A BLAISDELL BOOK IN THE
PURE AND APPLIED SCIENCES

CONSULTING EDITOR

William Prager

*University of California
at La Jolla*

A COURSE IN THERMODYNAMICS

Joseph Kestin

BROWN UNIVERSITY

A COURSE IN

THERMODYNAMICS

BLAISDELL PUBLISHING COMPANY

A Division of Ginn and Company

WALTHAM, MASSACHUSETTS · TORONTO · LONDON

DESIGNED BY *Larry Kamp*

To my little daughter

ANITA

Preface

IN RECENT YEARS, it has become customary to apologize for presenting the academic community with a new book on thermodynamics. The number of new textbooks on this subject has indeed been great and I, like my predecessors, feel that I must justify my efforts to my readers by the hope that I succeeded in anticipating and in answering questions which have not been anticipated and answered elsewhere.

The purpose of this book is frankly pedagogical, and I would like to think that it can be used to introduce the novice into the subject and to accompany him to a point when he feels that he understands the foundations and has acquired an appreciation of its power, its universality as well as of its limitations. Although it endeavors to speak to beginners, it makes no concessions as far as rigor is concerned and attempts to preserve a logical deductive sequence.

The education of engineers has undergone a deep transformation during the last decade, and it is, therefore, understandable that present-day textbooks must differ radically from those of the quite recent past. The scientific basis of this education has broadened, and more importance is attached to depth of understanding. The education of a modern engineer no longer proceeds along several clearly demarcated and isolated grooves, but aims at presenting the scientific basis of engineering in as unified a way as may be possible. Much public discussion has been spent on the desirable extent of courses in thermodynamics, on the role of statistical concepts in it and on the desirability of introducing the study of irreversible processes in continuous systems. The present book contains the author's views on these controversial topics in a detailed manner. In fact, so much detail has been given that it was found necessary to split the work into two volumes, of which this is the first, it being hoped that the sequel can be put into the hands of the reader with a minimum of delay.

The textbook has not been designed for a specific course of well-defined duration. Rather, it attempts to set out the experimental basis of the subject of classical thermodynamics and the generalizations which can be formulated from it in a connected way. I would like to think that I successfully avoided circular arguments as well as non sequiturs, and that I reduced anticipatory statements to a minimum. In addition, an attempt has been made to demonstrate the wide applicability of thermodynamics to a multitude of systems, emphasis being placed on the fact that the study is not restricted to systems characterized by only two independent parameters of state. Chapters 7 and 8 provide the necessary descriptive background for a physical understanding of a variety of systems, starting with the conventional pure substances, inclusive of heterogeneous systems and mixtures, galvanic and fuel cells, and so on. Beyond this, special attention is devoted to solid rods stressed elastically as well as plastically including the phenomena of creep and relaxation, and to interactions which occur through the intervention of gravitational, electrostatic, and magnetostatic fields. It is believed that the latter topics have received a more thorough treatment on an elementary level than has been available hitherto. In this manner, I hope to establish in the students' minds a clear link between thermodynamics and the parts of the curriculum which deal with mechanics, fluid mechanics, solid mechanics, and electromagnetic theory. In particular, the study of pure substances includes the often unappreciated limiting case of a gas whose properties are approximated by those of an incompressible fluid. These two chapters somewhat disrupt the continuity in the exposition of the Zeroth, First, and Second Laws of thermodynamics, but I have decided to tolerate the interruption in order to furnish the student with a set of clear physical ideas for future use.

Chapter 1 devotes a good deal of space to the study of systems of units and dimensions, it being recognized that an ability to work with a large variety of them is essential in our times. Although the MKSA system of units is favored, the view is taken that the use of quantity equations makes it unnecessary to work with a narrowly defined set of units and to become enmeshed in it.

The study of temperature, energy, and entropy with the aid of the three laws of thermodynamics is based on the mathematical properties of differential forms, and interpretations in terms of vector fields are used freely, because most contemporary students of engineering are familiar with them from their studies of mechanics. The First Law is first formulated for closed, uniform systems and then extended to the cases of open and continuous systems. Thus the student is introduced early to the essential concepts which he will require for the understanding of continuum (so-called irreversible) thermodynamics, and this has enabled me to include the study of various physical fields in a natural way. In order to prepare the ground still further, a distinction is made between quasistatic reversible and quasistatic irreversible processes in addition to the presentation of irreversible processes whose rates may not be infinitesimal.

The Second Law is presented in the manner of Clausius and Planck as well as in the manner of Carathéodory, Chapter 10 being devoted to the latter.

The last three chapters explore the consequences of the Second Law both for the derivation of relations between properties and fundamental equations of state, and for the introduction of the concepts of entropy production and maximum work. A formulation for open systems and the introduction of the chemical potential are also included.

Statistical concepts are used only when I thought that their inclusion contributes to a deeper understanding of the subject, but this has been done sparingly and heuristically only.

I am aware that I produced a discursive and occasionally repetitious volume. No real apology is made for that, because I believe that the modern tendency for shortening and compression has gone too far. Often it is preferable to study a more leisurely exposition rather than to grapple with an incomplete presentation over and over again, and most of us learn by repetition anyway. Certain basic ideas must be examined from different angles for clarification, and certain illustrations can well be used in several contexts.

Very few universities can devote enough time to a first course in thermodynamics in their curricula to allow them to expound the subject to the extent presented in this book. Instead of attempting to make the selection for them, I have deliberately included more than can be reasonably covered in one course. I trust that each instructor will not find it difficult to emphasize the aspects which he considers important and hope that the book can be used again in a second, deeper study. At the same time the student will not be left with the erroneous impression that the subject can be fathomed in all its profundity in a single pass and will be left with something which he can turn to later if a greater mastery of thermodynamics appears to him desirable.

The absence of tables may prove somewhat disconcerting to students, but they will find them all at the end of Volume II when it becomes available.

In concluding this preface I think that I ought to give expression to the admiration which I feel for a number of classical authors whose writing influenced me in my attempt to reorganize the subject for a new presentation. My interest was first aroused when I worked on the translation of Professor E. Schmidt's *Thermodynamics* about twenty years ago. I think that his book contains an excellent presentation of the more detailed engineering applications of the subject. At about that time I was deeply influenced by M. Planck's *Theory of Heat* and J. H. Keenan's *Thermodynamics*. Somewhat more recently, my work on the translation of A. Sommerfeld's magnificently concise *Thermodynamics and Statistical Mechanics* and my study of A. H. Wilson's book of the same title clarified to me the connection between the macroscopic and microscopic points of view. The fundamental simplicity of structure of the subject was revealed to me in H. B. Callen's *Thermodynamics*, and M. W. Zemansky's well-known textbook continuously served as a model of simplicity combined with accuracy. As I was preparing the present manuscript I was presented with a set of galley proofs of Howard Reiss' forthcoming *Methods of Thermodynamics* which contains a concise exposition of a point of view that I find very close to my own.

My colleagues R. Di Pippo, H. Reiss, V. L. Shah, J. H. Whitelaw, and R. Wood helped me greatly in reading the proofs and I wish to thank them for their time and effort. Mr. Di Pippo was also very helpful with the preparation of the illustrations, tables, list of symbols, and the index, and Mrs. Judi Bardsley patiently and competently typed several versions of the manuscript.

J. KESTIN

September 1965
Providence, R. I.

Contents

A COURSE IN THERMODYNAMICS

Definitions and Basic Concepts

1.1 The scope and methods of thermodynamics

The science of thermodynamics is a branch of physics. It describes natural processes in which changes in temperature play an important part. Such processes involve the transformation of energy from one form to another. Consequently, thermodynamics deals with the laws which govern such transformations of energy.

The student will recall that in the elementary presentation of the subjects of mechanics, electromagnetism, and fluid mechanics, it was tacitly assumed that the processes under consideration occurred at constant temperature and that the transformation of mechanical or electrical energy into heat was largely ignored. Thus, in the study of friction, the considerations were restricted to the calculation of the forces acting on bodies and only seldom was an attempt made to take into account the loss of mechanical energy, kinetic or potential, suffered by a body in the presence of friction. The study was mainly concentrated on *conservative systems* in which the sum of kinetic and potential energy remained constant, that is, to systems in which the amount of *mechanical* energy was conserved.

Experience teaches that real phenomena in mechanics are always accompanied by friction, that the flow of electric currents is always accompanied by the evolution of Joule heat, and so on. In general, all real phenomena in nature involve some *energy dissipation*. The subject of thermodynamics recognizes this fact and studies its consequences and to this effect makes a careful distinction between reversible and irreversible processes (Section 4.6). The systematic distinction between these two kinds of processes is one of the most characteristic and important features of thermodynamics.

Thermodynamics is firmly based on experiment. It is developed, principally, from four fundamental so-called *laws of thermodynamics*: the Zeroth Law (Section 2.3), the First Law (Section 5.3), the Second Law (Sections 8.2 and 9.1) and the Third Law (Volume II). Each of these laws constitutes an axiomatic generalization obtained on the basis of experience. In addition, as will be carefully pointed out in this exposition, it will be necessary to accept the validity of certain other generalizations, all of them based on experimental facts; in view of their more restricted scope, these additional principles are not given the rank of laws of thermodynamics.

It is essential to realize that the laws of thermodynamics cannot be directly and exhaustively verified by suitable experiments. They always represent bold generalizations obtained on the basis of restricted experiments and their truth is ascertained by inference, that is, from the fact that of all the consequences derived from them, none have failed to be verified experimentally.

Since thermodynamics deals with processes performed by real systems, it relies on our knowledge of their physical, or more precisely, *thermodynamic properties*. In principle the properties of systems must be measured experimentally. The science of thermodynamics does not provide methods whereby such properties can be evaluated theoretically. However, it will be shown that certain combinations of properties cannot exist in one particular substance if its behavior is not to contradict the basic laws of thermodynamics. In this manner, thermodynamics is able to provide tests for the consistency of measurements relating to the properties of substances, as well as methods of evaluating some of them if some others have been measured.

Instead of being measured, the properties of substances can sometimes be calculated from first principles by the use of special assumptions concerning the structure of matter, as they are made in *statistical mechanics*. The science of statistical mechanics or, as it is now also called, the science of *statistical thermodynamics* is a useful and necessary extension of *classical thermodynamics* and cannot be ignored entirely in its exposition. In this book we shall present some of its results, albeit in a descriptive manner, but it will be always necessary to make a sharp distinction between the methods of classical as opposed to statistical thermodynamics.

The principles embodied in the laws of thermodynamics and derived from them are very important in the design, operation, and performance of many present-day engineering systems and appliances. They are of particular importance in the production of power from the chemical energy of fuels and in the study of chemical and metallurgical engineering. Since the application of thermodynamics to the analysis of processes used in engineering is neither simple nor obvious, some attention will be devoted to the study of such applications.

Because thermodynamics extends the scope of the description of natural phenomena as compared with that given in mechanics, electromagnetism, and fluid mechanics, it will be necessary to assume that the student has a working knowledge of the rudiments of these disciplines. Furthermore, it will be necessary to re-examine and redefine the concepts of temperature and energy. These are undoubtedly familiar to the student, but for our purposes it will be necessary to provide them with a more general, and more precise physical and mathematical meaning.

In order to pave the way for the understanding of a large class of applications of thermodynamics to the solution of engineering problems, it will be necessary to recognize the existence of *continuous systems* (Section 6.1). Such systems occur in the study of fluid mechanics, heat transfer, electromagnetic theory, the mechanics of solid continua, and many other branches of engineering science. They are characterized by the fact that the thermodynamic properties of the system vary from point to point and, often, with time. The processes which occur in them effect a continuous transformation of mechanical energy into heat, because they are predominantly irreversible. For this reason, considerations of this kind are said to belong to the *thermodynamics of irreversible processes*† or, as we shall prefer to call it, to *continuum thermodynamics*. Continuum thermodynamics constitutes a relatively recent, but very important additional extension of classical thermodynamics; it is still undergoing a process of development and refinement through current research.

---

† The shorter and more easily pronounced term: *irreversible thermodynamics* is frequently used in this connection. However, this term is a misnomer, because a branch of science can be neither reversible nor irreversible.

1.2 Systems and units of measurement. Fundamental units

As in all branches of physics, a thorough understanding of the systems of units employed for the measurement of physical quantities is indispensable in thermodynamics. Although basically the systems of units employed in thermodynamics are identical with those already encountered in mechanics, a review of them is not entirely superfluous. In particular, it is important to distinguish between the essential features of the systems of units and those which depend merely on more or less convenient conventions. It is unfortunate that the historical development of science and engineering has made us heirs to a confusing multitude of systems of units, but this is a state of affairs which is not likely to be remedied in the near future and, accordingly, an ability to convert units from one system to another efficiently becomes indispensable.

1.2.1 Fundamental units

In any system of units all physical quantities are divided into two classes. A certain small number of them, the *primary* quantities, are regarded as simple and fundamental, and conventional standards are selected for their measurement. Quantities of this class are measured by comparing them with the standard directly or with suitably prepared replicas of it called secondary standards. The number resulting from such a comparison is called the *measure* of the physical quantity in terms of the specified unit. Hence, primary quantities are measured in terms of the *fundamental units* of the system. The usual number of fundamental units is three, but that number is dictated entirely by convenience. In thermodynamics this number is larger than three.

All physical quantities other than the primary ones are called *secondary* quantities and are measured in terms of *derived units*. The measurement of secondary quantities is not effected by direct comparison with another quantity of the same kind, the unit, but by more complicated rules involving the primary quantities. In making the preceding distinction between primary and secondary quantities, it is not necessary to insist that all measurements carried out in practice must be of these two opposing types. We are, of course, permitted to perform actual measurements in the most convenient way, that is, we are permitted to have standards for the secondary quantities as well as to measure primary quantities in terms of secondary quantities, if desired. The essential point lies in the fact that a small number of units, two, three, or four, characteristic of each system of units, is defined independently and that all other units are derived from them. Hence, a primary quantity in one system may become a secondary quantity in another system and vice versa.

1.2.2 Systems of units

The existing systems of units differ among themselves in three respects: In the choice of the number of fundamental units which is either three or four, in the choice of the physical nature of the fundamental units, and in the choice of the magnitude of the fundamental units.

The *magnitudes* of all present-day fundamental units derive from two stems, the metric and the English systems of units. The metric units are fixed by primary international agreements, whereas the English units are related to them by several conventional conversion factors.

Regarding the physical nature of the fundamental units, all systems include a unit of length and time. Depending on the choice of the third unit, systems are divided into physical or absolute systems and into gravitational or engineering systems. In the absolute or physical system of units, the unit of *mass* is chosen as fundamental whereas the gravitational or engineering systems replaces it by a unit of *force*, more precisely, by a unit of *standard weight*. The single system with four fundamental units, the MKSA system, makes use of the unit of electric current in addition to the three preceding ones, namely length, time, and mass.

At the present time it is necessary to be familiar with five different systems of units, three of them metric, and two English, each characterized by a different combination of arbitrary choices. The modern tendency is to favor G. Giorgi's† MKSA system of rational units which was adopted for universal use by the Ninth International Conference on Weights and Measures held in 1948 in Paris.‡ This system is far more convenient in practical applications than the remaining four, and it is hoped that it will become widespread without undue delay.

The *absolute MKSA* system is based on four units, the units of length, mass, time, and electric current. The unit of length is the meter (m), the unit of mass is the kilogram (kg), the unit of time is the second (sec), and the unit of electric current is the Ampere (A).§ The designation MKSA has been formed with the initial letters of the names of the units in the preceding order.‖ In branches of science in which there is no need to measure electrical quantities, the Ampere is not used, and the curtailed, three-unit system is known as the MKS system of units.

In the *absolute metric or CGS system* there are three fundamental units: the unit of length is the centimeter (cm), the unit of mass is the gram (g) or 1/100th part of the *mass* of the standard kilogram. The unit of time is the second (sec).

Until recently, the CGS system was favored by physicists in all countries, but is now being replaced by the MKSA system. The main disadvantage of the CGS system comes from the fact that the most important units, the gram, centimeter, and dyne (for force) are very small and this necessitates the frequent use of powers of 10.

The *gravitational* or *engineering metric* system is also based on three fundamental units, a unit of length which is the meter (m), a unit of time—the second (sec), and a unit of force—the kilogram-weight (kgf). The kilogram-weight is the attraction force exerted by the earth on the standard mass of 1 kg at a place where the gravitational acceleration has a *standard* value[#] of

$$\mathbf{g} = 9.80665 \text{ m/sec}^2. \tag{1.1}$$

In practical calculations this value is usually rounded off to

$$\mathbf{g} \approx 9.81 \text{ m/sec}^2. \tag{1.1a}$$

† See Bodea, E., *Giorgis rationales MKS-Massystem mit Dimensionskohärenz* (Basel: Birkhäuser, 1949).
‡ It was also adopted by the Fifth International Conference on Properties of Steam held in London in 1956.
§ According to international agreement, abbreviations for units which are derived from the names of famous scientists or engineers are written with a capital letter, all others being written with lower-case letters. The abbreviations for units are now written without a period at the end, and never assume the plural form.
‖ The system based on the above four units, augmented by the candela, a unit of light intensity, is distinguished, if necessary, by the symbol SI (Système International).
Constants which represent agreed numbers and which are, therefore, exact numbers are now distinguished by having the last digit printed in bold type. We shall follow this convention throughout the book.

This attraction force is called *weight*, or more precisely, *standard weight*. Generally speaking, the gravitational acceleration g depends on the geographical latitude and on the altitude above sea level.†

The fact that the same word, "kilogram," is used to describe the units of both mass and weight in two different systems of units is confusing. We shall always make a careful distinction between them. Several European countries have legally adopted the designations kilopond (kp) and pond (p) for the kilogram-weight and gram-weight respectively, still allowing the use of kg and g when no misunderstanding is likely to arise. In this book we shall consistently use the abbreviations kp for the kilogram-weight (kilopond) and p for the gram-weight (or gram-force).

The *English absolute* system of units makes use of the foot as its unit of length and of the pound-mass (lbm) as its unit of mass. The unit of time, the second, is common to all systems.

In the *English gravitational* or *engineering* system of units, the units of length and time (foot and second) remain unaltered, but the unit of force, the pound-weight (lbf) is the weight of a standard pound-mass at a place where the acceleration due to gravity has a value

$$g = 32.1740 \text{ ft/sec}^2 \tag{1.2}$$

or

$$g \approx 32.2 \text{ ft/sec}^2. \tag{1.2a}$$

The use of the word "pound" to denote two essentially different units in two different systems is as confusing as the double use of the word "kilogram." Unfortunately, no alternative name for the pound-force has been proposed so far, although its adoption would be highly desirable. We shall carefully distinguish between the two in the abbreviations: 1 lbm for the pound-mass and 1 lbf for the pound-force.

The fundamental units of the three metric and the two English systems of units are compared in Table 1.1.

The units of force in the absolute systems and the units of mass in the gravitational systems are secondary and will be discussed in Section 1.3.

1.2.3   Fundamental standards

All units listed in Table 1.1 are based on three internationally recognized *fundamental standards*, the standard meter, the standard kilogram, and the second of Ephemeris time.

Until recently, the fundamental standard of length, the *meter* (m) was defined as the distance between two marks on a suitably shaped bar when measured at a specified

---

† The gravitational acceleration at sea level is the following approximate function of the geographical latitude ϕ (International Gravity Formula):

$$g = 978.0495(1 + 0.005\,2892 \sin^2\phi - 0.000\,0073 \sin^2 2\phi) \text{ cm/sec}^2.$$

At a moderate altitude h m above sea level in free air, the gravitational acceleration g changes by

$$\Delta g = -0.000\,3086\, h \text{ cm/sec}^2.$$

In the presence of a rock of density $\rho(\text{g/cm}^3)$ the gravitational acceleration is increased by

$$\Delta g = +0.000\,9419\, \rho h \text{ cm/sec}^2.$$

TABLE 1.1
The Five Systems of Fundamental Units.

System	Number of fundamental units	Type	Length	Time	Mass	Force, weight
Metric						
MKS	3	abs	m	sec	kg	secondary
CGS	3	abs	cm	sec	g	secondary
Engineering	3	grav	m	sec	secondary	kp
English						
Absolute	3	abs	ft	sec	lbm	secondary
Engineering	3	grav	ft	sec	secondary	lbf

Note: The table lists the truncated MKS system and not the full MKSA system.

temperature (0°C). This primary meter bar is made of an alloy of platinum and iridium and is kept in Sèvres near Paris. When first conceived, it was intended to make it equal to 1/10,000,000th part of a quadrant of the terrestrial meridian. In 1960, the Eleventh General Conference on Weights and Measures held in Paris resolved to replace the meter bar by a descriptive standard which linked the unit of length with a particular wavelength of light. Accordingly, the meter is now defined as

$$1,650,763.73$$

wavelengths of the orange-red line† of the isotope 86 of krypton. The new standard is more easily reproducible in different laboratories and less likely to be influenced by the hazards to which the meter bar might be exposed, since it is believed that the wavelength of a specified kind of light is immutable. The new definition was so phrased as to render the length of the new standard as nearly equal to the old one as contemporary techniques permit. However, if higher-order differences should be detected in the future, the new and not the old standard will be retained.

In addition to the primary meter, the possible use of twelve secondary wavelength meter standards is admissible in cases when extreme accuracy is not required.‡

Decimal multiples and submultiples of the meter, as well as of all other metric units, may be designated by standard prefixes which can be found listed in Table I.§ For example, the *centi*meter (cm) is 1/100th of a meter, and so on.

The English foot (ft) is defined by the exact relation

$$1 \text{ ft} = 0.3048 \text{ m}$$

† 1 wavelength of the orange-red line = $6057.8021 \times 10^{-10}$ m approximately.
‡ Wavelengths of krypton 86:
 6,458.0720; 6,422.8006; 5,651.1286; 4,503.6162;
Wavelengths of mercury 198:
 5,792.2683; 5,771.1983; 5,462.2705; 4,359.5624;
Wavelengths of cadmium 114:
 6,440.2480; 5,087.2379; 4,801.2521; 4,679.4581;
all in units of 10^{-10} m.
§ Tables bearing Roman numerals have been collected together at the end of Volume II.

so that 1 inch (in), or 1/12th of a foot is

$$1 \text{ in} = 2.54 \text{ cm}$$

exactly. In this manner, to the same number of significant figures,

$$1 \text{ in} = 41,929,399 \text{ wavelengths}$$

of the orange-red line of krypton 86.

As the science of the structure of matter progresses, it is possible to discern a general tendency towards replacing artificially made standards by standards derived from atomic constants. There is no doubt that this tendency will continue and more fundamental standards will be of this obviously advantageous type.

For many years, the unit of time, the *second*, has been linked to the motion of the earth and was defined as the 86,400th part of the mean solar day. However, progress with the techniques of time measurement revealed that the mean solar day varies perceptibly, and the Tenth General Conference on Weight and Measures held in Paris in 1954 recommended a slight modification which was subsequently adopted by the Eleventh Conference in 1960. The amended definition links the unit of time with a particular year, and stipulates that one second shall be taken as the agreed fraction 1/31,556,925.975 of the tropical year 1900.0. Time measured with respect to the rotation of the earth relative to the fixed stars is described as *Ephemeris time*. Hence, the preceding unit is known as one second of Ephemeris time. Measurements in terms of Ephemeris time require tedious and protracted astronomical observations and are for that reason extremely inconvenient. On the other hand, the development of so-called atomic clocks whose operation depends on atomic vibrations and on extremely precise frequency measurements are much more accessible, and therefore preferable. Consequently, it is very likely that a time standard based on them will be adopted in the near future. As an interim measure, the U. S. National Bureau of Standards maintains a service of time signals on stations WWV and WWVH with reference to an atomic clock which emits a signal whose frequency is exactly equal to the frequency of a quantum transition in cesium in the ground state.[†] In terms of an Ephemeris second, the frequency of this transition is

$$9,192,631,770 \text{ cycles/sec.}$$

It is now believed that frequencies of quantum transitions are immutable in time. Frequencies can be measured with an accuracy of 2 parts in 10^{11}, so that time now constitutes that physical quantity which can be measured with the highest relative accuracy attainable.

Irrespective of the details of its definition, the unit of time is the same in all systems, and we shall not find it necessary to discuss it any further.

The units of mass in the absolute systems or the units of force in the gravitational systems are both defined with reference to a standard block of metal — also kept in Paris — and called a *kilogram*. The fact that the same block of metal is used to define units for two entirely different physical quantities — mass and force, combined with the unfortunate circumstance that both units are known under the same name — "kilogram," and under the same abbreviation — kg, proves to be a source of great confusion to the

† Natl. Bur. Std. (U.S.) Tech. News Bull., **45** (1961), 8.

beginner. Much of this confusion will be removed when the name kilopond (kp) for kilogram-force (kilogram-weight) becomes universal, as already intimated earlier.

Masses are measured by comparing them on a balance and in a uniform gravitational field with replicas of the standard mass, its multiples or subdivisions. These implements are loosely referred to as "weights," which also adds to the confusion. Mass† serves as a measure of the quantity of matter because its numerical value is independent of geographical location and of the variation of the gravitational acceleration with it.

Weights are measured by indicating the *force* with which the given mass is attracted by the earth. Since the strength of the gravitational field of the earth varies from location to location in a manner indicated in the footnote on page 5, the concept of a *standard weight* has been introduced by specifying a *standard* value of the gravitational acceleration g, as given in equations (1.1) and (1.2). Thus one *kilopond* is defined as the *standard weight* of the same lump of metal which serves as a standard for one *kilogram*.

The standard weight of a lump of matter is proportional to its mass and can, therefore, be used as a measure of quantity of matter. In fact, engineers in some European countries measure the quantity of substance by indicating its standard weight, that is a force. This is one more habit which leads to confusion, though it is acceptable in principle; it should, however, be discarded.

We shall bear the distinction between masses and weights, that is, between masses and forces, clearly in mind, and this will enable us to formulate a set of practical rules for the performance of numerical calculations without error (Section 1.3).

The related units of mass and force in the English systems of units, the pound-mass (lbm) and the pound-force (lbf) are defined by the equations

$$1 \text{ lbm} = 0.453 \ 592 \ 37 \text{ kg},$$
$$1 \text{ lbf } = 0.453 \ 592 \ 37 \text{ kp}.$$

The unit of *electrical current* can be defined with reference to the force acting between two electrical conductors carrying a current. It then becomes a derived unit. For example, in the CGS system, electric currents are measured in units of $cm^{1/2}g^{1/2} sec^{-1}$. Since the fractional exponents are considered awkward, the MKSA system resorts to the expedient of introducing an independent unit of electrical current, the Ampere (A). Nevertheless, the definition of 1 A is linked to the meter, kilogram, and second by stipulating that it is that current which causes two very thin parallel conductors to be attracted with a force of 2×10^{-7} Newton per 1 meter length. The Newton is the derived unit of force in the MKS system and will be defined in Section 1.3.

In addition to the previously discussed fundamental units, it is necessary to adopt a unit of temperature. The concept of temperature and the unit now employed to measure it will be discussed in detail in Chapter 2. Thus in thermodynamics use is made of four fundamental units.

In thermodynamics and in chemistry there is a need to provide a measure of the *quantity of a substance*. Since all matter is known to consist of discrete particles, molecules, or atoms, the unit of quantity of substance could be based on a specified number of such particles. The mol (or mole), which we shall define in Section 3.9 and then extensively use in this book, is formed in such a way; however, since most sub-

---

† In view of the equivalence of mass and energy epitomized by A. Einstein's famous equation $E = mc^2$, one must realize that it is the *rest mass*, that is, the mass measured at zero relative velocity, which is meant here.

stances do not consist of identical particles, and in some cases the precise nature of these particles is in doubt, an independent unit of the quantity of substance is required. The physical, the MKS, and the absolute English systems of units employ mass as the unit of quantity, as stated earlier.

1.3   Derived units. Dimensions

In the preceding section we have described in detail the main systems of units which are currently being used in science and engineering, enumerating the primary quantities and the fundamental units on which they are based as well as the relations between them. Owing to their large number, it is convenient to introduce a more general designation for a class of units of one kind. We say that all units employed to measure a particular physical quantity have the same *dimension* and use a separate symbol for it. Thus the concept of a dimension confers a name on a class of units; a particular unit constitutes an individual member of the class. The dimension of length will be denoted by **L**, those of mass, force, and time by **M, F**, and **T**, respectively. Hence, in each system, to the fundamental units, there correspond fundamental dimensions **L, M, T** in an absolute system, and **L, F, T** in a gravitational system. In order to distinguish between the units and dimensions, we shall use braces for the former and brackets for the latter. Hence, $[W]$ denotes the dimension of work, W, and $\{W\}$ will denote the unit. We emphasize once again that the number of fundamental dimensions in a given system, just as the number of fundamental units, is arbitrary, being dictated by custom and convenience.

1.3.1   Derived units

The secondary or derived quantities are measured with the aid of derived units which are formed from the fundamental units by the same algebraic operations as are used to evaluate a physical quantity in terms of the fundamental physical quantities. This relation between the derived and fundamental physical quantities may constitute a definition or a physical law, but from our present point of view this distinction is irrelevant. It is only important to realize that some such relation must be invoked. For example, units of velocity are formed with reference to the definition

$$v = \frac{dx}{dt},$$

where x denotes a displacement and t denotes time. Units of force or mass are formed with reference to an empirical law of nature – Newton's Second Law

$$F = ma, \tag{1.3}$$

where F is a force, m denotes a mass, and $a = d^2x/dt^2$ is the acceleration.

As another example, we may consider the work W of a force F acting over a collinear displacement x

$$W = Fx. \tag{1.4}$$

The dimension of work is

$$[W] = \mathbf{FL}$$

in a gravitational system or

$$[W] = \mathbf{ML^2T^{-2}}$$

in an absolute system. The respective units in the English systems are

$$\{W\} = \text{ft lbf} \qquad \text{(gravitational)}$$
$$\{W\} = \frac{\text{lbm ft}^2}{\text{sec}^2}. \qquad \text{(absolute)}$$

In dealing with physical quantities, the operations of addition or subtraction are reserved for quantities having identical dimensions and do not occur when derived quantities are defined. Such definitions involve only the operations of multiplication or division, and since repeated multiplication or division may be used, simple rational powers may also occur. Finally, a specified power of a derived physical quantity may be defined in terms of the fundamental quantities, all raised to some simple power. Hence, in general, the dimension of a derived quantity will be expressed as a *monomial product* of the fundamental dimensions each of which may be raised to a positive or negative power, the exponents being all rational, real numbers. For example, *all* derived dimensions in the absolute system have the form

$$\mathbf{M^\alpha L^\beta T^\gamma}, \tag{1.5}$$

and *all* derived dimensions in the gravitational system have the form

$$\mathbf{F^\delta L^\epsilon T^\eta}, \tag{1.6}$$

where the exponents $\alpha, \beta, \ldots, \eta$ are real, rational numbers (positive or negative). In particular cases all the exponents may be identically equal to zero. The corresponding physical quantity, X, is then said to be *dimensionless* with respect to the given set of dimensions, and we write

$$[X] \equiv 1.$$

It should be realized that the dimension of any physical quantity depends on the system used and differs from system to system; it does not, as is sometimes erroneously stated, express the "physical nature" of the quantity considered. Very often quantities of a different physical nature have the same dimensions in a particular system of units. For example, both a torque and a quantity of work have the dimension $\mathbf{FL}$ and are measured in ft lbf. In thermodynamics the specific heat (Section 5.14) and entropy (Section 8.10) have identical dimensions in spite of the fact that they are of an entirely different physical nature.† Conversely, a quantity which is dimensionless in one system need not necessarily be dimensionless in another.

We shall revert to this problem elsewhere. We shall then demonstrate that the forms (1.5) and (1.6) are necessary consequences of the fact that our systems of units are so arranged that the ratios of two measurements of any physical quantity (their measures) are independent of the units employed. If the unit is halved, for example, the number expressing a measure is necessarily doubled (principle of absolute significance of rela-

---

† " . . . The dimensions of a physical quantity are not inherent in it, but constitute a conventional property conditioned by the choice of the system of measurement. If this circumstance had always been properly appreciated, a great number of unfruitful controversies in physical literature . . . would have been avoided." M. Planck, *General Mechanics*, translated by H. L. Brose (Macmillan, 1933), p. 46.

tive magnitude).† We shall then also discuss the problem of trigonometric, logarithmic, and transcendental functions. At this point, it is sufficient to say that their arguments must be dimensionless in any adopted system of dimensions.

1.3.2 Defining equation; measure equation

In order to perceive clearly the relation between a derived unit and the equation which is used for its definition, we shall consider a particularly simple example taken from elementary geometry. The area A of a rectangle of sides a and b is *defined* as the product

$$A = ab. \tag{1.7}$$

The lengths a and b are measured with respect to a single fundamental unit, that of length. Hence, their dimensions are

$$[a] = [b] = \mathsf{L}. \tag{1.8}$$

In particular, in the MKS system

$$\{a\} = \{b\} = \mathrm{m}, \tag{1.8a}$$

or in the English system

$$\{a\} = \{b\} = \mathrm{ft}. \tag{1.8b}$$

The dimensional equation (1.8) stands for any one of the arbitrarily large number of equations (1.8a) and (1.8b) between the units.

The simplest convention for the unit of area $\{A\}$ or for the dimension of area $[A]$ is to choose a square for which $a = b$ and to adopt the area of this square as the derived unit of area. In order to preserve a trace of the defining equation (1.7) together with the conventions (1.8), (1.8a), and (1.8b), it is advantageous to write

$$[A] = \mathsf{L}^2$$

or, in the particular systems of units

$$\{A\} = \mathrm{m}^2 \quad \text{or} \quad \{A\} = \mathrm{ft}^2.$$

The alternative notation

$$\{A\} = \mathrm{sq\ m} \quad \text{or} \quad \{A\} = \mathrm{sq\ ft}$$

is distinctly inferior because it fails to recall the original conventions. Symbols of the latter kind will not be used in this book because they impede the efficient conversion of units which is so essential in the face of the multitude of systems of units.

By following the preceding set of rules it is possible to establish a consistent set of secondary units and to link it to a graphically simple set of equations of the type of equation (1.7). Equations (1.3) and (1.4) are also of this type. The only requirement for success is to agree on a universally acceptable set of units and to use it consistently in measurement and calculation. Calculations are performed only on the *measures* of secondary quantities, that is, on the numbers which express the ratio of the quantity to the appropriate unit, a consistent one in this case. It is then said that the equations of

---

† See Bridgman, P. W., *Dimensional Analysis* (2nd ed.: Yale Univ. Press, 1937), p. 21.

physics are interpreted as *measure equations*. The absence of such agreement forces us to examine alternative sets of conventions.

Frequently, a separate and independent unit is chosen for the secondary quantity, the area in our case. The acre is an example of such an independent secondary unit. The consistent unit of area in one system affords another example of a unit which is independent with respect to another system. The unit 1 m² is independent in the CGS system, whereas 1 cm² is independent in the MKS system. Clearly, in cases like these, equation (1.7) can no longer be retained, because the product *ab* measured in units of length ceases to be equal to the area measured in independent units. Instead, it becomes *proportional* to it, and we must replace equation (1.7) by the relation

$$A = k \, ab, \tag{1.9}$$

where k denotes a factor of proportionality. This factor depends on the choice of the units $\{a\} = \{b\}$ and $\{A\}$ or, more generally, on the choice of the dimensions $[a] = [b] = \mathbf{L}$ and $[A] = \mathbf{A}$. In order to preserve the link with equation (1.9), we are compelled to endow the factor of proportionality k with a dimension

$$[k] = \frac{\mathbf{A}}{\mathbf{L}^2}$$

since equation (1.9) is equivalent to

$$k = \frac{A}{ab}.$$

In our previous examples, for $A =$ acre and $a = b =$ ft, we will find

$$k = \frac{1}{4.356 \times 10^4} \frac{\text{acre}}{\text{ft}^2}, \tag{1.9a}$$

which is normally written without the braces { } for units because k is a constant for each particular choice of units. Similarly

$$k = 10^4 \frac{\text{cm}^2}{\text{m}^2} \quad \text{or} \quad k = 10^{-4} \frac{\text{m}^2}{\text{cm}^2}.$$

Thus the factor k is numerically equal to the reciprocal of the ratio of the independent unit of area to the consistent unit of area.

The preceding, second set of conventions is logically equivalent to the first set. In particular, it also interprets the equations of physics as measure equations, and insists on performing measurements as well as calculations in terms of a consistent system of units. It appears to give us complete freedom in the choice of units, but in practice it is very inconvenient. The disadvantage of the second system lies in the fact that the equations of physics acquire a cumbersome set of dimensional proportionality factors k which constitute an unnecessary burden on our memories. The burden is unnecessary because a more convenient system of conventions can be devised.

1.3.3 *Units of force, mass, energy, power, and pressure*

Before we proceed to outline a more flexible set of conventions, it is useful first to discuss the derived units of force in the absolute systems **L, M, T**, and the derived units of mass in the gravitational systems **L, F, T**. Both types of units are derived with refer-

ence to Newton's Second Law, equation (1.3). Hence, in a consistent absolute system

$$[F] = \mathbf{MLT^{-2}}. \tag{1.10}$$

In particular, in the MKS system, the unit of force is called 1 Newton (N), and

$$1 \text{ N} = 1 \frac{\text{kg m}}{\text{sec}^2}. \tag{1.11}$$

In the CGS system, the unit of force is 1 dyne, where

$$1 \text{ dyne} = 1 \frac{\text{g cm}}{\text{sec}^2}. \tag{1.11a}$$

Similarly, in the absolute English system of units, the unit of force is called 1 poundal, that is,

$$1 \text{ poundal} = 1 \frac{\text{lbm ft}}{\text{sec}^2}. \tag{1.11b}$$

In all cases, the unit of force is defined as that force which imparts a unit acceleration to a unit mass.

In a consistent gravitational system

$$[M] = \mathbf{FL^{-1}T^2}.$$

In particular, in the metric system, the unit of mass is

$$1 \frac{\text{kp sec}^2}{\text{m}};$$

it has no separate name. The unit of mass in the English gravitational system is called a slug. Thus

$$1 \text{ slug} = 1 \frac{\text{lbf sec}^2}{\text{ft}},$$

and in both cases the unit of mass is defined as that mass to which a unit acceleration is imparted by a unit force.

The derived units of force and mass together with the derived units of work, W, or energy, E, power, $\dot{W}$, and pressure, P, are listed in Table 1.2. The MKS unit of work and energy is called 1 joule (J), and that of power, that is, of the rate of the performance of work per unit time

$$\dot{W} = \frac{\mathrm{d}W}{\mathrm{d}t},$$

is called 1 watt (W). Since

$$[W] = \mathbf{FL} \quad \text{and} \quad [\dot{W}] = \mathbf{FL/T},$$

we have

$$1 \text{ J} = 1 \text{ Nm} = 1 \frac{\text{kg m}^2}{\text{sec}^2} \quad \text{and} \quad 1 \text{ W} = 1 \frac{\text{N m}}{\text{sec}} = 1 \frac{\text{kg m}^2}{\text{sec}^3}.$$

The CGS unit of energy is called erg; the unit of power in the CGS system, and the units of work and power in the English systems have no special names. The same is

TABLE 1.2
Units of Mass, Force, Energy, and Power.

System	Length	Time	Mass	Force, weight	Work, energy	Power	Pressure	Quantity of substance
Metric								
MKS	m	sec	kg	$N = \dfrac{kg\ m}{sec^2}$	$J = Nm = \dfrac{kg\ m^2}{sec^2}$	$W = \dfrac{N\ m}{sec} = \dfrac{kg\ m^2}{sec^3}$	$\dfrac{N}{m^2}$	kg
CGS	cm	sec	g	$dyne = \dfrac{g\ cm}{sec^2}$	$erg = \dfrac{g\ cm^2}{sec^2}$	$\dfrac{erg}{sec} = \dfrac{g\ cm^2}{sec^3}$	$\dfrac{dyne}{cm^2} = \dfrac{g}{cm\ sec^2}$	g
Engineering (gravitational)	m	sec	$\dfrac{kp\ sec^2}{m}$	kp	kpm	$\dfrac{kpm}{sec}$	$\dfrac{kp}{m^2}$	kp
English								
Absolute	ft	sec	lbm	$poundal = \dfrac{lbm\ ft}{sec^2}$	$\dfrac{lbm\ ft^2}{sec^2}$	$\dfrac{lbm\ ft^2}{sec^3}$	$\dfrac{lbm}{ft\ sec^2}$	lbm
Engineering (gravitational)	ft	sec	$slug = \dfrac{lbf\ sec^2}{ft}$	lbf	ft lbf	$\dfrac{lbf\ ft}{sec}$	$\dfrac{lbf}{ft^2}$	lbf

true about all consistent units of pressure P which is measured as the ratio of a force to an area. Hence,

$$[P] = \mathbf{ML}^{-1}\mathbf{T}^{-2} \quad \text{or} \quad [P] = \mathbf{FL}^{-2}.$$

An examination of Table 1.2 explains the practical difficulties of performing *measurements* with the aid of the consistent secondary units in any one of the five systems as opposed to the performance of *calculations*. The primary units are normally adjusted to a convenient size for measurement, but the same cannot carry over to the secondary units. For example, the MKS unit of pressure N/m² is far too small, and

$$1\ bar = 10^5\ N/m^2$$

is often preferred. Practical difficulties of this type are particularly acute in relation to the derived units of mass and force. The habit of measuring forces in kiloponds in the metric system and in pounds-force in the English system is so deeply ingrained that a change is unlikely. This would favor the adoption of the gravitational systems of units, as engineers have done for many years. However, in thermodynamics great inconveniences would arise from the need to use *specific quantities*.

If V is the volume of a homogeneous substance and m is its mass, then

$$v = \frac{V}{m}$$

is called the *specific volume* of the substance. Many similarly formed quantities, such as specific energy or specific heat are useful in thermodynamics. They all constitute, essentially, physical magnitudes which are referred to a unit of quantity of matter. In aerodynamics, and several other branches of science, the reciprocal of specific volume

$$\rho = \frac{m}{V}, \qquad (\rho v = 1) \tag{1.12}$$

called the *density* or *specific weight* of the homogeneous substance is widely used.

If a gravitational system were adopted, it would be necessary to refer such quantities to 1 kp sec²/m or to 1 slug = lbf sec²/ft. Hence,

$$\{v\} = \frac{m^4}{kp\ sec^2} \quad \text{and} \quad \{v\} = \frac{ft^4}{lbf\ sec^2}$$

or

$$\{\rho\} = \frac{kp\ sec^2}{m^4} \quad \text{and} \quad \{\rho\} = \frac{lbf\ sec^2}{ft^4}.$$

This is considered awkward by most people. The alternative device employed by Continental European engineers of measuring quantities of matter in units of standard weight is equally awkward.

It would therefore appear that a four-unit **MFLT** system might prove convenient. In such a system a unit force would not impart a unit acceleration to a unit mass. Instead, a unit weight acting on a unit mass — represented by the same lump of metal — would cause it to move with the standard gravitational acceleration **g**. Newton's Second Law would be written

$$F = kma \tag{1.13}$$

with

$$[k] = \frac{\mathbf{FT^2}}{\mathbf{ML}}.$$

In particular

$$k = \frac{1}{9.80665}\frac{kp\ sec^2}{kg\ m} = \frac{1}{32.1740}\frac{lbf\ sec^2}{lbm\ ft}.$$

Some authors who favor this system replace equation (1.13) by

$$F = \frac{1}{g_0} ma \tag{1.13a}$$

in which

$$g_0 = \frac{1}{k} = 9.80665\frac{kg\ m}{kp\ sec^2} = 32.1740\frac{lbm\ ft}{lbf\ sec^2} \tag{1.13b}$$

is *numerically*, but not dimensionally, equal to the standard gravitational acceleration **g**. The urge to replace the symbol g_0 by g is seldom resisted, and equations derived from Newton's Second Law acquire a quantity which suggests, erroneously, that the solution to a problem depends on terrestrial gravitation in cases when it does not. In the contrary case, the genuine appearance of the gravitational acceleration g leads to the emergence of a factor g/g_0 which is often omitted as being close to unity, with the result that no gravitational acceleration shows up in answers to problems in which it plays an essential part.

For these reasons, the retention of a dimensional factor k or g_0 in equations (1.13) and (1.13a) cannot be recommended.

1.3.4 Number of fundamental units

Before outlining the final conventions regarding units and numerical calculations to be adopted in this book, it is useful to examine the last arbitrary feature of any system of units, namely the choice of the number of fundamental units. We have seen before that three or four fundamental dimensions **M, L, T; F, L, T;** or **M, F, L, T** can be chosen with equal consistency. We shall now demonstrate that the number could be successfully reduced to two, if desired.†

Accordingly, we shall adopt two fundamental dimensions, length **L** and time **T**. In order to define the units of mass and force, it is sufficient to supplement Newton's Second Law $F = ma$, equation (1.3), with another, no less general law of mechanics, the law of universal gravitation. In a three-unit system the law of universal gravitation must be written with a dimensional constant, thus

$$F = \mathbf{G}\,\frac{m_1 m_2}{r^2}. \tag{1.14}$$

Here F denotes the force of gravity acting between the masses m_1 and m_2 at a distance r, and it is assumed that the *gravitational* mass in equation (1.14) is physically identical with the *inertial* mass in equation (1.3). The factor **G**, the universal gravitational constant, is analogous to the factor k in equations (1.9) and (1.1); it depends on the arbitrary choice of the units of force, mass, and length. In the MKS system

$$\mathbf{G} = (6.670 \pm 0.015) \times 10^{-11}\,\frac{\text{N m}^2}{\text{kg}^2}. \tag{1.15}$$

For the purpose of defining units with the aid of equation (1.1) it is necessary to put

$$\mathbf{G} \equiv 1. \tag{1.15a}$$

In this manner, the following dimensions would be obtained:

$$[m] = \mathbf{L}^3\mathbf{T}^{-2} \quad \text{and} \quad [F] = \mathbf{L}^4\mathbf{T}^{-4}.$$

In an MS system of units

$$\{m\} = \frac{\text{m}^3}{\text{sec}^2} \quad \text{and} \quad \{F\} = \frac{\text{m}^4}{\text{sec}^4}.$$

The MS system of units is sometimes used by astronomers, and the unit m³/sec² is known as the astronomical unit of mass. As a matter of curiosity, Table 1.3 lists the dimensions of mass, force, energy, power, and pressure in terms of **L** and **T**.

The reduction of the number of fundamental units by one has led to the suppression of a dimensional constant in the same way as the reduction from four to three fundamental units suppressed the constant g_0 in equation (1.13a). Similarly, the factor in equation (1.9) was suppressed when the number of fundamental geometrical units had been reduced from two to one. Moreover, instead of determining the dimensional constant by measurement when a physical law rather than a definition is involved, as was the case with **G** in equation (1.15), we agree to give it the value of unity by convention. The problem of measuring a physical constant is now replaced by that of producing a new physical standard.

The two-unit system could be easily adopted universally if it were found convenient. In engineering practice the need to employ Newton's law of universal gravitation from equation (1.14) occurs so rarely that the suppression in it of the dimensional factor **G** is not considered essential.

† See Planck, M., *General Mechanics*, translated by H. L. Brose (Macmillan, 1933), p. 46.

TABLE 1.3

*Dimensions of Several Derived Units in a Two-Unit System
Based on the Units of Length and Time.*

Quantity	Length	Time	Mass	Force	Energy	Power	Pressure
Dimension	L	T	L^3T^{-2}	L^4T^{-4}	L^5T^{-4}	L^5T^{-5}	L^2T^{-4}

1.3.5 Conversion equations; quantity equations

It has now been shown in detail that every physical dimension or unit is obtained by the same algebraic process as the corresponding physical quantity. It follows that dimensions and units are subject to the general rules of algebra, and that algebraic operations may be performed with them. Every physical quantity a may be interpreted as a product of its dimensionless measure $\tilde{a}$ (numerical value) and of the respective unit $\{a\}$:[†]

$$a = \tilde{a} \cdot \{a\}. \tag{1.16}$$

Accordingly, the symbols in a physical equation are interpreted as representing *the* physical quantity and not its measure in terms of a specific system of units. It is then said that the equations of physics are treated as *quantity equations*. Physical phenomena are independent of the choice of any particular system of units and standards, so that, for example, if we choose a smaller unit, the numerical measure increases proportionately, but the product remains the same. Since different units are never added together, all equations become *dimensionally homogeneous*; all additive terms in them have the same dimension in the adopted system of dimensions. Consequently, empirical factors must be regarded as being physical quantities, endowed with a dimension, if the equation is to be dimensionally correct.

The suppression of the constant g_0 in equation (1.13a) is algebraically equivalent to the substitution

$$g_0 \equiv 1$$

in equation (1.13b). With this substitution equation (1.13b) can be written

$$1 \text{ kp} = 9.80665 \text{ kg } \frac{\text{m}}{\text{sec}^2}$$

or

$$1 \text{ lbf} = 32.1740 \text{ lbm } \frac{\text{ft}}{\text{sec}^2}.$$

[†] This procedure can be justified rigorously from the point of view of higher algebra. See Landolt, M., *Grösse, Masszahl und Einheit* (Zürich: Birkhäuser, 1943). Also Bridgman, P. W., *Dimensional Analysis* (Yale Univ. Press, 1922); Drobot, S., "O Analizie Wymiarowej," (in Polish) *Zastosowania Matematyki*, I (1954), 233; Sedov, L. I., *Similarity and Dimensional Methods*, translated by M. Holt (Academic, 1959).

These are *conversion equations* which relate the arbitrary units of force to the consistent units of force in an absolute, three-unit system. They can be written more generally as

$$1 \text{ kp} = 1 \text{ kg} \cdot \mathbf{g} \; \Big\}$$
$$1 \text{ lbf} = 1 \text{ lbm} \cdot \mathbf{g}.$$

(1.16a)

Similarly, the substitution $k \equiv 1$ in equation (1.9a) leads to the conversion equation

$$1 \text{ acre} = 4.356 \times 10^4 \text{ ft}^2.$$

The suppression of the constant g_0 and the adoption of a gravitational system of units would lead to the conversion equations

$$1 \text{ kg} = \frac{1}{\mathbf{g}} \text{ kp},$$

$$1 \text{ lbm} = \frac{1}{\mathbf{g}} \text{ lbf},$$

which are algebraically identical with equations (1.16a). The conversion equation has the same structure as the defining equation for the respective units. Thus, equations (1.16a) appear in the form of Newton's Second Law; that is, force = mass × acceleration.

The use of dimensional conversion equations allows us to establish a simple algebraic formalism for the handling of practical computations. In this book all equations will be written in a three-unit† system of dimensions with all proportionality factors suppressed in them.‡ In particular, since the factor in Newton's Second Law is suppressed, the homogeneous form of the equations is the same in an absolute and in a gravitational system. All measured or tabulated quantities will be given in a set of units appropriate for the purpose, and regardless of the set of units in which calculations are performed. In order to express the final result in terms of a desirable unit, use will be made of the appropriate conversion equations. Every physical quantity will be handled as a whole; that is, inclusive of the unit, and every physical equation will be interpreted as a quantity equation.

It thus becomes necessary to record a large number of conversion equations. This is best done in tabular form. Table II§ contains several useful conversion equations. Tables III and IV contain conversion factors for pressure and energy; they are so composed that the unit on the left is equal to the product of the number on the same line and the unit at the top of the respective column. The conversion equations (1.16a) for the units of mass and force must constantly be borne in mind.

Several examples may serve to explain the details of this formalism.

As our first example, let us calculate the mean velocity of a body which covers a distance $x = 180$ miles in $t = 3$ hours (h). Hence,

---

† More precisely, in a four-unit system including temperature.
‡ However, empirical laws which express a relation between masses and forces, like the law of universal gravitation, will retain the proportionality factors. Fortunately, such laws will only seldom make their appearance in the course of this study.
§ All tables designated by Roman numerals are included at the end of Volume II.

$$V = \frac{x}{t} = \frac{180 \text{ mile}}{3 \text{ h}} = 60 \frac{\text{mile}}{\text{h}}.$$

If we wish to change to other units, for example to the metric system, we use the conversion equations

$$1 \text{ mile} = 1609.34 \text{ m}$$
$$1 \text{ h} = 3600 \text{ sec},$$

so that

$$V = 60 \frac{1609.34 \text{ m}}{3600 \text{ sec}} \approx 26.82 \frac{\text{m}}{\text{sec}}.$$

The latter equation can also be written

$$\frac{V}{\text{m/sec}} = 26.82.$$

When labeling coordinate systems in graphs and diagrams, it is very convenient to make use of this possibility and to divide the symbol of the quantity by the unit in which it is measured, treating the numerical values shown as dimensionless numbers. An example of this rational system of preparing graphs is shown in Figure 1.1 in which the velocity V of a material point has been plotted against distance, x.

Another example may further illustrate the ease of calculation which can be achieved by this method. Let us calculate the kinetic energy per unit mass, e, carried by a gas traveling at a velocity $V = 300$ ft/sec. We write

$$e = \tfrac{1}{2}V^2 = \tfrac{1}{2} (300 \text{ ft/sec})^2 = 45,000 \frac{\text{ft}^2}{\text{sec}^2}, \tag{a}$$

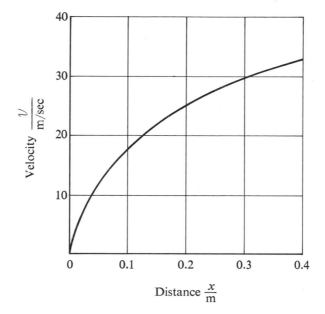

FIGURE 1.1. *Example of the dimensionally correct method of labeling coordinate axes.*

but since the unit ft²/sec² is unconventional, we prefer to transform it to ft lbf/lbm. We use the identity

$$1 \text{ lbf} = 1 \text{ lbm} \times 32.2 \text{ ft/sec}^2$$

from equations (1.16a) and substitute from it

$$1 \frac{\text{ft}^2}{\text{sec}^2} = \frac{1}{32.2} \frac{\text{ft lbf}}{\text{lbm}},$$

obtaining finally

$$e = 45{,}000 \frac{1}{32.2} \frac{\text{ft lbf}}{\text{lbm}} = 1398 \frac{\text{ft lbf}}{\text{lbm}}.$$

Alternatively, we may multiply the result in equation (a) by

$$\frac{1}{32.2} \cdot \frac{\text{lbf sec}^2}{\text{lbm ft}},$$

which is identically equal to unity, as seen from equations (1.16a) and does not, therefore, change the value of the quantity. In order to transform to the metric unit J/kg; we use the conversion equations

$$1 \text{ J} \approx 0.738 \text{ ft lbf}, \qquad \text{(Table IV)}$$
$$1 \text{ lbm} \approx 0.454 \text{ kg}, \qquad \text{(Table II)}$$

and write

$$e = 1398 \frac{\text{ft lbf}}{\text{lbm}} = 1398 \frac{\text{ft lbf}}{\text{lbm}} \cdot \frac{1}{0.738} \frac{\text{J}}{\text{ft lbf}} \cdot \frac{1}{0.454} \cdot \frac{\text{lbm}}{\text{kg}} = 4172 \frac{\text{J}}{\text{kg}}.$$

The last two groups of terms are identically equal to unity, and all undesirable units cancel.

1.3.6　Summary

Owing to the importance attached to an efficient ability to handle diverse units with assurance, it may be useful briefly to summarize the characteristics of the system of units (or dimensions).

(1) A system of units (or dimensions) is based on a small but arbitrary number n of fundamental or primary units (dimensions) P whose physical nature is also arbitrary.

(2) Quantities other than the fundamental ones are measured (expressed) in terms of derived units (dimensions), each of which is of the form of a monomial product.

(3) There exists an intimate link between the secondary or derived quantity S and the equation used to define it. The defining equation may be a law of nature or a primary definition. This link can be expressed in three alternative ways.

(3a) An independent unit is chosen for the new quantity S. The number of primary units is increased to $n + 1$, and the defining equation is written with a proportionality factor k. This factor appears in all equations whose derivation makes use of the defining equation.

(3b) A consistent unit is chosen for the new quantity S. The number of primary units remains equal to n, the defining equation is written with $k \equiv 1$, but measurements must be expressed in terms of the consistent unit.

The desire to express all measurements in terms of a consistent set of units is rooted in the interpretation of the equations of physics as relations between measures (measure equations).

(3c) An independent unit is chosen for the quantity S, but the defining equation is written with $k \equiv 1$, that is, in terms of the n fundamental units. The relation between the independent and consistent unit is expressed in the form of a conversion equation. All calculations are performed on physical quantities each of which is interpreted as the product of a numerical factor — the measure of the quantity — and the unit in terms of which they have been measured. Rules of algebra are used in conjunction with the required number of conversion equations to express the result in terms of any desired unit, and the equations of physics are interpreted as quantity equations.

Although all three alternatives lead to consistent procedures, the procedure (3c) has proved to be most flexible and, therefore, favorable from the point of view of avoiding needless numerical errors.

The preceding summary will be found useful in the study of *dimensional analysis*.

1.3.7   Units of pressure

We shall complete the discussion in this section by reviewing the units of pressure which are employed in contemporary practice because of the importance of the measurement of pressure in thermodynamics.

The force per unit area is termed *pressure*. In English units it should be measured in lbf/ft², but almost all pressure gauges are calibrated in lbf/in².† Thus,

$$1 \text{ lbf/in}^2 = 144 \text{ lbf/ft}^2.$$

In the MKS system pressure should be measured in N/m², but this unit is inconveniently small in practical applications. Consequently, use is made of its decimal multiple, the bar, defined as

$$1 \text{ bar} = 1 \times 10^5 \text{ N/m}^2 = 1 \times 10^6 \text{ dyne/cm}^2.$$

In the drafting of meteorological charts, the millibar (mbar), a unit 1000 times smaller, is generally favored.

Pressures are frequently measured in terms of an independent, empirical unit, the *standard atmosphere* (1 atm) which is equal to the pressure exerted by a column of mercury 760 mm high at 0°C, when the density of the mercury is 13.5951 g/cm³ and at a place where the gravitational acceleration has the standard value 980.665 cm/sec². The pressure corresponding to 1 mm of mercury under those conditions is called 1 Torricelli (1 Torr). Hence

$$1 \text{ atm} = 101{,}325 \text{ N/m}^2 = 760 \text{ Torr}.$$

and in English units

$$1 \text{ atm} = 14.6959 \text{ lbf/in}^2 \approx 14.7 \text{ lbf/in}^2.$$

In the metric gravitational system of units, pressures are measured in kp/m², or in the more convenient units of kp/cm² to which the name of one *technical atmosphere* (1 at)

---

† Sometimes abbreviated to psi. We shall avoid this abbreviation in order to exhibit the connection between this and the fundamental units so as to retain ease of conversion.

is sometimes given. The pressure of 1 kp/m^2 is equal to that exerted by a column 1 mm high of water at $+4°C$, when its density is a maximum; more precisely the height of the column should be 1.000028 mm because 1 kg of water occupies the volume of 1.000028 dm^3. The kilogram was originally defined as the mass of 1 dm^3 of water at $+4°C$ and under a pressure of 1 atm. In order to facilitate comparative measurements a standard kilogram of platinum–iridium was manufactured and its mass was made as nearly equal to that of 1 dm^3 of water as it was then possible to determine. Later, a small error in the standard was detected, with the result that a mass of water equal to the standard — that is, a volume of 1 liter, by definition — has a volume of 1.000028 dm^3. Nevertheless, the standard kilogram was retained, as it would create too much confusion to change it. We note, therefore, that

$$1 \; kp/cm^2 = 98066.5 \; N/m^2 = 0.980665 \; bar = 735.56 \; Torr = 0.967841 \; atm.$$

Pressures are also measured in mm and ft of water and in inches of mercury. The various units of pressure are compared in Table III. The table gives conversion factors of the highest possible accuracy, but in practical numerical work these may be, naturally, rounded off.

Sometimes, in practical measurements, the *gauge pressure* is used. This is the amount by which the true pressure exceeds the atmospheric pressure, and is so called because it is the value measured by an ordinary pressure gauge. It should be indicated by a different abbreviation† to distinguish it from the absolute pressure. We shall avoid these notations, always indicating absolute pressures.

1.4   The system and its surroundings. Open and closed systems

In the study of mechanics, as a rule, we are quite clear about the particular body or system of bodies whose behavior we wish to describe with the aid of Newton's laws of motion. Very often the analysis is formulated with respect to a portion of a body or structure and Newton's laws are applied to it rather than to the whole. This portion is always imagined *isolated* from the rest with the aid of *fictitious* cuts, that is, with the aid of a boundary in the form of a geometrical surface which may be partly fictitious and which may partly coincide with a real physical boundary. In fact, in any branch of physics, the analysis of a phenomenon or process in terms of the relevant physical laws must begin by mentally *isolating* a collection of bodies from the rest. Accordingly, in thermodynamics, we shall employ the concept of a *thermodynamic system*, or *system* for short. A system is any collection of material bodies imagined isolated from the rest with the aid of a clearly defined *boundary*. As is the case in mechanics, we shall not necessarily assume that the boundary is rigid; on the contrary, in most cases the boundary will deform when the system is subjected to some process which we wish to understand and to analyze. It should be quite clear, however, just as was the case in mechanics, that the definition of a particular system and of its boundary is entirely arbitrary and depends on the person who performs the analysis. The boundary may be a real one, or it may be drawn arbitrarily through space. Furthermore, again in similarity with the analyses performed in mechanics, the same general process or phenomenon

---

† The symbols psia and psig are often used to distinguish between the absolute (psia) and gauge (psig) pressure, both being measured in psi = lbf/in^2. In Germany the symbols ata and atü are used for the same purpose.

may be successfully and rigorously analyzed in terms of several alternative systems. The choice of a particular boundary enclosing a particular system is dictated exclusively by convenience and by our intuitive grasp of the subject.

The material objects not included in the system inside its boundary constitute its *surroundings*. We may be inclined to say at this point that the surroundings of a system, therefore, include "the rest of the universe." In order to avoid speculation about the nature of the universe, on whether it is contracting, expanding, or oscillating, it is not necessary to succumb to such an impulse. It is known from experience that the effect of any process on whose analysis we may wish to concentrate our attention decays with distance. At a sufficiently large distance from any system under consideration, the processes which occur within it cease to exert any measureable influence and may be ignored for all practical purposes. Consequently, experience shows that even in the surroundings of a system it is only necessary to include a limited number of material objects, namely, those present in its *immediate surroundings*. Again, the precise objects to be included, and the distance from the system at which the presence of further quantities of matter may be safely disregarded, will differ from case to case and will be dictated by our intuitive understanding of the phenomenon under consideration. It is quite clear, for example, that the extent of the surroundings of a system will be different when we analyze the operation of an internal combustion engine from that required in the analysis of the effects of an explosion of a nuclear device.

In the study of thermodynamics it is impossible to leave the surroundings completely out of account when phenomena in a system are studied because the system will invariably *interact* with it, that is, the system will be affected by it. In mechanics, the influence of the surroundings is taken into account by specifying the forces exerted on the system from a distance and at its boundary, including the "internal" forces at that portion of the boundary which results from a cut. In general, the way in which a system interacts with its surroundings and the extent of such interactions will depend on the physical nature of the walls or partitions which are adjacent to the boundary of the system. We shall find it, therefore, necessary to study the properties of such partitions. We shall begin by making one important distinction between systems and we shall resume the discussion of the properties of partitions in Chapter 2.

A system is called *closed* when its boundary is not crossed by matter. In the contrary case, we say that the system is *open*. It should be noted here that a closed system is one of constant mass, but that the converse is not the case. When a system loses matter through one channel and gains mass at exactly the same rate through another, its mass will remain constant, but the system is an open one.

The distinction between a closed and an open system in thermodynamics is analogous to the distinction between a Lagrangian and an Eulerian frame of reference in fluid mechanics.† In the Lagrangian frame of reference, the motion of a large mass of fluid is described by concentrating attention on a small element of fluid of fixed mass and by writing down its equation of motion. In this way, the problem of determining the whole motion consists in expressing the coordinates of every particle as functions of time. Each particle of fluid whose motion is analyzed as part of a more general problem constitutes a closed system. An alternative and often simpler method of representing the motion of a large expanse of fluid concentrates on an element of volume which is fixed in space and aims at describing the instantaneous motion at every point in space

† See Prandtl, L., *Essentials of Fluid Dynamics*, translated by W. M. Deans (London: Blackie, 1952), p. 32.

as a function of time. A small volume element does not contain the same fluid during the time under consideration because different fluid elements constantly flow through it; it constitutes, therefore, an open system. A "point in space" is treated as the mathematical limit of a fixed volume ΔV when $\Delta V \to 0$. This alternative mode of description is known as the Eulerian method.

In order to illustrate these very important concepts, we shall consider the cylinder of an internal combustion engine shown sketched in Figure 1.2. We assume that the reader is sufficiently familiar with the operation of such an engine. If we wish to analyze the processes which take place inside the cylinder, we will find it convenient to draw the boundary inside it, in the immediate neighborhood of the piston, cylinder bore and cylinder head as shown by the broken line in Figure 1.2. As the piston moves in and out of the cylinder, the boundary deforms and the volume of the system changes. During that part of the process when both valves are closed, the system includes a fixed amount of matter and is a closed one. The fact that the combustible mixture is made to explode during this process, that is, the fact that a chemical reaction takes place inside it does not affect the issue. Since no matter crosses the boundary, we say that the system is closed. During the process of induction when the mixture of air and gasoline vapor is drawn into the cylinder, and during the process of exhaust, when the burnt gases are expelled, the system included inside the boundary represented by the broken line in Figure 1.2 is an open one.

The surroundings of the system, as we have defined it, will include the metal of the engine, the cooling water and the atmosphere outside it. It is clear that the nature of the interaction between the system and its surroundings will depend on the properties of the metal walls and of the piston. The extent of the interaction will be different with metal walls as compared with the unrealistic case when they may be made of a plastic.

For the analysis of the same engine, we could, if we wished, have drawn the boundary immediately outside it, as shown by the chain-dotted line in Figure 1.2. In this case the system would be open, but the boundary would be rigid. The surroundings would include the atmospheric air just outside the engine. Finally, when analyzing, for example,

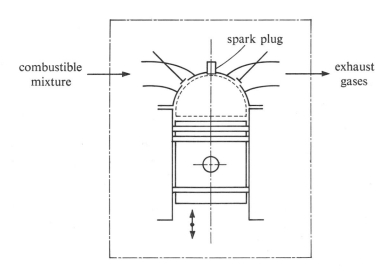

FIGURE 1.2. *Choice of system and of boundary.*

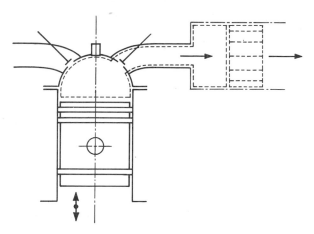

FIGURE 1.3. *Fictitious cylinder and piston used to define a closed system.*

the process of exhaust we could imagine that the exhaust duct is connected to a fictitious cylinder provided with a piston as shown in Figure 1.3. As the combustion gases
are expelled from the cylinder, the fictitious piston would move outwards, and the
system marked by the broken line in the diagram would become a closed one. Its
boundary, evidently, would not be rigid.

A nondeforming boundary of an open system is sometimes called a *control surface*,
the open system itself being said to constitute a *control volume*.

1.5 Macroscopic description of the state of a system. Classical thermodynamics

Having selected a system and its boundary, we shall proceed to describe it adequately in precise numerical terms. This is an essential step in any analysis of a problem in physics because it then allows us to conduct the analysis with the aid of mathematical formulae. A thermodynamic system is most easily described in terms of the
physical properties of its components. In general, we shall find that the system does not
necessarily consist of a single homogeneous substance, although the latter does constitute the simplest kind of system. In such cases we shall find that the system can very
often be divided into a finite number of homogeneous subsystems. The description of
the system will then include a description of all of its homogeneous subsystems. We
can, therefore, now concentrate on the description of homogeneous systems. We shall
describe them in terms of their physical properties as they are measured with the aid of
suitable laboratory instruments. These properties may include, for example, the pressure, the specific volume or density, the electrical properties such as conductivity, the
optical properties, such as refractive index, and so on For ease of expression, we say
that the system is in a given *state* when *all* its measurable physical properties have
fixed values, that is, when they are expressed by specifying a set of definite numbers.
All such numbers are, of course, endowed with dimensions and are expressed in terms
of the units of a particular system of units. The set of these numbers constitutes the set
of the *thermodynamic coordinates*, parameters of state, or (thermodynamic) *properties*
of the system.

No general rule can be laid down as to the particular properties required to describe the state of a particular system. These must be known from our familiarity with the system through experiment. For example, it is quite clear that to describe the state of a certain mass of gas contained in a vessel we shall use properties that are different from those which we shall require in order to define the state of a piece of iron in a magnetic field. Furthermore, it is known from experience that in many but by no means all cases the shape of the system need not be included in the description of its state, though its volume must be considered.

Experience teaches that the properties of a system do not change independently of one another and that a fixed, *finite* number of them determine all the others. A given mass of gas, or liquid, of a specified chemical composition, for example, changes its refractive index when its pressure and specific volume is varied. In other words, in the case of every system, a certain limited, finite number of properties *only* can be varied independently; if the values of that number of properties are fixed, all the others assume fixed values, and the state is fixed. Frequently importance is attached only to the *number* of properties which can be fixed independently, the actual properties chosen for the purpose being of secondary importance. In selecting the properties to be regarded as independent, it is only necessary to exclude such pairs of properties as specific volume and density; one being the reciprocal of the other, equation (1.12), we cannot adjust both of them independently.

The simplest systems encountered in thermodynamics, namely homogeneous substances, such as liquids or gases, are characterized by having *two* independent properties. For example, the state of a gas of fixed chemical composition is fixed, that is, *all* its properties have fixed values, when its pressure and specific volume are fixed. Examples of thermodynamic systems will be discussed more systematically from this point of view in Chapters 7 and 8.

Translating the preceding experimental observations into mathematical terms, we can say that any property, y, regarded as dependent, is a *single-valued function*† of the n independent properties $x_1, x_2, \ldots, x_n$, and we can write

$$y = \mathrm{f}(x_1, x_2, \ldots, x_n), \tag{1.17}$$

there being only one value y for a given set of values of $x_1, x_2, \ldots, x_n$. An equation of this form is known as an *equation of state* or *characteristic equation* for a given system. It must be determined experimentally from measured data; in certain cases it can be derived from first principles by methods used in other branches of physics, such as statistical thermodynamics formerly known as *statistical mechanics*. Depending on circumstances, the results of measurements can be represented by one or several empirical formulas which fit the data, by a suitable graph, a digital computer program, or by simply tabulating them. We shall encounter all alternative forms of the equation of state in this book. The precise form in which the equation of state (1.17) is given is not, in itself, important. The essential fact is that in thermodynamics we shall always assume its *existence* for all systems under consideration.

The equation of state represents the dependent variable as a function of n independent variables and it is clear that the mathematical theory of functions of a finite

† In the study of the properties of certain anomalous substances such as water, Section 7.5.9, or in the study of supercooling and supersaturation, Section 7.5.11, it might appear that the equation of state is not single-valued. Such an impression is erroneous, as will be explained in Section 7.5.10.

number of independent variables will play an important part in thermodynamics. Since in the mathematical study of such functions the emphasis and notation differ from those required in thermodynamics, we shall find it necessary to review this subject in Sections 3.3 to 3.7.

It is easy to indicate systems which cannot be described by the preceding scheme. For example, in order to specify the state of a very high column of atmospheric air at rest it will not be sufficient to indicate its density or pressure because both quantities vary *continuously* with height. Instead of two properties it is necessary to indicate two continuous functions, that is, two infinities of properties. It must, therefore, be recognized that the generalizations of thermodynamics do not apply to such systems *directly*. We shall revert to this problem in Chapter 6, where we shall be able to extend our present concepts to include such *continuous systems*. However, even today, the analysis of some very important systems cannot be formulated with the aid of the methods of thermodynamics because the nature of the variables needed to describe their state is unknown.

In the preceding definition of the state of a system, it was not found necessary to speculate about the structure of matter and to inquire whether it consists of discrete particles such as atoms and molecules or to go even further, and to include the elementary particles, protons, neutrons, electrons, and so on. Since all the properties of systems were assumed measured with the aid of full-scale instruments, it was implied that matter can be treated as a continuous medium because this is the impression we gain from such experiments. Whenever such a view is taken, we say that a *macroscopic* description of the system has been provided.† The consequences of this point of view form the subject of inquiry in *classical thermodynamics* which will constitute the principal topic of this book. An alternative method of description, to be reviewed in the succeeding section, is adopted by *statistical thermodynamics*. The extension needed to include the analysis of contiunous systems are also considered to fall outside the realm of classical thermodynamics; they are said to belong to *continuum thermodynamics*.

1.6   Microscopic description of thermodynamic systems. Statistical thermodynamics; classical and quantum mechanics

In contrast with the macroscopic description, we can attempt to describe and to analyze the systems encountered in nature by accepting the view that matter consists of discrete particles, that is, of atoms and molecules. According to this point of view, for example, a certain quantity of gas enclosed in a vessel consists of an enormously large number of molecules which move chaotically in all directions colliding with one another and bouncing against the walls of the container. In developing this hypothesis, we shall find it necessary to make further assumptions regarding the nature of these collisions, to state, for example, whether or not they are elastic, and to specify whether the molecules interact during collisions only or whether they also exert long-range forces on one another. Finally, we shall be forced to speculate about the nature of the bonds which link atoms in a molecule, whether they are rigid, elastic, or otherwise. In other words, we shall be forced to *postulate* a suitable *molecular model* for every substance.

† The reader can find additional interesting considerations on this subject in Bridgman, P. W., *The Nature of Thermodynamics* (Harvard Univ. Press, 1941).

It is quite clear that no direct experiments to verify the correctness of such models are possible. Any instrument which we might use for the purpose would be enormously large compared with the size of a molecule and could not, therefore, serve to measure the forces acting on the latter. The only way in which we can judge whether any assumed model is adequate is to deduce from it the behavior of a large collection of molecules, that is, of a macroscopic system, and to compare the predicted behavior with large-scale experiments. Models which result in agreement with the experiments are retained, models which conflict with them are rejected or modified. Here, of course, agreement always leaves a margin of experimental error and refinements in the model usually accompany refinements in measuring techniques. By this means, the preceding *microscopic* description is made to agree with the macroscopic description in spite of the apparent, but superficial, discrepancy between them.

Adopting the microscopic point of view, we would say that two states of a system are identical if all molecules have identical positions and move with identical velocities in both cases. The natural way of describing such a *microstate* in the case of molecules which move like material points would be to introduce a system of coordinates x, y, z, and to specify for every molecule its position vector $\mathbf{r}(x, y, z)$ and its velocity vector $\mathbf{c}(u, v, w)$ by indicating its components u, v, w along x, y, z, respectively. In actual calculations of this nature, it has been found preferable to specify the components p_x, p_y, p_z of the linear momentum $\mathbf{p} = mc$ of the molecules (of mass m), instead of the components of velocity. If the system contains N molecules, we would require $6N$ coordinates to define its state. The number of molecules, N, even in a minute macroscopic system is very large. From comparisons between calculations and experiment, for example, it is known that 1 cm³ of a gas at atmospheric pressure and at the temperature of melting ice contains $N = \mathbf{L} = 2.687 \times 10^{19}$ molecules!† It is quite clear, therefore, that the preceding obvious scheme is impractical, even if methods for measuring the positions and momenta of molecules did exist. The number of coordinates would simply be impossibly large.

An alternative method consists in dividing the *physical space* in which the molecules perform their motion into cubical or rectangular cells whose volume is given by $\Delta x \Delta y \Delta z$, Figure 1.4(a). We concentrate on a typical cell which encloses the portion of the physical space contained between the coordinates x, y, z and $x + \Delta x, y + \Delta y, z + \Delta z$. Instead of describing the momenta of all molecules contained in the cell, we again concentrate on those whose momenta are contained between the values p_x, p_y, p_z and $p_x + \Delta p_x$, $p_y + \Delta p_y$, $p_z + \Delta p_z$. If we imagine the three momentum components represented on the three axes of a Cartesian system of coordinates, Figure 1.4 (b), we obtain the *momentum space*. Hence, a molecule is represented by two associated points, one in each of the two spaces. In order to represent a molecule by one point, we can imagine, even if we cannot visualize, a six-dimensional space, the *phase space for a molecule* or μ space, whose Cartesian coordinates are x, y, z, p_x, p_y, p_z and to isolate from it a typical cell of volume

$$\Delta\Omega = \Delta x \cdot \Delta y \cdot \Delta z \cdot \Delta p_x \cdot \Delta p_y \cdot \Delta p_z. \tag{1.18}$$

† More precisely

$$\mathbf{L} = (2.68719 \pm 0.00010) \times 10^{19} \frac{1}{\text{cm}^3};$$

the universal constant of physics $\mathbf{L}$ is called the Loschmidt number.

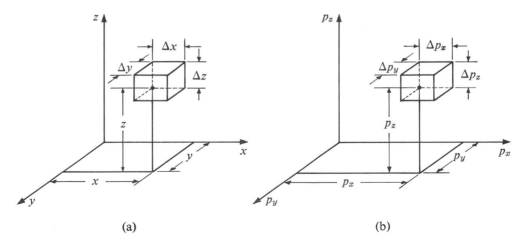

FIGURE 1.4. *Cells in the physical and momentum spaces.*
(a) *Physical space.* (b) *Momentum space.*

In this way the study of the distribution of momentum components over the molecules has been made equivalent to the study of the distribution of points in the phase space. For a given network of cells, it now suffices to indicate the number of molecules, n, contained in each cell, the so-called *occupation numbers*, in order to complete the description.

Even this scheme is not entirely acceptable, because molecules cannot be counted and their momenta cannot be measured. Instead, we specify the *probable* occupation numbers n and this allows us to use the methods of probability and statistics in the theory. In fact, the preceding scheme for describing the state has been devised with that object in view. Hence, the branch of physics which uses these methods is called *statistical* thermodynamics.

On further examination it turns out that not all systems can be analyzed in terms of the μ space and it is necessary to introduce a different phase space, the *phase space proper* or Γ space, whose coordinates represent the position and momenta of *all* molecules. An additional complication is introduced when polyatomic molecules are considered. Such molecules can accumulate additional energy by virtue of their rotation about an axis passing through them and by performing internal vibrations. This introduces further coordinates which supplement the momenta considered so far. Hence, the Γ space possesses $6N$ dimensions for a monatomic molecule and more for polyatomic molecules; and a particular microstate is represented by a single point in that space. We shall, however, refrain from pursuing this matter any further owing to its complexity. We shall be able to illustrate the main points sufficiently well, if inexactly, by confining our attention to the μ space for a monatomic molecule alone.

Since to each cell in the μ space there corresponds an average position in the physical space, x, y, z, and an average position in the momentum space, p_x, p_y, p_z, the average energy of a molecule is specified. Its potential energy depends on position and its kinetic energy is $\frac{1}{2}(p_x^2 + p_y^2 + p_z^2)/m$. It follows, further, that one macroscopic state, or *macrostate* of a system, may correspond to a multitude of microstates, and that the behavior of a macroscopic system derived by this method will be determined by the details of the molecular model as well as by the coarseness of the lattice used for the cellular subdivisions in the μ space. This is conditioned by the fact that large-scale instruments which measure thermodynamic macrostates are insensitive to rapid fluctuations caused by the motion of molecules. Such instruments are sensitive only to *average* forces, and it is intuitively evident that a given average or macrostate may be the same for a large number of microstates.

Comparing the two methods of analysis, we see that the science of classical thermodynamics leads to laws which are independent of any assumptions regarding the structure of matter but from which the properties of substances, that is, their equations of state, cannot be derived. On the other hand, the science of statistical thermodynamics begins with suitable hypotheses, from which equations of state as well as the laws of classical thermodynamics can be obtained. As already stated, these hypotheses must be subjected to subsequent verification by macroscopic experiments.

It might be supposed that the accuracy of the description of a thermodynamic system increases as the size of a cell in the phase space is made to decrease and that it is possible to carry out the analysis by passing to the limit of infinitely small cells with $\Delta\Omega \to 0$, and by integrating over the phase space. This is the method used in *classical statistical thermodynamics* (or *kinetic theory* in the case of gases). It leads to many results which agree with experiments but also to some which are in glaring contradiction with them. In 1900 Max Planck discovered that these very important contradictions can be removed only by postulating that the cells in the phase space have a finite volume. In the μ space of a monatomic molecule this volume must be equal to $\Delta\Omega = \hbar^3$, where $\hbar$ is a universal constant of physics and the same for all systems. It is easy to verify that its dimension (length $\times$ momentum), equation (1.18), is

$$[\hbar] = [x]\,[p] = \mathsf{ML^2T^{-1}},$$

and is equal to that of the product of energy and time (or "action"). In the absolute physical system the related constant, $\mathbf{h} = 2\pi\hbar$, known as *Planck's constant*, or the "*quantum* of action," has the value

$$\left.\begin{aligned} \mathbf{h} &= (6.62517 \pm 0.00023) \times 10^{-27} \text{ erg sec,}\\[6pt] \hbar &= \frac{\mathbf{h}}{2\pi} = (1.05443 \pm 0.00004) \times 10^{-27} \text{ erg sec.} \end{aligned}\right\} \qquad (1.18a)$$

The preceding postulate constitutes the starting point of *quantum statistics*. This is contrasted with *classical statistics* when the passage to the limit $\Delta\Omega \to 0$ is performed.

It should be realized that the process of passing to the limit $\Delta\Omega \to 0$ implies that the energy of a molecule, like its position, can change continuously, that is, that the difference between the energies associated with two neighboring cells in the phase space can be made arbitrarily small. The assertion that the volume of a cell in the phase space is finite means that this energy difference cannot be smaller than a certain quantum. As a molecule moves from one cell of the phase space to its neighbor, it is said to undergo a *quantum jump*.

Finally, it can be seen that the total number of microstates possible for a given number of molecules, N, is finite in quantum statistics. In classical statistics the number of possible microstates increases *ad infinitum* with increasing fineness of the lattice and becomes a continuum in the limit when the lattice is made infinitely fine. In quantum statistics this number is finite and the totality of microstates forms a so-called *discrete* group.

As a matter of interest we may note here that quantum statistics puts a restriction on the *volume* of an element, $\Delta\Omega$, and not on all its sides. Assuming, for the sake of simplicity that $\Delta x = \Delta y = \Delta z = \epsilon$ and $\Delta p_x = \Delta p_y = \Delta p_z = \delta$ we see that the product $\epsilon\delta = \hbar$. If the lattice is made finer in the physical space, it must be made correspondingly coarser in the momentum space. Consequently, we may assert broadly, that if the position of a molecule is known more and more exactly ($\epsilon \to 0$), its velocity will be specified less and less exactly ($\delta \to \infty$). This fact is proved in all its generality in quantum mechanics and is known as *Heisenberg's uncertainty principle*.

Heisenberg's uncertainty principle is intimately connected with the experimentally established dual nature of elementary particles which exhibit corpuscular as well as wave-like characteristics. The latter are brought into evidence by the diffraction patterns produced by streams of elementary particles and normally associated with waves. The motion of elementary particles, unlike that of large macroscopic bodies, is not governed by Newtonian (or classical) mechanics but by *Schrödinger's equation* (or quantum mechanics). Schrödinger's equation, which will be introduced to the reader in Volume II, constitutes a theoretical formulation of the laws of quantum mechanics and fully accounts for the wave-like aspects of microscopic particles and naturally leads to Heisenberg's uncertainty principle. Thus the uncertainty principle, contrary to the literal meaning of the word "uncertainty," does not relate to the normal uncertainty or limited precision associated with the use of necessarily imperfect measuring instruments which are subject to constant improvement; it brings into evidence the more subtle uncertainty in describing the position and momentum of an elementary particle under conditions when its wave-like nature comes to the fore.

We have outlined some of the essential concepts of statistical thermodynamics which can be based on classical or on quantum mechanics, depending on circumstances. This was done with the aid of the model of a gas, pictured as a collection of freely and randomly moving molecules. The models which are suitable for the study of the properties of liquids or solids are evidently different. In actual fact, no successful microscopic model for a liquid has yet been proposed. In the case of solids, crystalline materials are imagined to consist of regular arrays of atoms arranged in characteristic *lattices* in the physical space. Every crystal lattice is assumed to consist of a large number of identical unit cells, and the resulting symmetries are said to determine the characteristic shapes and properties of macroscopic crystals. The atoms in the lattice are supposed to be linked to all others with elastic bonds. The only motions in which the atoms can participate are characteristic vibrations under the restoring forces which the links exert upon them. In metals, for example, the arrangement of atoms in the lattice is not always perfect, and some of them may become misplaced giving rise to *dislocations* which cause important differences in the strength and, generally, in the behavior of metals as compared with perfect crystals.

The preceding description of a microstate was cast entirely in mechanical terms and it is not quite clear how the mechanical quantities which characterize such a microstate or a series of microstates associated with one macrostate are related to the properties used in the macroscopic description of the system. It has already been mentioned that measuring instruments are not sensitive to instantaneous and rapid changes in the microstate. It follows, therefore, that macroscopic parameters can only be represented by the common *averages* of the mechanical characteristics of the microstates which correspond to a given macrostate. For example, the pressure exerted on the walls of a vessel by a gas contained in it is interpreted as the average result of the very many impulses which they suffer as the molecules impinge on them at high velocities and in large numbers. We shall encounter additional connections between averages of microscopic characteristics and macroscopic parameters in Volume II. Here it is sufficient to note that the science of statistical thermodynamics provides a systematic interpretation of macroscopic properties in terms of averages taken over suitable microscopic quantities. It is known from mathematical statistics that only systems containing large numbers of particles will show statistically insignificant departures from averages. In other words, meaningful averages, that is meaningful and measurable macroscopic properties can be associated only with statistically large collections of particles. Hence, it follows that small collections of molecules cannot be analyzed by the methods of classical thermodynamics because in them departures from average states are large. Thus, for example, the concept of pressure cannot be associated with a vessel which contains several molecules only, because their impacts occur so rarely that the effect is not equivalent to a uniform constant pressure, as is the case with collections containing enormous numbers of molecules.

In the study of thermodynamics it is essential to keep the above two points of view, the classical and macroscopic, as opposed to the statistical or microscopic, sharply separated in one's mind if no confusion is to result. In this book we shall provide a rigorous formulation of the laws of classical thermodynamics. The results of statistical thermodynamics, whether based on classical or quantum mechanics, will be introduced in a descriptive and heuristic manner only.[†]

1.7 On passing to the limit $\Delta V \to 0$

In developing our subject, as was the case in mechanics, it is often necessary to perform integrations over some space filled with matter, with electric charges, magnetic dipoles, and so on. For example, when the mass of a certain fluid on nonuniform density is calculated the result is written

$$m = \iiint\limits_{V} \rho(x, y, z) \, \mathrm{d}V. \tag{1.19}$$

The preceding mathematical symbol implies two limiting processes. First, the density is defined as the limit

$$\rho = \lim_{\Delta V \to 0} \frac{\Delta m}{\Delta V} \tag{1.19a}$$

of the mass Δm contained in a volume ΔV of space, as this volume is made arbitrarily small. The microscopic description of systems presents us here with the following

---

[†] A full presentation of the theory of statistical thermodynamics can be found in Tolman, R. C., *The Principles of Statistical Mechanics* (Oxford Univ. Press, 1938). See also, Rushbrooke, G. S., *Introduction to Statistical Mechanics* (Clarendon Press, 1949); Fast, J. D., *Entropy* (McGraw-Hill, 1962); MacDonald, D. K. C., *Introductory Statistical Mechanics* (Wiley, 1963); Landau, L. D., and Lifshitz, E. M., *Statistical Physics*, translated by E. and R. F. Peierls (Pergamon and Addison-Wesley, 1958); Reif, F., *Fundamentals of Statistical and Thermal Physics* (McGraw-Hill, 1965). Fay, J. A., *Molecular Thermodynamics* (Addison-Wesley, 1965).

quandary. As long as the volume ΔV is large enough to contain a very large number of molecules, the fact that these molecules move in and out of the element ΔV has little effect on its mass Δm and the series of values of $\Delta m/\Delta V$ appears to converge to a limit, and this limit is defined as the average density over the volume ΔV. However, as the volume ΔV is progressively decreased in the process of making it "arbitrarily small," eventually it will become so small that it will contain a few molecules only. Now, as these molecules move at high velocities, the number of them contained in the volume ΔV will fluctuate and at some stage the volume ΔV will become so small that during part of the time it will contain no molecules at all. Under the circumstances it is difficult to see whether the limit (1.19a) does exist, and whether a continuous function $\rho(x, y, z)$ which represents the spatial density distribution can be said to exist. In fact, the preceding analysis gives the impression that the passage to the limit (1.19a) will tend to yield a function such as the one sketched in Figure 1.5. It is realized that the second limit implied by the process of integration in equation (1.19) exists only if the continuous function $\rho(x, y, z)$ can be said to exist.

This genuine quandary can only be resolved by an appeal to observation and experiment. These show that systems which consist of very large numbers of molecules behave like *continua*. This means that on passing to the limit $\Delta V \to 0$, it is possible at every instant to assign to every point in space a value of density ρ equal to the limiting value, lim $\Delta m/\Delta V$, which is reached when ΔV is still large compared with molecular dimensions. Thus, the existence of a continuous function $\rho(x, y, z)$ of space coordinates may be assumed and the complications which arise from allowing ΔV to tend to zero without limit may be disregarded. Conversely, the mass contained in a finite volume V can be computed by the integral (1.19).

The assumption that a thermodynamic system can be treated as a continuum underlies all derivations employed in classical and continuum thermodynamics (as well as in continuum mechanics, electromagnetic theory, fluid mechanics, and so forth), and its correctness is inferred from the fact that the resulting description does not conflict with observation. The fact that this assumption is made, just as the interpretation of macroscopic measurable properties in terms of microscopic quantities, is seen, once again, to exclude the applicability of these branches of science to systems which contain only small numbers of molecules, atoms, electrons, and so on.

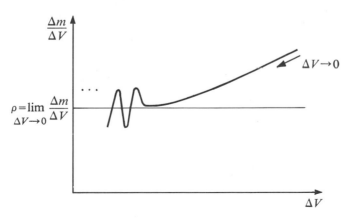

FIGURE 1.5. *Passing to the limit* $\Delta V \to 0$.

1.8 Extensive, intensive, and specific properties

Examining all the possible macroscopic thermodynamic properties of systems, we shall find it useful to distinguish between two classes of them. When the value of a property in a homogeneous system is independent of its mass, we shall call the property *intensive*. Pressure, P, is an example of such a property because it has the same value for the whole system as for any of its parts. The velocity, $\mathcal{V}$, of a system moving uniformly is another example of an intensive property. In contradistinction, properties whose values in homogeneous systems are proportional to the mass will be called *extensive*. More generally, a quantity whose value for the whole system is equal to the sum of the values for the subsystems into which the system can be divided is called extensive. Volume, V, is a familiar example of an extensive property, because its value is, for example, halved for half the system. The energy, kinetic or potential, of a macroscopic system of mass m is also an example of an extensive property. In this book all extensive properties will be denoted by capital letters.

It was already mentioned in Section 1.3 that in a homogeneous system it is convenient to consider its specific volume or volume per unit mass

$$v = \frac{V}{m}.$$

In general, it will be found convenient to make frequent use of *specific quantities* of homogeneous systems by dividing their extensive properties by their mass. Hence, if Z denotes any extensive property, the associated specific property is defined as

$$z = \frac{Z}{m},$$

and we shall follow the convention of using capital and lower case symbols to make the distinction. The kinetic energy per unit mass, $e = \frac{1}{2}\mathcal{V}^2$, considered in Section 1.3 is also a specific property.

Very often, particularly in problems involving chemical reactions, specific quantities are referred to one mol (Section 3.9) rather than to a unit of mass of the system. We then obtain molar (specific) quantities. We shall use the subscript m to distinguish them from the usual specific quantities, but only when absolutely necessary; otherwise, we shall simply use the corresponding lower case symbol. Thus, in a system containing n mols of a homogeneous substance, the molar (specific) volume is

$$v_m = \frac{V}{n} \quad \text{measured in} \quad \frac{m^3}{\text{kmol}} \quad \text{or} \quad \frac{\text{ft}^3}{\text{lbmol}}.$$

In general

$$z_m = \frac{Z}{n}, \tag{1.20}$$

sometimes also written

$$z = \frac{Z}{n}. \tag{1.20a}$$

It will be remembered from mathematics that a function, f, of the independent variables x_1, x_2, . . . , which has the property that

$$f(\lambda x_1, \lambda x_2, \ldots) = \lambda^m f(x_1, x_2, \ldots), \tag{1.21}$$

where λ is an arbitrary constant, is called homogeneous of degree m.† It is seen that when all variables of a homogeneous function are multiplied by a constant, the function itself is multiplied by the same constant raised to a power which describes the degree of the function. It is easy to see that an equation of state for any extensive property of a homogeneous system must be homogeneous of order $m = 1$ in terms of other extensive properties; indeed if the extensive properties which are considered independent are multiplied by a constant λ, the mass of the system becomes multiplied by it, and the same applies to the dependent extensive property. An intensive dependent property must be homogeneous of degree $m = 0$ in terms of extensive properties, because its value cannot change as the mass of the system is changed. An equation of state which is expressed in terms of intensive and specific or molar properties only is independent of the mass of the system and refers to a unit mass or to one mol of it, as the case may be.

List of Symbols for Chapter 1

Latin letters

A	Area
a	Acceleration; length; general physical quantity
b	Length
$\mathbf{c}$	Velocity vector
e	Kinetic energy per unit mass
$\mathbf{F}$	Dimension of force
G	Universal gravitational constant
g	Gravitational acceleration
$\mathbf{g}$	Standard gravitational acceleration
g_0	Coefficient of proportionality in Newton's Second Law, equation (1.13a)
$\mathbf{h}$	Planck's constant
$\hbar$	$= \mathbf{h}/2\pi$
k	Coefficient of proportionality in equation (1.9) and in Newton's Second Law, equation (1.13)
$\mathbf{L}$	Loschmidt number
$\mathbf{L}$	Dimension of length
m	Mass; order of homogeneous function, equation (1.21)
$\mathbf{M}$	Dimension of mass
N	Number of molecules
n	Number of fundamental units (dimensions); number of independent properties; number of molecules per cell (occupation number)
P	Pressure; fundamental units (dimensions)
$\mathbf{p}$	Linear momentum

† See also Section 7.5.3.

p_x, p_y, p_z	Components of linear momentum
r	Position vector
t	Time
T	Dimension of time
u	Velocity component in x direction
V	Volume
v	Specific volume; velocity component in y direction
$\mathcal{V}$	Velocity
v_m	Molar (specific) volume
w	Velocity component in z direction
X	Physical quantity
x	Displacement; independent property; coordinate
y	Dependent property; coordinate
Z	Extensive property
z	Coordinate; specific property

Greek letters

α	Exponent, equation (1.5)
β	Exponent, equation (1.5)
γ	Exponent, equation (1.5)
δ	Exponent, equation (1.6); measure of cell in velocity space
ϵ	Exponent, equation (1.6); measure of cell in physical space
η	Exponent, equation (1.6)
λ	Constant, equation (1.21)
ρ	Density; specific weight
Ω	Volume in phase space

Special symbols

[ ]	Dimension of a physical quantity
{ }	Unit of measure for respective physical quantity
$\sim$	Above a letter—denotes numerical value of physical quantity.

CHAPTER 2

Temperature and Temperature Scales. Equilibrium

2.1 General remarks. Adiabatic and diathermal walls

In this chapter, we shall concentrate our attention on the very important concept of *temperature* and on the methods of measuring it in terms of conventional *temperature scales*. The concept of temperature is linked in our minds with a definite, intuitive idea based on our temperature sense which enables us to distinguish "hot" from "cold." This sense, however, is insufficient to establish a scientifically rigorous concept or a quantitative measure of temperature. We shall find it necessary first to examine certain phenomena which occur in systems when their interaction with the surroundings is controlled by different walls, ranging from what are called "good thermal insulators" to "good thermal conductors." In this way we shall be able to transform our subjective sense impressions into objective, measurable statements. A definition of a physical quantity which provides a clear indication on how to measure it, or on the operations which are required in order to determine it in the laboratory, is called an operational definition. Thus the following remarks can be said to aim at providing an *operational definition of temperature.*

When a thermodynamic system† is enclosed in a vessel and is allowed to interact with the surroundings such as the terrestrial atmosphere, it is found that its independent properties change with time. After a sufficiently long time, the length of time depending on the details of the experiment, the independent properties of the system always assume fixed values and no further change is observed. It is implied, of course, that no measurable changes can be observed in the surroundings during the experiment. The system is then said to have reached a *state of thermal equilibrium.*

The speed with which the state of a system tends to equilibrium depends on the walls in which it is enclosed. With certain walls, such as thin metal sheets, the speed is very high, with others, such as thick asbestos layers, or the walls of Dewar flasks, it is very low. Thus, available walls can be arranged in a series and the limiting case when the system attains its state of thermal equilibrium in a very short time, compared with the time during which the system is observed, is said to occur with a *diathermal wall*; a diathermal wall is an idealized case of a "good thermal conductor."

When a system is allowed to reach a state of thermal equilibrium with the surroundings, it is further found that not all its independent properties can be adjusted to assume arbitrarily prescribed values. For example, experimenting with a system consisting of a

† In this section we shall consider only *closed, uniform* systems contained within rigid walls.

37

fixed mass m of gas in a rigid diathermal vessel of fixed volume V, we find that the pressure P assumes a fixed value determined by the volume. We can change the pressure by changing the volume and we can establish that the two are connected by a functional relationship

$$f(P, V) = 0 \qquad\qquad (2.1)$$

different for each experiment. We then say that the state of thermal equilibrium reached through a diathermal wall is characterized by *restricted values* of the properties of the system. With more independent properties than two, a relationship of the type of equation (2.1) will still be found to exist, except that the number of variables will be increased.

In the other extreme case, when the process of reaching equilibrium extends over a longer and longer period of time, it is found that there is more and more freedom in adjusting the independent properties to give them independently prescribed values. This occurs when thicker and thicker walls are used, that is, when "better thermal insulators" are employed. In the limiting, idealized case there is complete freedom to adjust *all* independent properties and no restricting relation (2.1) is found to exist. We then say that the walls are *adiabatic*. An adiabatic wall *isolates* the system from its surroundings, whereas a diathermal wall *couples* the system to it.

In general, the walls of the vessel will play some part in the processes under observation. Again, it is found by experiment that the part played by the walls can be made less and less important and for our present purposes we may assume that a diathermal or an adiabatic wall determines only whether a restricting equation, such as equation (2.1), is or is not imposed on the independent properties of the system. Otherwise the wall can be entirely left out of consideration.

Under actual experimental conditions it is invariably observed that the system never reaches a state of thermal equilibrium *exactly*. If observations are made with very sensitive instruments, *some* changes in the properties, namely *fluctuations* about a fixed state can be detected. This possibility is disregarded in classical thermodynamics because it has its origin in the molecular structure of matter. Thus its study properly belongs to the subject of statistical mechanics.†

2.2 Thermal equilibrium between systems

We have so far considered only the case when a single system is allowed to interact with the atmosphere (itself assumed to be in a state of thermal equilibrium, unaffected by the presence of the system) in which most of our experiments are carried out. We now proceed to consider the interaction between two or more systems, independently of the atmosphere. We shall, therefore, examine the behavior of systems enclosed in a *rigid adiabatic vessel*.

When two systems, 1 and 2, whose independent properties are $x_1, y_1, \ldots ; x_2, y_2, \ldots ,$ respectively, are allowed to interact with each other, Figure 2.1, across a diathermal wall, it is observed that, in general, both systems will undergo a change in state and that their independent properties will vary. After a time, they will assume fixed states and are said to be in thermal equilibrium with each other. Any change in the state of one system will, in general, cause a change in the state of the other system. If the state of one system is kept constant, after equilibrium has set in, as was assumed to be the case

† For references see footnote on p. 32.

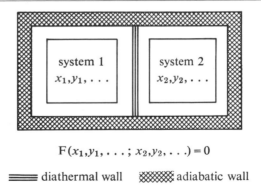

$$F(x_1, y_1, \ldots; x_2, y_2, \ldots) = 0$$

▬▬▬ diathermal wall   ▨▨▨▨ adiabatic wall

FIGURE 2.1. *Two systems interacting across a diathermal wall.*

with the atmosphere in the preceding section, the state of the other system can only be varied within limits. Once again, the independent properties of the other system will vary in a restricted way satisfying an *equation of constraint*

$$f(x_2, y_2, \ldots) = 0. \tag{2.2}$$

A similar equation of constraint will exist for the first system, and we can make the general statement that for two systems interacting across a diathermal wall there exists an equation of constraint between the independent properties of both systems, for, when the state of system 1 is changed, equation (2.2) will change as well. This can be written

$$F(x_1, y_1, \ldots; x_2, y_2, \ldots) = 0. \tag{2.3}$$

Now, if the diathermal wall is replaced by an adiabatic wall, Figure 2.2, no such constraint can be observed. The states of either system can be adjusted entirely independently of each other.

In the first case, the two systems were coupled; a change of state in one involved a change of state in the other. In the second case no such coupling existed, the systems were isolated. Clearly, it is advantageous to say that two systems coupled across a diathermal wall have a *common property* after they have attained thermal equilibrium. Later, we shall call this property the common *temperature* of the two systems but at this stage it would be premature to do so. A property of a system must be fixed when *its* state is fixed and so far we have simultaneously fixed two states of *different* systems, equation (2.3).

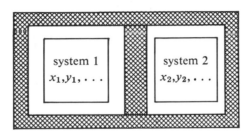

FIGURE 2.2. *Two systems interacting across an adiabatic wall.*

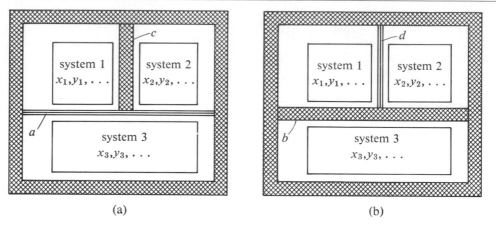

(a)　　　　　　　　　　　　　　　　　(b)

FIGURE 2.3. *The Zeroth Law of thermodynamics.*

2.3　The Zeroth Law of thermodynamics

In order to follow up on the preceding idea, we shall now consider an important imaginary experiment with three systems, Figure 2.3(a). We shall suppose that three thermodynamic systems, 1, 2, and 3, are enclosed in a rigid adiabatic container. Systems 1 and 2 are not coupled having been made to interact across an adiabatic wall c. Systems 1 and 2 are each coupled with system 3 and interact with it across a diathermal wall a. In this manner we can say that system 1 is in thermal equilibrium with system 3, and that system 2 is in thermal equilibrium with system 3. We feel intuitively, that is, on the basis of our everyday experience, that systems 1 and 2, in spite of the fact that they are separated by an adiabatic wall, are also in thermal equilibrium with each other. In fact, we can imagine that the diathermal wall a has been replaced by an adiabatic wall b, Figure 2.3(b), and that the adiabatic wall c has been replaced by the diathermal wall d. Now only systems 1 and 2 are coupled, and it is an experimental fact that the change in the arrangement of the partitions from Figure 2.3(a) to Figure 2.3(b) *produces no change in the state of systems 1 and 2.* We express this fact in general terms by asserting that

Two systems in thermal equilibrium with a third system are in thermal equilibrium with each other.

At first the preceding statement may appear trivial to the reader. This is so because it expresses an experimental fact with which we are all very familiar. In general, however, it cannot be said that two systems which behave in the same way with respect to a third, behave in the same way with respect to each other. For example, two substances (such as hydrogen and oxygen) which are inert with respect to a third (for example, argon) need not be chemically inert with respect to each other. A mixture of hydrogen and oxygen will explode violently when ignited, but a mixture of either of them with argon will not.

The italicized statement, which constitutes a generalization derived from experimental observations and which is assumed to be universally valid, is known as the *Zeroth Law of thermodynamics.* It was first formulated by R. H. Fowler in 1931.†

---

† See also Fowler, R. H., and Guggenheim, E. A., *Statistical Thermodynamics* (Cambridge Univ. Press, 1949), p. 56.

Since the so-called First and Second Laws of thermodynamics were formulated much earlier (see Sections 5.3, 8.2, and 9.1), and since in a logical development of the subject it must be stated before them, it has been agreed to designate it as the Zeroth Law. The Zeroth Law permits us to assert that *all* systems in thermal equilibrium with each other have a common property. This statement agrees with our temperature sense, because we know that two systems which have been in contact with each other for a sufficiently long period of time are equally "hot" or "cold."

2.4 Temperature

In order to facilitate expression, we shall confine out attention to systems whose state is described by two independent variables. We shall denote these variables by the symbols x and y, distinguishing between systems by appending suitable subscripts. The extension of the succeeding considerations to systems with any number of variables is immediate and does not affect the argument.

When two systems, 1 and 2, are coupled across a diathermal wall, their independent variables are constrained by equation (2.3) which can now be written

$$F(x_1, y_1, x_2, y_2) = 0. \tag{2.4}$$

Similarly, for systems 1 and 3, we have

$$G(x_1, y_1, x_3, y_3) = 0, \tag{2.4a}$$

because, in general, the form of the equation will be different. The Zeroth Law then asserts that systems 2 and 3 must also be in equilibrium, or that a relation

$$H(x_2, y_2, x_3, y_3) = 0 \tag{2.4b}$$

between their independent variables must exist.

Suppose now that the state of one of the systems, say 1, is fixed; it will be denoted by a. All possible states for systems 2 and 3 which are in equilibrium with it will trace curves

$$g_a(x_2, y_2) = 0 \quad \text{and} \quad h_a(x_3, y_3) = 0 \tag{2.5a, b}$$

in the coordinates x_2, y_2 and x_3, y_3, respectively, as shown in Figure 2.4. In the case of three variables all these states would trace a surface in space, and with more variables we would have a hypersurface in hyperspace. If we now change the state of system 1 from a to b, we shall find that the loci of states for systems 2 and 3 will change, and that

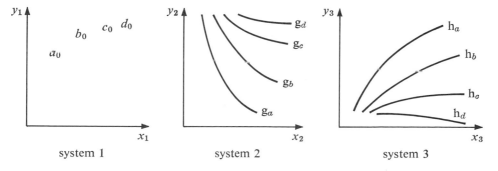

FIGURE 2.4. *Corresponding isotherms for two systems.*

two new curves,

$$g_b(x_2, y_2) = 0 \quad \text{and} \quad h_b(x_3, y_3) = 0 \qquad (2.5\text{c, d})$$

will be traced. Experience teaches that these curves need not necessarily have continuously turning tangents like the ones shown in Figure 2.4. By varying the state of system 1 still further, we can obtain additional pairs of curves, g_c, h_c, g_d, h_d, and so on. The Zeroth Law shows that each pair of curves g and h has the property that *all* states on one are in equilibrium with *all* states on the other because they are in equilibrium with a third state. We shall call such pairs of curves (surfaces or hypersurfaces for systems with more than two independent variables) *corresponding isotherms*. Since systems 2 and 3 are quite arbitrary, it is seen that for any system it is possible to trace a net of isotherms and that for any two systems it is possible to indicate corresponding isotherms. Consequently, it is possible to ascribe numerical values to corresponding isotherms by adopting a suitable *convention* and to define these numbers as the common temperature t of *all* systems in thermal equilibrium. It is easy to see that whenever the state of the system is fixed by fixing the values of its properties x and y, its temperature is fixed, and hence *temperature is a property*. More precisely, it is an *intensive* property, because it has the same value for a system and for its possible subdivisions. It is, namely, that property which determines whether or not the system is in thermal equilibrium with other systems. Equal temperatures imply thermal equilibrium, different temperatures imply its absence. Finally, since the state of the reference system 1 can be changed continuously, the isotherms of a system will transform continuously one into another and cover the whole plane x, y. However, through any point of the plane there passes one and only one isotherm.

The preceding argument can be summarized, that is, *formalized*, in more general terms, using a more precise mathematical mode of expression. We consider three systems, system 1 whose l independent properties are $x_1, \ldots, x_l$, system 2 whose m independent properties are $y_1, \ldots, y_m$, and system 3 whose n independent properties are $z_1, \ldots, z_n$. If the three systems were in thermal equilibrium in pairs, there would exist the following three equations of constraint:

$$\left. \begin{aligned} F(x_1, \ldots, x_l;\ y_1, \ldots, y_m) &= 0, \\ G(x_1, \ldots, x_l;\ z_1, \ldots, z_n) &= 0, \\ H(y_1, \ldots, y_m;\ z_1, \ldots, z_n) &= 0. \end{aligned} \right\} \qquad (2.6)$$

Since the three systems are quite arbitrary, the functions F, G, H will, in general, be of a different form for each pair of systems. The Zeroth Law states that if two of the above conditions are satisfied for a particular set of values $x_1^\circ, \ldots, y_1^\circ, \ldots, z_1^\circ, \ldots z_n^\circ$, then the third condition follows as a physical consequence.

The somewhat lengthy argument which led us to the formulation of this concept of temperature rested on a not quite rigorous demonstration of the fact that the equations of constraint (2.6) must necessarily be of the form

$$\left. \begin{aligned} f(x_1, \ldots, x_l) - g(y_1, \ldots, y_m) &= 0, \\ f(x_1, \ldots, x_l) - h(z_1, \ldots, z_n) &= 0, \\ g(y_1, \ldots, y_m) - h(z_1, \ldots, z_n) &= 0, \end{aligned} \right\} \qquad (2.7)$$

that is, that the variables describing the state of one system must appear in them in separate combinations $f(x_1, \ldots, x_l)$, $g(y_1, \ldots, y_m)$, $h(z_1, \ldots, z_n)$, so that, for example, terms like $x_1^a y_2^b$ and so on cannot occur. This also means that

$$F = f - g; \qquad G = f - h; \qquad H = g - h. \tag{2.8}$$

It follows, therefore, that equation (2.7) can be written

$$t_0 = f(x_1^\circ, \ldots, x_l^\circ) = g(y_1^\circ, \ldots, y_m^\circ) = h(z_1^\circ, \ldots, z_n^\circ) \tag{2.9}$$

for a particular set of values denoted by a superscript $^\circ$ for which the three systems are in thermal equilibrium. The common value t_0 of the three functions f, g, h is called the common temperature of the three systems at that particular state of thermal equilibrium.

A proof of the preceding propositions can be indicated by the following reasoning. First, it is noted that conditions (2.7) are *sufficient* to satisfy equations (2.6). For example, if the first equation (2.7) is subtracted from the second, the third is obtained; thus, the validity of the first two implies the third. The same can be shown for any pair of equations (2.7) by addition or subtraction. However, the validity of (2.8) or (2.9) demands that this must always be the case and not simply for one particular form of the functions F, G, H such as (2.8). In other words, it is essential to prove that the conditions (2.8) are also *necessary*.

A glance at the Zeroth Law in the form of equations (2.6) shows that the existence of two equations of constraint containing the *three* sets of variables, $x_1, \ldots, x_l; y_1, \ldots, y_m; z_1, \ldots, z_n$ must lead to the existence of a *third* relation involving only *two*, say $y_1, \ldots, y_m; z_1, \ldots, z_n$. In other words, the functions F, G, H must all be of a form which allows us to *eliminate* one set of variables from two relations. This is done by calculating one, say x_l, from two equations, and equating the result, thus

$$\begin{aligned} x_l &= F'(x_1, \ldots, x_{l-1}; y_1, \ldots, y_m) \\ &= G'(x_1, \ldots, x_{l-1}; z_1, \ldots, z_n). \end{aligned} \tag{2.10}$$

The last relation, as seen from the third equation (2.6), must *not* contain $x_1, \ldots, x_{l-1}$. If the state of system 1 were described by *one* independent variable, x_l, this would always be possible. With more independent variables this is possible if, and only if, the variables $x_1, \ldots, x_l$ enter the relation in the form of a combination $f(x_1, \ldots, x_l)$ which can be determined. For this to be possible, we must replace equation (2.10) by

$$f(x_1, \ldots, x_l) = g(y_1, \ldots, y_m),$$

which is identical with (2.8), and the proposition is proved.

2.5 Empirical temperature scales

The process of assigning numerical values to all the corresponding isotherms of all systems is entirely arbitrary and its details are governed by convenience and by convention. It amounts to selecting a standard to measure temperatures, that is, it amounts to establishing a scale on which the temperatures of a system could be arranged in a continuous sequence. This process corresponds to the selection of a fundamental unit, such as the selection of a standard kilogram for the comparison of masses. Length and mass are extensive properties and have a natural zero associated with zero length or mass. In this respect, temperature, being an intensive property, resembles time, and the establishment of a scale for its measurement requires the fixing of an origin (the

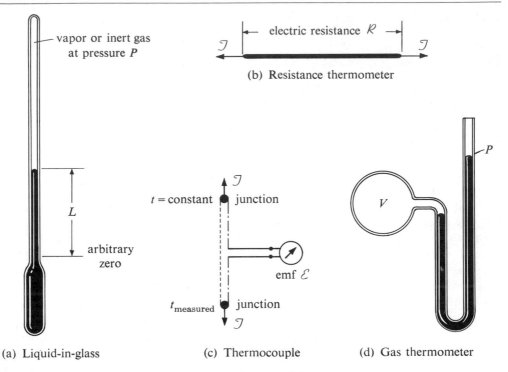

FIGURE 2.5. *Principal types of thermometers.*

"zero") as well as of a unit. Just as was the case with other units, there are now in existence several temperature scales, and this unfortunate fact is a source of confusion.

In order to establish a temperature scale we shall first choose a particular reference system, that is, a *thermometer*. *A priori*, there are no restrictions as to the type of system to be chosen but certain systems are simpler and more convenient than others. Many systems are used in practice, but four basic types of systems, Figure 2.5, have withstood the test of time, and we need only consider these from now onward; they have the common feature that their state is determined by two independent properties. The most frequently encountered thermometer, Figure 2.5(a), consists of a glass capillary tube with a bulb at one end and with its other end sealed. The bulb is filled with a liquid such as mercury or alcohol, and the space above it is occupied by the vapor of the liquid at a very low, but variable, pressure or by an inert gas. The state of such a liquid-in-glass thermometer is fixed when the pressure P of the gas or vapor is fixed and when the length of the thread, L, measured from an arbitrary zero, is fixed. The second class of system consists of a thin metal wire, such as platinum or nickel, whose state is determined by its electrical resistance R and the tension J applied to its ends. The third system consists of a pair of dissimilar wires, such as platinum and an alloy of platinum and rhodium, or copper and constantan, arranged in a loop, Figure 2.5(c), with two junctions. One junction is kept at a constant temperature, and the state of the loop, or *thermocouple*, is fixed when the electromotive force (emf) $\mathcal{E}$ generated in the loop and the tension on the wires, J, is fixed. Finally, Figure 2.5(d), we can use a fixed quantity of a gas in a bulb, and in this case the state, as already mentioned previously, is defined by the pressure P and volume V of the gas. It should be realized that these four types of thermometers represent an extremely large variety of systems if individual details are taken into account. Hence, the specification of the standard thermometer which is used for the definition of a temperature scale must include an exact description of the minute details of its manufacture.

Having chosen a system, we must now choose a rule for assigning numbers to its isotherms. This will assign numerical values to the corresponding isotherms of all systems. The simplest way of doing this is to keep one property constant and to relate the temperature to the other property which is then known as the *thermometric property*. The process is illustrated in Figure 2.6, where the property y has been fixed at a value Y and temperatures along the isotherms t_1, t_2, . . . are measured in terms of the values x_1, x_2, ... Any rule of correspondence, that is, any single-valued function $t(x)$ can be arbitrarily assigned to establish the scale. This function is known as the *thermometric function*. It is easily seen from Figure 2.6 that this is not the only set of rules which can be adopted. Instead of fixing one particular value of the property y, it is possible to stipulate an arbitrary function

$$\phi(x, y) = 0$$

represented by the dotted curve in the diagram, and to relate the temperature t to the values x_1', x_2', ...

Considering the four systems discussed earlier, Figure 2.5, it is found convenient to keep the tension constant in the case of the resistance wire and thermocouple. In the case of the gas thermometer, it is possible to maintain either the pressure or the volume constant and to measure temperatures in terms of the other property. In the case of the liquid-in-glass thermometer it is usual to seal it as mentioned before. This has the effect of imposing a relation

$$\phi(P, L) = 0$$

on the thermometer, because the pressure will adjust itself to a given length of thread. The length of thread is then chosen as the thermometric property. Consequently, we have to consider five basic types of thermometers, as listed in Table 2.1.

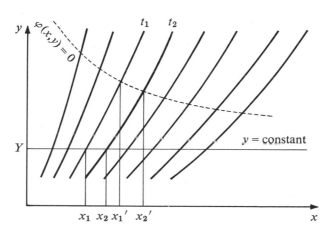

FIGURE 2.6. *Assigning numbers to isotherms.*

TABLE 2.1
Basic Types of Thermometers.

System	Variable y	Variable x (Thermometric property)
1. Liquid in glass; prescribed relation $\phi(P, L) = 0$	Pressure P	Length of thread L
2. Thin resistance wire	Tension $\mathcal{T}$	Electrical resistance $\mathcal{R}$
3. Thermocouple (Pair of dissimilar wires with two junctions)	Tension $\mathcal{T}$	Electromotive force $\mathcal{E}$
4. Gas in a bulb	Pressure P	Volume V
5. Gas in a bulb	Volume V	Pressure P

The simplest thermometric function which we can stipulate is one of direct proportionality

$$t = Ax. \tag{2.11}$$

Clearly, it is not the only possible relation; the next one in order of complexity might be a linear relation

$$t = ax + b \tag{2.11a}$$

or a quadratic relation†

$$t = \alpha x^2 + \beta x + \gamma. \tag{2.11b}$$

Logarithmic thermometric functions have also been proposed.

In all thermometric functions an appropriate number of constants has been inserted and it is necessary to determine them according to some rule. It is possible, for example, to assign arbitrary numerical values to these constants, but if this were done the resulting temperature scale would depend to a very large extent on the details of the design of the particular thermometer. Owing to the high degree of arbitrariness in the definition of a temperature scale, measurements performed by different observers would be extremely difficult to compare, and it is essential to devise methods to facilitate such intercomparisons.

It is known from experiment that certain processes always occur at fixed temperatures.‡ For example, water under atmospheric pressure boils at a fixed temperature. Substances melt or solidify at fixed temperatures if the pressure is maintained at a

---

† Since the relation $t(x)$ must be single-valued, only a portion of the parabola in equation (2.11b) can be used.
‡ This can be ascertained without reference to a temperature *scale*, it being sufficient to note that the thermometric property preserves its value.

constant value, and so on. Systems undergoing such processes can be used as *fixed thermometric points* to great advantage. If conventional values are assigned to such fixed thermometric points, it is certain that all temperature scales will coincide at those points and intercomparison will be greatly facilitated. Consequently, rather than assign arbitrary values to each of the constants in equations (2.11), (2.11a), (2.11b), we choose as many fixed points as there are constants in the thermometric equation and determine them by assigning conventional values of temperature to the fixed points.

In the case of equation (2.11) we can assign a value t_r to one such fixed point noting that the thermometric property then has a value x_r. Hence, we must have

$$t_r = Ax_r \quad \text{and} \quad A = t_r/x_r,$$

so that equation (2.11) becomes

$$t = \frac{x}{x_r} t_r; \tag{2.12}$$

it states that temperatures are *proportional* to the values of the thermometric property. In the case of equation (2.11a) we would choose two fixed points $t_1(x_1)$ and $t_2(x_2)$ giving

$$a = \frac{t_2 - t_1}{x_2 - x_1} x + \frac{x_2 t_1 - x_1 t_2}{x_2 - x_1}. \tag{2.12a}$$

A temperature scale established in accordance with the above rules is known as an *empirical temperature scale*. The correlation of "hotter" states with larger and positive temperatures and of "colder" states with lower or negative temperatures is achieved by a suitable choice of the thermometric function together with the fixed thermometric points. The position at which $t = 0$ is also arbitrary and depends on the same choices.

Until recently, it was customary to use the thermometric equation (2.11a) and the following two fixed points: The *steam point*, or the temperature assumed by a system consisting of pure water in equilibrium with its vapor at the pressure of one standard atmosphere which is commonly known as the "boiling point of water"; the *ice point* is the temperature of equilibrium between air-saturated water and ice at normal atmospheric pressure, or "the melting point of ice."

On the *Celsius scale*† the steam point, t_s, and the ice point, t_i, are assigned the values

$$t_s = 100°C \quad \text{and} \quad t_i = 0°C. \tag{2.13}$$

On the *Fahrenheit scale* the agreed fixed points are

$$t_s = 212°F \quad \text{and} \quad t_i = 32°F, \tag{2.13a}$$

so that

$$t_s - t_i = 180°F, \tag{2.14}$$

and

$$1°C = 1.8°F. \tag{2.15}$$

† This scale was previously known as the *centigrade scale*. By international agreement, reached at the Ninth Conference on Weights and Measures held in 1948 in Paris the older name is now considered obsolete and should not be used.

Denoting the values of the thermometric property x measured at the steam and ice points respectively by x_s and x_i, we obtain from equation (2.12a)

for the Celsius scale $\qquad t(x) = 100\dfrac{x - x_i}{x_s - x_i},$ $\qquad\qquad$ (2.16)

for the Fahrenheit scale $\qquad t(x) = 32 + 180\dfrac{x - x_i}{x_s - x_i}.$ $\qquad\qquad$ (2.16a)

If we made a number of thermometers, even of one kind and differing only in details, and compared the different scales defined by them with the aid of suitable measurements, we would find that the respective temperature scales did not coincide, except for the ice and steam points. In other words, if we immersed a mercury-in-glass thermometer in a bath which brought the thread up to, say, mark 50, we should notice that the thread of an alcohol thermometer, the resistance of a resistance thermometer or the emf of a thermocouple immersed in the same bath would not precisely indicate a temperature of 50 (°C or °F as the case may be). This would even be the case if we used a *different* mercury-in-glass thermometer. The surprising thing, however, is that the differences in the indications of quite different thermometers would not be very large, as seen from Table 2.2. In spite of the complete dependence of an empirical temperature scale on the fortuitous properties of a particular system, a large measure of uniformity has been achieved owing to the device of determining the constants in equation (2.11) with the aid of conventional fixed points.

A close scrutiny of Table 2.2 shows that the different empirical temperature scales defined by the four gas thermometers differ from each other by very small quantities only and that these differences are appreciably smaller than for the remaining temperature scales. It is natural to suppose that by performing extensive experiments with gas thermometers it might be possible to evolve a more universal temperature scale. We shall examine this question in the next section and we shall show that this is, indeed, the case.

2.6   The perfect-gas temperature scale

A gas thermometer is a very difficult instrument to operate. It requires great skill in handling and is subject to a number of corrections when very precise results are aimed at. It is also bulky, compared with a resistance thermometer or thermocouple, and requires a long time to reach thermal equilibrium with the system whose temperature is being measured. For all these reasons gas thermometers are never used as instruments to measure temperatures. However, when used as systems to define a temperature scale, they offer the best chance of making the standard virtually independent of the details of their design and of ensuring good reproducibility, as already stated in connection with Table 2.2.

When defining an empirical temperature scale with the aid of a gas thermometer, it is most convenient to follow an original suggestion made in 1854 by Lord Kelvin and later revived by W. F. Giauque in 1939, that is, to use the thermometric equation (2.11) which contains only one constant and which, consequently, requires only *one fixed point* for calibration. This suggestion has now been adopted by the Tenth International Conference on Weights and Measures held in 1954. The fixed point adopted is the so-called *triple point of water*. It is known, and we shall study this question in much greater detail in Section 7.4.5, that a single, pure chemical substance, such as water, can exist

TABLE 2.2
Comparison of Empirical Temperature Scales; Bath at a Nominal Temperature of 50°C.
(Estimates)

Type of thermometer	Reading, $t(°C)$
1. Constant-volume helium thermometer	49.999
2. Constant-pressure helium thermometer	49.990
3. Constant-volume nitrogen thermometer	50.046
4. Constant-pressure nitrogen thermometer	50.046
5. Platinum-resistance thermometer	50.40
6. Platinum — 90% Pt 10% Rh thermocouple	49.10
7. Platinum-copper-constantan thermocouple	48.30
8. Mercury-in-glass thermometer	50.12
9. Alcohol-in-glass thermometer	50.45

in at most three states of aggregation in one system in equilibrium. Moreover, as long as the three states of aggregation† are present in the system, its pressure and its temperature have fixed values which are characteristic of the chemical nature of the substance. The temperature or the pressure of such a system can be changed only if one of the phases has been allowed to disappear, for example, by heating or by compression. However, as long as all three phases are observed and as long as the system is in equilibrium and remains uncontaminated by other substances, its temperature (and, incidentally, its pressure) has a fixed value. Thus, the triple point, once attained, will maintain a fixed temperature. That fixed temperature depends solely on the purity of the substance used, and is, in this respect, superior to the ice and steam points which depend on their pressure being maintained at one atmosphere exactly as well as on the purity of the substance.

The temperature of the triple point of water, to be denoted by θ_3, has been fixed by convention at a value of

$$\theta_3 = 273.16°K \qquad (2.17)$$

the symbol °K denoting a temperature on the resulting *Kelvin scale*. In order to distinguish between the present scale and those discussed in Section 2.5, we shall now denote temperatures by the symbol θ. It may seem surprising that the temperature assigned to the triple point of water by convention is so awkward and that no simple rounded-off value has been chosen. The reason for it is of a practical nature, as will be shown later. The present choice ensures that one degree on the Kelvin scale is nearly equal to one degree on the Celsius scale, the difference being so slight that it cannot be detected even by quite sensitive instruments. The conventional value of the temperature of this triple point of water should be regarded as a *universal constant of physics*.

Depending on whether the chosen thermometric property is the pressure, P, or the volume, V, of the gas, we obtain from equation (2.11)

for the $V = $ const thermometer $\qquad \theta(P) = \dfrac{P}{P_3}\,\theta_3,$ $\qquad\qquad (2.18)$

for the $P = $ const thermometer $\qquad \theta(V) = \dfrac{V}{V_3}\,\theta_3,$ $\qquad\qquad (2.18a)$

† We shall call them *phases* later. An exact definition of a phase is given in Section 7.4.1.

where P_3 and V_3 denote the values of these parameters measured at the triple point in the gas, and θ_3 has the value from equation (2.17).

Instead of using the pressure or volume as the thermometric property, it is also possible to use their product, PV, as the thermometric property in a gas thermometer. Since both pressure and volume are properties, their product is also a property and has a fixed value when the state of the gas is fixed. We can, therefore, choose the product PV together with either the pressure or the volume as the two independent properties for a gas. When this is done, equation (2.11) assumes the form

$$\theta(PV) = \frac{PV}{(PV)_3}\,\theta_3. \tag{2.18b}$$

In principle it is necessary to specify a constant path, for example, $P = $ const or $V = $ const, in conjunction with equation (2.18b) but experience shows that the isotherm of a gas at low density approximates very closely the equation

$$PV = \text{const}, \tag{2.19}$$

and it follows that the temperature scales defined by equation (2.18b) differ very little from each other when either $P = $ const or $V = $ const is specified. If the isotherm of a gas were represented by equation (2.19) exactly, there would be no difference at all.

The temperature scales defined by any one of the three equations (2.18), (2.18a), (2.18b), differ very little from each other, as already intimated in Table 2.2. For most purposes, particularly for most engineering applications, they can be regarded as being equivalent. However, in work of the highest precision it is found that these small differences depend to a large extent on the gas used in the thermometer. Even with the same gas, the empirical temperature scales will differ somewhat depending on the mass of gas used in a given volume. That mass is best specified by indicating the pressure, P_3, of the gas contained in the given volume at the triple point of water. In many laboratories, a standard value $P_3 = 1000$ Torr is used.

The most important discovery in connection with gas thermometry is made when experiments are performed at different values of the pressure P_3, for it is then found that as the pressure P_3 is made to decrease, the differences between all the empirical gas-thermometer scales show a tendency to disappear. The manner in which this happens is shown in Figure 2.7, which represents the result of the determination of the temperature of the steam point with the aid of several gas thermometers each of which was used at several values of P_3. It is seen from the diagram that the maximum discrepancy between the temperature of the steam point as measured on the different temperature scales has decreased from 0.5°K at $P_3 = 1000$ Torr to 0.2°K at $P_3 = 400$ Torr. It is also seen that for each particular thermometer, the indicated temperature depends on pressure and is a linear function of P_3. There is, of course, a limit of P_3 below which measurements become impossible, and in general, measurements with lower values of P_3 which correspond to decreasing quantities of gas in the bulb, become increasingly difficult. It is, however, characteristic that *all* of the straight lines which correspond to the different thermometers in Figure 2.7 intercept *the same* temperature

$$\theta_s = 373.15°\text{K} \tag{2.20}$$

on the axis of abscissae $P_3 = 0$. In other words, if the readings of gas thermometers are *extrapolated to zero pressure*, in the limit, all empirical gas-thermometer scales *become*

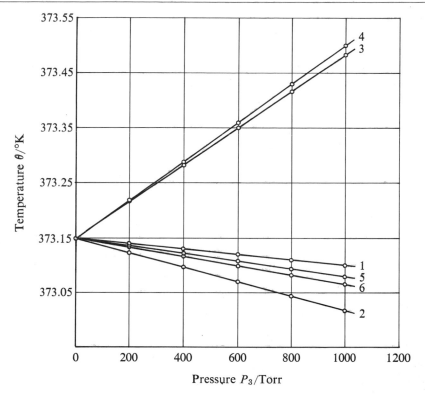

FIGURE 2.7. *Comparison between gas-thermometer scales measuring*
the temperature of the steam point.
1. *Constant-volume hydrogen thermometer*
2. *Constant-pressure hydrogen thermometer*
3. *Constant-volume air thermometer*
4. *Constant-pressure air thermometer*
5. *Constant-volume helium thermometer*
6. *Constant-pressure helium thermometer*

NOTE: The points shown in the diagram have been calculated rather than measured. For relevant theory see Volume II.

identical. This occurs irrespectively of the temperature measured, and, for example,
the same feature would be observed if the ice-point temperature were measured, all
indications extrapolating then to

$$\theta_i = 273.15°\text{K}. \tag{2.20a}$$

In addition, the extrapolated value becomes independent of the nature of the gas used
as well as of the thermometric property.

The process of extrapolation to $P_3 = 0$ performed graphically in Figure 2.7 corresponds mathematically to the evaluation of the limit of the expressions in equations
(2.18), (2.18a), and (2.18b) as $P_3 \to 0$, and the fact that the limit is a common one can be
written

$$\theta = \lim_{P_3 \to 0} \frac{P}{P_3} \theta_3 = \lim_{P_3 \to 0} \frac{V}{V_3} \theta_3 = \lim_{P_3 \to 0} \frac{PV}{(PV)_3} \theta_3. \tag{2.21}$$

It is clearly advantageous to adopt a new empirical scale, namely, that common scale which arises from the extrapolation of the readings of any gas thermometer to zero pressure in the bulb. This common scale is known as the *perfect-gas temperature scale*. It does not, any longer, depend on the properties of any particular substance; it depends only on the common behavior of all real gases as their pressure is reduced. It is, further, independent of the details of the design and manufacture of the thermometer and does, therefore, ensure good reproducibility. This is achieved, it is true, at the cost of considerable complication in experimentation, but, in practice, experiments with gas thermometers are performed very rarely and are confined to fundamental calibrations only.

In order to facilitate expression, it has become customary in thermodynamics to introduce the concept of a *perfect* (or ideal) *gas*. A perfect gas is defined as a gas which behaves at all pressures like a real gas when the behavior of the real gas is extrapolated to zero pressure. Hence, if a perfect gas could be obtained, the perfect-gas temperature scale would be defined by equation (2.21) with the operator lim omitted, indicating that no extrapolation to $P_3 = 0$ is necessary. Hence, we would have

$$\theta = \frac{PV}{(PV)_3}\, \theta_3 \qquad\qquad (2.22)$$

exactly. Thus, to every *real gas*, air, hydrogen, helium, and so on, there corresponds a *perfect gas*, air, hydrogen, helium, and so on. This justifies the name given to this new empirical temperature scale. We shall show later (Sections 9.8 and 10.3.2) that from the Second Law of thermodynamics it is possible to derive a temperature scale which is entirely independent of the properties of any substance whatsoever. Its existence is conditioned only by the physical truth expressed in a fundamental law of nature; it is called the thermodynamic temperature scale, T, and it will be shown that it is identical with the perfect-gas temperature scale (Section 12.3). Hence, the perfect-gas temperature scale defined by the equation

$$\theta = \lim_{P_3 \to 0} \frac{PV}{(PV)_3}\, \theta_3 \qquad\qquad (2.23)$$

(or by equations (2.21)) is the one finally adopted for use in thermodynamics. It is reasonable to suppose, and practice fully confirms, that the adoption of such a fundamental scale in preference to an arbitrary empirical scale will lead to considerable simplifications in the equations of thermodynamics. However, for the time being, that is until the equivalence of these two scales will have been proved, we shall assume that all temperatures under consideration are measured on the perfect-gas temperature scale, denoted by the symbol θ.†

It will be noted from equation (2.23), which contains only positive quantities on the right-hand side, that the perfect-gas temperature is always a positive quantity. In contrast with the Celsius and Fahrenheit scales described in Section 2.5, the perfect-gas temperature scale has no zero, because the product PV of a real gas cannot, by its nature, be equal to zero, or extrapolate to a zero value. Furthermore, so far the scale can only be used at temperatures at which gases do not liquefy and is, therefore, only defined down to the lowest point of liquefaction of a real gas. Helium has the lowest

† Failure to make this distinction between the two temperatures, the perfect-gas temperature, θ, and the thermodynamic temperature, T, has often landed the expositors of the subject of thermodynamics in circular arguments in which that which is to be proved has been earlier implied in the assumptions.

point of liquefaction of all gases ($\theta = 4.215°K$ at 1 atm for the more abundant isotope He⁴) and this adequately describes the lower limit on the scale. Thus, the perfect-gas temperature scale cannot, in itself, be used, for example, for measurements in liquid helium. When discussing the equivalent thermodynamic temperature scale, it will be shown (Section 9.8) that the latter does have a natural zero point and covers all temperatures which are possible in nature with the only exception of a class of very special systems to which negative temperatures can be assigned (Section 10.4). From this point of view the thermodynamic temperature scale proves to be a necessary extension of the perfect-gas temperature scale.

2.7 Relations between the different scales. The unit of temperature

The temperatures measured on either of the two equivalent scales, the thermodynamic scale and the perfect-gas temperature scale, are called *absolute* because they are measured from the natural zero point on the thermodynamic scale and not from an artificial zero point as on the Celsius or Fahrenheit scales. Since all these scales, together with an absolute scale which corresponds to the Fahrenheit scale, are used in practice, we must devote some time to a discussion of their mutual relationships.

First, it should be realized that a perfect-gas Celsius and a perfect-gas Fahrenheit temperature scale can be set up by adopting the same rules as were used in Section 2.5 for the establishing of the corresponding empirical scales. In the past use was made of equation (2.11a) together with the fixed points (2.13) or (2.13a), and the product PV of a real gas was employed as the thermometric property. We then had:

on the Celsius scale, equation (2.16)

$$t = \lim_{P_3 \to 0} \; 100 \frac{(PV) - (PV)_i}{(PV)_s - (PV)_i} \tag{2.24}$$

and on the Fahrenheit scale, equation (2.16a)

$$t = \lim_{P_3 \to 0} \; 32 + 180 \frac{(PV) - (PV)_i}{(PV)_s - (PV)_i} \tag{2.24a}$$

Since on the perfect-gas absolute scale measurements show that

$$\theta_s - \theta_i = 100°K, \tag{2.25}$$

equations (2.20) and (2.20a), and since by definition

$$t_s - t_i = 100°C \tag{2.25a}$$

we find that

$$1°C \approx 1°K. \tag{2.26}$$

In fact, the approximate equality in equation (2.26) is not accidental, as already mentioned. The value $\theta_3 = 273.16°K$ was so chosen as to make sure that this should be so and explains the, at first, puzzling choice made. However, the values $\theta_s = 373.15°K$ and $\theta_i = 273.15°K$ are *experimental* values subject to future correction in the light of more precise determinations. For this reason, equation (2.26) is only approximately true.

Assuming that the best measurements of the ice and steam points reveal systematic errors $\Delta\theta_i$ and $\Delta\theta_s$, and that they have been performed with uncertainties not exceeding

$\pm\epsilon_i$ and $\pm\epsilon_s$, respectively, equation (2.25) should be written

$$\theta_s - \theta_i = 100°\mathrm{K} + (\Delta\theta_i + \Delta\theta_s) \pm (\epsilon_i + \epsilon_s). \tag{2.25b}$$

Thus equation (2.26) becomes

$$1°\mathrm{C} = [1 + 0.01(\Delta\theta_i + \Delta\theta_s) \pm 0.01(\epsilon_i + \epsilon_s)]°\mathrm{K}, \tag{2.26a}$$

because $\theta_s - \theta_i = 100°\mathrm{C}$ by definition.

The most accurate values of the perfect-gas temperatures of the ice and steam points known today are

$$\theta_i = (273.1500 \pm 0.0002)°\mathrm{K},$$
$$\theta_s = (373.1464 \pm 0.0036)°\mathrm{K},$$

so that

$$\theta_s - \theta_i = (99.9964 \pm 0.0038)°\mathrm{K}$$

and

$$1°\mathrm{C} = (0.999964 \pm 0.000038)°\mathrm{K}. \tag{2.26b}$$

Here, $\Delta\theta_i = 0$, $\Delta\theta_s = -0.0036°\mathrm{K}$, $\epsilon_i = \pm0.0002°\mathrm{K}$, and $\epsilon_s = \pm0.0036°\mathrm{K}$.

In order to remove this link with experimental techniques, it is possible to redefine the Celsius scale by assuming that equation (2.26) holds exactly, that is, that one degree represents the same *change in temperature* on both scales. If, in addition, it is stipulated that at the ice point $t_i = 0°\mathrm{C}$, a scale is obtained which for all practical purposes is identical with the Kelvin scale, except that its zero is displaced to

$$\theta_i = 273.15°\mathrm{K} + \Delta\theta_i \pm \epsilon_i. \tag{2.26c}$$

Indeed, reverting to equation (2.23), we can write

$$\lim_{P_3 \to 0} PV = \frac{\theta}{\theta_3}(PV)_3; \qquad \lim_{P_3 \to 0}(PV)_i = \frac{\theta_i}{\theta_3}(PV)_3;$$

$$\lim_{P_3 \to 0}(PV)_s = \frac{\theta_s}{\theta_3}(PV)_3.$$

Substituting these values into equation (2.24), we obtain

$$t = 100\,\frac{\theta - \theta_i}{\theta_s - \theta_i},$$

which, by virtue of equation (2.25), simplifies to

$$\theta = \theta_i + t. \tag{2.27}$$

The only quantity in this equation which is subject to future correction is the temperature of the ice point on the absolute scale, equation (2.26c). Equation (2.27) shows that the absolute Kelvin scale differs from the Celsius scale only by a shift in the zero point, as asserted, on condition that both scales are based on the perfect-gas, or better, on the thermodynamic temperature scale. Adopting the value of $\theta_i = 273.15°\mathrm{K}$ we can write

$$0°\mathrm{C} = 273.15°\mathrm{K} \quad \text{and} \quad 0°\mathrm{K} = -273.15°\mathrm{C}. \tag{2.28}$$

We can proceed similarly with the Fahrenheit scale. In this connection it is sufficient to assume that

$$1°C = 1.8°F \tag{2.28a}$$

and to apply the same factor to the value $\theta_3 = 273.16°K$. The resulting absolute scale is called the *Rankine scale*, and on it we have

$$\theta_3 = 491.688 \quad \text{and} \quad 1°F \approx 1°R. \tag{2.29}$$

Similarly,

$$\left.\begin{array}{l} \theta_i = 491.688°R, \qquad \theta_s = 671.688°R, \\ \theta = (\theta_i - 32) + t = 459.688 + t. \end{array}\right\} \tag{2.30}$$

This latter course has been recommended for adoption by the Tenth International Conference on Weights and Measures. We shall use it throughout this book.

The relations between the four scales are shown graphically in Figure 2.8. In most applications the constants in the equations may be rounded off and we may put

$$\left.\begin{array}{ll} \theta = t + 273 & \text{for the Kelvin-Celsius scales,} \\ \theta = t + 460 & \text{for the Rankine-Fahrenheit scales.} \end{array}\right\} \tag{2.31}$$

More correctly

$$\left.\begin{array}{l} \theta \approx t\dfrac{°K}{°C} + 273°K, \\[2mm] \theta \approx t\dfrac{°R}{°F} + 460°R. \end{array}\right\} \tag{2.31a}$$

From the preceding description of the four scales which are currently in use, it is clear that the temperature scales as well as the units of temperature have been defined independently of the remaining fundamental units. Consequently, we are free to ascribe a new dimension to temperature, and we shall denote it by Θ. The units of temperature on the Celsius and Kelvin scales are for all intents and purposes identical, as seen from equation (2.26a). Those on the Fahrenheit and Rankine scales are also practically identical, equation (2.29). The conversion equation between the two pairs of scales is contained in the definitions (2.28a) and (2.29).

The reader should note that the Celsius and Fahrenheit scales, being defined with the aid of equation (2.11a), contain *two* arbitrary constants and require two measurements for calibration, one each at the steam and ice points. The point which corresponds to the zero point on the thermodynamic scale—the so-called *absolute zero*—is not fixed on them. It is numerically equal to the ice-point temperature on the Kelvin scale, and to the ice-point temperature minus the conventional value of 32°F on the Rankine scale and is, therefore, dependent on the exact determination of these values. Being dependent on experimental results, it is liable to undergo slight modifications as techniques of temperature measurement progress. On the other hand, the Kelvin and Rankine scales contain only *one* arbitrary constant equation (2.11), and only one calibration —at the triple point of water—is required. The absolute zero is fixed on either scale and will not be changed in the future. However, the values ascribed to the ice and steam points may need revision. These differences are unimportant in most scientific, and certainly in most engineering, applications and may be disregarded. In measurements of the highest precision, particularly in low-temperature physics, the differences are significant and may lead to discrepancies. The two absolute scales avoid these errors and are fundamentally much more satisfactory.

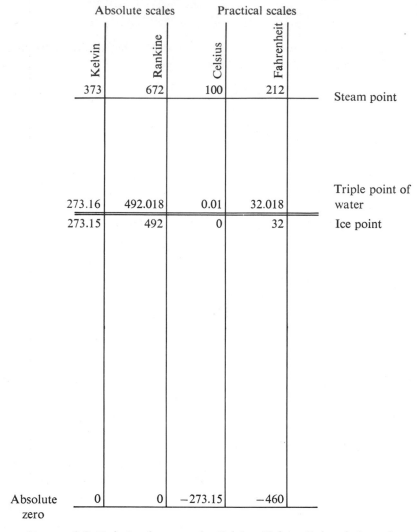

FIGURE 2.8. *Relation between the Celsius, Kelvin, Fahrenheit, and Rankine temperature scales. Rounded values.*

2.8 The International Practical Temperature Scale

As the accurate measurement of temperature by means of a gas thermometer is a difficult and tedious process, a more convenient scale was agreed on by the Seventh General Conference on Weights and Measures held in 1927. The scale is now known as the International Practical Temperature Scale and has been revised several times since its original inception. The present version, revised in 1960, is known as the International Practical Temperature Scale of 1948,[†] since its basic features were established in that year. The scale is defined by a number of melting and boiling points of pure substances which have been determined as accurately as possible on the perfect-gas temperature scale in the scientific establishments of various countries. Between these

[†] See H. F. Stimson, "International Practical Temperature Scale of 1948" (Text Revision of 1960). *J. Res. Natl. Bur. Std.* A. **65** (1961) 139.

fixed points, temperatures are interpolated by means of resistance thermometers, thermocouples, and radiation thermometers (pyrometers). Special rules have been established for the determination of temperature from the readings of these intruments. The Celsius scale rather than the Kelvin scale is used, but conversion from the one to the other is simple and can be effected with reference to equation (2.27) with $\theta_i = 273.15°$K. If necessary, and in order to emphasize the fact that this particular version of the international scale has been employed, the symbol $t°$C(Int. 1948) can be used.

The essential rules defining the International Practical Temperature Scale of 1948 are:

1. The Kelvin thermodynamic[†] scale is recognized as the fundamental scale to which all temperature measurements should ultimately be referable. The magnitude of the degree on this scale is defined by the adoption of the convention fixing the thermodynamic temperature of the triple point at exactly 273.16°K.

2. The International Practical Temperature Scale of 1948 is based on six reproducible temperatures, defining fixed points, to which numerical values have been assigned, and on formulas establishing the relation between temperature and instruments calibrated by means of values assigned to the six defining fixed points. These fixed points are defined by specified equilibrium states, each of which, except the triple point of water, is under a pressure of 101,325 N/m² (1 standard atmosphere).

3. The fixed points of the scale and the exact numerical values assigned to them are given in Table 2.3 below:

TABLE 2.3
Defining Fixed Points.
(International Practical Temperature Scale of 1948)

Exact values assigned. The pressure is 1 standard atmosphere, except for the triple point of water.

	Temperature, $t/(°C)$ (Int. 1948)
Temperature of equilibrium between liquid oxygen and its vapor (oxygen point)	−182.97
Temperature of equilibrium between ice, liquid water, and water vapor (triple point of water)	+ 0.01
Temperature of equilibrium between liquid water and its vapor (steam point)	100.00
Temperature of equilibrium between liquid sulphur and its vapor (sulphur point)	444.6[a]
Temperature of equilibrium between solid silver and liquid silver (silver point)	960.8
Temperature of equilibrium between solid gold and liquid gold (gold point)	1063

[a] In place of the sulphur point, it is recommended to use the temperature of equilibrium between solid zinc and liquid zinc (zinc point) with the value 419.505°C (Int. 1948). The zinc point is more reproducible than the sulphur point, and the value which is assigned to it has been so chosen that its use leads to the same values of temperature on the International Practical Temperature Scale as does the use of the sulphur point.

† See Sections 9.8 and 10.3.2.

4. It is usually practically impossible to control the pressure at which the fixed points are realized in the laboratory, with the exception of the triple point of water which exists under a constant pressure of 0.006228 kp/cm² (Sections 7.4.5 and 7.4.9). It becomes, therefore, necessary to correct the temperatures of the fixed points to the prevailing, barometric pressure p. This can be done by means of the following formulae:

Oxygen point
$$t_p/°C = -182.97 + 9.530\pi - 3.72\pi^2 + 2.2\pi^3. \tag{2.32}$$

Steam point
$$t_p/°C = 100 + 28.012\pi - 11.64\pi^2 + 7.1\pi^3. \tag{2.33}$$

Sulphur point
$$t_p/°C = 444.6 + 28.012\pi - 11.64\pi^2 + 7.1\pi^3. \tag{2.34}$$

Zinc point, silver point, gold point
No correction required.

In the above formulae

$$\pi = \frac{p}{p_0} - 1,$$

and p_0 is the reference pressure of 1 standard atmosphere, expressed in the same units as p.

5. The procedures for interpolation lead to a division of the scale into four parts.

(a) From 0°C to 630.5°C (antimony point) the temperature t is defined by the formula

$$R_t = R_0(1 + At + Bt^2), \tag{2.35}$$

where R_t is the resistance at temperature t of the platinum wire resistor of a standard resistance thermometer, and R_0 is the resistance at 0°C. The constants R_0, A, and B are to be determined from the values of R_t at the triple point of water, at the steam point, and at the sulphur point (or the zinc point). The platinum wire of a standard resistance thermometer shall be annealed, and its purity shall be such that R_{100}/R_0 is not less than 1.3920.

(b) From the oxygen point to 0°C the temperature t is defined by the formula

$$R_t = R_0[1 + At + Bt^2 + C(t - t_{100})t^3], \tag{2.36}$$

where R_0, A, and B are determined in the same manner as in the preceding range a. The constant C is determined from the value of R_t at the oxygen point, and $t_{100} = 100°C$.

(c) From 630.5°C to the gold point, the temperature t is defined by the formula

$$\mathcal{E} = a + bt + ct^2, \tag{2.37}$$

where $\mathcal{E}$ is the electromotive force of a standard thermocouple of platinum and platinum-rhodium alloy, when one of the junctions is at 0°C and the other at the temperature t. The constants a, b, and c are to be determined from the values of $\mathcal{E}$ at 630.5°C, at the silver point, and at the gold point. The value of the electromotive force at 630.5°C is to be determined by measuring this temperature with a standard resistance thermometer, but the temperature itself is that of the freezing point of antimony. The wires of the thermocouple must be annealed, and the platinum wire must be of a purity to guarantee that the ratio R_{100}/R_0 is not less than 1.3920. The platinum-rhodium wire must consist of nominally 90% platinum and 10% rhodium by weight. The completed thermocouple must produce the following electromotive forces with respect to 0°C:

at the gold point $\mathcal{E}_{Au} = 10300\ \mu V \pm 50\mu V$

at the silver point $\mathcal{E}_{Au} - \mathcal{E}_{Ag} = 1183\ \mu V + 0.158(\mathcal{E}_{Au} - 10300\ \mu V) \pm 4\ \mu V$

at the antimony point $\mathcal{E}_{Au} - \mathcal{E}_{630.5} = 4766\ \mu V + 0.631(\mathcal{E}_{Au} - 10300\ \mu V) \pm 8\ \mu V$.

(d) Above the gold point the temperature t is defined by the formula

$$\frac{J_t}{J_{Au}} = \frac{\exp\left[\dfrac{c_2}{\lambda(t_{Au} - T_0)}\right] - 1}{\exp\left[\dfrac{c_2}{(t + T_0)}\right] - 1}, \tag{2.38}$$

where J_t and J_{Au} are the radiant energies† per unit wavelength interval at wavelength λ emitted per unit time per unit solid angle and per unit area of a black body at the temperature t and at the gold point respectively; c_2 is Planck's second radiation constant with the value $c_2 = 0.014\,38$ m°C, the wavelength λ is in meters, and $T_0 = 273.15$°C.

In order to facilitate measurements, the International Practical Temperature Scale has been supplemented by an additional series of fixed points based on substances easily obtained in sufficient purity. They are given in Table 2.4.

TABLE 2.4
Secondary Reference Points.
(International Practical Temperature Scale of 1948)

A = allotropic transition	M = melting point
B = boiling point	S = sublimation point
F = freezing or melting point	Tr = triple point

All under a pressure of 1 standard atmosphere, except for triple points.

		Temperature, $t/(°C)$ (Int. 1948)
Carbon dioxide	S	−78.5
Mercury	F	−38.87
Ice point (water)[a]	F	0.000
Phenoxybenzene (diphenyl-ether)	Tr	26.88
Sodium sulphate decahydrate	A	32.38
Benzoic acid	Tr	122.36
Indium	F	156.61
Naphthalene[b]	B	218.0
Tin	F	231.91
Benzophenone[c]	B	305.9
Cadmium	F	321.03
Lead	F	327.3
Mercury[d]	B	356.58
Aluminum	F	660.1
Copper (in reducing atmosphere)	F	1083
Nickel	F	1453
Cobalt	F	1492
Palladium	F	1552
Platinum	F	1769
Rhodium	F	1960
Iridium	F	2443
Tungsten	M	3380

[a] Temperature of equilibrium between ice and *air-saturated* water.

[b] $t_n/(°C) = 218.0 + 44.4\pi - 19\pi^2 \qquad \pi = \dfrac{p}{p_0} - 1.$

[c] $t_p/(°C) = 305.9 + 48.8\pi - 21\pi^2.$

[d] $t_p/(°C) = 356.58 + 55.552\pi - 23.03\pi^2 + 14.0\pi^3.$

† For details of the phenomenon of radiation see for example, Schmidt, E. *Thermodynamics*, translated by J. Kestin (Oxford: Clarendon Press, 1949), pp. 465 ff. or Sommerfeld, A. *Thermodynamics and Statistical Mechanics* (Vol. V of *Lectures on Theoretical Physics*) translated by J. Kestin (Academic, 1956), pp. 135 and 246.

The International Practical Temperature Scale is defined by a very complicated specification, but has the advantage of being easily reproducible. No gas- or liquid-filled thermometers are required. The platinum resistance thermometer serves for interpolation from −183°C up to 660°C, but from this temperature up to the gold point a platinum versus platinum-rhodium thermocouple is used, for at such high temperatures a platinum wire becomes sensibly thinner by evaporation, which results in an increase in resistance, but does not affect the emf of a thermocouple. The scale is not defined below the oxygen point (−182.97°C or 90.18°K).

By progressive revisions the International Practical Temperature Scale is made to coincide as closely as possible with the perfect-gas temperature scale, but it must be remembered that it is not identical with it. On the other hand, all equations of thermodynamics are written in terms of the perfect-gas or thermodynamic temperature scale. Furthermore, with progress in measuring techniques, discrepancies show up and very often the fixed points and interpolation techniques of the international scale are retained; its errors can be neglected except in work of the very highest accuracy for which the necessary corrections can be applied separately. This course is similar to that followed in the definition of other units as was the case with the kilogram and liter described on page 22.

At present the deviations of the International temperature scale with respect to the perfect-gas or thermodynamic temperature scale can only be determined by direct comparison. This is normally done with the aid of gas thermometers, even though other possibilities exist (Volume II). Since these deviations are, by design, as small as possible, the determination of a definitive set of corrections is very difficult, and has not yet been attained.†

In the range from the oxygen point (−182.97°C) to the ice point (0°C), the deviations do not exceed the difference $t_{\text{thermo}} - t_{\text{int}} = +0.04°C$. At the oxygen point, the thermodynamic temperature is, most probably, $t_{\text{oxy}} = -182.982°C$ (thermo). In the range from 0°C to the sulphur point (444.4°C), it is possible to use the interpolation formula‡

$$t = \frac{t_{\text{thermo}} - t_{\text{int}}}{°C} = \frac{t}{t_{100}}\left[-0.0060 + \left(\frac{t}{t_{100}} - 1\right)\left(0.04106 - 7.363 \times 10^{-5}\,\frac{t}{°C}\right)\right]. \qquad (2.39)$$

This gives

$$t_{\text{steam}} = 99.994°C \qquad \text{(thermo)}$$

and

$$t_{\text{sulph}} = 444.70°C \qquad \text{(thermo)}.$$

Similarly, the best (average) present values for the other fixed points are

$$t_{\text{silver}} = 961.55°C \qquad \text{(thermo)}$$

and

$$t_{\text{gold}} = 1064.06°C \qquad \text{(thermo)}.$$

Above the gold point, the International Temperature Scale is identical with the thermodynamic temperature except for the reference value at the gold point.

---

† See Stimson, H. F., *International Practical Temperature Scale of 1948* (Text Revision of 1960). *J. Res. Natl. Bur. Std., A.* **65** (1961), 139. Also Moser, H. "A review of recent determinations of thermodynamic temperatures of fixed points above 419°C," *Temperature*, ed., C. M. Herzfeld (Reinhold, 1962), III, p. 167.
‡ J. A. Beattie, *Temperature* (Reinhold, 1955), II, p. 63.

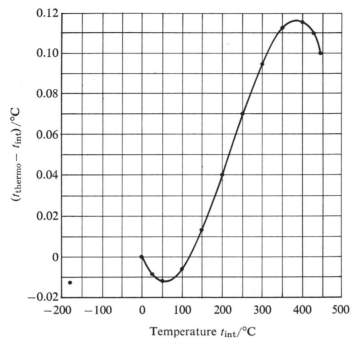

FIGURE 2.9 (*a*) *Corrections* $\Delta t = t_{thermo} - t_{int}$ *to be applied to temperature measurements on the International, Practical Scale (1948). After H. F. Stimson.*

The diagram in Figure 2.9(a) shows these deviations graphically in the range from the ice point to the gold point. An alternative set of corrections to be applied between the sulphur point and the gold point is shown in Figure 2.9(b). The graphs show that the possible errors of this most carefully established temperature scale are not insignificant

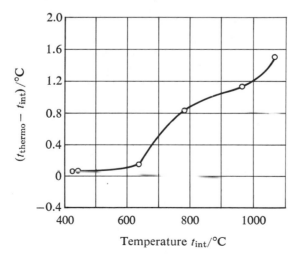

FIGURE 2.9 (*b*) *Corrections* $\Delta t = t_{thermo} - t_{int}$ *to be applied to temperature measurements from the sulphur point to the gold point. After H. Moser.*

at higher temperatures. It is therefore pointless, for instance, to retain any decimals when indicating temperatures above 1500°C or 2500°F.

The gap below the oxygen point (−182.97°C = 90.18°K) is partly filled by three empirical temperature scales, all designed for use at very low temperatures. The *magnetic temperature* scale is based on the magnetic properties of certain paramagnetic salts (Volume II); it has been used from the lowest temperature ever attained (0.0014°K) to approximately 1°K, but it has not been adopted internationally as a standard. Two other scales of temperature are based on the unique relation between the vapor-pressure and temperature of two isotopes of helium, helium 3, and helium 4 (Volume II). They are known, respectively, as the 1958 He^4 Vapor Pressure Scale of Temperatures, or T_{58} for short, and the 1962 He^3 Vapor Pressure Scale of Temperatures, abbreviated to T_{62}. The former is used in the temperature range from 1°K to 5.2°K, and the latter from 0.2°K to 3.324°K.

2.9 Practical temperature measurement†

In all temperature measurements it is essential to secure full thermal equilibrium between the system whose temperature is being measured and the thermometer being used. This requirement presents difficult problems in experimentation and implies that the state of the system does not vary, or fluctuate with time. For this reason, the measurement of varying temperatures is usually very difficult. It must be borne in mind that every thermometer measures temperatures *on its own* empirical temperature scale which depends on the nature and design of the thermometer as well as on the thermometric equation used. It is therefore always necessary to ascertain whether the discrepancies between a particular empirical temperature scale and the International Practical Scale or even the thermodynamic scale are tolerable for the purpose in hand. If this is not the case, more or less elaborate calibrations must be undertaken and suitable corrections introduced.

2.9.1 *Liquid-expansion thermometers*

The ordinary mercury-in-glass thermometer can be used from the freezing-point of mercury at −36.87°C up to about +300°C, if the space above the mercury is free of any gas except mercury vapor. Its range can be extended considerably above the normal boiling-point of mercury (356.7°C) if the boiling-point is raised by filling the thermometer with nitrogen, carbon dioxide, or argon under pressure. It is possible to reach 600°C with a pressure of 20 atm, while with a pressure of 70 atm and a quartz capillary as much as 800°C is attainable.

The quality of a thermometer depends largely on the quality of the glass of which it is made. Inferior glass has a considerable thermal lag: The volume change lags behind the temperature change, reaching its final value only after several hours. Thus, if a thermometer is immersed in an ice-water bath shortly after having been used at a higher temperature, the mercury column falls somewhat below the 0°C mark. This effect is known as "ice-point depression." Good quality thermometers have an ice-

† This section reproduces almost verbatim the author's translation of Section I 3 of E. Schmidt's *Thermodynamics* (Oxford: Clarendon Press, 1949), pp. 7 ff. (With the kind permission of Prof. E. Schmidt and Springer Verlag.)

point depression of less than 0.05°C on cooling from 100°C. The following kinds of glass are most widely used in Germany:

Jena standard glass 16^{III} up to 350°C,
Jena borosilicate glass 59^{III} up to 500°C,
Jena "supremax" glass 1565^{III} up to 700°C.

Good-quality mercury thermometers are very accurate and convenient, and have the advantage — not shared by electrical thermometers — of indicating the temperature directly without the use of auxiliary apparatus. They are, however, unsuitable for defining the thermodynamic temperature scale, because the coefficients of thermal expansion of both mercury and glass (the latter about one-eighth of the former) depend on the thermodynamic temperature in a very complicated way.

Table 2.5 gives so-called standard divisions, that is, the position of the mercury meniscus at various temperatures t, provided the capillary is perfectly cylindrical and uniformly divided.

TABLE 2.5
Standard Divisions of Mercury Thermometers.

t	16^{III}	59^{III}	1565^{III}
−30°C	−30.28°C	−30.13°C	—
0	0.00	0.00	0.00°C
+50	+50.12	+50.03	+50.05
100	100.00	100.00	100.00
150	149.99	150.23	150.04
200	200.29	200.84	200.90
250	261.1	252.2	252.1
300	302.7	304.4	303.9
350	—	358.0	356.6
400	—	412.6	410.5
500	—	526.9	523.1
600	—	—	644
700	—	—	775

For lower temperatures, down to −100°C, the thermometer is filled with alcohol, for use down to −200°C it is filled with petroleum, ether, or commercial pentane. However, as glass is wetted by these substances, the accuracy is far less than that of a mercury thermometer.

When subdividing the scale of a mercury thermometer the whole of the mercury is assumed to be at the same temperature, but in actual measurement the upper part of the mercury column — the so-called exposed, or emergent, thread — is usually at a different temperature. If t is the temperature reading, t_0 is the mean temperature of the exposed thread, a is the length of the exposed thread in scale degrees, and c is the net linear coefficient of expansion of mercury in the glass, it can easily be seen that the reading should be corrected by an amount

$$a(t - t_0)c. \qquad (2.40)$$

Values of *c* for different quantities of glass are listed in Table 2.6.

TABLE 2.6

Correction Factor c for the Exposed Thread.

Glass	$c/(°C)$
Glass 16^{III}	0.000158
″ 59^{III}	0.000164
″ 1565^{III}	0.000172
Quartz glass	0.000180

The mean temperature of the exposed thread can either be estimated, or alternatively measured by means of the Mahlke, or emergent-thread, thermometer, if greater accuracy is required. The emergent-thread thermometer consists of a long cylindrical mercury vessel communicating with a narrow capillary tube. It is placed near the main thermometer so that the top of the cylindrical mercury vessel is level with the meniscus of the main thermometer column, as in Figure 2.10. The emergent-thread thermometer then measures the mean temperature of that length of the main thermometer thread

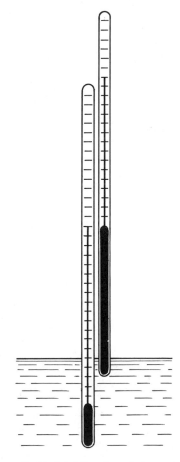

FIGURE 2.10. *Mahlke thread thermometer.*

lying alongside its own cylindrical mercury vessel, and this length must be substituted for a in the equation (2.27). If the projecting thread of the main thermometer is longer than the vessel of the emergent-thread thermometer, an additional emergent-thread thermometer is required. With temperatures of the order of 300°C the projecting thread correction may amount to as much as 10°C.

It is not appropriate here to embark on a full discussion of the many errors to which liquid-filled (and other) thermometers are liable in practice; such questions are exhaustively dealt with in the literature.†

2.9.2   Resistance thermometers

The principle of the electrical-resistance thermometer is based on the fact that the electrical resistance of any pure metal increases by about 0.004 of its value at 0°C for each 1°C of temperature rise. This temperature coefficient of resistance is, remarkably enough, approximately the same as the coefficient of expansion of gases, a fact which can be explained by the statistical theory of electrical conduction in metals.

Alloys have much lower temperature coefficients of resistance than pure metals, and are therefore unsuitable for resistance thermometers. With manganin and constantan, for instance, the resistance in the vicinity of room temperature is practically independent of temperature.

Pure platinum is the most suitable metal for resistance thermometers on account of its great resistance to chemical attack and its high melting point. The platinum-resistance thermometer is the interpolation instrument used to define the lower parts of the International Practical Temperature Scale, that is, from −190°C to +600°C (see page 58). Apart from platinum, copper and nickel are the most widely used metals.

Certain sintered metallic oxides, or so-called thermistors, have large electrical resistivities which strongly depend on temperature. Their temperature coefficients of resistance are negative and an order of magnitude larger (a factor of approximately 10) than those of pure metals. However, even if they are very carefully manufactured and aged, their properties change with time fairly strongly. They can also be used as resistance thermometers, but on condition that they are subjected to frequent recalibration. Carbon and germanium (with 0.0016% indium) resistors can also be used as thermometers, particularly at low temperatures.

In manufacturing a resistance thermometer it must be remembered that its state depends on strain as well as on temperature, and care must be taken to secure strain-free mounting, particularly after cooling. As a rule it is necessary to provide suitable protective tubes because contamination produces changes in the resistivity of the thermometer. Any suitable method for measuring resistance can be used. The most convenient is the Wheatstone bridge, shown diagrammatically in Figure 2.11. Here R_t is the resistance of the thermometer, R_a and R_b are known fixed resistances, and R_c is an adjustable measuring resistance; $\mathcal{E}$ is a source of current, and G a null-point galvanometer. By adjustment of the variable resistance R_c the reading of the galvanometer

---

† See Knoblauch, O., and Hencky, K., *Anleitung zu genauen technischen Temperaturmessungen* (2nd ed.; Munich and Berlin, 1926); *Technical Data on Fuel*, ed. Spiers, (5th ed.; British National Committee, World Power Conference, 1952); *International Critical Tables*, section on thermometry; *Temperature, Its Measurement and Control in Science and Industry*, The American Institute of Physics (Reinhold, 1941, 1954, and 1962).

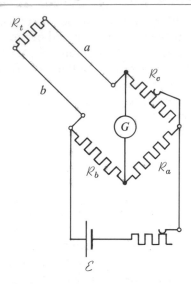

FIGURE 2.11. *Resistance thermometer in Wheatstone bridge.*

can be reduced to zero, when the unknown resistance of the thermometer is given by the equation

$$\frac{R_t}{R_c} = \frac{R_b}{R_a}.$$ (2.41)

When the bridge is balanced, the resistance thermometer passes a current

$$I = \frac{\mathcal{E}}{R_t + R_c},$$

which must be kept very small in order to suppress its effect on the temperature of the resistance R_t itself through Joule heating.

As a rule, the resistance R_l of the thermometer leads, a and b, cannot be neglected in comparison with the thermometer resistance R_t. This resistance cannot be subtracted by measuring it, particularly if it is realized that the temperature of the resistance leads ranges from that being measured at the element R_t and room temperature at the terminals. The effect of the leads can be eliminated by duplicating them as nearly as possible and by shunting the duplicate $a'b'$ into the opposite arm R_c of the bridge, Figure 2.12. The dummy leads must be placed as near to the main leads as possible so as to make sure that the junction c is at the temperature of the thermometer and that the temperature distribution between it and the terminals is also as nearly the same as possible. It is clear from equation (2.41) that now

$$(R_t + R_l)R_a = (R_l + R_c)R_b$$

and R_c can be made equal to R_t only if $R_a = R_b$ is chosen. Thus,

$$R_t = R_c \quad \text{if} \quad R_a = R_b.$$ (2.41a)

The two leads a' and a can be replaced by one, when the so-called *three-lead resistance thermometer* is obtained, Figure 2.13. For high-precision operation it is possible to

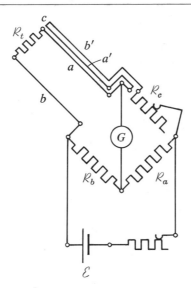

FIGURE 2.12. *Resistance thermometer with compensated leads.*

obtain more complete compensation of the effects of the leads, as well as compensation for contact resistances at the terminals, when a four-lead resistance thermometer is used in conjunction with a so-called Mueller bridge.† A Kelvin bridge can also be employed.

Very often it is preferable to utilize a high-precision potentiometer for resistance measurement because the same instrument can also serve to measure the emf of ther-

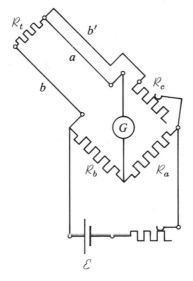

FIGURE 2.13. *Three-lead resistance thermometer.*

† For more details see Baker, H. D., Ryder, E. A., and Baker, N. H., *Temperature Measurement in Engineering* (Wiley, 1961), II, p. 34.

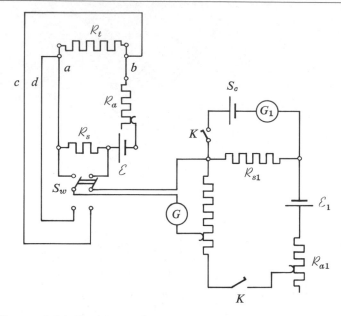

FIGURE 2.14. *Resistance thermometer in a potentiometer circuit.*
R_t—resistance thermometer   *$\mathcal{E}, \mathcal{E}_1$—sources of emf*
R_s, R_{s_1}—standard resistances   *S_c—standard cell*
R_a, R_{a_1}—adjustable resistors   *S_w—change-over switch*
G, G_1—null-point galvanometers   *K—key*

mocouples. The required circuit is shown in Figure 2.14. A very small current is passed through the resistance thermometer R_t via the relatively heavy current leads a and b, and that current is determined by measuring the voltage drop across a very accurate standard resistance R_s. The variable resistor R_a is used to adjust the current to the desired magnitude. The accompanying voltage drop across the thermometer is measured directly on the potentiometer circuit by connecting it through the high-resistance leads c and d. The potentiometer circuit is, in essence, identical with the one shown in Figure 2.15 for a thermocouple circuit.

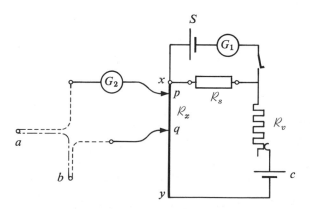

FIGURE 2.15. *Potentiometer circuit for thermocouple.*

A resistance thermometer made of wire can be distributed as desired, and is therefore very suitable for the measurement of mean temperatures over large areas.

2.9.3   Thermocouples

If two wires of different metals are joined to form a closed circuit, an electric current will flow round the circuit as long as the two junctions are kept at different temperatures. If a galvanometer is inserted into the circuit at any point, its reading will be a measure of the temperature difference between the junctions. Such an arrangement is widely used in practical temperature measurement. One of the junctions may be kept at room temperature, in a bath of melting ice at 0°C, or better still, in a triple-point cell. In the first case it can be omitted altogether, the two wires being connected to the terminals of the galvanometer, which then forms the cold junction.

By comparison with the liquid-filled thermometer, the thermocouple has the advantage of small size, which makes it particularly suitable for use in restricted spaces. Like the resistance thermometer, the thermocouple requires auxiliary measuring equipment, only one set of which is required, however, for any number of thermocouples. Consequently, for temperature measurement at a number of points the thermocouple method is cheaper and quicker than any other.

The emf produced by the temperature difference between the two junctions can be measured either by means of a potentiometer or other null-point method, or directly by an indicating instrument.

A simple potentiometer circuit is shown in Figure 2.15, where a is the thermocouple and b the cold junction, which is immersed in melting ice. An accumulator c causes current to pass round the circuit through the variable resistance R_v, the fixed standard resistance R_s, and the potentiometer wire xy. The current is standardized by adjusting the variable resistance R_v until the voltage drop across R_s is just equal to the emf of the standard cell S, as indicated by a zero reading of the galvanometer G_1. The potentiometer tappings p and q are then adjusted until the emf of the thermocouple is balanced by the voltage drop along the potentiometer wire between them, indicated by a zero reading of the galvanometer G_2. If the resistance of the potentiometer wire from p to q is R_x and the emf of the standard cell is $\mathcal{E}_s$, we have

$$\text{emf of thermocouple} = \mathcal{E}_s \cdot \frac{R_x}{R_s}.$$

The tappings p and q are usually arranged to give coarse and fine adjustment respectively. For a more detailed account of potentiometers for the measurement of thermal emf's, the reader may consult some specialized treatises on the subject.[†]

An alternative form of null-point circuit is shown in Figure 2.16; a_1 and a_2 are two thermocouples, and b is the cold junction, which may be common to any number of hot junctions; c is a multiple switch by means of which any one of a number of hot junctions may be selected, and G is a center-zero galvanometer. R_s is a known fixed resistance, A a current instrument, d a source of current, and R_v a variable resistance. To take a reading the resistance R_v is adjusted until the galvanometer G reads zero, when the current I passing through the current instrument A is noted. The emf of the thermocouple is then equal to the voltage drop IR_s across the fixed resistance R_s. When using

† Baker, H. D., Ryder, E. A., and Baker, N. H., *Temperature Measurement in Engineering* (Wiley, 1961), II.

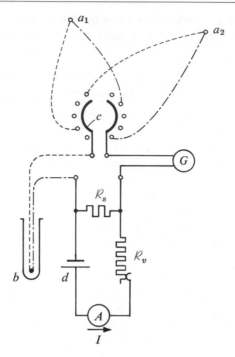

FIGURE 2.16. *Thermocouples with null-point circuit.*

an indicating instrument for direct measurement, it must be remembered that the reading is less than the true emf by the voltage drop across the thermocouple caused by the current flowing.

Table 2.7 lists the more important pairs of metals used in thermocouples, giving in each case the emf per 100°C temperature difference and the maximum temperature permissible for a reasonable useful life. For the measurement of lower temperatures, copper-constantan and manganin-constantan thermocouples are preferred. Constantan is an alloy of 60 percent copper and 40 percent nickel, while manganin consists of 84 percent nickel.

To avoid secondary or "nuisance" emf's at the terminals of the measuring instrument, the temperature of which often differs from room temperature owing to frequent handling, it is usual to connect the instrument in that side of the circuit composed of the metal having the smaller thermal emf with respect to copper, for example, in the copper or manganin side. In work of higher precision it is preferable to connect instruments and switches (whose terminals are made of pure copper) by means of electrolytic copper wires. This can always be achieved if it is remembered that one leg of a thermocouple can be cut, the cuts being joined by a copper wire. The additional two junctions will produce exactly equal and opposite emf's if they are kept at the same temperature. This is achieved by special junction boxes, usually made of a large block of copper kept in a Dewar flask. The common temperature need not be equal to the temperature of the cold junction, but the equality of temperature secures the cancellation of the two additional emf's. By contrast, it is practically impossible to maintain the terminals of potentiometers and others at the same temperature.

There is no simple relationship between temperature and emf for any couple over its whole working range; the applicability of any formula is more or less restricted, as for instance equation (2.37) for the platinum versus platinum-rhodium couple defining part of the international temperature scale. For small ranges of temperature it is often sufficient to assume a linear relationship. Generally speaking, it is necessary to calibrate thermocouples against other instruments; the emf figures in Table 2.7 are, of course, nothing more than a rough comparison of sensitivities.

TABLE 2.7

*Electromotive Force and Approximate Maximum Permissible
Working Temperature of Thermocouples of Different Metals.*

(The metal mentioned first is positive with respect to the other at the hot junction.)

Pair of metals	Maximum working temperature (°C)	Approx. emf per 100°C (mV)	Approx. temperature difference per microvolt
Copper *vs.* Constantan (Eureka)	400	4	0.025°C
Manganin *vs.* Constantan (Eureka)	700	4	0.025
Iron *vs.* Constantan (Eureka)	800	5	0.020
Chrome-nickel *vs.* Constantan	1,000	4–6	0.016–0.020
Chrome-nickel *vs.* Nickel	1,100	4	0.025
Platinum-rhodium *vs.* Palladium-gold	1,200	4	0.025
Chromel *vs.* Alumel	1,350	5	0.020
Platinum-rhodium *vs.* Platinum (90% Pt, 10% Rh)	1,500	1	0.1
Iridium *vs.* Iridium-rhodium (40% Ir, 60% Rh)	2,000	0.5	0.2
Iridium *vs.* Iridium-rhodium (90% Ir, 10% Rh)	2,300	0.5	0.2
Tungsten *vs.* Tungsten-molybdenum (75% W, 25% Mo)	2,600	0.3	0.35

2.9.4   Radiation thermometers or pyrometers

Pyrometers are suitable for the measurement of temperatures of over 700°C. They can be used at a distance and are the only possible form of thermometer for the measurement of very high temperatures. In most types the luminosity of an electrically heated wire is compared with that of an optical image of the body whose temperature is being measured, the image being projected into the plane of the wire by means of a lens. The luminosities of the image and of the wire are made equal either by adjustment of the heating current through the wire, or by adjustment of their relative strengths by means of variable apertures, Nicol prisms, or wedges of tinted glass. Apart from such subjective instruments there are objective types in which the image of the hot body falls on a thermocouple, the emf of which serves as a measure of the temperature of the body. The relationship between temperature and radiation is, however, only known accurately for a theoretical blackbody, to which the nearest practical approach is a hollow box with a small hole for the emission of radiation from the interior. Ordinary surfaces, particularly bright metallic surfaces, have a lower luminosity than a blackbody at a given temperature.

2.10   Additional remarks concerning equilibrium

In order to conclude this chapter, it will be found useful to revert to the concept of equilibrium and to restate the principles established in Section 2.1 in terms of the newly acquired concept of temperature. The concept of temperature and our ability to perform reproducible temperature measurements rely on the fact that systems show a tendency towards thermal equilibrium. More precisely, it is maintained that systems, however complex, which are made to interact across diathermal walls within a rigid adiabatic enclosure *always* reach a state of thermal equilibrium. This state is characterized by the fact that no changes in the state of any subsystem can be observed and that all sub-systems acquire a common temperature. In actual fact no perfect equilibrium is ever attained, and if sufficiently sensitive thermometers are used, it is always possible to detect small temperature differences between parts of a system enclosed in an insulating envelope. Furthermore, the temperature at any particular point within the system usually varies with time. This behavior of real systems is, however, attributed to the lack of perfection in the properties of the approximation to an adiabatic enclosure employed in a particular instance. Thus, the preceding assertion is seen to constitute a generalization and extrapolation of observed facts, rather than a simple statement of experimental fact; its truth can only be ascertained by subjecting its consequences to experimental verification.

The importance of the preceding assertion has been clearly recognized by Josiah Willard Gibbs. Recently, it has been proposed to elevate the statement to the rank of a principle of thermodynamics and an attempt has been made† to derive the First as well as the Second Laws of thermodynamics from it (Volume II).

In the future it will be useful to visualize the process of attaining equilibrium in the form of the following, simplified process. First, it is imagined that an arbitrary number of systems, Figure 2.17(a), are enclosed in rigid adiabatic containers, and sufficient time is allowed for every one of them to reach a state of equilibrium characterized by the fact that the temperature of any part of each system is the same within it. It is asserted that this will *always* happen. Next, the systems are all brought within a common, rigid adiabatic enclosure, Figure 2.17(b), and subsequently, the inner adiabatic partitions are replaced by diathermal ones, Figure 2.17(c). It is once more asserted that all systems will always reach a state of equilibrium characterized by the fact that the temperature is uniform throughout.

Similar phenomena are known from mechanics. If a mass *m* is placed on a horizontal wall in the gravitational field of the earth, Figure 2.18, in a larger vessel, so that it is at rest, or as it is said, so that it is *constrained* to be at rest, it is found that the removal of the constraint will cause the mass to fall; but the mass will come to rest eventually. The system, the mass *m*, has reached a state of *mechanical equilibrium*. The adiabatic partitions removed in the experiment depicted in Figure 2.17 constitute thermal constraints

† Hatsopoulos, G. N., and Keenan, J. H., "A single axiom for classical thermodynamics," *J. Appl. Mech.* Transactions of the ASME. Ser. E. **29** (1962) 193. See also, Hatsopoulos, G. N., and Keenan, J. H., *Principles of General Thermodynamics* (Wiley, 1965).

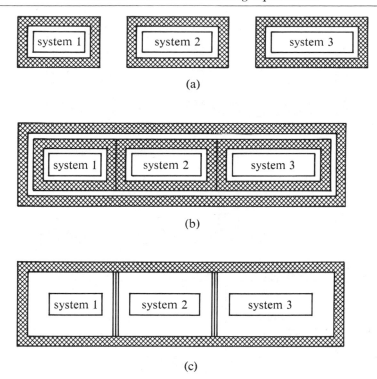

FIGURE 2.17. *The process of attaining thermal equilibrium after the removal of thermal constraints.*

in the same way as the horizontal wall in Figure 2.18 constituted a mechanical constraint. The removal of a constraint is seen to allow a system to perform a process whereby it reaches a new "final" state of equilibrium from an initial state of equilibrium.

Another example is afforded by the experiment illustrated in Figure 2.19 in which two quantities of gas are enclosed in adiabatic cylinders and are separated by an adiabatic, rigid wall. If the wall, the mechanical constraint, is replaced by a piston, the pressures of the two gases will eventually become equalized after first performing some oscillations, and the systems will be said to have reached mechanical equilibrium. If, further, the thermal constraint is removed, in that the adiabatic piston is replaced by a diathermal one, the systems will reach thermal equilibrium in addition to maintaining

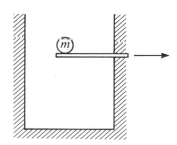

FIGURE 2.18. *The process of attaining mechanical equilibrium.*

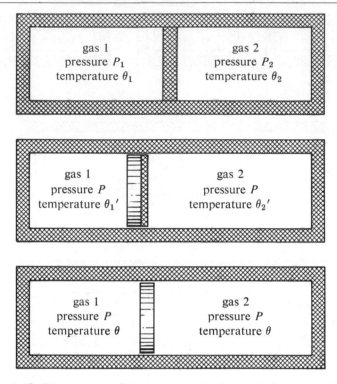

FIGURE 2.19. *The process of attaining mechanical and thermal equilibrium.*

mechanical equilibrium. It is also observed that very often mechanical equilibrium is reached after a number of characteristic oscillations. However, when thermal equilibrium is attained across rigid walls, no temperature oscillations are observed.

The perceptive reader will have undoubtedly noticed that in the example of Figure 2.18 the mass m, imagined in the form of a small sphere, could have attained stable equilibrium if the bottom of the vessel were concave upwards, unstable equilibrium if it were convex upwards, or neutral equilibrium with the flat bottom sketched. The type of equilibrium in existence depends on the behavior of the systems with respect to *small disturbances*. Similar considerations apply to the more general systems studied in thermodynamics, and they also can reach any one of the three kinds of equilibrium mentioned.

List of Symbols for Chapter 2

Latin letters

A Constant in equations (2.11), (2.35), and (2.36)
a Constant in equations (2.11a) and (2.37)
B Constant in equations (2.35) and (2.36)
b Constant in equations (2.11a) and (2.37)
C Constant in equation (2.36)
c Constant in equation (2.37)

c_2	Planck's second radiation constant
$\mathcal{E}$	Electromotive force
I	Electric current
J	Radiant energy per unit wavelength per unit time per unit solid angle per unit area of a blackbody
L	Length
m	Mass
P	Pressure
p	Barometric pressure
p_0	Standard barometric pressure, 1 standard atmosphere
$\mathcal{R}$	Electrical resistance
t	Temperature on Celsius or Fahrenheit scale
$\mathcal{J}$	Tension
V	Volume
x	Independent property
y	Independent property

Greek letters

α	Constant in equation (2.11b)
β	Constant in equation (2.11b)
γ	Constant in equation (2.11b)
Δ	Error in respective quantity
ϵ	Uncertainty
θ	Temperature on perfect-gas scale
Θ	Dimension of temperature
λ	Wavelength
π	$= (p/p_0 - 1)$ in equations (2.32), (2.33), and (2.34)

CHAPTER 3

The Equation of State

3.1 General remarks. Criteria for properties

The equation of state constitutes a functional relationship between one dependent and n independent variables. The relation is single-valued and also continuous, but its derivatives are not necessarily continuous. In order to apply mathematical analysis to the equation of state, it is necessary to recapitulate some of the relations which are proved in the mathematical theory of functions of several variables, and so to establish a firm link between the mathematical and the thermodynamical concepts. In addition, it will be useful to obtain geometrical representations of the equation of state in order to be in a position to visualize them more clearly.

Not all quantities encountered in thermodynamics are directly related to the independent properties by a functional relationship. They arise as a result of the performance of certain mathematical operations, in particular, as we shall see in Section 4.1, as a result of the computation of line integrals. Consequently, such quantities are related to the independent variables in a more complex way, and do not form with them an equation of state. In other words, these quantities do not assume fixed values once the thermodynamic state of the system is fixed. Hence, by studying the mathematical properties of functions of several variables it will be possible to indicate exact *criteria* by which a property can be distinguished from the other quantities encountered in thermodynamics, it being clear that any *property* can always be represented as a *function* of the n independent variables of the system.

The preceding remarks do not provide a method whereby this function can be determined; they merely suggest that such a functional relation *exists*. As a rule, this relation must be determined experimentally by direct measurement. In particular cases, it can be determined by the methods of statistical thermodynamics after a suitable *molecular model* has been found to provide results which agree with macroscopic experiments. An equation of state cannot always be written down in a closed, mathematical form, for example, by means of an algebraic expression. More frequently, it will be given in the form of tables, such as the steam tables, Tables X, XI, and XII in Volume II, or even in the form of diagrams. Many such state diagrams will be introduced throughout this book.

There is no difficulty in indicating our first criterion for a property. Any algebraic combination of properties, or any explicit function of properties, is also a property, because each of them assumes a fixed value whenever the properties in terms of which they have been expressed, assume fixed values. For example, the expressions $c\theta + Pv$ or $\ln (Pv/c\theta)^\gamma$, in which c and γ stand for constants, are properties. A number of such composite expressions will be introduced later in the book, because they play an important part in the science of thermodynamics. The expression $k = \phi(P, v)$, where ϕ denotes an arbitrary single-valued function of the independent variables P, v is also a property.

The distinction between quantities which are and which are not connected to the independent variables of a system by a functional relationship is a vital one in thermodynamics. It will be shown in Chapters 4 and 5 that the two very important quantities: work and heat do not belong to this class. For this reason, it will be necessary to develop additional criteria for the existence of an equation of state, Section 4.2.

3.2   Thermal equations of state

An equation of state which contains temperature as a variable is often referred to as a *thermal equation of state*. Since every empirical temperature scale is defined in relation to the properties of a particular system, it follows that the thermal equation of state for that system, and in terms of that particular temperature, is partly given in the definition of the temperature scale. More precisely, the definition of the temperature scale implies a specified temperature variation of the thermometric property under conditions when all the remaining independent properties are kept at fixed, constant values. For example, if an empirical temperature scale θ is adopted in terms of the resistance of a length of platinum wire, then the adopted thermometric function constitutes the thermal equation of state for platinum wires at the stipulated constant value of tension $\mathcal{T}_0$. If a linear scale of the form

$$\theta = \theta_3 \frac{\mathcal{R}}{\mathcal{R}_3} \qquad \text{at} \quad \mathcal{T}_0 = \text{const} \tag{3.1}$$

had been defined, it is seen that any empirical thermal equation of state for platinum wires in terms of the platinum temperature scale would reduce to equation (3.1) for $\mathcal{T} = \mathcal{T}_0$, its general form being

$$\mathrm{f}(\mathcal{T}, \theta, \mathcal{R}) = 0, \tag{3.2}$$

so that

$$\mathrm{f}(\mathcal{T}_0, \theta, \mathcal{R}) = \theta - \theta_3 \frac{\mathcal{R}}{\mathcal{R}_3}. \tag{3.3}$$

In the case of gases, the perfect-gas temperature scale has been defined in terms of the product PV, and the thermometric equation becomes itself the thermal equation of state for the hypothetical perfect gas defined in Section 2.6. Hence, *by virtue of the universal adoption of this scale*, the thermal equation of state for a perfect gas is identical with equation (2.18b), or

$$\theta = \frac{PV}{(PV)_3} \theta_3. \tag{3.4}$$

In this equation, the temperature θ_3 of the triple point is a universal constant, and the value $(PV)_3$ is a characteristic, measured quantity for a given mass of any particular gas, such as air or helium. In the product $(PV)_3$, the pressure P is an intensive property, and the extensive property V can be represented as the product

$$V = mv \tag{3.5}$$

of mass and specific volume. Thus, the quantity

$$R = \frac{(Pv)_3}{\theta_3} \tag{3.6}$$

is a characteristic constant of the given gas, and equation (3.4) can be written

$$PV = m R \theta. \tag{3.7}$$

Equation (3.7) constitutes a very convenient form of the thermal equation of state of a perfect gas. The quantity R is known as the *gas constant* of the particular perfect gas (air, helium, and so on), and its units are

$$\{R\} = \frac{\text{lbf ft}}{\text{lbm °R}}; \quad \frac{\text{kpm}}{\text{kg °K}}; \quad \frac{\text{kcal}}{\text{kg °K}}; \quad \frac{\text{Btu}}{\text{lbm °R}}; \quad \frac{\text{J}}{\text{kg °K}}; \quad \text{or} \quad \frac{\text{atm m}^3}{\text{kg °K}};$$

depending on the system of units preferred at the time. The measured values of gas constants for different, perfect gases can be found in Table V. The thermal equation of state for any other substance must be determined by suitable measurements; it can, as already stated, sometimes be derived from a suitable model by the methods of classical and quantum statistics.

The definition of the perfect-gas temperature scale requires that the values of the products PV and $(PV)_3$ in equation (3.4) should be obtained as a result of extrapolation to zero pressure from measurements on real gases, perfect gases constituting non-existent, but convenient idealizations. Consequently, the thermal equation of state of a real gas will differ from equation (3.4) and will be more complex in its mathematical form. However, when the product PV is calculated from it for different pressures P at any constant temperature θ and the process of passing to the limit $P \to 0$ is performed on the results, the limit must agree with equation (3.7). On the one hand, this puts a constraint on the possible, empirically admissible forms of the function $f(P, V, \theta)$ for a gas, when experimental results are represented, or, as it is said, *correlated* by a mathematical expression. The same remains true for cases when graphical or tabular representations are used. On the other hand, the results of measurements must extrapolate to the so-called *asymptotic form* (3.7). If in any particular case they do not, it is certain that the measurements contain serious experimental errors. For example, the temperature scale used in the correlation may not have been corrected to the perfect-gas scale, the vessel may have leaked, causing the mass to change, or the gas may have become contaminated with another gas directly or owing to a chemical interaction between the gas and the cylinder containing it.

Instead of using the mass as a measure of quantity, it is possible to make use of the chemical unit, the mol. The use of the mol leads to a considerable simplification in the form of the thermal equation of a perfect gas which will be dealt with in Sections 3.9 and 3.10.

3.3 Geometrical representation as a surface

The thermal equation of state for a unit mass of gas or liquid of specified chemical composition, or a so-called pure substance, has the general form

$$F(P, v, \theta) = 0. \tag{3.8}$$

The function can, at least in principle, be solved with respect to any one of the three variables, so that it can be written in three equivalent forms:

$$P = P(v, \theta); \quad v = v(P, \theta); \quad \text{and} \quad \theta = \theta(P, v). \tag{3.8a}$$

A similar equation of state can also be written down for a solid of specified chemical composition and subjected to a uniform pressure acting on its surface; the solid then also constitutes a pure substance.

Certain liquids, such as water or liquid bismuth, exhibit an interesting, anomalous behavior. The specific volume of liquid water or bismuth passes through a maximum (minimum density) at a given temperature, for example, $+4°C$ for water, at atmospheric pressure, Figure 3.1. Thus, in the range, say, of $0°C$ to $6°C$, there exist two different states of water of identical specific volume and pressure but different temperatures. It would appear, therefore, that the second thermal equation of state (3.8a) for such anomalous substances is double-valued, contrary to what has been asserted earlier and in Section 1.5. Similar examples are encountered in the study of phase equilibria, Section 7.4.10, when it will be discovered that macroscopically differing forms of pure substances, such as different states of aggregation (liquid, solid, or gaseous forms of a substance) or different *allotropic modifications* of a solid can sometimes exist in a given, common range of pressures and temperatures, though the specific volumes are different. In such cases it is necessary to realize that an understanding of the process always allows us to determine, independently of the equation of state, which of the possible states has actually been attained. This knowledge has the effect of rendering the equation single-valued.

When an isotropic solid body is subjected to a complex, three-dimensional system of stresses, its state can no longer be described by two independent properties, the number increasing to four in the elastic range. The equation of state becomes accordingly more complex.

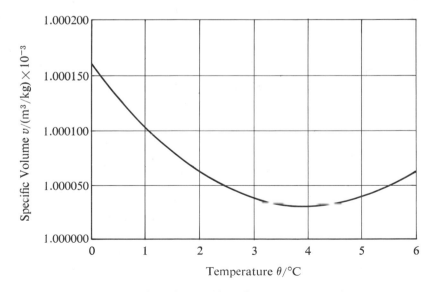

FIGURE 3.1. *The specific volume of liquid water at atmospheric pressure.*

In the case of simple systems whose state is described by two independent variables, the equation of state constitutes a relation between three variables and can be represented geometrically by means of a surface in three-dimensional space. For example, the surface of state of a perfect gas, equation (3.7), written for a unit mass in the form

$$Pv = R\theta \tag{3.9}$$

is represented by a so-called hyperbolic paraboloid shown in an isometric projection in Figure 3.2. The coordinates in Figure 3.2 are θ, P, and v. In actual practice it is very awkward, and inconvenient, to make use of such pictures or of three-dimensional models made of wood, cardboard, or others. Instead, surfaces of this kind are easily depicted on a sheet of paper by drawing on it a suitable contour diagram, in the same way as a mountainous region is described by means of contours on a map. It is imagined that the surface is intersected by an equidistant family of planes $P = $ const, $\theta = $ const, or $v = $ const, and that the resulting curves are projected in the directions, P, θ, or v, respectively, that is, into the v, θ; P, v; or P, θ planes, and labeled with the value of that variable which remains constant. Three such contour maps for a perfect gas are shown in Figure 3.3. For example, the contours in the P, v plane are rectangular hyperbolae $Pv = $ const, where the constant is equal to $R\theta$. In Figure 3.3(a), the values of temperature, rather than of the product $R\theta$, have been indicated. The remaining contours, as is easy to verify from equation (3.9), are simply straight lines emanating from the respective origins.

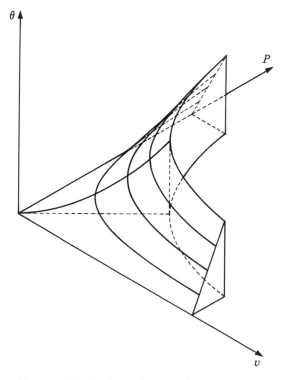

FIGURE 3.2. *Surface of state of a perfect gas.*

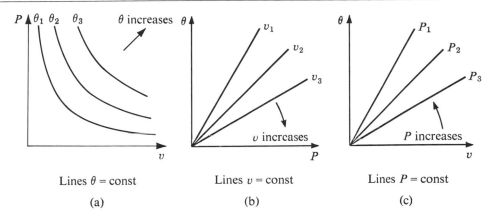

FIGURE 3.3. *Contour projections of the surface from Figure 3.2.*

When the number of independent variables increases beyond two, say to n, the tracing of contours becomes impossible. The equation of state is then represented by a hypersurface of n dimensions in a space of $n + 1$ dimensions. It will be noted that in such cases an isotherm is no longer a line, as in the case of two independent variables, but becomes a geometrical subspace of $n - 1$ dimensions. It is a surface for systems with three independent variables.

3.4 Notation

The essential mathematical characteristic of a thermodynamic property is that it assumes a definite value at a definite thermodynamic state. When the state of the system is made to undergo a continuous series of changes, the system is said to have performed a *process*. If the system undergoes a process at the end of which it returns to the initial state, it is said to have performed a *cyclic process* or *cycle* for short. At the end of a cycle all properties of the system assume their initial values irrespective of the nature of the cycle. Thus, a state is represented by a point in the space of $n + 1$ dimensions discussed in the preceding section, and a process is represented by a curve. A cycle is represented by a closed curve.

Since the equation of state expresses a relation between a thermodynamic property regarded as the dependent variable and n independent properties, it will be often necessary to consider derivatives with respect to one property, when the others are kept constant. In other words, partial derivatives are likely to, and do, play an important part in the study of thermodynamics.

For example, in the case of the relation

$$\theta = \theta(P, v), \tag{3.10}$$

we shall be interested in the partial derivatives

$$\frac{\partial \theta}{\partial P} \quad \text{and} \quad \frac{\partial \theta}{\partial v}.$$

In writing down such partial derivatives in thermodynamics, it is customary to indicate the variable which is kept constant in the process of differentiation by displaying it as a subscript. In the case of equation (3.10) we shall write

$$\left(\frac{\partial \theta}{\partial P}\right)_v \quad \text{and} \quad \left(\frac{\partial \theta}{\partial v}\right)_P . \tag{3.10a}$$

This somewhat cumbersome notation is essential in thermodynamics, though it is found superfluous in mathematics. The reason for it lies in the difference in interest in the two branches of science. It is very important to realize that the *mathematical* symbols

$$z = \mathrm{f}(x, y) \quad \text{or} \quad z = z(x, y) \tag{3.11}$$

denote particular functional relationships between the dependent variable z and the independent variables x, y. In mathematics it is immaterial to enquire into the nature of these quantities, because the study is centered on the *relation* between them, that is, on the *form* of the function. Thus, the functions in equation (3.11) may stand for the linear relation

$$z = ax + by,$$

where $\mathrm{f}(x, y)$ means

$$\mathrm{f}(x, y) = ax + by.$$

If it is necessary to discuss another function in the same context, such as the quadratic relation

$$z = Ax^2 + Bxy + Cy^2,$$

the symbol $\mathrm{f}(x, y)$ would no longer be employed, but would be replaced by another, say

$$\phi(x, y) = Ax^2 + Bxy + Cy^2,$$

and the distinction between $z = \mathrm{f}$ and $z = \phi$ would be in the form of their relation to the independent variables x, y. Thus, when discussing partial derivatives, preference is given to the symbols

$$\frac{\partial \mathrm{f}}{\partial x}, \frac{\partial \mathrm{f}}{\partial y}, \frac{\partial \phi}{\partial x}, \frac{\partial \phi}{\partial y}, \cdots, \text{ instead of } \frac{\partial z}{\partial x}, \frac{\partial z}{\partial y}, \cdots,$$

since the functions f and ϕ have been clearly defined beforehand. Consequently, the preceding symbols are unambiguous, it being always evident which, and how many, independent variables have been kept constant during the process of differentiation.

In thermodynamics, as in all branches of physics, a symbol denotes a *physical quantity*, irrespectively of how it is related to other quantities. Thus, in the equation of state

$$\theta = \theta(P, v), \tag{3.12}$$

it may become necessary to perform a change of variables, replacing, for example, the specific volume v by the refractive index n. We would still write

$$\theta = \theta(P, n) \tag{3.12a}$$

retaining the symbol θ for temperature, regardless of the fact that the mathematical forms (3.12) and (3.12a) cannot, in general, be identical. In mathematics, as explained, two different symbols would be used to emphasize this fact. In forming partial derivatives in thermodynamics we would write

$$\left(\frac{\partial \theta}{\partial P}\right)_v \quad \text{and} \quad \left(\frac{\partial \theta}{\partial v}\right)_P \qquad \text{for equation (3.12),}$$

and

$$\left(\frac{\partial \theta}{\partial P}\right)_n \quad \text{and} \quad \left(\frac{\partial \theta}{\partial n}\right)_P \qquad \text{for equation (3.12a),}$$

placing the emphasis on the physical quantity, θ in this example, rather than on the functional relation which links it to the properties chosen as independent. Without the subscripts, the first partial derivatives would both be written $\partial \theta / \partial P$ and the symbol would become ambiguous, since $(\partial \theta / \partial P)_v$ and $(\partial \theta / \partial P)_n$ denote two different physical quantities as well as two different mathematical forms. In the case of more independent variables, it is necessary to display more than one subscript to the parenthesis.

For these reasons, the subscript notation for partial derivatives

$$f_x \text{ for } \frac{\partial f}{\partial x}, \qquad \phi_y \text{ for } \frac{\partial \phi}{\partial y}, \qquad \text{and so on,}$$

which is found so convenient in mathematics, cannot be employed in thermodynamics.

The thermodynamic notation for partial derivatives has the additional advantage that the symbol displays the independent variables of the function whose derivative is being considered in an unambiguous manner. These appear in the subscript outside the parenthesis and as the variable with respect to which the derivative is taken. Thus, for example, the symbol

$$\left(\frac{\partial \theta}{\partial v}\right)_P$$

indicates that θ is treated as the function $\theta = \theta(v, P)$, whereas

$$\left(\frac{\partial \theta}{\partial n}\right)_P$$

shows that a change of variables to $\theta = \theta(n, P)$ has been performed.

3.5   Geometrical representation of partial derivatives

The geometrical interpretation of the partial derivatives (3.10a) is illustrated in Figure 3.4. The area contained by the oval in the figure represents a portion of the surface defined by equation (3.10). The lines a_1 and a_2 are curves of intersection of the surface with two planes $v = \text{const}$ which have been chosen a distance dv apart. The line b_1 and b_2 are curves of intersection with two planes $P = \text{const}$ at dP apart. Both pairs of curves delineate a small quadrilateral 1234. Two planes $\theta = \text{const}$ are passed through points 1 and 3, the highest and the lowest one in the quadrilateral, respectively, the distance between them being $d\theta$. The resulting curves of intersection with the surface are c_1 and c_2.

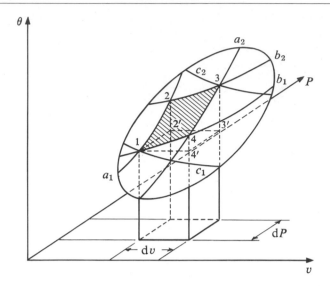

FIGURE 3.4. *Geometrical illustration of the differentiation of an equation of state.*

The partial derivative $(\partial\theta/\partial P)_v$ represents the gradient of path 12 which is parallel to the θ, P plane, that is, one for which $v = $ const. Its numerical value is that of the tangent of the angle between 12 and the P, v plane. The distance 22' represents the difference in altitude which is covered by progressing along 12 by dP. The *principal value* of this difference in altitudes is given by the product

$$\left(\frac{\partial\theta}{\partial P}\right)_v dP.$$

Similarly, the partial derivative $(\partial\theta/\partial v)_P$ represents the gradient of path 14 parallel to the plane, that is, one for which $P = $ const, and is equal to the tangent of the angle formed by 14 and the P, v plane. The distance 44' represents the difference in altitude which is overcome on progressing along 14 by dv, and its principal value is given by the product

$$\left(\frac{\partial\theta}{\partial v}\right)_P dv.$$

The principal value of the total difference dθ in altitude which is overcome when progressing along the surface from 1 to 3, that is by dP and dv simultaneously or in succession in any order is equal to the sum of the above two. The resulting expression

$$d\theta = \left(\frac{\partial\theta}{\partial P}\right)_v dP + \left(\frac{\partial\theta}{\partial v}\right)_P dv \tag{3.13}$$

is known in mathematics as the *total differential* of the function $\theta(P, v)$. It represents the principal value of the change in the value of the dependent variable (in this case θ), when the independent variables (in this case P and v) change by given, small amounts (in this case dP and dv).

In dealing with a quantity w which is a function of three independent variables x, y, z, we would write

$$dw = \left(\frac{\partial w}{\partial x}\right)_{y,z} dx + \left(\frac{\partial w}{\partial y}\right)_{z,x} dy + \left(\frac{\partial w}{\partial z}\right)_{x,y} dz, \tag{3.14}$$

and similarly for any *finite* number n of variables of a quantity $y(x_1, \ldots, x_n)$, we would use the symbol

$$dy = \sum_{1}^{n} \left(\frac{\partial w}{\partial x_i}\right)_{x_j} dx_i, \tag{3.14a}$$

where x_j stands for all the n variables $x_1, \ldots, x_n$ except x_i.

By interchanging the parts played by the variables P, v, θ, we can obtain two further total differentials

$$dP = \left(\frac{\partial P}{\partial v}\right)_{\theta} dv + \left(\frac{\partial P}{\partial \theta}\right)_{v} d\theta \tag{3.15}$$

and

$$dv = \left(\frac{\partial v}{\partial P}\right)_{\theta} dP + \left(\frac{\partial v}{\partial \theta}\right)_{P} d\theta. \tag{3.15a}$$

The partial derivatives which appear in the expressions for total differentials constitute new physical quantities some of which are sufficiently important to be given a name and a symbol to themselves. It is clear that they are all definite functions of the independent variables, even if some of the latter drop out accidentally in the process of differentiation. Consequently, they are all properties, because their values are fixed when the values of the independent properties are fixed.

When a homogeneous substance is heated at constant pressure ($dP = 0$), the change in volume dv will be related to the change in temperature $d\theta$ according to the equation

$$dv = \left(\frac{\partial v}{\partial \theta}\right)_{P} d\theta.$$

Instead of dealing with the derivative $(\partial v/\partial \theta)_P$ itself, it is customary to consider the relative change in volume dv/v and to define the quantity

$$\beta = \frac{1}{v}\left(\frac{\partial v}{\partial \theta}\right)_{P} \tag{3.16}$$

which represents the relative change in volume of the system per unit change of temperature in a process during which the pressure P = const. The resulting physical quantity is called the *coefficient of volume expansion* or *coefficient of expansion* for short. It is measured in reciprocal degrees

$$\{\beta\} = \frac{1}{°K} \quad \text{or} \quad \frac{1}{°R}.$$

If heating is performed at constant volume, $dv = 0$, equation (3.9) shows that the resulting change in pressure $dP = (\partial P/\partial \theta)_v d\theta$. By analogy we can define the *coefficient of tension*

$$\pi = \frac{1}{P} \left(\frac{\partial P}{\partial \theta} \right)_v \tag{3.17}$$

which represents the relative change in pressure per unit degree of temperature when heating at constant volume. Again

$$\{\pi\} = \frac{1}{^\circ \mathrm{K}} \quad \text{or} \quad \frac{1}{^\circ \mathrm{R}}.$$

Finally, if the pressure is increased at constant temperature by compressing the volume, we have

$$\mathrm{d}v = \left(\frac{\partial v}{\partial P} \right)_\theta \mathrm{d}P.$$

The relative change in volume per unit pressure change forms the basis of the definition of the *isothermal coefficient of compressibility:*

$$\kappa = -\frac{1}{v} \left(\frac{\partial v}{\partial P} \right)_\theta. \tag{3.18}$$

The negative sign is added owing to the fact that for all known substances the pressure and volume changes are of opposite signs during a process of compression or expansion at constant temperature. Hence, the coefficient κ itself is positive. This property that $\mathrm{d}P \cdot \mathrm{d}v < 0$ for all isothermal processes is connected with the stability of systems and will be discussed more fully in Volume II. The adjective "isothermal" is added to distinguish the present coefficient from the *isentropic coefficient of compressibility* introduced in Section 12.7. In some textbooks the reciprocal of κ is used. It is then called the isothermal bulk modulus and is denoted by B.† Thus,

$$B = -v \left(\frac{\partial P}{\partial v} \right)_\theta. \tag{3.18a}$$

The preceding coefficients play a very small part in the study of processes involving gases. In such cases some form of the equation of state is usually known and there is no advantage in using additional concepts. However, in processes involving liquids or solids, the above coefficients, in particular, the coefficient of thermal expansion β and the isothermal coefficient of compressibility κ retain very nearly constant values over considerable ranges of pressure and temperature. Then, their use introduces simplifications in the resulting equations which are found convenient.

3.6 Equation of state interpreted as a scalar field‡

In thermodynamics it is frequently more useful to adopt a different interpretation of the equation of state from that given in Section 3.3, and to consider that it can be

---

† In some older textbooks the changes $\mathrm{d}P$, $\mathrm{d}v$ are made relative to the pressure P_0 or volume v_0 of the substance at a specified state. Hence, in equations (3.16) and (3.18), the instantaneous v is replaced by the volume v_0 at the ice point and pressure P in the first instance, and by the volume v_0 at the ice point and standard atmospheric pressure $P_0 = 1$ atm in the second instance. Similarly, in equation (3.17), P is replaced by the pressure P_0 at the ice point and the same specific volume.
‡ For a clear treatment of the differential calculus of scalar fields see Apostol, T. M., *Calculus* (Blaisdell, 1962), Vol. II. pp. 156 ff.

represented as a *scalar field*. Since all thermodynamic properties which describe the state of a system are scalars, to each system there corresponds a scalar field, that is, a field in which a particular value of a scalar quantity – the dependent variable – is associated with a state, that is, with a point in the space of n dimensions defined by the n independent variables. For example, if a system possesses three independent properties, so that its equation of state is

$$w = f(x, y, z), \qquad (3.19)$$

with each point in the space x, y, z, there will then be associated a value w of the scalar quantity $w(x, y, z)$. The representation of the equation of state in the form of a field enjoys the advantage, as compared with its representation as a hypersurface, in that it requires a space of only n dimensions, as against $n + 1$ dimensions needed previously; it is, therefore, particularly advantageous in the case of $n = 2$ when it can be represented on a two-dimensional diagram or in the case of $n = 3$ when an isometric drawing can be used.

In a field, it is convenient to draw the loci along which the dependent property remains constant. These are known as level lines, surfaces or hypersurfaces, depending on the number of independent properties. In the case of the function (3.19) these loci will be the surfaces

$$f(x, y, z) = \text{const.}$$

In the case of systems with two independent variables

$$w = \phi(x, y), \qquad (3.19a)$$

they will be the lines

$$\phi(x, y) = \text{const.}$$

The lines or surfaces of constant property are identical with the contours discussed in Section 3.3. In fact, the contours in Figure 3.3 represent the level lines for the three fields which can be used interchangeably to depict the equation of state of a perfect gas, depending on which pair of the three variables P, v, θ is chosen as independent. It is convenient to label the level lines or surfaces with that value of the dependent variable which remains constant by simply writing it alongside the locus, Figure 3.5. Depending on the physical nature of the dependent property, such loci are given different names: isotherms for temperature, isobars for pressure, isochores for volume, and so on.

The rate of change of the dependent variable along a given curve, that is along the path C of a thermodynamic process, Figure 3.6, is given by the so-called *directional derivatives*. We shall suppose that the path C of the process is described in parametric form

$$x(s), y(s), z(s),$$

where s is measured along the arc of the curve; alternatively the time, t, can be chosen as a parameter. Then the directional derivatives are

$$\frac{dw}{ds} = \left(\frac{\partial w}{\partial x}\right)_y \frac{dx}{ds} + \left(\frac{\partial w}{\partial y}\right)_x \frac{dy}{ds} \qquad (3.20a)$$

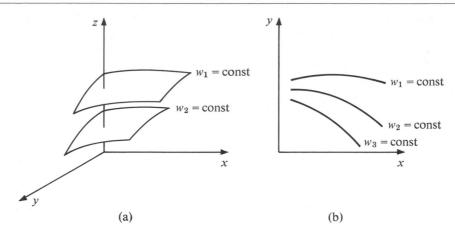

FIGURE 3.5. *Loci along which a scalar quantity remains constant in a field.*
(a) Two independent variables. (b) Three independent variables; surfaces.

or

$$\frac{dw}{ds} = \left(\frac{\partial w}{\partial x}\right)_{y,z}\frac{dx}{ds} + \left(\frac{\partial w}{\partial y}\right)_{z,x}\frac{dy}{ds} + \left(\frac{\partial w}{\partial z}\right)_{x,y}\frac{dz}{ds} \tag{3.20b}$$

and so on, for n variables. The derivatives dx/ds, dy/ds, and dz/ds are equal to the direction cosines formed by the vector ds, whose components are dx, dy or dx, dy, dz, with the axes of coordinates. Thus this rate of change depends only on the direction of the curve at the point in question. If the direction is that of one of the axes, the directional derivative becomes identical with the respective partial derivative. The rate of change in a given field and at a given point is maximum when the curve C is *normal* at that point to the level curve or line. This can be easily ascertained by rendering the expressions in equations (3.20a, b) a maximum with respect to the directional cosines.† The

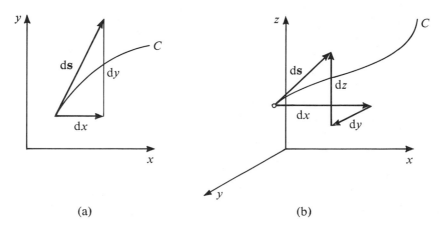

FIGURE 3.6. *Directional derivative. (a) Two independent variables.*
(b) Three independent variables.

---

† A simple, explicit proof can be found, for example, in Sokolnikoff, I. S., and Redheffer, R. M., *Mathematics of Physics and Engineering* (McGraw-Hill, 1958), pp. 243–5.

maximum rate of change then becomes

$$\sqrt{\left[\left(\frac{\partial w}{\partial x}\right)_y\right]^2 + \left[\left(\frac{\partial w}{\partial y}\right)_x\right]^2} \quad \text{or} \quad \sqrt{\left[\left(\frac{\partial w}{\partial x}\right)_{y,z}\right]^2 + \left[\left(\frac{\partial w}{\partial y}\right)_{z,x}\right]^2 + \left[\left(\frac{\partial w}{\partial z}\right)_{x,y}\right]^2}. \quad (3.21)$$

It is, therefore, convenient to introduce a vector whose components at a point are equal to the partial derivatives and which is, evidently, normal to the level line or surface at that point. Its length will be equal to that given in equation (3.21). The total differentials for equation (3.19) or (3.19a) are written

$$dw = \left(\frac{\partial w}{\partial x}\right)_{y,z} dx + \left(\frac{\partial w}{\partial y}\right)_{z,x} dy + \left(\frac{\partial w}{\partial z}\right)_{x,y} dz$$

or

$$dw = \left(\frac{\partial w}{\partial x}\right)_y dx + \left(\frac{\partial w}{\partial y}\right)_x dy.$$

Along a level line $dw = 0$, the preceding equations become

$$\left(\frac{\partial w}{\partial x}\right)_{y,z} dx + \left(\frac{\partial w}{\partial y}\right)_{z,x} dy + \left(\frac{\partial w}{\partial z}\right)_{x,y} dz = 0 \qquad (3.22a)$$

and

$$\left(\frac{\partial w}{\partial x}\right)_y dx + \left(\frac{\partial w}{\partial y}\right)_x dy = 0. \qquad (3.22b)$$

The increments dx, dy, dz or dx, dy are now no longer independent, since the equations apply only to a level surface or line. Thus, they can be interpreted as the components of a vector $\mathbf{dr}(dx, dy)$ or $\mathbf{dr}(dx, dy, dz)$ which has the same direction as the tangent to the level surface or line at the point. Hence, equations (3.22a, b), which have the form of scalar products, express the fact that the vectors whose components are $\mathbf{G}\{(\partial w/\partial x)_{y,z}, (\partial w/\partial y)_{z,x}, (\partial w/\partial z)_{x,y}\}$ or $\mathbf{G}\{(\partial w/\partial x)_y, (\partial w/\partial y)_x\}$ are normal to the level surface or line as the case may be. The vector defined in the preceding manner is known as the *gradient of the scalar field*, and is written

$$\mathbf{G} = \text{grad } w. \qquad (3.23)$$

Thus, with every *scalar* field it is possible to associate a vector field, its gradient, the components of the gradient being equal to the partial derivatives of the scalar at a given point. Two such gradient fields are seen sketched in Figure 3.7. The dotted lines are everywhere tangent to the vector $\mathbf{G}$; they are known as the field lines and will be discussed further in Sections 4.2 and 10.2. The definitions discussed in this section for scalar fields with two and three independent variables can be easily extended to any number n of independent variables.

3.7   Relations between partial derivatives

The partial derivatives which appear in the total differentials discussed in the preceding sections are not independent of each other, and it is useful to make the relations between them explicit. In general, we shall be interested in three classes of relationships: (1) Relations between the partial derivatives which occur in one perfect differential, that is, between the components of the gradient, (2) Relations which obtain be-

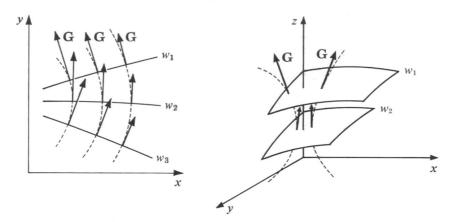

FIGURE 3.7. *Gradient field associated with scalar fields:* **G** = *grad w.*

tween the partial derivatives when the parts played by the dependent and independent variables are interchanged, and (3) Relations which are valid when the independent variables are replaced by other independent variables. We shall take these relations in turn.

3.7.1   Condition of integrability

It will be remembered from analysis that higher, mixed partial derivatives are independent of the order of differentiation. For the purpose of writing down the consequences of this statement, it will be convenient to introduce separate symbols for the first partial derivatives which appear in equations (3.19a) and (3.19). Thus for equation (3.19a), we shall write

$$\left(\frac{\partial w}{\partial x}\right)_y = M(x,\,y) \quad \text{and} \quad \left(\frac{\partial w}{\partial y}\right)_x = N(x,\,y), \tag{3.24}$$

so that the perfect differential becomes

$$\mathrm{d}w = M(x,\,y)\,\mathrm{d}x + N(x,\,y)\,\mathrm{d}y. \tag{3.24a}$$

Similarly for equation (3.19a), we put

$$\left(\frac{\partial w}{\partial x}\right)_{y,z} = P(x,\,y,\,z); \left(\frac{\partial w}{\partial y}\right)_{z,x} = Q(x,\,y,\,z); \left(\frac{\partial w}{\partial z}\right)_{x,y} = R(x,\,y,\,z); \tag{3.25}$$

and obtain

$$\mathrm{d}w = P(x,\,y,\,z)\,\mathrm{d}x + Q(x,\,y,\,z)\,\mathrm{d}y + R(x,\,y,\,z)\,\mathrm{d}z. \tag{3.25a}$$

Since the second derivatives must be independent of the order of differentiation, it is clear that the components of the gradients **G**$(M,\,N)$ or **G**$(P,\,Q,\,R)$ cannot be prescribed arbitrarily. In fact, the following relations must be satisfied

$$\left\{\frac{\partial M(x,\,y)}{\partial y}\right\}_x = \left\{\frac{\partial N(x,\,y)}{\partial x}\right\}_y \tag{3.26}$$

for equation (3.24a) and

$$\left\{\frac{\partial P(x,\,y,\,z)}{\partial y}\right\}_{x,z} = \left\{\frac{\partial Q(x,\,y,\,z)}{\partial x}\right\}_{y,z}$$

$$\left\{\frac{\partial P(x,\,y,\,z)}{\partial z}\right\}_{x,y} = \left\{\frac{\partial R(x,\,y,\,z)}{\partial x}\right\}_{y,z} \qquad (3.26\text{a})$$

$$\left\{\frac{\partial Q(x,\,y,\,z)}{\partial z}\right\}_{y,x} = \left\{\frac{\partial R(x,\,y,\,z)}{\partial y}\right\}_{z,x},$$

there being progressively more such relations as the number of independent variables is increased. In general, the number of relations is equal to the number of second derivatives in a function of n variables, that is, to the number $\frac{1}{2}n(n-1)$ of unordered pairs which can be formed with n objects.

For our future needs it is more convenient to write the preceding relations in the form of more symmetric differences, assigning a new symbol to each difference. It is also convenient to use the mathematical notation for derivatives in which subscripts are omitted. Thus, equation (3.26) can be rewritten

$$\omega_z = \frac{\partial N}{\partial x} - \frac{\partial M}{\partial y} = 0, \qquad (3.27)$$

and equations (3.26a) can be replaced by

$$\omega_x = \frac{\partial R}{\partial y} - \frac{\partial Q}{\partial z} = 0,$$

$$\omega_y = \frac{\partial P}{\partial z} - \frac{\partial R}{\partial x} = 0, \qquad (3.27\text{a})$$

$$\omega_z = \frac{\partial Q}{\partial x} - \frac{\partial P}{\partial y} = 0.$$

In all these relations, the subscript for the difference, ω, and the variables x, y, z with respect to which derivatives are taken follow each other cyclically, as suggested by Figure 3.8.

An expression of the type (3.24a) or (3.25a) is known as a *linear differential form*, a *Pfaffian form*, or a *Pfaffian* for short. It is clear that when a Pfaffian form is written down at random, the conditions (3.27) or (3.27a) will not, in general, be satisfied. How-

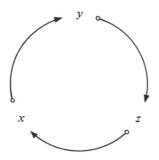

FIGURE 3.8. *Cyclic sequence.*

ever, if the Pfaffian form is derived from a scalar field, these relations will be satisfied. Thus, the class of Pfaffians derived from a scalar function—an equation of state—is a special one. In the latter case it forms a perfect differential, whereas in the general case when the functions M, N or P, Q, R are arbitrary, it does not.

The conditions in equations (3.27) or (3.27a) evidently constitute necessary conditions for the existence of a functional relationship $w(x, y)$ or $w(x, y, z)$, as the case may be, that is for the existence of an equation of state. In other words, if such functional relationships exist, the conditions (3.27) or (3.27a), known as the *conditions of integrability*, are satisfied. Conversely, it can be shown that these conditions are also sufficient. In other words, given two functions M, N or three functions P, Q, R which satisfy the conditions of integrability, it is possible to assert that they are the first partial derivatives of some function $w(x, y)$ or $w(x, y, z)$.† Similar conditions are sufficient in the case of n variables.

A given function w has a unique perfect differential, but a given perfect differential corresponds to an infinity of functions w which differ from each other by a constant; this constant disappears upon differentiation. Thus the sum

$$w' = w + w_0 \tag{3.28}$$

possesses the same perfect differential as w, if w_0 is an arbitrary constant, and the conditions of integrability (3.27) and (3.27a) imply the existence of families of functions. Interpreting this result geometrically, we notice that such families of surfaces or hypersurfaces consist of identical geometrical entities which are merely displaced with respect to each other in the direction of the dependent variable. Moreover, the contours of all members of such a family are identical. This means that the level lines in the respective scalar fields are identical, the only difference being that the numbers associated with them differ by a constant amount w_0, Figure 3.9. It is said that such families define a *potential*, that is, a set of potential lines, surfaces, and so on.

Let us suppose now that for some thermodynamic system we are given the properties $M(x, y)$ and $N(x, y)$ or $P(x, y, z)$, $Q(x, y, z)$, $R(x, y, z)$ which satisfy the relations

---

† See Courant, R., *Differential and Integral Calculus*, translated by E. J. McShane (2nd ed.; London: Blackie, 1937), p. 353 or Sokolnikoff, I. S., and Redheffer, R. M., *Mathematics of Physics and Modern Engineering* (McGraw-Hill, 1958), pp. 381 and 401.

In the case of two variables it is easy to prove the existence of w by simply constructing it. Let $\xi = \int_0^x M dx$.

Then $\partial \xi / \partial x = M$ and $\partial^2 \xi / \partial x \partial y = \partial M / \partial y$; but $\partial M / \partial y = \partial N / \partial x$. Therefore

$$\frac{\partial}{\partial x}\left(\frac{\partial \xi}{\partial y}\right) = \frac{\partial N}{\partial x} \quad \text{or} \quad \frac{\partial}{\partial x}\left(N - \frac{\partial \xi}{\partial y}\right) = 0.$$

Hence, $N - \partial \xi / \partial y$ is a function of y only. Let us denote it by $\mathrm{f}'(y)$. Then

$$N = \frac{\partial \xi}{\partial y} + \mathrm{f}'(y).$$

We assert that $w = \xi + \mathrm{f}(y)$, and verify

$$\frac{\partial w}{\partial x} = \frac{\partial \xi}{\partial x} = M; \qquad \frac{\partial w}{\partial y} = \frac{\partial \xi}{\partial y} + \mathrm{f}'(y) = N.$$

For a proof in the case of three variables see Apostol, T. M. *Calculus* (Blaisdell, 1962), II, p. 196.

(3.27) or (3.27a). Can we assert that the family of functions $w' = w + w_0$ whose existence is thereby implied determines a new thermodynamic property of the system? A moment's reflection will suggest that the answer is only partially affirmative. When the values of the independent properties are fixed, the state is fixed. Consequently, the value of the property w is fixed, except for the value of the constant w_0, which is arbitrary. Physical quantities which possess this mathematical property are known as potentials as the student will readily remember from his study of fluid mechanics or electromagnetic theory. A potential can be made into a property by the simple device of assuming a conventional value for the arbitrary constant w_0. In actual fact, it is more convenient to assign a conventional value w_0 to the potential when a reference state of the system is determined by conventional values of the independent properties x_0, y_0, z_0. Thus we postulate

$$w_0 = w(x_0, y_0, z_0). \tag{3.29}$$

This convention is equivalent to assigning an agreed value to the arbitrary constant w_0. When a convention of this kind is adopted, a potential becomes a property in the thermodynamic sense of the word.

Irrespective of whether the convention (3.29) is or is not adopted, a thermodynamic property and a potential have one mathematical property in common. Given *two states*, say A and B in Figure 3.9, it is readily seen that the *difference* between the potentials

$$w(B) - w(A) = w'(B) - w'(A)$$

is independent of the process which the system may have undergone in changing its state from A to B. This is indicated in the figure by showing two curves a and b each of which represents two distinct processes. Such curves, drawn on a *state diagram* like the one considered, are referred to as *paths*. We can now state our result succinctly by asserting that *the difference in potentials between two states is independent of the path connecting them*. It is evident that the same is true about any thermodynamic property. This fact follows immediately by making reference to the original concept of a thermodynamic property. Thus the only difference between a potential and a thermodynamic

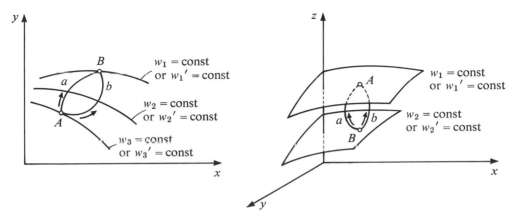

FIGURE 3.9. *Potential surfaces.*

property consists in the fact that the former contains an arbitrary constant in its definition, while the latter does not.

The preceding argument has, therefore, provided an additional test. The test is for a physical quantity to be a potential, and since the difference between a property and a potential is of secondary importance only, the test will be used in cases when a distinction between thermodynamic properties and potentials on the one hand, and physical quantities of a different nature on the other, becomes important.

It was found in the preceding paragraphs that the difference between the values which a property or a potential assume at some given final state B and some given initial state A is independent of the process which the system may have undergone. It follows as a corollary that the total change for a cycle is zero. That this is so can be easily seen with reference to Figure 3.9 and by considering the arbitrary cycle $AaBbA$. Since $w(B) - w(A)$ is independent of the path, the total change for the cycle is

$$[w(B) - w(A)] + [w(A) - w(B)] = 0.$$

The result would not be zero for a quantity other than a property or a potential as we shall see in detail in Chapter 4. The converse is also true, and we can assert that a physical quantity whose change is independent of the path and whose net change around a cycle is, therefore, zero, constitutes a potential or, in special cases, a thermodynamic property.

Frequently changes around cycles are calculated step-by-step, Figure 3.10. The path is divided into small steps ab, such that the difference in the independent properties between them is dx and dy, respectively. The principal value of the change in the independent property is then given, as explained in Section 3.2, by the total differential

$$dw = M dx + N dy \tag{3.30}$$

in which $M(x, y)$ and $N(x, y)$ satisfy the integrability condition (3.27). The total change between a final state B and an initial state A is obtained by integration, and is written

$$w(B) - w(A) = \int_A^B M dx + N dy. \tag{3.30a}$$
along curve C

The resulting integral is known as a *line integral*. The value of this line integral, as

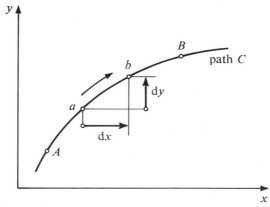

FIGURE 3.10. *Step-by-step calculation and the meaning of a line integral.*

shown earlier, is independent of the path, that is, of the curve C, and the note under the integrand in equation (3.30) could have been dropped. When the integration is performed around a cycle, the symbol $\oint$ is used to denote that the initial and final states are identical. The line integral is then known as a *circular integral*, and it is possible to write

$$\oint_{\text{along curve } C} M\,dx + N\,dy = 0, \qquad (3.31)$$

but only on the assumption that the functions $M(x, y)$ and $N(x, y)$ are partial derivatives of a property w or of a potential $w' = w + w_0$ and satisfy the integrability condition. The extension of these remarks to any number of independent properties requires no further comment.

The quantities ω_x, ω_y, and ω_z which vanish in equations (3.27) and (3.27a) when a perfect differential dw is involved can be readily interpreted as the components of yet another vector $\mathbf{R}(\omega_x, \omega_y, \omega_z)$, known as the curl of $\mathbf{G}$ and written

$$\mathbf{R} = \text{curl } \mathbf{G}.$$

The components of the curl field of a gradient field are trivial, being identically zero everywhere. They will have definite values for vector fields which are not derived from a potential, and we shall resume their discussion in Section 4.1. For the present, we note that

$$\text{curl grad } w = 0, \qquad (3.32)$$

and that, furthermore,

$$\mathbf{G} \cdot \text{curl } \mathbf{G} = 0, \qquad (3.32a)$$

since curl $\mathbf{G} = 0$. A vector field $\mathbf{G}$ whose curl vanishes identically is known as an *irrotational* or *potential* field. Similar considerations apply to functions of $n \geq 3$ variables, except that the differences ω can no longer be interpreted as components of a vector; they become antisymmetric tensors.[†]

At first sight the interpretation of the derivatives which occur in conjunction with an equation of state and which constitute thermodynamic properties of different physical dimensions as the components of a *vector* may appear uncomfortable to the student. In this connection it should be pointed out that we are dealing here with a mathematical concept which constitutes a convenient geometrical *interpretation of relations* between physical quantities. In this it is equivalent to the interpretation of a physical equation in the form of a graph in which the coordinates of a point, that is lengths, have different physical dimensions. The difference is only in the nature of the geometrical concept, a point in one case and a vector in the other.

3.7.2 *Change in the role of the variables*

A different type of relation exists when the parts played by the dependent and independent variables are interchanged. In thermodynamics, these relations find an applica-

---

[†] For further mathematical details see Brillouin, L., *Tensors in Mechanics and Elasticity* (Academic Press, 1964). Such considerations are not essential in thermodynamics, beyond supplying rigorous proofs for the intuitively plausible statement that the preceding observations can be easily extended to n independent variables.

tion mainly when only two independent variables are involved, and we shall restrict our attention to this case only, illustrating the argument with reference to the equation of state $F(P, v, \theta) = 0$. Choosing P, v, θ in turn as the dependent variable, we can write three total differentials

$$\left.\begin{array}{l} dP = \left(\dfrac{\partial P}{\partial v}\right)_\theta dv + \left(\dfrac{\partial P}{\partial \theta}\right)_v d\theta, \\[2mm] dv = \left(\dfrac{\partial v}{\partial P}\right)_\theta dP + \left(\dfrac{\partial v}{\partial \theta}\right)_P d\theta, \\[2mm] d\theta = \left(\dfrac{\partial \theta}{\partial P}\right)_v dP + \left(\dfrac{\partial \theta}{\partial v}\right)_P dv, \end{array}\right\} \tag{3.33}$$

as already explained in Section 3.5. Thus we are led to the consideration of a total of six partial derivatives. It is easy to see that only three of them are independent, since they occur in pairs like

$$\left(\frac{\partial P}{\partial v}\right)_\theta \quad \text{and} \quad \left(\frac{\partial v}{\partial P}\right)_\theta,$$

in which one is equal to the reciprocal of the other. Since, however, ultimately only two variables are independent, it follows that the three partial derivatives must satisfy one more relation. Considering the first total differential in equation (3.33), we can apply it to a path of constant pressure, $dP = 0$. Since the relation expressed by the total differential is always true, it is certainly true for this particular case. Hence,

$$\left(\frac{\partial P}{\partial v}\right)_\theta dv + \left(\frac{\partial P}{\partial \theta}\right)_v d\theta = 0 \qquad \text{along } P = \text{const.}$$

This is equivalent to writing

$$\left(\frac{\partial P}{\partial v}\right)_\theta + \left(\frac{\partial P}{\partial \theta}\right)_v \left(\frac{\partial \theta}{\partial v}\right)_P = 0,$$

or in a more symmetric form

$$\left(\frac{\partial P}{\partial v}\right)_\theta \left(\frac{\partial v}{\partial \theta}\right)_P \left(\frac{\partial \theta}{\partial P}\right)_v = -1 \tag{3.34}$$

in which the symbols P, v, θ follow each other cyclically in the numerator, denominator, and index of each partial derivative. It is easy to see that applying the same argument to the remaining two total differentials would lead to an identical relation.

Introducing the three coefficients β, π, and κ equations (3.16), (3.17), and (3.18) (coefficient of thermal expansion, coefficient of tension, isothermal coefficient of compressibility), into equation (3.34), it is easy to derive the following relation which must be satisfied by them at any state of a homogeneous, chemical system. We would then obtain

$$\beta = \pi \kappa P. \tag{3.35}$$

Given any two of the coefficients from experiment, we can calculate the third.

3.7.3   Change in independent variables. Jacobians

Still another type of relation is obtained when a *change in independent variables* is considered. Suppose that in the equation of state

$$w = w(x, y), \tag{3.36}$$

it becomes necessary to represent the dependent variable, w, in terms of new independent variables u and v. The latter, being properties, will also be given in the form of the equations of state

$$u = u(x, y) \quad \text{and} \quad v = v(x, y). \tag{3.36a}$$

When all the equations of state are given in the form of explicit mathematical expressions, the desired result will be obtained by direct substitution, thus

$$w = w[x(u, v), y(u, v)]. \tag{3.36b}$$

This implies that x and y can be evaluated from equations (3.36a), and that u and v are really independent variables. These conditions are not necessarily always satisfied, and it becomes useful to study the mathematical properties of transformations of this type. For example, the form of the functions (3.36a) may be such that x and y cannot be calculated readily. Alternatively, the two relations in (3.36a) may be such that a functional relation between u and v is implied. If, for example, u and v† were chosen as the specific volume and density, respectively, their product, equation (1.12), would always be equal to unity, whatever the values of x, y. In other words, it would then be possible to eliminate both independent variables x, y simultaneously and a relation

$$F(u, v) = 0 \tag{3.36c}$$

would result. Furthermore, in the study of thermodynamics, as already mentioned earlier, more often than not, the *existence* of the equations of state (3.36) and (3.36a) is assured, but no explicit expressions are given, or even known. Thus the analysis is frequently concerned with partial derivatives and relations between them rather than the functions themselves. Hence, often it is more important to calculate the derivatives

$$\left(\frac{\partial w}{\partial u}\right)_v \quad \text{and} \quad \left(\frac{\partial w}{\partial v}\right)_u \tag{3.37}$$

than to establish the explicit form (3.36b).

The problem thus outlined is of a mathematical nature and can always be solved by the application of the chain-rule for the differentiation of functions of functions and of implicit functions. However, if it is considered that, ultimately, we shall be concerned with a choice of two of eight possible independent variables, giving 28 acceptable pairs, it is realized that the problem, though fundamentally simple, can become very complex in its details, and that it is useful to establish some general rules of procedure and to devise a compact system of notation. The latter is achieved by the introduction of so-called *Jacobians*.

---

† In this section the symbols u and v stand for arbitrary properties and v does not necessarily denote specific volume.

If the equation of state $w = w(x, y)$ is interpreted as a scalar field, then the change of variables to u, v amounts to a *geometrical transformation* or *mapping* of the plane x, y into the plane u, v which has the property that to every point (x, y) there corresponds one, and only one point (u, v) in a certain domain.† To these corresponding points there corresponds one and the same value of the dependent variable w: It follows that the mathematical theory of such transformations‡ is directly applicable. In particular, as illustrated in Figure 3.11, it is noted that to a contour $w = $ const in the x, y plane there corresponds a, generally different, contour $w = $ const in the u, v plane, and that, furthermore, to any curve C in the x, y plane (such as the path of a line integral) there corresponds a different curve C' in the u, v plane, a closed curve being mapped into another closed curve.

By the application of the chain-rule for differentiation it is possible to establish relations for the derivatives (3.37) in terms of known functions, thus

$$\left.\begin{aligned} \left(\frac{\partial w}{\partial x}\right)_y &= \left(\frac{\partial w}{\partial u}\right)_v \left(\frac{\partial u}{\partial x}\right)_y + \left(\frac{\partial w}{\partial v}\right)_u \left(\frac{\partial v}{\partial x}\right)_y, \\ \left(\frac{\partial w}{\partial y}\right)_x &= \left(\frac{\partial w}{\partial u}\right)_v \left(\frac{\partial u}{\partial y}\right)_x + \left(\frac{\partial w}{\partial v}\right)_u \left(\frac{\partial v}{\partial y}\right)_x. \end{aligned}\right\} \tag{3.38}$$

Here, $(\partial w/\partial x)_y$, $(\partial w/\partial y)_x$, $(\partial u/\partial x)_y$, $(\partial u/\partial y)_x$, $(\partial v/\partial x)_y$ and $(\partial v/\partial y)_x$ are known, and it is necessary to calculate $(\partial w/\partial u)_v$ and $(\partial w/\partial v)_u$. This involves the solution of the two linear, algebraic equations (3.38). The result is best written in terms of the functional determinant

$$J = \begin{vmatrix} \left(\dfrac{\partial u}{\partial x}\right)_y & \left(\dfrac{\partial v}{\partial x}\right)_y \\[2ex] \left(\dfrac{\partial u}{\partial y}\right)_x & \left(\dfrac{\partial v}{\partial y}\right)_x \end{vmatrix} = \left(\frac{\partial u}{\partial x}\right)_y \left(\frac{\partial v}{\partial y}\right)_x - \left(\frac{\partial u}{\partial y}\right)_x \left(\frac{\partial v}{\partial x}\right)_y, \tag{3.38a}$$

which is called a *Jacobian* and which can also be written symbolically as

$$J = \frac{\partial(u, v)}{\partial(x, y)}. \tag{3.38b}$$

This symbol suggests the expansion (3.38a) in an easily remembered way, and furthermore, as will be seen later, makes it possible to memorize the rules governing transformations without much difficulty. It is noted that the Jacobian (3.38a or b) contains only derivatives of the new variables u, v with respect to the old variables x, y, but does not contain the dependent variable w. Hence, it is a function of x, y only and its numerical value varies from point to point. Since, however, to each point of the x, y plane there corresponds one point of the plane u, v, it can also be conceived as a function

---

† That this must be so is a consequence of the single-valuedness of equations of state and not of the general properties of such transformations.
‡ For a lucid account see Courant, R., *Differential and Integral Calculus*, translated by E. J. McShane (2nd ed.; London: Blackie, 1937), II, pp. 133–159. See also Apostol, T. M., *Calculus* (Blaisdell, 1962), II, pp. 84 and 94.

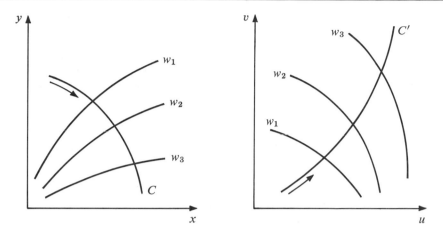

FIGURE 3.11. *Change of independent variables or mapping.*

12 9421

of u and v which varies from point to point. Its value is the same for two corresponding points, and, in general, its form characterizes the type of mapping of the x, y plane into the u, v plane defined by equations (3.36a).

It is recalled from the theory of linear, algebraic equations that the system (3.38) has a unique pair of solutions on condition that

$$J = \frac{\partial(u, v)}{\partial(x, y)} \neq 0$$

identically. If this is the case, it is not difficult to see that we then have

$$\left(\frac{\partial w}{\partial u}\right)_v = \frac{\begin{vmatrix} \left(\frac{\partial w}{\partial x}\right)_y & \left(\frac{\partial v}{\partial x}\right)_y \\ \left(\frac{\partial w}{\partial y}\right)_x & \left(\frac{\partial v}{\partial y}\right)_x \end{vmatrix}}{\frac{\partial(u, v)}{\partial(x, y)}} = \frac{\frac{\partial(w, v)}{\partial(x, y)}}{\frac{\partial(u, v)}{\partial(x, y)}}. \tag{3.38c}$$

The preceding equation can be simplified very considerably by the application of several properties of Jacobians which we proceed to enumerate without proof. A complete derivation can be found in the references quoted in the footnote of p. 98, and the reader unfamiliar with this mathematical topic can appreciate the fact that, essentially, the properties to be discussed are consequences of the application of the chain-rule of differentiation as outlined in equations (3.38).

(a) A change in the order of the variables u, v or x, y produces a change in the sign of the Jacobian. Thus, for example

$$\frac{\partial(u, v)}{\partial(x, y)} = -\frac{\partial(v, u)}{\partial(x, y)} = \frac{\partial(v, u)}{\partial(y, x)}. \tag{3.39}$$

(b) The ratio of two corresponding, elementary areas in the two planes is equal to the Jacobian of the transformation at the point.

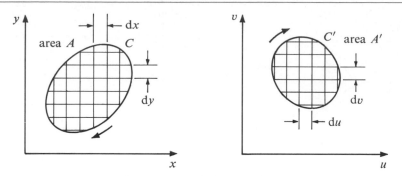

FIGURE 3.12. *Calculation of areas.*

The diagram in Figure 3.12 represents a curve C which encompasses a finite area A in the x, y plane. The corresponding curve C' in the u, v plane encompasses an area A', and, evidently

$$A = \iint_C dx\, dy \qquad \text{whereas} \quad A' = \iint_{C'} du\, dv.$$

Here, $dx\, dy$ and $du\, dv$ represent elementary rectangles produced in the two diagrams by infinitely closely spaced lines which are parallel to the coordinate axes.

The *area property* of a Jacobian asserts that

$$A = \iint_C dx\, dy = \iint_{C'} \frac{\partial(x, y)}{\partial(u, v)}\, du\, dv, \tag{3.40}$$

and reciprocally

$$A' = \iint_{C'} du\, dv = \iint_C \frac{\partial(u, v)}{\partial(x, y)}\, dx\, dy. \tag{3.41}$$

On passing to the limit of a point, we have

$$\frac{dx\, dy}{du\, dv} = \frac{\partial(x, y)}{\partial(u, v)} \tag{3.42}$$

or

$$\frac{du\, dv}{dx\, dy} = \frac{\partial(u, v)}{\partial(x, y)}. \tag{3.42a}$$

Thus it can be said that the value of the Jacobian measures the *local distortion* in area produced by the mapping $(u, v) \to (x, y)$ or reciprocally. In the particular case when the Jacobian of a transformation is a constant in the whole domain of interest, its value represents the ratio of any two areas in the two diagrams, since then

$$\frac{A}{A'} = \frac{\displaystyle\iint_C dx\, dy}{\displaystyle\iint_{C'} du\, dv} = \frac{\partial(x, y)}{\partial(u, v)} = \text{const.} \tag{3.42b}$$

It is this special case which is important in thermodynamics. In Section 9.12 we shall become acquainted with a transformation of variables for which both Jacobians are equal to unity, and this will prove important for the derivation of a number of important relations in Chapter 12.

(c) Owing to an ingenious choice of symbols for Jacobians, the numerator and denominator $\partial(x, y)$, $\partial(u, v)$, and so on, can be "cancelled" in the same way as the symbols dx, dy, and so on, can be "cancelled" in the formulas involving ordinary derivatives. Thus

$$\frac{\partial(x, y)}{\partial(u, v)} \cdot \frac{\partial(u, v)}{\partial(x, y)} = 1 \tag{3.43}$$

as is clear from equations (3.42) and (3.42a).

Equally, for successive mappings $(x, y) \to (\xi, \eta) \to (u, v)$ it is possible to write

$$\frac{\partial(x, y)}{\partial(u, v)} = \frac{\partial(x, y)}{\partial(\xi, \eta)} \cdot \frac{\partial(\xi, \eta)}{\partial(u, v)}. \tag{3.44}$$

Application of this rule to equation (3.38c) permits us to write

$$\left(\frac{\partial w}{\partial u}\right)_v = \frac{\partial(w, v)}{\partial(u, v)}. \tag{3.45}$$

This form, of great importance in thermodynamics, is very easy to remember if it is noticed that symbols within the parentheses, in this case the symbol v, may also be "cancelled" on condition that they then appear as a subscript. This is done as follows:

$$\left(\frac{\partial w}{\partial u}\right)_v = \frac{\partial(w, \phi)}{\partial(x, y)} \cdot \frac{\partial(x, y)}{\partial(u, \phi)}. \tag{3.45a}$$

By this rule, we can write immediately

$$\left(\frac{\partial w}{\partial v}\right)_u = \frac{\partial(w, u)}{\partial(x, y)} \cdot \frac{\partial(x, y)}{\partial(v, u)} = \frac{\partial(w, u)}{\partial(v, u)}. \tag{3.45b}$$

However,

$$\frac{\partial(w, x)}{\partial(x, y)} = -\left(\frac{\partial w}{\partial y}\right)_x \tag{3.45c}$$

as seen from equation (3.39).

These rules greatly facilitate the computation of partial derivatives when a change of variables is performed.

(d) When the determinant (3.38a) vanishes identically, it is when

$$J = \frac{\partial(u, v)}{\partial(x, y)} \equiv 0 \tag{3.46}$$

in a domain in x, y, and so also in the corresponding domain in u, v, the pair of linear algebraic equations (3.38) does not lead to a unique set of solutions for $(\partial w/\partial u)_v$ and $(\partial w/\partial v)_u$. A full discussion of all possible cases is of little importance in thermodynamics since the existence of condition (3.46) signifies that u and v are not independent, and that a relation of the form (3.36c) exists. In other words, the variables x and y can be eliminated from the two equations (3.36a) simultaneously. In general, only one variable can be eliminated, leading to one of two relations

$$\phi(u, v, x) = 0 \quad \text{or} \quad \psi(u, v, y) = 0 \tag{3.46a, b}$$

as desired. The vanishing of the Jacobian constitutes both a necessary and sufficient condition for the existence of the relation $F(u, v) = 0$. More precisely, when $u(x, y)$ and $v(x, y)$ are substituted into the function F, namely

$$F\{u(x, y), v(x, y)\} = 0,$$

the resulting relation is an identity, and does not contain either x or y. This fact can be easily appreciated with reference to the area property of Jacobians, equation (3.42b). Given a curve C in x, y which encloses an area, it is found that the area enclosed by the image curve is identically zero. Hence, an area in x, y is mapped into a *single curve*, the curve $F(u, v) = 0$ in u, v, as sketched in Figure 3.13. This type of mapping is described as degenerate.

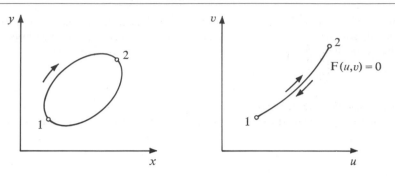

FIGURE 3.13. *Degenerate mapping.*

In order to illustrate the ease with which relations between partial derivatives can be derived when Jacobians are employed, it is instructive to rederive equation (3.34). When the index which appears in each of the three derivatives is "absorbed" to form a Jacobian, we obtain

$$\left(\frac{\partial P}{\partial v}\right)_\theta\left(\frac{\partial v}{\partial \theta}\right)_P\left(\frac{\partial \theta}{\partial P}\right)_v = \frac{\partial(P,\,\theta)}{\partial(v,\,\theta)}\cdot\frac{\partial(v,\,P)}{\partial(\theta,\,P)}\cdot\frac{\partial(\theta,\,v)}{\partial(P,\,v)}.$$

It is now seen that terms like $\partial(P,\,\theta)$ and $\partial(\theta,\,P)$ appear in pairs on the right-hand side. They can be "cancelled" after the order in one has been inverted, and this has the effect of changing the sign. Thus the right-hand side of the above equation is

$$(-1)(-1)(-1) = -1,$$

as proved previously.

The preceding account has been restricted to the discussion of systems involving two independent variables, because they are by far the most important ones in thermodynamics. There are no essential difficulties in extending the concept of a Jacobian to more than two variables,

$$J = \frac{\partial(u_1,\,u_2,\,\ldots,\,u_n)}{\partial(x_1,\,x_2,\,\ldots,\,x_n)} = \begin{vmatrix} \dfrac{\partial u_1}{\partial x_1} & \dfrac{\partial u_1}{\partial x_2} & \cdots & \dfrac{\partial u_1}{\partial x_n} \\[2mm] \dfrac{\partial u_2}{\partial x_1} & \dfrac{\partial u_2}{\partial x_2} & \cdots & \dfrac{\partial u_2}{\partial x_n} \\[2mm] \cdots & \cdots & \cdots & \cdots \\[2mm] \dfrac{\partial u_n}{\partial x_1} & \dfrac{\partial u_n}{\partial x_2} & \cdots & \dfrac{\partial u_n}{\partial x_n} \end{vmatrix}, \tag{3.47}$$

where the variables held constant have been omitted for simplicity. It is noteworthy that the "cancelling" rule indicated in equation (3.45a) remains valid, but a full discussion of the case of more than two independent variables would exceed the needs of this book.†

3.8   Fundamental equations of state

In order to complete our discussion of the nature of equations of state, we might usefully investigate the following problem. Suppose that we wish to consider a system with two independent variables x and y. The reader will appreciate that, once again, the extension of the present argument to systems with more than two independent properties involves no new concepts, and that two independent properties have been chosen for ease of expression. Suppose, further, that we wish to consider several dependent

† For futher details see Courant, R., *op. cit.* Examples of the convenience which results from the use of Jacobians in thermodynamics can be found in Chapter 12.

properties, z_1, z_2, and so on. It is clearly important to know whether the relations $z_2(x, y)$, $z_3(x, y)$ and so on can be calculated, if *one* relation, say $z_1(x, y)$ is known from experiment or from statistical mechanics. At any given state x, y, the values of z_2, z_3 and so on as well as of z_1 must be fixed, because all these quantities are known to be properties. Hence, the existence of the functions $z_2(x, y)$, $z_3(x, y)$ and so on is assured. The problem that we wish to analyze in general terms here is this: knowing that the functions $z_2(x, y)$, $z_3(x, y)$ and so on exist, can we calculate them from $z_1(x, y)$?

It is obvious that for this to be the case, the dependent variables must necessarily be related to each other mathematically in some way. In particular cases it is not always apparent that either a relation exists or what its nature is. In this connection the methods of statistical mechanics often reveal relations which are difficult to obtain empirically. However, assuming the existence of such a relation, the question still remains as to whether it is sufficient for our purpose. It is clear from the discussion in Section 3.2 that this is certainly the case sometimes. For example, given the thermal equation of state $v(P, \theta)$, we can immediately indicate the equation of state for the coefficient of thermal expansion $\beta(P, \theta)$, as only differentiation and division by v, equation (3.16), is involved. The result will not contain any constants to be determined, because no new constants arise when differentiation is performed.

It is equally clear that the inverse problem, that is, the evaluation of $v(P, \theta)$ from $\beta(P, \theta)$ will not provide a complete solution. It is possible to integrate equations (3.16) as follows:

$$\ln v(P, \theta) = \int \frac{1}{v}\left(\frac{\partial v}{\partial \theta}\right)_P d\theta \qquad \text{along} \quad P = \text{const}$$

or

$$\ln v(P, \theta) = \int \beta(P, \theta) \, d\theta \qquad \text{along} \quad P = \text{const.}$$

The resulting integral will contain a constant of integration which is a function of pressure, and we can write generally

$$\frac{v(P, \theta)}{v(P_0, \theta)} = \exp\left\{\int_{\theta_0}^{\theta} \beta(P, \theta) \, d\theta + \psi(P)\right\}.$$

The function $\psi(P) = \ln v(P, \theta_0) - \ln v(P_0, \theta_0)$ must be evaluated from information which is not contained in the equation of state $\beta = \beta(P, \theta)$, that is, from additional experimental data if we confine ourselves to classical thermodynamics. Here, $v(P_0, \theta_0)$ denotes the value of v at the reference state given by P_0, θ_0 which must also be known.

The preceding argument leads to an important distinction between different forms of equations of state. Given a set of dependent variables z_2, z_3, and so on, and an equation of state $z_1(x, y)$, we discern two cases. In the first case all properties z_2, z_3, and so on, depend on property z_1 through relations involving differentiation only. In this case, the functions $z_2(x, y)$, $z_3(x, y)$, and so on can be determined without further measurement, and the equation of state $z_1(x, y)$ is called a *fundamental equation*. Whether an equation is fundamental or not depends as much on the properties which appear in it, in the preceding example z_1, x, and y, as on the properties z_2, z_3, and so on which are of interest.

It is worth noting that the thermal equation of state for a homogeneous pure substance, also known as the pressure-volume-temperature relation, or P, V, T relation for short, does *not* constitute a fundamental equation in thermodynamics. We shall study this equation in greater detail in Sections 12.2 and 12.11.

3.9 The mol

Although the student is undoubtedly familiar with the use of the mol as an alternative unit of quantity of matter, we shall find it advantageous to recapitulate the concept in this section, and to show how it can be utilized to simplify the thermal equation of state of perfect gases.

Experiments performed on gases at very low pressures or, more precisely, experiments performed at modest pressures and extrapolated to zero pressure reveal a very important regularity in their behavior.

If the masses of equal volumes of different gases are compared under conditions when their temperatures θ and pressures P are equal, it turns out that the masses are to each other in nearly fixed ratios. As the pressure P is made to tend to zero, the equality becomes asymptotically exact. Furthermore, when subjected to chemical reactions, gases combine in simple ratios of volume, and hence mass. Since the volumes are the same, the ratios of the masses are asymptotically equal to the ratios of densities, and to the inverse of the ratios of specific volumes. Hence, for gases 1 and 2

$$\lim_{P\to 0} \frac{m_2}{m_1} = \lim_{P\to 0} \frac{m_2/V}{m_1/V} = \lim_{P\to 0} \frac{\rho_2}{\rho_1} = \lim_{P\to 0} \frac{v_1}{v_2}, \qquad \text{at} \begin{cases} P = \text{const}, \\ \theta = \text{const}. \end{cases}$$

Recalling the definition of a hypothetical perfect gas from Section 2.6, we can omit the process of passing to the limit $P \to 0$, and write

$$\frac{m_2}{m_1} = \frac{\rho_2}{\rho_1} = \frac{v_1}{v_2} \qquad \text{at } P = \text{const}, \theta = \text{const} \tag{3.48}$$

for perfect gases. This ratio of masses is *defined* as the *ratio of the molecular masses*† of the two gases. Denoting the molecular mass of a gas by the symbol M, we can record the definition in the relation

$$\frac{m_2}{m_1} = \frac{\rho_2}{\rho_1} = \frac{v_1}{v_2} = \frac{M_2}{M_1}, \tag{3.48a}$$

valid for any pressure P and temperature θ common to both gases. In order to agree on a definite scale of molecular masses for gases, it is sufficient to *assume* an arbitrary value for one of them. The molecular mass of any other gas will then be determined by a single measurement of one of the ratios m_2/m_1, ρ_2/ρ_1, or v_1/v_2 at an arbitrary pressure P and temperature θ. In practice, this ratio is determined from the values of specific volume (or density) at the *normal pressure* of 1 atm and the *normal temperature* of 273.15°K, suitably corrected for the change in value which would be obtained as a result of extrapolation to zero pressure at that temperature. The combined conditions of normal pressure and temperature are often described by the abbreviation NTP.‡

† Some authors use the inconsistent term: "ratio of molecular *weights*" which was coined at a time when quantities of matter were measured by their weights in the gravitational system of units.
‡ An alternative, conventional set of conditions known as STP (standard pressure and temperature) stipulates a pressure of 30 in Hg and a temperature of 60°F.

Hydrogen was first used as a reference substance, and its molecular mass was assigned the value $M_{H_2} = 2$ exactly, corresponding to the fact that chemical experiments lead to the microscopic hypothesis that a hydrogen molecule is diatomic. On this scale the molecular mass of oxygen gas, which is also diatomic, would be $M_{O_2} = 31.74$. Since oxygen combines readily with a larger number of elements than hydrogen, the convention was changed and based on oxygen as a reference substance. It was then *assumed* that

$$M_{O_2} = 32 \text{ cxactly.} \tag{3.49}$$

Since the discovery of isotopes, it has become recognized that the preceding definition lacks precision because the isotopic composition of oxygen depends on the mode of its preparation. Atmospheric oxygen consists of three isotopes in the ratio

$$O_2^{16} : O_2^{18} : O_2^{17} = (560 \pm 10) : 1 : (0.204 \pm 0.008).$$

Accordingly, on the older *chemical scale* the value (3.49) is assigned to "natural" oxygen in which the isotopes occur in the preceding abundance ratios. On the newer *physical scale*, the value (3.49) is assigned to the pure isotope O_2^{16}. More recently, the International Union of Pure and Applied Physics (IUPAP, 1960) and the International Union of Pure and Applied Chemistry (IUPAC, 1961) adopted an international scale based on the isotope 12 of carbon, because carbon combines readily with a very large number of elements. On the *carbon 12* or *international* scale

$$M_{C^{12}} = 12. \tag{3.49a}$$

Thus, there exist side-by-side three scales of molecular masses: the chemical scale, the physical scale and the carbon 12 scale. However the differences between them are at most of the order of 1 part in 3000 and can be ignored except for cases when utmost precision is called for. In such extreme cases, it is necessary to ascertain precisely which scale is meant. The hydrogen scale is now obsolete, and most of the older tables use the chemical scale.

A mass of gas in pounds, grams, or kilograms which is *numerically* equal to the conventional molecular mass M is called one *mol* (or *mole*). In many applications it is convenient to use the mol as a unit of quantity of substance. Depending on the units of mass used, mols are designated as 1 gmol (gram-mol) for grams, 1 kmol (kilomol) for kilograms or 1 lbmol (pound-mol) for pounds-mass. Thus 1 mol represents a new unit of quantity of matter which has been defined independently of the unit of mass, and a conversion equation is required for it. According to its definition

$$\left. \begin{array}{l} 1 \text{ gmol} = M \text{ g} \\ 1 \text{ kmol} = M \text{ kg} \\ 1 \text{ lbmol} = M \text{ lbm.} \end{array} \right\} \tag{3.50}$$

Consequently, the units of molecular mass are

$$\{M\} = \frac{\text{g}}{\text{gmol}}; \frac{\text{kg}}{\text{kmol}}; \quad \text{or} \quad \frac{\text{lbm}}{\text{lbmol}}.$$

When the quantity of matter is expressed in mols, we shall use the symbol n for it, and

$$\{n\} = \text{mol (gmol, kmol, lbmol, as the case may be).}$$

The physical equation relating the number of mols n to the mass m of a quantity of gas has the form

$$nM = m \tag{3.50a}$$

whose relation to the conversion equations (3.50) should be noted. The molecular mass M plays here the part of the conversion factor k in an equation in which the units — for the number of mols and mass in the present case — are defined independently. Conceived as a quantity equation, equation (3.50a) should be written

$$n = m, \tag{3.50b}$$

noting that the conversion factor M from $\{n\}$ to $\{m\}$ depends on the chemical nature of the gas.

The molecular masses of different gases are seen listed in Table V in terms of the three existing scales. Table V lists several additional properties of gases which will be introduced later in the course of our study.

3.10   The universal gas constant. Avogadro's hypothesis

The experimental fact expressed in equation (3.48a) leads to the conclusion that $M_1 v_1 = M_2 v_2$, that is, to the conclusion that the product Mv for any perfect gas has the same value at a given pressure or temperature. This product represents the volume v_m of one mol of any gas. It follows that the *molar volumes* v_m of all gases are the same at a given pressure and temperature. In particular, at NTP

$$\left.\begin{array}{l} v_{m,0} = (22.4207 \pm 0.0006) \text{ m}^3/\text{kmol} \quad \text{(physical scale)} \\[2pt] \text{or} \\[2pt] v_{m,0} = (22.4146 \pm 0.0006) \text{ m}^3/\text{kmol} \quad \text{(chemical scale).} \end{array}\right\} \tag{3.51}$$

When the quantity of the gas is represented by the number of mols n, its volume is

$$V = n v_m \tag{3.52}$$

and its mass is

$$m = nM. \tag{3.52a}$$

Consequently, equation (3.7) can be modified to

$$P v_m = M R \theta. \tag{3.52b}$$

In this equation, the molar volume v_m is the same for all perfect gases for a given pressure P and a given temperature θ. For example, for two different perfect gases 1 and 2 at the same pressure and temperature

$$P v_m = M_1 R_1 \theta,$$
$$P v_m = M_2 R_2 \theta.$$

Hence, it follows that the product

$$\mathbf{R} = MR = \frac{P v_m}{\theta} \tag{3.53}$$

is the same for all perfect gases and constitutes a universal constant of physics. In MKS and in English units

$$\mathbf{R} = (8316.96 \pm 0.34) \; \frac{J}{kmol \; °K}$$
$$= (1545.81 \pm 0.06) \; \frac{ft \; lbf}{lbmol \; °R}$$

(3.54)

on the physical scale. Values of this *universal gas constant* **R** in alternative units are given in Table VI. Table VI also contains a note on the conversion factors which link the three sets of mol units.

Multiplying both sides of equation (3.52b) by the number of mols n, and noting that $n v_m = V$ and that $MR = \mathbf{R}$, we find that the thermal equation of a perfect gas assumes the *universal form*

$$PV = n \, \mathbf{R} \, \theta$$

(3.55)

which is valid for any perfect gas whatsoever. This, evidently, constitutes a significant practical simplification. Moreover, equation (3.53) provides a ready means of calculating the gas constant of any perfect gas when its molecular mass is known.

Referring to equation (3.53), it is noted that the numerical value of the universal gas constant **R** depends on the scale chosen for the measurement of molecular masses. Depending on the scale, one mol of a specified chemical substance represents a different *mass*, and hence also a different *molar* volume, v_m. On the other hand, the individual gas constant, that is, the ratio $R = \mathbf{R}/M$, is independent of this choice. That this should be so is evident because the unit of *mass* is independent of the convention regarding *molecular* masses.

The preceding experimental facts led Avogadro (1776–1856) to enunciate the now evident microscopic hypothesis, known as *Avogadro's principle*, which states that one mol of any perfect gas (in practice a real gas at low density) contains the same number of molecules. This number, known as the *Avogadro number*,† is

$$\mathbf{N} = (6.02486 \pm 0.00016) \times 10^{26} \; molecules/kmol$$
$$= (2.73283 \pm 0.00007) \times 10^{26} \; molecules/lbmol$$

(3.56)

on the physical scale.

The universal gas constant referred to one molecule

$$\mathbf{k} = \frac{\mathbf{R}}{\mathbf{N}}$$

(3.56a)

is known as Boltzmann's constant. It has the value

$$\mathbf{k} = (1.38044 \pm 0.00007) \times 10^{-23} \; J/°K.$$

(3.56b)

Further values of Avogadro's number and Boltzmann's constant in alternative units are listed in Table VII.

The reader should satisfy himself that Avogadro's hypothesis naturally leads to the conclusion that one mol of any perfect gas must occupy the same volume as that of any other. When combined with the additional hypothesis that during chemical reactions the products consist of the same atoms, only arranged differently, as the

---

† The Loschmidt number in Germany. In works in the English language, the constant
$$\mathbf{L} = \mathbf{N}/v_m = (2.68719 \pm 0.00010) \times 10^{19} \; molecules/cm^3,$$
is referred to as the Loschmidt number.

reactants, Avogadro's hypothesis accounts for the fact that chemical reactions at low pressures consume and produce gases whose *volumes* bear simple ratios to each other.

At this stage, it is useful to summarize the various forms of the perfect-gas law for easy reference.

Per unit mass

$$Pv = R\theta, \qquad R = \mathbf{R}/M. \tag{3.57a}$$

For m units of mass

$$PV = mR\theta, \qquad V = mv. \tag{3.57b}$$

Per one mol of gas

$$Pv_m = \mathbf{R}\,\theta. \tag{3.57c}$$

For $n = m/M$ mols

$$PV = n\,\mathbf{R}\,\theta; \quad V = nv_m; \quad m = nM. \tag{3.57d}$$

3.11   Molar quantities

One mol of a gas, a different mass in each particular case, is frequently employed in the formation of specific quantities. They are known as *molar specific quantities*. There are many advantages attendant on this choice of units; they will become apparent to the reader after he has become familiar with the chapter on chemical reactions in Volume II. At this stage it is sufficient to notice that in each particular case the quantity relates to M units of mass rather than to one unit of mass. The units for molar specific volume v_m are

$$\{v_m\} = \frac{\text{m}^3}{\text{kmol}}; \quad \frac{\text{cm}^3}{\text{gmol}}; \quad \text{or} \quad \frac{\text{ft}^3}{\text{lbmol}}.$$

It should be clear to the reader that the equations of thermodynamics remain unaffected by the choice of the specific quantities used for numerical calculations. For this reason we find it superfluous to introduce a separate set of symbols for molar specific quantities and will rely on the fact that the nature of the quantity is usually clear from the content or from the unit quoted. Thus, instead of the form in equation (3.57c) we shall frequently write

$$Pv = \mathbf{R}\,\theta,$$

the appearance of the universal gas constant indicating that v denotes here the molar specific volume. On the rare occasions when confusion may result, the molar specific quantities will be distinguished by the subscript m as was done in equation (3.57c).

List of Symbols for Chapter 3

Latin letters

A Constant; area
a Constant
B Constant; isothermal bulk modulus, equation (3.18a)

b	Constant
C	Constant
G	Gradient vector of a scalar
J	Jacobian
k	Boltzmann's constant
M	Quantity defined by equation (3.24); molecular mass
m	Mass
N	Quantity defined by equation (3.24)
n	Number of independent variables; number of mols
N	Avogadro's number
P	Pressure; quantity defined by equation (3.25)
Q	Quantity defined by equation (3.25)
R	Quantity defined by equation (3.25); gas constant
R	Curl of vector **G**; universal gas constant
r	Vector; position vector
$\mathcal{R}$	Electric resistance
s	Displacement
t	Time
$\mathcal{T}$	Tension
u	Coordinate
V	Volume
v	Specific volume; coordinate
v_m	Molar volume
w	Quantity defined in equations (3.14) and (3.14a)
x	Independent variable; coordinate
y	Independent variable; coordinate
z	Dependent variable; coordinate

Greek letters

β	Coefficient of (volume) expansion
η	Coordinate
θ	Temperature measured on empirical temperature scale
κ	Isothermal coefficient of compressibility, equation (3.18)
ξ	$= \int_0^x M dx$ in footnote on p. 92; coordinate
π	Coefficient of tension, equation (3.17)
ρ	Density
ω	Component of the curl of a vector defined in equations (3.27) and (3.27a)

Special symbols

{ }	Unit of measure for respective physical quantity

CHAPTER 4

Work. Reversible, Irreversible, and Quasistatic Processes

The concept of work in thermodynamics is a natural extension of the concept of work in mechanics. This extension is required to take into account the greater variety of phenomena encountered in thermodynamics. Since a complete understanding of the physical concept of work and of its mathematical nature is of utmost importance, it would appear opportune first to review the more familiar concept of work in mechanics.

4.1 The concept of work in mechanics

The most elementary definition of *work* in mechanics is formulated in relation to the simplest mechanical system, a material point in equilibrium, Figure 4.1. Such a system is visualized as being acted upon by a force F which is balanced by an equal and opposite "opposing" force $-F$. The system will then be at rest, and in order to perform work it is necessary to displace it, say by increasing the force F by a small quantity ΔF. Under the action of the two forces, $F + \Delta F$ and $-F$, the system will accelerate, and the acceleration will be smaller and smaller as ΔF is made to decrease towards zero. In the limit, we *say* that the material point, though always in equilibrium, is displaced "infinitely slowly" or "quasistatically." The product

$$W = Fx \tag{4.1}$$

of force F and displacement x is *defined* as the work done by the force F and against force $-F$. In thermodynamics, it is necessary to specify which one of the forces, F or $-F$, is included as part of the system, that is, it is necessary to determine the force exerted by the system upon its surroundings. If the force F is exerted by the system, we shall say that the work is done *by* the system.

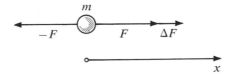

FIGURE 4.1. *Elementary definition of work.*

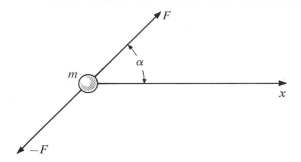

FIGURE 4.2. *Force at an angle to the displacement.*

This elementary definition is generalized to include progressively more complex mechanical systems. When the force varies with distance, $F(x)$, an elementary distance, dx, is considered, and the limit

$$W = \int_1^2 F(x) \, dx \tag{4.1a}$$

is defined as the work performed by the system against the variable, opposing force $-F(x)$. If the force is known as a function of a parameter, say time t, then the displacement $x(t)$ must be known in terms of it, and the expression for work is written

$$W = \int_{x_1(t)}^{x_2(t)} F(t) \, \dot{x}(t) \, dt, \tag{4.1b}$$

where $\dot{x} = dx/dt$ is the rate of change of displacement with time. When the force and the displacement are not collinear, Figure 4.2, these definitions are changed to

$$W = Fx \cos \alpha, \tag{4.2}$$

$$W = \int_{x_1}^{x_2} F(x) \, \cos \alpha(x) \, dx, \tag{4.2a}$$

$$W = \int_{x_1(t)}^{x_2(t)} F(t) \, \cos \alpha(t) \, \dot{x}(t) \, dt, \tag{4.2b}$$

respectively.

In more complex cases it is convenient to frame the definition of work in terms of vector concepts since both the force and the displacement have the mathematical properties of *vectors*. The *scalar* quantity, work, is defined as the *scalar* product of force and displacement,

$$W = \mathbf{F} \cdot \mathbf{x} \tag{4.3}$$

in the simplest case when the system, mass m, is displaced quasistatically along a straight line against the action of a constant force $-\mathbf{F}$.

If a material point m is displaced along a given known curve C, Figure 4.3, under the action of a known, but variable external force $\mathbf{F(r)}$ forming part of the system, where $\mathbf{r}$ is the radius vector drawn from an arbitrary origin, it is convenient to regard

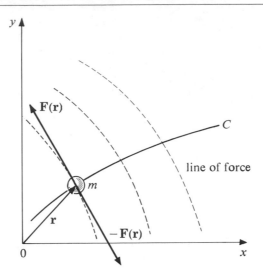

FIGURE 4.3. *Work in a field.*

the opposing force, specified here in terms of the space coordinates $\mathbf{r}(x, y, z)$, as being defined by the vector field $-\mathbf{F}(F_x, F_y, F_z)$. The work is then defined as the limit

$$W = \int_{\mathbf{r}_1}^{\mathbf{r}_2} \mathbf{F} \cdot d\mathbf{r}. \tag{4.4}$$
along curve C

The process of evaluating the integral in equation (4.4) is identical with that known in mathematics as the calculation of a *line integral*.† A field of forces is a particular example of a *vector field*, a concept which plays an important part in the study of fluid mechanics, electromagnetic theory, and other branches of physics. The line integral which is analogous to the expression (4.4) is known as *circulation* in fluid mechanics, if the vector field is a velocity field $\mathcal{V}(x, y, z, t)$, and if the curve C is closed, Figure 4.4.

Hence, more precisely, work is defined as a line integral in a field of forces which is evaluated along a prescribed curve C from an initial point 1 to a final point 2. Evidently, the course of the curve must be given, say in the form of a vector function $\mathbf{r}(t)$ of a parameter t, for example the time.

It is useful now to write out explicitly the operations involved in the evaluation of the work W from the definition (4.4) in a Cartesian system of coordinates x, y, z, Figure 4.3. The integrand can then be written

$$\mathbf{F} \cdot d\mathbf{r} = P(x, y, z)dx + Q(x, y, z)dy + R(x, y, z)dz, \tag{4.5}$$

where

$$P(x, y, z) \equiv F_x; \quad Q(x, y, z) \equiv F_y; \quad \text{and} \quad R(x, y, z) \equiv F_z.$$

In evaluating the line integral for work, it must be remembered that the material point m moves along the curve C, prescribed or otherwise known. We shall assume that

† See for example, Courant, R., *Differential and Integral Calculus* translated by E. J. McShane (London: Blackie, 1936), II, p. 343; and Apostol, T. M., *Calculus* (Blaisdell, 1962), II, p. 219.

it is given in parametric form, that is, in the form of three equations: $x(t)$, $y(t)$, and $z(t)$. Thus, it is necessary to substitute $x(t)$, $y(t)$, $z(t)$ into the component functions $P(x, y, z)$, $Q(x, y, z)$, $R(x, y, z)$, and this ensures that only forces along the curve are considered. The three functions P, Q, R thus become functions of the single variable, t, $P[x(t), y(t), z(t)]$; $Q[x(t), y(t), z(t)]$; $R[x(t), y(t), z(t)]$. Similarly, the component displacements dx, dy, dz are not arbitrary, because the material point m is known to move along the curve C. This will be the case if

$$dx = \dot{x}(t)dt; \quad dy = \dot{y}(t)dt; \quad dz = \dot{z}(t)dt,$$

where the dots above the symbols denote differentiation with respect to the parameter t, as before. Finally, the initial and end points 1 and 2 correspond to prescribed values, t_1 and t_2, of the parameter. In this manner, the work of the force is equal to the *definite* integral of a function of the *single variable* t,

$$W = \int_{t_1}^{t_2} \{P[x(t), y(t), z(t)] \, \dot{x}(t) + Q[x(t), y(t), z(t)] \, \dot{y}(t)$$
$$+ R[x(t), y(t), z(t)] \, \dot{z}(t)\} \, dt. \tag{4.6}$$

In the preceding recapitulation we have deliberately adopted the method of writing down equations which is appropriate, and convenient, in mathematics. As already remarked in Section 3.4, in the study of thermodynamics, the notation is more closely linked with the corresponding physical quantities. Accordingly, it is convenient to provide a symbol for the integrand (4.5) of the line integrals (4.4) or (4.6), that is to reserve a symbol for the "element of work." In this connection the symbol

$$dW = \mathbf{F} \cdot d\mathbf{r} = P \, dx + Q \, dy + R \, dz \tag{4.7}$$

naturally suggests itself. However, this symbol can be misleading, unless the mathematical operations outlined earlier are clearly borne in mind; in particular, it must be remembered that the specification of the curve C exerts an essential influence on the required substitutions. The appearance of equation (4.7) seems to admit the statement

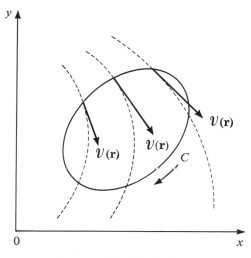

FIGURE 4.4. *Circulation.*

that "both sides" of the equation can be integrated, giving on the left-hand side

$$\int_1^2 dW = W_2 - W_1. \tag{4.8}$$

This, however, is an erroneous interpretation. The integral (4.8) implies that W is a variable, and that the very simple function of that single variable, namely unity, is being integrated. Under such conditions, the integral is equal to the difference between the values of the variable at the ends of the interval of integration, in the same manner as

$$\int_1^2 f(x)dx = F(x_2) - F(x_1),$$

where the function of one variable, $f(x)$, is being integrated, and where the primitive $F(x)$ is known to exist. A glance at equation (4.6) shows that the line integral is formed differently, and that in the above, obviously erroneous interpretation, the specification of the curve C has been lost sight of. Work, W, is not a function of the independent variables x, y, z, because its value, equation (4.6), is seen to depend on the shape of the curve, that is, on the functions $x(t), y(t), z(t)$, as well as on the coordinates (x_1, y_1, z_1) and (x_2, y_2, z_2) of the end points of the path.

In order to see this more clearly, it is natural to enquire as to how the result of the integration (4.6) depends on the shape of the curve C. In particular, given a fixed initial point 1 and a fixed final point 2, it is pertinent to ask whether or not the work W in the given field of forces will change when the curve C, that is the *path* joining points 1 and 2, changes. An examination of the expression in equation (4.6) leads to the immediate conclusion that, *generally*, the value of W in equation (4.6) will change as the curve is changed. This is due to the fact that the functions $x(t), y(t), z(t)$, and so the functions $\dot{x}(t), \dot{y}(t), \dot{z}(t)$ will change as already mentioned. Given three arbitrary functions $P(x, y, z), Q(x, y, z), R(x, y, z)$, there is no reason for different substitutions to lead to identical values of W.

We can, therefore, state quite generally that the work performed by a material point which is displaced in a given field of forces between two fixed points depends on the path. Using the terminology of thermodynamics, the preceding observation can be restated by asserting that work in mechanics is neither a property nor a potential.

4.2   Further criteria for properties

Comparing the present argument with that given in Section 3.7.1, we note the similarities, and the differences. In the present argument P, Q, R stand for arbitrary functions and consequently the conditions of integrability (3.27a) are *not necessarily* satisfied. A field of this kind is known in mechanics as *nonconservative*, or *rotational*.

In particular cases it may so happen that the field of forces is such that the components P, Q, R do satisfy the conditions (3.27a) identically at every point. They then constitute the partial derivatives of some potential $w(x, y, z)$, as pointed out in Section 3.7.1, and the field becomes irrotational, that is, potential. In a potential field, the computation of the line integral (4.6) proceeds differently since the latter is equal to the difference in the values of the potential at the endpoints, irrespective of the detailed specification of curve C. As we already know from Section 3.7.1, we then have

$$W = \int_1^2 P\,dx + Q\,dy + R\,dz = w(x_2, y_2, z_2) - w(x_1, y_1, z_1). \tag{4.9}$$

It follows as a corollary that

$$\oint (P\,dx + Q\,dy + R\,dz) = 0 \tag{4.9a}$$

for *any* cyclic path. It is understood, of course, as will be seen in more detail in Section 10.2, that the circular line integral (4.9a) may vanish for some particular closed paths even in a rotational field. Hence, the importance of the qualification "any" in the preceding statement.

In terms of vector concepts, the conditions of integrability (3.27a) can be written

$$\text{curl } \mathbf{F} = 0, \tag{4.10}$$

and since the vanishing of the curl of a vector field is associated with the absence of local rotations, the field is called irrotational. Furthermore, the field can also be written

$$\mathbf{F} = \text{grad } w. \tag{4.11}$$

The conditions (4.9), (4.9a), (4.10), or (4.11) for a field to be irrotational and potential are both necessary and sufficient, as stated in Section 3.7.1.

The remark concerning notation can now be rephrased as follows. The expression

$$dW = P\,dx + R\,dy + Q\,dz, \tag{4.12}$$

or, more generally,

$$dW = \sum_n X_i\,dx_i \tag{4.12a}$$

stands for a Pfaffian form with *n* functions X_i of the *n* independent variables x_i, that is, for an integrand of a line integral. Sometimes (when the associated vector field is irrotational), it is equal to the difference in the values of a scalar potential function, since the potential function exists. Then, the result

$$\int_1^2 dW = W_2 - W_1$$

has a meaning, and applies: the Pfaffian constitutes a *perfect differential*. However, *in general*, this is not the case, the potential function $W \equiv w$ does not exist, the Pfaffian constitutes an *imperfect differential*, and we write

$$\int_1^2 dW = W_{1,2}$$

which is a shorthand notation for the operations indicated in full in equation (4.6).

Summing up, we can state that the vector field $\mathbf{F}(X_1, \ldots, X_i, \ldots, X_n)$ associated with a Pfaffian expression $dW = \sum_n X_i dx_i$ can be of one of two types: conservative, or nonconservative.

In a conservative field $\mathbf{F}$

(a) The curl vanishes identically curl $\mathbf{F} = 0$.

(b) There exists a potential w, such that $\mathbf{F} = \text{grad } w$.

(c) Any line integral taken in the field is independent of the path; its value depends only on the initial point 1 and on the final point 2, so that it is equal to the difference between the values of the potentials at these points or

$$W_{1,2} = \int_1^2 \mathbf{F} \cdot d\mathbf{r} = w(2) - w(1).$$

(d) Any circular integral (the circulation in a velocity field in fluid mechanics) vanishes in the field, or

$$\oint \mathbf{F} \cdot d\mathbf{r} = 0$$

for any cyclic path.

(e) The Pfaffian is a perfect differential, and its components satisfy the conditions of integrability (3.27) or (3.27a).

It is proved in vector analysis,[†] and it was stated in Section 3.7.1, that any one of the preceding statements is both *necessary and sufficient* for a field to be irrotational which means that the truth of any one statement implies that all the others are satisfied, and conversely, that if any one condition is absent, all are absent. In thermodynamic terms, it is possible to state that the preceding conditions (a) to (e) apply to properties and to potentials. In fact, we shall make frequent use of them to decide whether a given quantity is a property or potential and so, conditions (a) to (e) constitute the *criteria for properties* mentioned first in Section 3.1.

The preceding description has been phrased principally in relation to three-dimensional vector fields. Its applicability to two-dimensional vector fields is evident, and its extension to spaces of more dimensions presents no difficulty and can be performed by mathematical induction. The condition of integrability for two-dimensional fields is very easy to write down. In the case of three dimensions, the following symbolic form is worth remembering:

$$\text{curl } \mathbf{F} = \begin{vmatrix} \mathbf{i} & \mathbf{j} & \mathbf{k} \\ \dfrac{\partial}{\partial x} & \dfrac{\partial}{\partial y} & \dfrac{\partial}{\partial z} \\ F_x & F_y & F_z \end{vmatrix} = 0. \tag{4.13}$$

The symbol is expanded like a determinant in terms of the three unit vectors $\mathbf{i}, \mathbf{j}, \mathbf{k}$, and when each of the factors of the unit vectors is equated to zero, equations (3.27a) are obtained. The "products" $F_y \cdot \partial/\partial x$ and so on are interpreted as the derivatives of $\partial F_y/\partial x$ and so on.

The reader may wish to be reminded (Section 3.7) that in the case of n dimensions, the number of equations increases from 3 to $\frac{1}{2}n \, (n-1)$. Such n-dimensional vector fields do not occur naturally when force fields in space are considered, but they play a part in the derivation of the mathematical consequences of the Second Law of thermodynamics, Chapters 9 and 10.

4.3 The theorems of Stokes and Gauss

The criteria for the existence of a potential are all implied in Stokes' theorem, and can be inferred from it. Stokes' theorem links the value of a line integral in a vector field $\mathbf{F}$, taken around a closed curve C, as shown in Figure 4.5(a), with the surface integral of the normal component of the vector $\mathbf{R} = \text{curl } \mathbf{F}$ taken over a surface σ spanning the curve C. This surface integral represents the flux of vector $\mathbf{R}$ across the

[†] See, for example, Apostol, T. M., *Calculus* (Blaisdell, 1962), II, p. 238 or Sokolnikoff, I. S., and Redheffer, R. M., *Mathematics of Physics and Modern Engineering* (McGraw-Hill, 1958), p. 378.

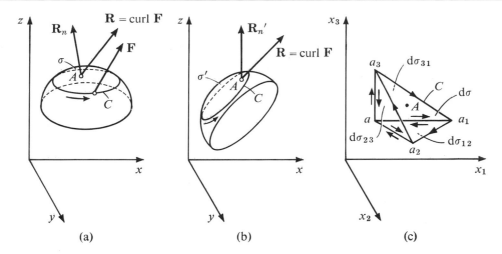

FIGURE 4.5. *Stokes' theorem.*

surface σ, and the theorem is written

$$\oint_C \mathbf{F} \cdot d\mathbf{r} = \iint (\text{curl } \mathbf{F})_n \, d\sigma \tag{4.14}$$

for any curve C and any surface σ† spanning it. In the case of a two-dimensional field the preceding equation specializes to

$$\oint \mathbf{F} \cdot d\mathbf{r} = \iint \omega_z \, d\sigma, \tag{4.14a}$$

since $\mathbf{R} = \text{curl } \mathbf{F}$ possesses only one component, namely ω_z. This special form of Stokes' theorem is often referred to as Gauss' theorem in the plane. As the line integral can be applied to any curve, we can imagine that the curve is contracted to a point, such as A in Figure 4.5(a). Thus, if the line integral vanishes for any curve C, the normal component of the curl, R_n, will vanish at that point. This proves that $\mathbf{R} = \text{curl } \mathbf{F}$ can have at most a component tangent to surface σ at point A. However, by drawing a different curve C' and spanning a different surface σ' through point A and curve C', it is possible to prove that the normal component R'_n in a *different direction* also vanishes, and that $\mathbf{R} = \text{curl } \mathbf{F}$ can at most have a component tangent to surface σ' at point A, as shown in Figure 4.5(b). By repeating this process a third time, it is possible to show that the three components of the vector $\mathbf{R} = \text{curl } \mathbf{F}$ vanish at an arbitrary point A, so that the vanishing of the circular integral implies the vanishing of the curl, and *vice versa*, on condition that the circular integral vanishes for *any*, and not just for some, closed curve C. The vanishing of a circular integral implies that any line integral is independent of the path, that is that a potential exists, or that the associated Pfaffian is a perfect differential. Thus, it is seen, as asserted before, that statements (a) to (e) quoted in the

† Strictly speaking, the theorem only applies to simply connected regions, but this restriction will always be satisfied in our applications.

preceding section are all equivalent and can be used interchangeably. Stokes' theorem combines them in a terse and condensed form. The same can be said about Gauss' theorem in the plane, the procedure being simplified by the fact that $\mathbf{R} = \text{curl } \mathbf{F}$ possesses a single component ω_z normal to the plane.

For the sake of completeness, we shall write down Stokes' theorem for the case when the number of independent variables is $n > 3$.[†] The system of orthogonal coordinates consists then of n mutually perpendicular axes which we shall number $x_1, x_2, \ldots, x_n$. The "vector" $\mathbf{F}$ (so-called n-vector) will now possess n components $F_1, F_2, \ldots, F_n$. The integrability conditions involve two derivatives, namely the derivative $\partial F_i/\partial x_j$ of one component, say F_i, in a direction x_j normal to it, and the reciprocal derivative $\partial F_j/\partial x_i$, where both indices, i and j, range over 1, 2, $\ldots$, n, but are never equal ($i \neq j$). Thus we can write down $n(n-1)$ differences

$$\omega_{ij} = \frac{\partial F_i}{\partial x_j} - \frac{\partial F_j}{\partial x_i}. \tag{a}$$

The number is $n(n-1)$ because each of the n indices i must be associated with $n-1$ indices j owing to the requirement that $j \neq i$.

When *all* differences (a) vanish, the integrability conditions are satisfied. In actual fact

$$\omega_{ij} = -\omega_{ji}, \tag{b}$$

as is easy to verify, and the number of independent integrability conditions is only $\frac{1}{2}n(n-1)$ as anticipated in Section 3.7.1 on p. 91. For the sake of symmetry, however, it is convenient to consider the $n(n-1)$ quantities ω_{ij}. It was mentioned earlier on p. 95 that the quantities ω_{ij} can be interpreted as the components of a vector only when $n = 3$, because then also $\frac{1}{2}n(n-1) = 3$. In general, however, $\frac{1}{2}n(n-1) \neq n$, and the $n(n-1)$ quantities ω_{ij} constitute the components of an antisymmetric tensor. This circumstance need not trouble the reader unfamiliar with tensor calculus, as it has no bearing on our argument.

In order to write down the required form of Stokes' theorem it is convenient first to revert to $n = 3$ variables and to rewrite the by now familiar equation in a more symmetric form. Accordingly, we consider the elementary triangle $a_1\, a_2\, a_3$ shown in Figure 4.5(c). The elementary triangle represents curve C, about to be contracted to point A, and encompasses area $d\sigma$. We now introduce the projections of $d\sigma$ on planes perpendicular to the coordinate axes, namely the elementary areas $aa_2a_3|x_1$, $aa_3a_1|x_2$, and $aa_1a_2|x_3$, denoting their areas by $d\sigma_{23}$, $d\sigma_{31}$, and $d\sigma_{12}$, respectively. It is easy to verify from the figure that the line integral around curve C is equal to the sum of three line integrals taken around the elementary triangles aa_2a_3, aa_3a_1, aa_1a_2, because the portions along aa_1, aa_2, and aa_3 cancel, since they are traversed twice in opposite directions. Hence,

$$\oint_C \mathbf{F} \cdot d\mathbf{r} = \oint_{aa_2a_3} F_1 \, d\sigma_{23} + \oint_{aa_3a_1} F_2 \, d\sigma_{31} + \oint_{aa_1a_2} F_3 \, d\sigma_{12}, \tag{c}$$

each integral involving one component of $\mathbf{F}$ only. Applying Gauss' theorem in each of the planes, we can write

$$\oint_C \mathbf{F} \cdot d\mathbf{r} = \iint_{aa_2a_3} \omega_1 \, d\sigma_{23} + \iint_{aa_3a_1} \omega_2 \, d\sigma_{31} + \iint_{aa_1a_2} \omega_3 \, d\sigma_{12}, \tag{d}$$

each of the double integrals extending over one elementary area. Each of the components ω_1, ω_2, ω_3 is equal to one of the components ω_{ij} from equation (a). A change in the order of the

---

[†] A more complete and more general derivation can be found in Brillouin, L., *Tensors in Mechanics and Elasticity* (Academic Press, 1964), p. 81.

indices from ij to ji changes the sign, equation (c). Similarly, if $d\sigma_{ij}$ is changed to $d\sigma_{ji}$, the sign of the elementary area changes. Hence, if we take the six terms

$$\Sigma \iint \omega_{ij}\, d\sigma_{ij} \quad \text{with} \quad i \neq j, i = 1, 2, 3; j = 1, 2, 3,$$

we obtain *twice* the sum on the right-hand side of equation (d). Consequently, Stokes' theorem can also be written

$$\oint \mathbf{F} \cdot d\mathbf{r} = \tfrac{1}{2} \sum_{ij} \omega_{ij}\, d\sigma_{ij}, \qquad (i \neq j; i, j = 1, 2, 3). \tag{e}$$

In the case when $n > 3$, equation (e) remains valid, because the integral can now be split into $n(n-1)$ line integrals, and hence, by Gauss' theorem in the plane, also into $n(n-1)$ surface integrals for the $n(n-1)$ components ω_{ij}. Thus,

$$\oint \sum_{ij} F_i\, dx_i = \tfrac{1}{2} \sum_{1}^{n} \iint \omega_{ij}\, d\sigma_{ij} \quad (i \neq j; i, j = 1, 2, 3, \ldots, n). \tag{f}$$

The only difficulty in deriving equation (f) stems from the fact that we cannot visualize more than three mutually perpendicular axes. With n variables there are exactly $\tfrac{1}{2}n(n-1)$ coordinate planes, and Figure 4.5(c) can be interpreted as a projection from the n-dimensional space into the three-dimensional space x_1, x_2, x_3 or, more precisely, a projection of this projection on a two-dimensional sheet of paper.

The vanishing of the line integral around a curve C contracting to point A assures the vanishing of all the $n(n-1)$ quantities ω_{ij} which means that the $\tfrac{1}{2}n(n-1)$ conditions of integrability are satisfied. Thus, a potential $w(x_1, \ldots, x_n)$ must exist, and

$$\frac{\partial F_i}{\partial x_j} = \frac{\partial F_j}{\partial x_i} = \frac{\partial^2 w}{\partial x_i\, \partial x_j} \left(= \frac{\partial^2 w}{\partial x_j\, \partial x_i} \right). \tag{g}$$

Consequently, the statements (a) to (e) made in Section 4.2 remain true for any number of variables.

4.4   The definition of work in thermodynamics

In generalizing the preceding concept of work to include phenomena other than those encountered in mechanics, an attempt must be made to divorce it from the need to consider forces, and yet to preserve its essential physical characteristics. We can recognize the latter by rephrasing the definitions of the preceding section in thermodynamical terms. The first important characteristic to recognize is that work was not associated with a particular position of the mass, or with a particular configuration within the field. In other words, it was not associated with a particular state of the system. Work was performed when the system changed position, that is when a process was performed.

For example, Figure 4.6, when a mass m of weight $G = mg$ is raised infinitely slowly in the gravitational field of the earth, the change of state from 1, characterized by elevation z_1 above some reference level, to state 2 described by elevation z_2, is accompanied by the performance of work. As is usual, the positive direction for z has been chosen upwards and opposite to the direction of the gravitational field. The system, that is, the mass m, is acted upon by the force G created by gravitation. We shall include this force in the system and consider it to be positive. In order to raise the mass, an external agent—the surroundings—must provide an equal and opposite force $F = -G$. Hence, according to the preceding conventions regarding signs, we shall say that the

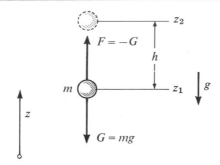

FIGURE 4.6. *Raising of a weight in the gravitational field of the earth. The weight $G = mg$ is considered to be positive. The opposite force $F = -G$ is exerted by the surroundings, and is negative.*

system has performed work

$$W_{1,2} = F\,h = -G\,h, \tag{4.15}$$

where $h = z_2 - z_1$ is the distance traversed. This work is negative when $z_2 > z_1$ ($h > 0$), and positive when $z_2 < z_1$ ($h < 0$). In the former case work is performed *on* the system; it is performed *by* the system in the latter case.

We now assert that the performance of any mechanical work by a system is always equivalent to the raising of a weight in a gravitational field. That this is so can be ascertained with reference to Figure 4.7. The system, mass m, is acted upon by the field which produces the positive force **F** included with the system. The surroundings apply the negative force $-\mathbf{F}$ which maintains a static balance. Work is done when the system is displaced, and we reckon that it is positive when the displacement is in the direction of **F**; it is negative in the opposite case. We now imagine that the surroundings (the force $-\mathbf{F}$) are removed and replaced by a fictitious mechanism whose sole function is to provide the instantaneous, external force $-\mathbf{F}$ with the aid of a weight G in a fictitious, uniform gravitational field. One such possible mechanism is shown sketched in Figure 4.7; it consists of a suitably shaped cam which provides a force of the re-

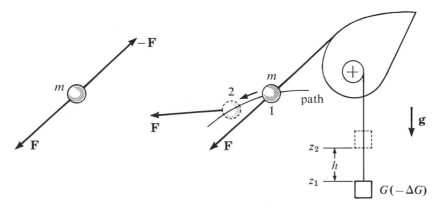

FIGURE 4.7. *Equivalence of work and the raising of a weight. The positive force **F** is included in the system. The negative force $-\mathbf{F}$ is supplied by the surroundings.*

quired direction and magnitude to overcome the action of force **F** by the action of weight G. If necessary, idle pulleys, gears and other mechanisms may be added even during the process, and all that is required of them is that they should be ideal, that is frictionless. By such means it is always possible to ensure that at every step

$$\mathrm{d}W = \mathbf{F} \cdot \mathbf{dr} = G\mathrm{d}z, \tag{4.15a}$$

where z is reckoned positive upwards. For the whole process, we then have

$$W_{1,2} = G\,h. \tag{4.15b}$$

The difference in the signs in equations (4.15) and (4.15a) stems from the circumstance that in equation (4.15) G denotes the weight of the system itself, whereas in equation (4.15b) G refers to a fictitious, external weight. Thus, in Figure 4.6 the positive direction of displacement $\mathrm{d}z$ has been chosen opposite to the positive downward force $G = mg$; in Figure 4.7 the displacement is regarded as positive when it is codirectional with the positive force **F**.

Adopting the preceding mode of description we shall advance the following general definition of the work performed by a thermodynamic system:

> *Work is performed by a system on its surroundings during a given process if the only effect external to the system* **could** *be the raising of a weight.*

The quantity of work is measured by the product G of the prescribed weight and the distance h traveled by it, and the convention is adopted that work performed *by* the system under consideration is *positive*. In the preceding example, Figure 4.7, it was imagined that the weight G was decreased by an amount $\Delta G \to 0$, and it was said that the *system* performed work. Work would have been performed by the surroundings on the system if instead of decreasing weight G by $\Delta G \to 0$, it had been increased by that amount thus displacing the mass m in the opposite direction. This suggests that

> *Work is performed on a system by its surroundings during a given process if the only effect external to the surroundings* **could** *be the raising of a weight.*

Work performed on the system will be regarded as negative, and the sketch in Figure 4.8 will help to memorize this, quite arbitrary, convention. In fact, in many books, particularly on physical chemistry and chemical thermodynamics, the opposite convention is followed. This has the effect of changing the appearance of the equations in that $-W_{1,2}$ must be substituted for $+W_{1,2}$ (or $-\mathrm{d}W$ for $+\mathrm{d}W$) in them to achieve agreement with this and similar books. Historically, the convention illustrated in Figure 4.8 stems from the fact that the stimulus to develop the science of thermodynamics came from the study of heat engines which are used to produce work, that is to perform it *on* their surroundings.

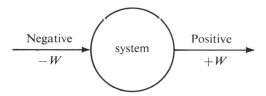

FIGURE 4.8. *Sign convention for work.*

The definitions of positive and negative work given earlier are clearly seen to be entirely equivalent to, and yet more general than the definitions adopted in mechanics. They are based on a definition first intimated by M. Planck† and later developed by J. H. Keenan.‡

It may appear puzzling at this stage that negative work has not been defined as that interaction between the system and its surroundings whose sole effect, external to the system, could be the *lowering* of a weight. The precise reasons for the unacceptability of such a definition cannot be given here; they must be deferred to Chapter 5, and particularly to Section 5.7 which discusses the concept of heat. It will then be shown that the same effect upon a system as is produced by the lowering of a weight outside it can also be produced by the addition of heat, a quantity known to us from everyday experience, but, so far, undefined in precise terms.

4.5 The calculation of work

From the definition of work given in the preceding section it is clear that work is neither a property nor a potential. Work is measured during a process, and its value is not fixed when the state of the system is fixed. This does not exclude the possibility that under very special circumstances the quantity of work may become a function of the independent properties only and hence equal to a difference in potentials. One such example was encountered in Section 4.1, namely the example of mechanical work in a conservative system. Another important example will be discussed in Section 5.3. In a nonconservative field, work was given by a Pfaffian which was not a perfect differential. It must not, however, be concluded that work in thermodynamics is always given by a Pfaffian as we shall see later in this section. It is now proposed to derive expressions for work in relation to a very simple system which is of great importance in the study of thermodynamics.

4.5.1   Simple substance expanding behind a piston

When a simple substance, a gas, a liquid, or a mixture of both is confined in a cylinder enclosed with the aid of a piston, Figure 4.9, and performs a process which causes the volume to increase or to decrease, it is clear that work is performed. In order to calculate it, we shall imagine that the surroundings have been replaced by the mechanism shown in the figure. If the piston is weightless, and if the piston as well as the mechanism are frictionless, it is possible to balance the force $F = PA$ exerted on the piston of area A by the pressure P when the weight G suspended from the arm is such that

$$GR = APr. \qquad (4.16)$$

The system is in equilibrium and the addition or subtraction of an "infinitely small" weight ΔG will cause the system to expand ($\Delta G < 0$) or to be compressed ($\Delta G > 0$) quasistatically. In the limit, when $\Delta G \to 0$ we encounter a set of conditions identical with those analyzed in Section 4.1 in connection with Figure 4.3. The principal feature

† See Planck, M., *Theory of Heat*, translated by L. Brose (Macmillan, 1932), p. 56.
‡ Keenan, J. H., *Thermodynamics* (Wiley, 1941), p. 8.

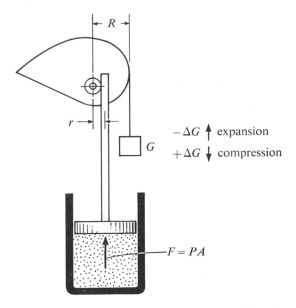

FIGURE 4.9. *Simple substance expanding behind a piston.*

of the process consists in the fact that the system, the contents of the cylinder, is always in equilibrium (like the mass m in Figure 4.3) even though we imagine that it expands or contracts, as the case may be. During an elementary process, when the piston moves upwards by a distance dx, the work performed by the system, in accordance with the definition given previously, is

$$dW = AP\,dx$$

which can also be written

$$dW = P\,dV, \qquad (4.17)$$

since $A\,dx = dV$. It is not stipulated that P must be constant, but it is clear that during a particular process there will exist a unique relation between the pressure P and the volume V of the system. Selecting the pressure P and the volume V as the independent variables, it is possible to represent the process in the diagram of Figure 4.10. The process begins at state 1, traverses a continuous sequence of equilibrium states and ends at state 2. Since the strip shown shaded in Figure 4.10 has an area equivalent to (4.17), the total work during the process is equal to the area $a12b$ under the curve which represents the process. The work is positive during process $1 \rightarrow 2$ but negative during the reverse process $2 \rightarrow 1$, and it is seen that the system can perform either of them equally well.

Not all processes will possess the idealized characteristics discussed above. For example, if the piston in Figure 4.9 were to move with friction, it would be possible to obtain mechanical equilibrium with values of ΔG different from zero. During the process, local temperature increases would be observed near the piston, and the system could not be in equilibrium at *every step* of the process. This suggests that there

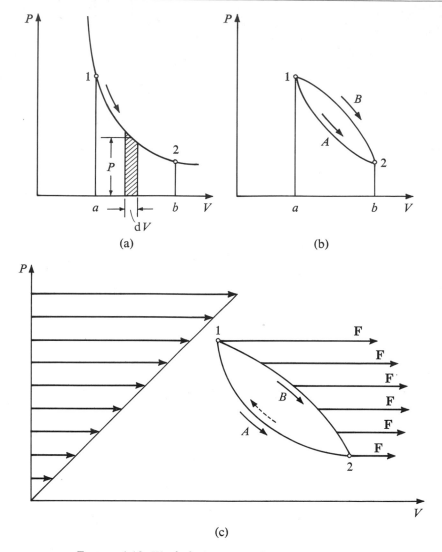

FIGURE 4.10. *Work during expansion or compression.*

exists a fundamental difference between the above two types of processes, and we shall recognize it, and discuss it in detail in Section 4.6. For the present it is sufficient to realize that the expression given in equation (4.17) applies to the idealized process, that is to a process which we shall learn to call *reversible*.

The expression in equation (4.17) is a very simple form of a Pfaffian, and its very simplicity causes difficulties in recognizing this fact. First, with reference to Figure 4.10(b), it is noticed that the quantity of work performed between states 1 and 2 depends on the details of the process. Considering two such processes, 1*A*2 and 1*B*2, it is evident that the work of the former is equal to area *a*1*A*2*b*, whereas that of the latter is *a*1*B*2*b*. These two areas are unequal, which confirms that the work in the case under consideration is not a property, since it depends on the path, 1*A*2 or 1*B*2, as the case may be. These paths are analogous to the curve C in the discussion of the line integral in Section 4.1. The mathematical nature of the expression in equation (4.17) can be clearly recognized if it is rewritten in the form

$$dW = P\,dV + 0\,dP$$

which shows that it is equivalent to the Pfaffian

$$dW = M(P, V)\,dV + N(P, V)\,dP$$

with the very simple substitutions

$$M(P, V) \equiv P,$$
$$N(P, V) \equiv 0.$$

The associated vector field is seen sketched in Figure 4.10(c); its component in the V direction, the factor of dV, is simply equal to P, and the other component is everywhere equal to zero. Thus the vector field $\mathbf{F}(P, 0)$ has the same appearance as the velocity field in pure shear or Couette flow.† It is now evident that the work in a process is given by the line integral

$$W_{1,2} = \int_1^2 P\,dV \qquad\qquad (4.17a)$$
$$\text{along curve } C$$

which depends on the path C of the process. It is instructive to verify that the vector field is rotational employing all the criteria given in Section 4.2. The integrability condition gives

$$\frac{\partial M}{\partial P} = \frac{\partial P}{\partial P} = 1 \quad \text{and} \quad \frac{\partial N}{\partial V} = \frac{\partial 0}{\partial V} = 0,$$
$$\text{curl } \mathbf{F} = -1 \neq 0,$$

and is not satisfied. Hence, it is seen that the integrals

$$\int_1^2 P\,dV \quad \text{and} \quad \int_1^2 P\,dV$$
$$\text{along } 1A2 \qquad\qquad \text{along } 1B2$$

are not equal, as shown previously, and the circular integral

$$\oint P\,dV \qquad \text{around} \quad 1A2B1$$

is different from zero since it is proportional to the area enclosed by the curve $1A2B1$. In the latter calculation it is imagined that the process $1B2$ is made to occur in the reverse order, so that the work is then negative and equal to the negative area $a1B2b$, Figure 4.10(b). This must be subtracted from the positive area $a1A2b$, and the result is the positive area $1A2B1$ as asserted previously. Thus, on all counts, the work $dW = P\,dV$ is not a property of the system.

The expression $dW = PdV$ is particularly simple owing to a felicitous, and so far accidental, choice of independent variables. If the variables θ, P had been chosen as

---

† See, for example, Schlichting, H., *Boundary Layer Theory*, translated by J. Kestin (4th ed.; McGraw-Hill, 1960), p. 67.

independent, the integrand $P \mathrm{d}V$ would be transformed to

$$\mathrm{d}W = P\left(\frac{\partial V}{\partial \theta}\right)_P \mathrm{d}\theta + P\left(\frac{\partial V}{\partial P}\right)_\theta \mathrm{d}P, \tag{4.18}$$

since

$$\mathrm{d}V = \left(\frac{\partial V}{\partial \theta}\right)_P \mathrm{d}\theta + \left(\frac{\partial V}{\partial P}\right)_\theta \mathrm{d}P.$$

Here its mathematical nature is more clearly perceived.

It is useful to introduce the coefficient of thermal expansion β and the isothermal compressibility κ from equations (3.16) and (3.18) into equation (4.18), when we obtain

$$\mathrm{d}W = \beta P V \, \mathrm{d}\theta - \kappa P V \, \mathrm{d}P. \tag{4.19}$$

Sometimes, particularly in liquids and solids the coefficients β and κ can be assumed constant and the change in volume can be neglected. When this is the case we obtain, approximately

$$W_{1,2} \approx \left\{ \beta V \int_{\theta_1}^{\theta_2} P \, \mathrm{d}\theta \right\} - \left\{ \tfrac{1}{2}\kappa V (P_2^2 - P_1^2) \right\}. \tag{4.19a}$$

It will be seen later that for many systems it will be possible to choose the variables in such a way as to obtain forms analogous to (4.17) rather than to (4.18). It is also noted that in the form (4.17) the factor P in $P \mathrm{d}V$ is an intensive property whereas the perfect differential $\mathrm{d}V$ is that of an extensive property.

4.5.2 *General compression or expansion*

In the case of a system of arbitrary shape, Figure 4.11, which undergoes a process consisting of a sequence of equilibrium states, that is, during which at every step the internal pressure P of the system is constantly balanced by an equal external pressure, the work in a step in the process can be calculated by a simple extension of the preceding equation (4.16). The force acting on an element $\mathrm{d}\sigma$ of the boundary of the system is

$$P \, \mathrm{d}\sigma.$$

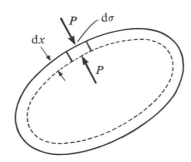

FIGURE 4.11. *General compression or expansion.*

The work performed by this force as the area $d\sigma$ recedes by a distance dx is

$$P \, d\sigma \, dx,$$

and the work for the whole system is

$$dW = \iint\limits_{\text{surface } \sigma} P \, d\sigma \, dx = P \iint\limits_{\text{surface } \sigma} d\sigma \, dx,$$

since during the process of integrating over the surface the pressure P remains unchanged. It is easy to verify that

$$\iint\limits_{\text{surface } \sigma} d\sigma \, dx = dV,$$

which is the change in volume represented by the volume enclosed between the full and broken curves in Figure 4.11. Hence, in this case too

$$dW = P \, dV. \tag{4.20}$$

It should be noted that in the derivation of equation (4.20), the tacit assumption was made that only normal forces, that is, pressures, act on the surface σ during the process, to the exclusion of tangential forces, that is, to the exclusion of shear.

4.6   Reversible, irreversible, and quasistatic processes

Before taking up the problem of calculating work for other systems, it is important to revert to the discussion of the distinction between the two processes, the ideal expansion, and the expansion with friction mentioned in Section 4.5.1. This will be done in an attempt to generalize their differences and to obtain a classification of processes which is essential to the study of thermodynamics. The distinction is a fundamental one, and forms the basis of an important generalization in thermodynamics, the Second Law introduced in Chapters 9 and 10.

The process of expansion or compression illustrated in Figure 4.9 was admittedly an idealized one. Strictly speaking, neither compression nor expansion could occur if the weight G exactly balanced the pressure on the piston through the ideal mechanism. However, by a stretch of imagination, it was accepted that a process, compression or expansion, as desired, could be performed "infinitely slowly" or, as is sometimes said, *quasistatically*. Moreover, when such a process was performed, the system remained in equilibrium at *every stage*; it consisted of a *continuous sequence of states of equilibrium*. An ideal process of this type is said to be *reversible*.

A reversible process can be easily represented in a state diagram, such as the P, V diagram of Figure 4.12. Since it consists of a continuous sequence of states of equilibrium, its geometrical image is a continuous curve, say curve a in the sketch. A reversible process will be represented by a continuous curve regardless of the number of independent variables which enter into its equation of state. During a reversible process from one equilibrium state, state 1, to another equilibrium state, state 2, to *every* point on the curve in the interval (1, 2) there corresponds *some* state assumed by the system. In fact, without using the term, several reversible processes or reversible cycles have been depicted on diagrams on the preceding pages of this book.

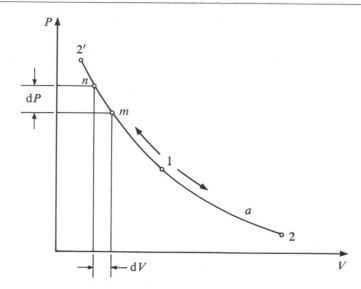

FIGURE 4.12. *Graphical representation of reversible process.*

When the system is in a given equilibrium state, for example state 1, and is so contained, or, as we shall say *constrained*, that it can perform reversible processes only, it is possible to cause it to traverse equilibrium states in *either* of the two directions, $1 \rightarrow 2$ or $1 \rightarrow 2'$. Moreover, the direction can be reversed at any stage of the process without the performance of additional work. All that is required is to add or subtract an "infinitely small" weight, that is, a weight ΔG which is *imagined* smaller than any quantity, however small. The ability to do so turns entirely on the characteristics of the ideal mechanism shown in Figure 4.9. The mechanism which makes it possible for a system to perform a reversible process will be different, depending on the nature of the system. For example, in order to charge or discharge an electric cell an ideal motor-generator will be required. The corresponding mechanism is shown sketched in Figure 4.13. The electric cell is imagined connected to an electric machine which can operate as an ideal motor or as an ideal generator, depending on the direction of rotation. In this manner, depending on whether a weight $\Delta G \rightarrow 0$ is added to or subtracted from G, the cell will discharge, performing work on the surroundings, or it will be charged and the weight G will perform work upon it.

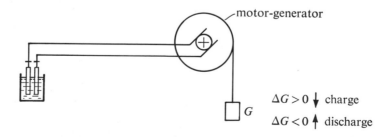

FIGURE 4.13. *Reversible process in electric cell.*

Another important characteristic of a reversible process can be discerned when the processes occurring in the surroundings of the system are also examined. When a system performs a reversible process $1 \to 2$, its state, as well as the state of the surroundings, change. Upon reversing the process, that is upon traversing the preceding sequence of states in the reverse order $2 \to 1$, the increments in the changes in the properties of the system will reverse their sign at each step. For example, when a gas is compressed during process $1 \to 2$, Figure 4.12, it will be expanded during the reverse process $2 \to 1$. Moreover, at any intermediate step, such as *mn* in the sketch, the corresponding increments dP and dV will retain their values, but will reverse their signs upon reversal. During the elementary process $m \to n$ the pressure increment is positive (d$P > 0$) whereas the corresponding volume increment is negative (d$V < 0$). During the reversed process $n \to m$ these increments will change their signs, but will retain the same absolute values for the same pairs of states, such as *m* and *n* in the present example. This will have the effect of changing the sign, but not the absolute value of the element of work

$$\mathrm{d}W = P\,\mathrm{d}V.$$

The same can be said about the process undergone by the surroundings; the reverse process is an exact "mirror image" of the forward process. Consequently, when a reversible process is reversed completely, the initial state of the system *as well as that of its immediate surroundings* will be completely restored.

Identical features can be discerned in the case of the electric cell shown in Figure 4.13.

Real processes are obviously different from the preceding idealization. Real processes occur at a finite speed, there is friction present, parts of the system undergo accelerations and so on. When the system is in an initial equilibrium state, it is not possible to start the process by the removal or addition of an infinitesimal weight ΔG only, but a finite change is required. The system can then be pictured constrained by the two pegs p_1 and p_2 shown in Figure 4.14. When this constraint is removed, an expansion or com-

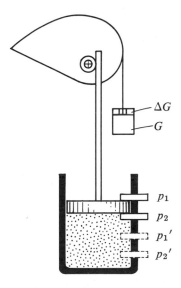

FIGURE 4.14. *Start of an irreversible process.*

pression will occur, depending on whether the finite weight ΔG has been added or subtracted. The process will occur at a finite rate, which may be slower or faster, depending on the magnitude of the weight ΔG, and will come to an end when the piston will meet another constraint, say when the pegs are reinserted at p_1' and p_2'.

As already mentioned, during the process the system will cease to be in equilibrium; temperature, pressure, and velocity differences will be observed, and it will no longer be possible to describe its state by indicating only two properties, its pressure and volume. Thus the initial state, state 1, Figure 4.15, can be represented by a point in the diagram, but the subsequent states cannot be so represented. When, at a later stage, the motion of the piston is arrested, the system will eventually assume another state of equilibrium, say state 2 in the sketch, which can once again be represented by a point in the diagram. Processes of this type are called *irreversible* in contrast with the reversible processes discussed earlier. It is clear that *all natural processes are irreversible* and that reversible processes constitute convenient idealizations only.

When the system under consideration performed an irreversible process, for example, the expansion $1 \rightarrow 2$ in Figure 4.15, it did so in a definite direction which, moreover, could not be changed while the process was in progress without profoundly altering its nature. Expansion could be obtained by reducing the weight by a finite amount ΔG, and an equilibrium state 2' could be attained ultimately. However, *during this process the direction could not have been reversed*, that is, the system could not have been made to follow the original path in the opposite direction.

Another instructive example of an irreversible process which occurs, like the preceding one, when a constraint (in the previous example the pegs) is removed is depicted in Figure 4.16. We can imagine a quantity of gas confined in volume V_1 at pressure P_1 in an adiabatic cylinder by means of a perfectly fitting slide S, there being a vacuum on the other side of it, Figure 4.16(a). The system is in equilibrium, and its state is represented by point 1 in the diagram of Figure 4.17. The slide is now removed, Figure 4.16(b), and since it is perfect, no work is required to do so. As soon as the slide is cracked open, the gas will rush into the evacuated space. Its motion will become complex, it may become highly turbulent, temperature and pressure differences will appear in it, and its state will no longer be described by two independent parameters. Eventually, the system will reach another state of equilibrium owing to the existence of the

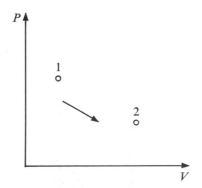

FIGURE 4.15. *Graphical representation of irreversible process.*

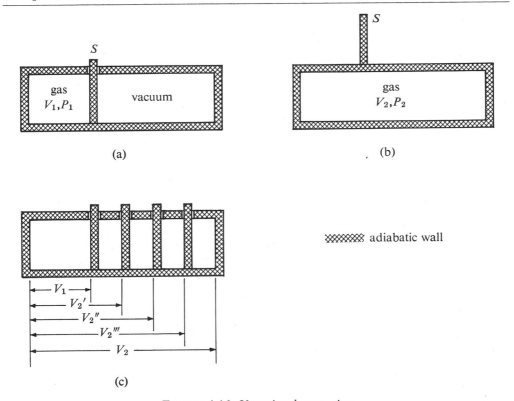

FIGURE 4.16. *Unresisted expansion.*

constraint provided by the chamber of volume V_2, and its state will now be described by the values P_2 and V_2 of the independent properties. Once again its state will be represented by a point, point 2 in the diagram. This process is known as unresisted adiabatic expansion, it being clear that no work has been done by or on the system, since the sole effect, external to the system, could not be the raising of a weight, be-

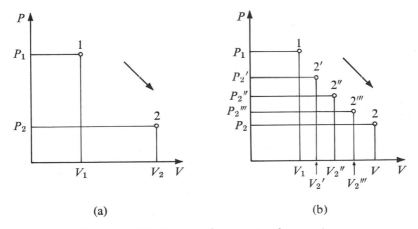

FIGURE 4.17. *Diagram for unresisted expansion.*

cause the cylinder is rigid, and so

$$W_{1,2} = 0. \tag{4.21}$$

We can summarize the characteristics of an irreversible process by listing them as follows:

(a) An irreversible process occurs at a finite rate.

(b) It proceeds in a definite direction.

(c) It is started from an equilibrium state as a consequence of the removal of a constraint, and ends by the system assuming an equilibrium state.

(d) The system is not in equilibrium during the process.

(e) It cannot be reversed without introducing changes in the immediate surroundings and in the constraints of the system.

The last characteristic requires some further comment, in that it must be emphasized that the term "irreversible" used to describe natural processes is somewhat misleading if its meaning is taken literally. When an irreversible process 1 → 2 has been performed, it is not implied that equilibrium state 1 can *never* be restored from equilibrium state 2. In fact, it must be assumed that it is *always* possible to achieve this through a suitable interaction with the surroundings. In the example of unresisted expansion, Figures 4.16(a), (b), the initial state of the system could be restored by replacing one end of the cylinder by a piston, that is by a scheme similar to the one sketched in Figure 4.9. At this stage the reader may not perceive that the initial state of the system can be restored completely by these means and feels intuitively that some additional interaction is necessary. This is, in fact, the case, as it would be necessary to extract heat in order to restore the initial state by this mechanism. However, since heat is a concept still unknown, we must defer the complete discussion of this point to Section 5.7. Nevertheless, it is clear that the process of restoring the initial state of the system does not constitute a simple reversal of a sequence of states, as was the case with reversible processes. In particular, the interactions with the surroundings are entirely different during the forward process and during the reverse process of restoring the original state of the system. Thus, when the initial state of the system is restored completely, the initial state of the surroundings is not restored simultaneously, in marked contrast with a reversible process.

The need for the stipulation that the initial state 1 can *always* be restored from state 2 which had previously been reached by an irreversible process is fundamental to the development of thermodynamics because only then is it possible to determine the properties of systems by measurements conducted prior to the performance of a process. Without the knowledge of properties, no process could be analyzed in quantitative terms. Not all systems encountered in nature possess this attribute. A notable exception is afforded by all living organisms. Superficially, living organisms perform an irreversible process during their life cycle, but in stating this we yield to the impulse of using the term "irreversible process" semantically, and not in its technical meaning appropriate in thermodynamics. For this reason, systems like biological ones cannot be analyzed in terms of the equations of thermodynamics† because no earlier state of such

† In modern times, the principles of thermodynamics are being applied in biology. The possibility of doing so rests on the acceptance of additional hypotheses. A detailed discussion of their nature would, however, exceed the scope of this course.

a system can ever be restored from a later state. Loosely speaking, one can say that a thermodynamic system possesses no "memory" or "history." A given state of the system is always described by its properties as they are measured at that state, and not by the details of the process which enabled the system to assume the state under consideration.

The process of unresisted, adiabatic expansion discussed in conjunction with Figure 4.16 could be subdivided into smaller and smaller steps by the provision of progressively more intermediate constraints in the form of ideal slides, as shown in Figure 4.16(c). In this manner the system could be made to assume the intermediate equilibrium states $2'$, $2''$, $2'''$, and so on, shown in the state diagram of Figure 4.17(b). It is noteworthy, however, that at each step, no matter how small, the system would exhibit the characteristic features of an irreversible process. The same can be said about the example with friction discussed in relation to Figure 4.14. The weight ΔG could be placed or removed in small steps, and the pegs could be replaced at intermediate positions, allowing the system to assume a number of intermediate equilibrium states. In this manner, the successive equilibrium states are made to differ from each other by progressively smaller amounts. In the example of the expansion against a piston, the process can be made slower and slower by the progressive reduction in the excess weight ΔG, and by a suitable spacing of the positions of the constraining pegs. As a result, the thermodynamic properties which characterize the successive states of equilibrium can be made to differ by less and less. By these means, the irreversible process may be made to occur "infinitely slowly," that is, quasistatically. Nevertheless, even in the limit, such a process would retain the essential features of an irreversible process. In particular, it would proceed in a definite direction, and a change in direction would not cause the system as well as its surroundings to traverse the same sequence of steps but in the opposite direction. In the example when the piston moved with friction, the local temperatures near the two rubbing surfaces would *increase* regardless of whether the gas were compressed or expanded. It should be realized that in the case of an irreversible process, even in the limit of a quasistatic process which can be traversed in both directions, the processes in the surroundings are not exactly reversed.

When a system performs a quasistatic irreversible process, it departs from exact equilibrium only slightly. It is then said to be in a *near-equilibrium* state. Under the circumstances, the image of the process can be *approximated* by a continuous line in a state diagram. It must, however, be noted that a point on such a diagram does not precisely represent the state of the system. It represents that state which would result if the process were arrested and the system were allowed to attain equilibrium adiabatically. For this reason, unlike a reversible process, the image curve in the state diagram does not constitute a continuous sequence of states of equilibrium; it can, however, be described as a continuous sequence of near-equilibrium states. In order to emphasize this circumstance, we shall follow the convention of representing quasistatic irreversible processes in state-diagrams by broken lines.

Thus for every irreversible process which occurs between two states of equilibrium 1 and 2, it is possible to provide two distinct idealizations. When the process is so idealized that all phenomena, such as friction and unresisted expansion which are inherently irreversible, are eliminated, the limit constitutes a reversible process. When the process is merely slowed down, the limit constitutes an irreversible, quasistatic process. It follows that all reversible processes are quasistatic, but that the converse is not true.†

The sketch in Figure 4.18(b) provides a pictorial representation of an irreversible process together with its two limits, a reversible process, Figure 4.18(a), and a quasistatic irreversible process, Figure 4.18(c).

The distinction between reversible and irreversible processes exemplified by the diagrams in Figure 4.18 impels us to re-examine the mathematical operations of differentiation and integration when they are applied to them. In passing to the mathematical limit, it is implied that two points, that is, two states of equilibrium, can be made to approach each other as closely as we please. This can be done for quasistatic processes only, but not for irreversible processes, because the latter consist of a *discrete* sequence of states of equilibrium. It follows that differential forms can be used only in relation to quasistatic processes. Irreversible processes must be described by expressions which do not contain differentials or their integrals. However, as we shall see in detail in the succeeding section, the physical interpretation of a differential form is not the same for quasistatic reversible, and for quasistatic irreversible processes.

The distinction between a reversible and an irreversible or natural process must always be made in terms of a definite, closed system. It is rather obvious that a change in the system used in a particular analysis may change the classification of the process. For example, if a gas is made slowly to expand against a frictionless piston which in turn actuates a friction brake, Figure 4.19, we shall say that the process is irreversible if the whole system is considered. The process undergone by the system consisting of the gas alone within boundary *B* can be idealized to a reversible one.

4.7   Quasistatic reversible, and irreversible compression and expansion

In order to gain a clear appreciation of the physical meaning of differential forms, it will be instructive to evaluate the work performed on a gas during compression or expansion in a cylinder when the process is conducted quasistatically, but irreversibly.

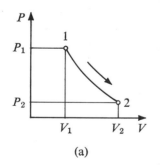
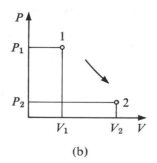
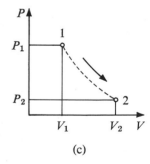

(a)   (b)   (c)

FIGURE 4.18. *Pictorial representation of processes.*
    (a) Reversible, and ipso facto quasistatic.
    (b) Irreversible.
    (c) Quasistatic, irreversible.

† In some textbooks on thermodynamics the term "quasistatic process" is used in a more restricted sense which makes it the equivalent of a reversible process. In this book the term is used more literally so that it means "nearly-static," that is, "very slow" or, in the limit, "infinitely slow."

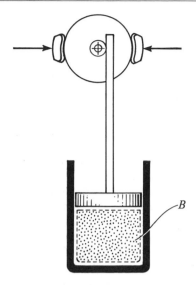

FIGURE 4.19. *Relation between the classification of a process and the choice of the system.*

Accordingly, we shall examine the counterpart of the system discussed in Section 4.5.1 in connection with Figure 4.9. In order to render the process irreversible, it is possible to visualize that the ideal piston is connected to a series of rods *f*, as shown in Figure 4.20, which move along the bushings *b* with considerable friction.

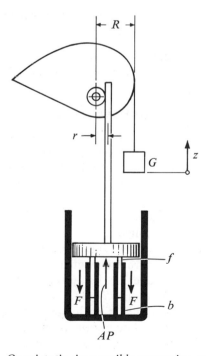

FIGURE 4.20. *Quasistatic, irreversible expansion or compression.*

In order to ensure that the process is quasistatic, the weight G must just balance the force AP on the piston and the sum F of all the friction forces exerted on the rods. Thus, the weight G will be different during compression and expansion, and equation (4.16) will be replaced by the two equations

$$GR = (AP + F)r \qquad \text{for compression,} \qquad (4.22a)$$

and

$$GR = (AP - F)r \qquad \text{for expansion.} \qquad (4.22b)$$

It follows, in marked contrast to the example of reversible expansion, that the work performed ceases to be equal to the integral of PdV. In order to see this more clearly, it is convenient to replace the expression GR/r by the equivalent, instantaneous external pressure P_{ext} which would provide an equal balancing force on the piston of area A. Consequently,

$$AP_{ext} = GR/r$$

and it is seen that

$$P_{ext} = P + F/A \qquad \text{for compression,}$$

and

$$P_{ext} = P - F/A \qquad \text{for expansion.}$$

Since the friction force F always opposes the motion, F is always positive, and it is noted that

$$\left. \begin{array}{ll} P_{ext} > P & \text{for compression, whereas} \\ P_{ext} < P & \text{for expansion.} \end{array} \right\} \qquad (4.23)$$

When the weight G is displaced by a distance dz performing positive or negative work Gdz, the volume of the system changes by dV, and the positive or negative work can be expressed as

$$dW = P_{ext}\, dV, \qquad (4.24)$$

and is no longer given by the expressions in equations (4.17) or (4.17a) in which the pressure P of the system appeared instead of the equivalent, instantaneous pressure P_{ext}. This is an essential difference, because the value of P_{ext} is not related to the state of the system and depends on the magnitude of the friction force, F in this example. In general, we can state it depends on the mode in which the quasistatic, irreversible process is performed. Even more importantly, it follows that the expression for work given in equation (4.24) no longer constitutes a Pfaffian form, because P_{ext} no longer represents a function of the independent properties of the system. In the case of the reversible process, the pressure P as well as the volume V could be regarded as functions of the independent variables of the system and were related to them mathematically through equations of state; they could, themselves, be chosen as independent variables. In the present example, this is no longer the case; the element of work is no longer a Pfaffian form, and its integration requires a knowledge of the relation between P_{ext} and V which cannot be acquired from an equation of state of the system, but must be derived from direct observation or from a knowledge of the details of the process. It is possible to express this difference by stating that in the irreversible case the work must be *measured* rather than *calculated*, because a knowledge of the properties of the system and of the sequence of states during the process is insufficient to determine the amount of work performed. Even if the appearance of equations (4.17) and (4.24) is superficially the same, their mathematical form, and, even more importantly, their relation to the equation of state of the system, that is their physical meaning, are different.

It is easy to see now that in an irreversible, quasistatic process

$$W_{1,2} = \int_1^2 P_{\text{ext}} \, \mathrm{d}V, \tag{4.24a}$$

and it is instructive to compare this expression with the integral

$$\int_1^2 P \mathrm{d}V$$

which would apply if the process were reversible; the latter can always be computed from a knowledge of the path of the process. It is convenient to introduce here the quantity

$$W_{\text{loss}} = \left| \int_1^2 \frac{F}{A} \, \mathrm{d}V \right|$$

which can be described as "work lost"; it is the work done against the forces of friction in the present example, but it may be due to other causes in other examples.

On comparing the actual work $W_{1,2}$ exchanged during the quasistatic, irreversible process with that which would be done in an equivalent reversible process, that is a reversible process which follows the same path, we can see that for compression

$$\left| \int_1^2 P_{\text{ext}} \, \mathrm{d}V \right| - \left| \int_1^2 P \mathrm{d}V \right| = W_{\text{loss}} > 0.$$

Since $\mathrm{d}V < 0$, both integrals are negative, and the equation expresses the fact that more work must be done *on the system* during an irreversible than during an equivalent reversible process. Similarly, for expansion, when $\mathrm{d}V > 0$,

$$\int_1^2 P \, \mathrm{d}V - \int_1^2 P_{\text{ext}} \, \mathrm{d}V = W_{\text{loss}} > 0.$$

Now, the work done by the system during an irreversible process turns out to be smaller than that which would be done by the system during an equivalent, reversible process. Both equations can be contracted to

$$W_{1,2} = \int_1^2 P \, \mathrm{d}V - W_{\text{loss}}; \qquad W_{\text{loss}} > 0. \tag{4.25}$$

The equation shows clearly that the work in a quasistatic, irreversible process is no longer equal to the area under the curve representing the process, or to the line integral taken along it in the vector field $\mathbf{F}(P, 0)$ discussed in Section 4.5.1.

The preceding calculations exhibit an important superiority of reversible processes over irreversible processes which will be discussed and studied more systematically in Chapters 9, 10 and 13 on the subject and consequences of the Second Law of thermodynamics. It will then be shown quite generally, in particular in Section 13.7, that an irreversible process is always inferior, from the practical point of view, to an equivalent reversible process: other things being equal, it produces less (positive) work, or requires more (negative) work, depending on whether work can be derived from it, or whether work must be supplied to perform it.

There is no difficulty in recognizing that the preceding equations apply to any volume change, and not only to changes produced by pistons, in complete analogy with the case of a reversible process discussed in Section 4.5.2.

In practical applications, the integral which appears in equation (4.24a) is important in two special cases, since in both the equivalent external pressure is given directly by the conditions of the process. In the first case, the vessel is rigid, and $P_{ext} = 0$, leading to

$$W_{1,2} = 0. \tag{4.24b}$$

This case is already familiar to the reader from the discussion of unresisted expansion in the preceding section. The second case of importance occurs when the equivalent external pressure is constant; it occurs, for example, when a cylinder operates in the atmosphere, or when a constant weight G is needed to balance it. Integration then yields

$$W_{1,2} = P_{ext} (V_2 - V_1) \qquad (P_{ext} = \text{const}). \tag{4.24c}$$

4.8 General form of expressions for work in other reversible and quasistatic processes

In order to establish expressions for reversible and quasistatic irreversible work for systems other than the one considered in Section 4.5, it is first necessary to study empirically their general characteristics, and to establish their equations of state; in particular, it is necessary to determine the number n of independent variables which uniquely define a state. This will be done more systematically in Chapters 7 and 8. It can, however, be stated at the outset that the reversible work can be represented by a single product of the form

$$dW = Y \, dZ \tag{4.26}$$

in the case of system with two independent variables. Here, Y is always an intensive property and Z is always an extensive property. The form of equation (4.26) is identical with that for the work $dW = PdV$, equation (4.20). It is also identical with that for the work performed by a force F as the latter is displaced by a distance dx in its own direction, namely

$$dW = F \, dx.$$

This similarity induces us to call all intensive properties Y which appear in the expression for elementary work by the common designation of *generalized forces*, whereas all extensive properties Z are known as *generalized displacements*. The generalized force and the generalized displacement which occur in a single expression for work in the form of equation (4.26) are termed *conjugate*. Thus the pressure P is a generalized force, whereas the volume V constitutes the respective conjugate (generalized) displacement.

When the number of independent variables exceeds $n = 2$, the elementary, reversible work turns out to be a sum of, say, ν terms of the form (4.26), namely,

$$dW = \sum_1^\nu Y_i \, dZ_i. \tag{4.26a}$$

The preceding generalization was first clearly recognized by C. Carathéodory in 1909; his main contributions to the study of thermodynamics will be discussed in Chapters 5 and 10.

In relation to quasistatic, irreversible processes which constitute sequences of near-equilibrium states, it is also possible to assert that the preceding forms for work remain unaltered, except that the generalized forces, and sometimes the generalized displacements, cease to have values which together with the other properties of the system satisfy the equation of state. An example of this type was given in equation (4.24).

The general statements given in this section are derived from experimental facts. In our case, so far, they have been based on the consideration of the properties of one type of system, a simple, homogeneous substance being compressed or expanded. As the subject is developed, and as more types of systems are taken into consideration, it will become progressively clearer that the above statements are, indeed, true. However, it seems useful to adduce at least one more example of a system and to show that its behavior follows the same general pattern. Accordingly, we shall consider a galvanic cell, first mentioned in Section 4.6, relying on the fact that its properties are sufficiently familiar to the student.

4.8.1   Work of a galvanic cell

Everyday experience with an automobile accumulator of electricity, commonly called a "battery," shows that its state is described by indicating its temperature θ and charge z. The charge z is usually, if somewhat crudely, determined by measuring the density ("specific gravity") of the electrolyte. Hence, the electromotive force or emf $\mathcal{E}$ of the accumulator is a unique function of temperature and charge,

$$\mathcal{E} = \mathcal{E}(\theta, z). \tag{4.27}$$

For example, in winter, when the temperature θ is low, even a fully charged accumulator shows strain on starting, because its emf, $\mathcal{E}$, is low. Similarly, the emf is low when the accumulator is "run down," that is, when its electric charge z is reduced.

An accumulator will persist in equilibrium when its emf is exactly balanced by a potentiometer, Figure 4.21. The potentiometer can then be used to determine the "open-circuit" emf $\mathcal{E}$ of the accumulator, as is well known. When the emf of the potentiometer is increased or decreased by an amount $\Delta\mathcal{E}$, electricity is made to flow into or out of the accumulator, in the same way as the volume of the system in Figure 4.9 could be made to change, thus starting a process by the addition or a subtraction of a weight ΔG. In the limit when $\Delta\mathcal{E} \to 0$, and in complete analogy with the limit $\Delta G \to 0$ for Figure 4.9, we shall say that the accumulator is charged or discharged *reversibly*. During such a process, as was shown in detail in Section 4.6 in connection with Figure 4.13, work is done by or on the system. During the process of discharge when $dz < 0$, the accumulator performs work on its surroundings. In the opposite

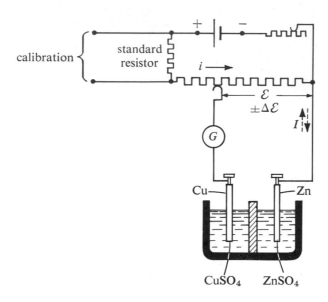

FIGURE 4.21. *Accumulator in equilibrium.*

process of charging, $dz > 0$, and work is done upon the accumulator by the immediate surroundings—the potentiometer circuit. The reader should satisfy himself that either of these processes possesses all the five characteristics of a reversible process listed on pages 127 to 129.

A transfer of electricity in an amount dz per time dt is described as the flow of an electric current of intensity

$$I = \frac{dz}{dt}.$$

The student will well know that a current flowing as a result of a potential difference $\mathcal{E}$ performs work at the rate

$$\dot{W} = \mathcal{E}I.$$

Since $\dot{W} = dW/dt$ and $I = dz/dt$, we can easily show that the reversible work of charging or discharging an accumulator is

$$dW = -\mathcal{E}\,dz. \tag{4.28}$$

The negative sign has been added to satisfy the convention that $dz > 0$ implies *negative work*, that is, work done on the system, whereas $dz < 0$ implies *positive work*, that is, work done by the system. Thus, in the case of an accumulator, or any galvanic cell, the reversible work dW has the general form (4.26) valid for systems with two independent variables. The emf $\mathcal{E}$ is independent of the mass of the system and constitutes an intensive property—the generalized force for a galvanic cell. The charge z is evidently an extensive property; it plays the part of the conjugate generalized displacement.

When an accumulator is charged or discharged, the excess emf $\Delta\mathcal{E}$ must have a finite value, and close observation shows that the temperature throughout the electrodes and electrolyte ceases to be exactly uniform in this case. This is analogous to the local changes in temperature produced by friction in the case of compression or expansion against a piston. Even when the excess emf $\Delta\mathcal{E}$ and the electric current I are very small, the system is not in exact thermal equilibrium. However, under suitable conditions the departures from equilibrium are small in the same way as was the case with the system depicted in Figure 4.20. The system traverses a sequence of near-equilibrium states and performs a quasistatic but irreversible process. The process which is analogous to friction in the case of compression and which causes departures from the idealized case of complete reversibility is colloquially described by the statement that the charging or discharging of an accumulator involves dissipation through the evolution of "Joule heat," and is due to the fact that an accumulator possesses a finite internal electric resistance R.

In order to understand the process more clearly, we can assume that an ideal accumulator has been connected to a resistor R in a manner sketched in Figure 4.22. In actual fact the resistance R is not separated from the accumulator but distributed throughout it. The flow of a current I causes a voltage drop $\Delta\mathcal{E}$ to appear across this hypothetical resistance R, and its magnitude is $\Delta\mathcal{E} = RI$. Thus, during charging, the external emf, $\mathcal{E}_{ext}$, exceeds the ideal emf $\mathcal{E}$ which would be measured in the limit $I \to 0$ by an amount RI. Similarly, during discharging, the opposing emf, $\mathcal{E}_{ext}$, would become smaller than $\mathcal{E}$ by the same amount. In analogy with (4.23), we can state that

$$\left.\begin{array}{ll} \mathcal{E}_{ext} > \mathcal{E} & \text{for charging } (W < 0) \\ \mathcal{E}_{ext} < \mathcal{E} & \text{for discharging } (W > 0) \end{array}\right\} \tag{4.29}$$

so that

$$\mathcal{E}_{ext} = \mathcal{E} + RI \qquad \text{for charging} \qquad (dz > 0),$$

whereas

$$\mathcal{E}_{ext} = \mathcal{E} - RI \qquad \text{for discharging} \qquad (dz < 0).$$

We observe once again that the work performed during the process can be written

$$dW = -\mathcal{E}_{ext}\, dz, \tag{4.30}$$

but that now $\mathcal{E}_{ext}$ is not linked to the properties θ and z by the equation of state of the accumulator.

Pursuing the analogy with the example discussed in Section 4.7, we can write

$$W_{1,2} = -\int_1^2 \mathcal{E}_{ext}\, dz, \tag{4.30a}$$

noting that

$$W_{1,2} \neq -\int_1^2 \mathcal{E}\, dz.$$

Furthermore, the work lost is

$$W_{loss} = \pm\left|\int_1^2 RI\, dz\right|$$

and

$$\left\{-\int_1^2 \mathcal{E}\ \mathrm{d}z\right\} - \left\{-\int_1^2 \mathcal{E}_{\mathrm{ext}}\ \mathrm{d}z\right\} = W_{\mathrm{loss}} > 0. \qquad (4.31)$$

The reversible work $-\int_1^2 \mathcal{E}\ \mathrm{d}z$ can be represented by an area in an $\mathcal{E}$, z diagram or by a line integral in the vector field associated with the Pfaffian $-\mathcal{E}\ \mathrm{d}z$. The same is not true with regard to the work $-\int_1^2 \mathcal{E}_{\mathrm{ext}}\ \mathrm{d}z$ in an equivalent, irreversible, quasistatic process.

When the external potentiometer from Figure 4.22 is so adjusted that the current I is not small, that is, when $\Delta\mathcal{E} = I\mathcal{R}$ is large, the accumulator will perform an irreversible process. The process of moving the slider from a position of equilibrium when $\mathcal{E} = \mathcal{E}_{\mathrm{ext}}$ to one in which $\mathcal{E}_{\mathrm{ext}} \gtrless \mathcal{E}$ is equivalent to the removal of a constraint and is analogous with the removal of the mechanical slide in Figure 4.16. The system now performs an irreversible process during which its state is far removed from equilibrium. The reader feels, however, that the new state of equilibrium reached by the system will not occur under conditions when the "open" emf $\mathcal{E}$ has again become equal to the external emf $\mathcal{E}_{\mathrm{ext}}$ owing to a suitable change in charge z. This is entirely due to the fact that in an accumulator the open emf, $\mathcal{E}$, is practically independent of the charge z and depends almost exclusively on the temperature θ. Thus, the new state of equilibrium in the case when $\mathcal{E}_{\mathrm{ext}}$ differs markedly from $\mathcal{E}$ involves some damage to the accumulator caused by too rapid a rate of charging or discharging. Nickel–iron (Ni–Fe) accumulators do not exhibit this unpleasant characteristic because in them the open emf $\mathcal{E}$ depends on the charge z to a much larger extent.

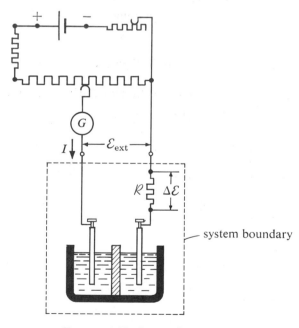

FIGURE 4.22. *Internal resistance.*

4.8.2   *Further remarks concerning reversible work*

It has been stated before that the reversible work in a simple system with two independent variables can be represented by a truncated Pfaffian, equation (4.26), in terms of a generalized force Y which is an intensive property and its conjugate generalized displacement Z which is an extensive property. It is easy to see that this is due to a judicious choice of variables, as already pointed out in Section 4.5.1. A simple change of variables would increase the number of terms to two. Since both quantities depend on the independent variables x_1, x_2 of the system, we may put

$$dZ = \left(\frac{\partial Z}{\partial x_1}\right)_{x_2} dx_1 + \left(\frac{\partial Z}{\partial x_2}\right)_{x_1} dx_2,$$

and

$$dW = X_1(x_1, x_2)dx_1 + X_2(x_1, x_2)dx_2,$$

where

$$X_1(x_1, x_2) = Y(x_1, x_2) \cdot \left(\frac{\partial Z}{\partial x_1}\right)_{x_2}$$

and

$$X_2(x_1, x_2) = Y(x_1, x_2) \cdot \left(\frac{\partial Z}{\partial x_2}\right)_{x_1}.$$

In developing the subject of thermodynamics it is often convenient and instructive to derive relations between the properties of a simple system of the type under consideration with reference to one particular system, most usually a simple chemical system. It should be clear that these relations can be immediately translated to apply to any system with two independent variables by substituting the new pair of conjugate force and displacement for the old pair.

Very often, more complex systems are obtained by coupling several simpler systems together, or even more simply, by including in one boundary several simpler systems. More complex systems can also appear when several processes of a different nature occur simultaneously in one system. For example, a rod of paramagnetic material may be simultaneously subjected to a variable axial force and a variable magnetic field. Very often, but not always, the element of work in the more complex case turns out to be the sum of the elements of work for the simpler processes assumed to occur independently of each other. When this is the case, it is said that *superposition* can be applied, otherwise, it is said that an *interaction* occurs. Whether or not superposition is admissible in any particular case must be known from experiment. In any case, the element of work for a system whose state is determined by n independent variables x_i will have the general form of equation (4.26a), that is,

$$dW = \sum_{1}^{n} X_i(x_i) \, dx_i, \tag{4.32}$$

where every function X_i depends, in principle, on all the n variables x_i. In special cases, that is, by virtue of a suitable choice of independent variables, the number of terms in equation (4.32) may be reduced to one which is smaller than n.

4.9   General remarks about the flow of work

The work performed by a system during a reversible process can be computed by observing the system itself, because all quantities in the expression for work can be expressed in terms of its state. In the general case this is impossible and the interaction between the system and its surroundings must be known in detail.

When various interactions are observed it becomes apparent that they can be divided into two classes: those that affect the system exclusively through its boundary and those that affect the whole of it. In mechanics, this distinction corresponds to the occurrence of surface forces in the first case and to the appearance of body forces in the second case. In the majority of phenomena which are studied in thermodynamics, only interactions which occur through the boundary need to be considered. Long range interactions are produced by various fields. The effect of a gravitational field was examined in a preliminary way in Section 4.1. It was then assumed that the field constituted a part of the system, and only the work of the external force acting through the boundary was taken into consideration. The effects caused by electrostatic and magnetic fields will be discussed in Sections 8.5.6 and 8.5.8. In all other cases we shall confine our attention to work transmitted through the boundary only. In this connection we shall use the graphic phrase that work "flows" through the boundary of the system. Furthermore, we shall be interested in three mechanisms whereby work is made to flow into or out of a system: (a) work associated with the deformation of the boundary, (b) work transmitted by a rotating shaft, and (c) electrical work.

4.9.1   Work associated with the deformation of a boundary

When the surroundings exert forces on a system, its boundary is deformed and work is transmitted. The force exerted per unit area of boundary is called stress, **T**, and in the general case the stress forms an angle α with the normal **n** to the element of surface dA, Figure 4.23. It is usually convenient to decompose the stress **T** into a normal component $\sigma = \mathbf{T}\cos\alpha$ and a tangential or shear component $\tau = \mathbf{T}\sin\alpha$. The negative of the normal component σ is called compression. Compression is related to pressure in a complex way which will be examined in Volume II. The work performed by a uniform

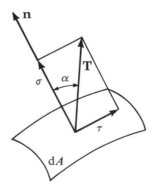

FIGURE 4.23. *Stress at a boundary.*

pressure P_{ext} has been calculated in Section 4.7, where it was shown that

$$dW = P_{ext}\, dV.$$

In reciprocating engines, work is performed by expanding gases against pistons performing reciprocating motions in cylinders. Consequently, such pistons move with varying velocities between the two dead centers, which very often reach magnitudes of the order of 50–60 ft/sec. Thus, the question arises as to how far such circumstances affect the expressions $dW = P\, dV$ or $dW = P_{ext}\, dV$ which are valid for reversible and irreversible quasistatic processes, respectively. In most cases, the accelerations and decelerations imparted to the piston can be disregarded, and under such conditions the force exerted by the piston on the surroundings is always equivalent to a pressure $P_{ext} = F/A$. If the piston moves with an instantaneous velocity $\mathcal{V}$, the instantaneous rate of performing work, or *power* is

$$\dot{W} = F\mathcal{V}$$

or

$$\dot{W} = AP_{ext}\, \mathcal{V}.$$

The rate of change of volume dV/dt, is then equal to $A\mathcal{V}$, and the preceding equation can be written

$$\dot{W} = \frac{dW}{dt} = P_{ext}\frac{dV}{dt}, \tag{4.33}$$

which is equivalent to $dW = P_{ext}\, dV$. In the case of a reversible process P_{ext} can be replaced by the cylinder pressure P, and the effect of velocity does not come into play when work is calculated.

Another complication arises from the fact that along the cylinder the pressure will change from the cylinder head to the fast-moving piston, a pressure gradient being created to match the velocity distribution in the gas, since the velocity of the latter varies from zero at the head to $\mathcal{V}$ at the piston. A detailed analysis of this process turns on the equations of fluid mechanics for continuous systems; the latter will be introduced in Section 6.1. At this stage it is possible to state[†] that even this complication has a negligible effect on the application of the preceding formulae for the calculation of work in engine cylinders. This is due to the fact that the element of work, dW, will always be equal to the product PdV, if P now denotes the pressure at the piston itself.

The contribution from the shearing stresses τ plays an important part in the study of elasticity and fluid mechanics. Owing to the complex nature of the resulting relations, the work is best expressed in terms of the components of the *stress tensor* $\boldsymbol{\sigma}$ and the *strain tensor* $\boldsymbol{\varepsilon}$ or the *rate-of-strain* tensor $\dot{\boldsymbol{\varepsilon}}$, but we shall defer the full discussion of this problem to Volume II.

4.9.2 Shaft work

Many engines encountered in practical applications produce or absorb power by the rotation of a shaft. When drawing the boundary of a system it may become necessary, or simply convenient, to include in it an imaginary cut through a shaft, Figure 4.24.

---

† See Kestin, J., and Glass, J. S. "Influence of high piston velocities on pressure distribution and piston work." *Aircraft Eng.*, **22** (1950) 163.

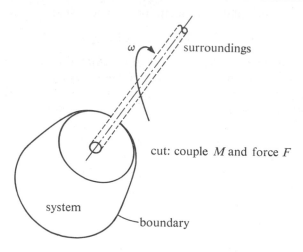

FIGURE 4.24. *Shaft work.*

Thus, the boundary will include a rotating area, the area of the shaft, over which there exists a distribution of shearing stresses τ. In general the vector sum of all these shearing stresses is equivalent to a couple M, and a transverse force F, but only the couple performs work since the force is not displaced. By the application of the principles of mechanics, or by the definition of work given in Section 4.2, it can be ascertained that in time dt, the shaft performs work

$$dW = M \, d\alpha,$$

where $d\alpha$ is the angle through which the shaft has turned during that time. Since $\dot{W} = dW/dt$ and $d\alpha/dt = \omega$ is the angular velocity, we have

$$\dot{W} = M\omega.$$

Frequently, the latter is given in terms of the rotational speed n in revolutions per minute (rpm), so that

$$\omega = \frac{2\pi n}{60},$$

and

$$\dot{W} = \frac{2\pi n M}{60}. \tag{4.34}$$

4.9.3   Electrical work

When the boundary of the system is pierced by wires carrying an electric current, work is performed, as was shown on the example of a galvanic cell in Section 4.8.1. The electrical work is calculated from a knowledge of the voltage $\mathcal{E}$ and the current I. When a steady, direct current performs work, we have

$$\dot{W} = \mathcal{E}I,$$

there being no difficulty in discerning whether the flux of power is positive or negative with respect to the system. In the case of an alternating current in which the voltage and current are out of phase by angle ϕ, we can write

$$\dot{W} = \overline{\mathcal{E}}\,\overline{I}\,\cos\phi,$$

where $\overline{\mathcal{E}}$ and $\overline{I}$ denote the rms values, as is well known from the elementary study of electricity. More complex cases need not be considered here since they are usually discussed in detail in courses on electricity.

List of Symbols for Chapter 4

Latin letters

A	Area
$\mathcal{E}$	Electromotive force
$\overline{\mathcal{E}}$	Electromotive force, rms value
F	Force
$\mathbf{F}$	Force vector
G	Weight
g	Gravitational acceleration
h	Linear displacement
I	Electric current
$\overline{I}$	Electric current, rms value
M	Function in Pfaffian expression; moment of couple
m	Mass
N	Function in Pfaffian expression
n	Number of revolutions per minute
P	Quantity defined in equation (4.5); pressure
Q	Quantity defined in equation (4.5)
R	Quantity defined in equation (4.5); radius, Figures 4.9 and 4.20
$\mathcal{R}$	Resistance
r	Radius, Figures 4.9 and 4.20
$\mathbf{R}$	Vector in Figure 4.5
$\mathbf{r}$	Radius vector
$\mathbf{T}$	Vector of stress
t	Time
u	Coordinate
v	Coordinate
V	Volume
$\mathcal{V}$	Velocity
W	Work
X_i	Function in Pfaffian expression, equation (4.12a)
x	Coordinate, displacement; independent variable
$\mathbf{x}$	Displacement vector
Y	Generalized force
y	Coordinate
Z	Generalized displacement
z	Coordinate; electric charge

Greek letters

α Angular displacement
β Coefficient of thermal expansion
Δ Increment of respective quantity
$\boldsymbol{\varepsilon}$ Strain tensor
θ Temperature, specifically when measured on empirical temperature scale
κ Isothermal compressibility
σ Surface in Figure 4.5
$\boldsymbol{\sigma}$ Stress tensor
τ Shearing stress
ϕ Phase angle
ω Angular velocity
ω_z Component of curl in z direction

CHAPTER 5

The First Law of Thermodynamics

5.1 General and historical remarks

Having provided precise definitions of the concepts of state, property, and work and having acquired some understanding of the distinction between reversible and irreversible processes, we are now in a position to formulate the first major generalization in thermodynamics, known as the *First Law* or *First Principle* of thermodynamics. The expression "formulate" is used here deliberately, because the First Law cannot be derived from simpler premises. Instead, limited experiments are interpreted in terms of the fundamental concepts just mentioned, their validity is extended to apply to all processes which occur under precisely the same conditions, and the result is in turn given an exact mathematical form. In order to achieve this final, mathematical formulation of the First Law, it will be found necessary to introduce two new concepts, those of the *energy of a system* which will prove to have the mathematical properties of a potential, and that of *heat* which will turn out to be a line integral for reversible processes, and thus analogous to work. Both heat and work will then be interpreted as two different forms of *energy in transition*, that is, two forms of energy exchanged between the system and its surroundings during a process.

In earlier days heat was thought of as a weightless fluid which could pass from one body to another. Joseph Black, a professor at Glasgow University, was one of the principal adherents to this theory. He introduced in 1760 the concept of specific heat — or the "capacity for heat fluid" to use his way of expression — and thus introduced a clear distinction between the concepts of temperature and quantity of heat which were previously often confused. The fact that heat is a form of energy was, however, perceived by some of his contemporaries.

Considerable support for this latter view was supplied by Count Rumford of Munich (the former Benjamin Thompson) in 1798. When boring cannon barrels, he found that it was possible to create any quantity of heat from mechanical work by means of friction. In spite of the convincing character of these experiments, the belief that heat was a material fluid survived for another fifty years.

The equivalence of heat and mechanical energy was lucidly formulated for the first time by a physician from Heilbronn, Robert Mayer. He also calculated the conversion factor of heat and mechanical energy, the mechanical equivalent of heat, from the experimental values of specific heats, at constant pressure and constant volume, supplied by Gay-Lussac. How little the time was ripe for such a discovery can be seen from the fact that the famous editor Poggendorf refused to publish Mayer's paper in the *Annalen der Physik*. It only appeared in 1842, when Liebig accepted it for the *Annalen der Chemie und Pharmazie*.

James Prescott Joule determined the value of the mechanical equivalent of heat in 1843, having had no previous knowledge of Mayer's work. He carried out the experiment which will form the basis of our generalization. For many years, well into the twentieth century, the result of Joule's fundamental experiment was only imperfectly understood and explained. In our exposition we shall adopt the interpretation put on it by M. Born and his co-worker C. Carathéodory in 1909.†

5.2 Joule's experiment

Joule contained a quantity of water in a rigid cylinder, Figure 5.1, which was insulated adiabatically from its surroundings. The cylinder was provided with a paddle wheel driven by a weight G traveling through a height h. The thermometer shown in the sketch of Figure 5.1 served to determine the initial as well as the final state of the system, the pressure P_a remaining constant and equal to atmospheric during the process. Thus, the state of the system, conceived as the cylinder with its contents, but without the weight, as shown, was changed by performing work upon it *adiabatically*. It was then observed that given an initial state described by temperature θ_1 and pressure P_a, a given amount of work $W_{ad} = Gh$ performed adiabatically always produced the same final state, described by temperature θ_2 and pressure P_a. Similar experiments with somewhat different arrangements have been performed later by Joule himself and by many other investigators. In some, the weight was replaced by an electric motor, and the electrical work performed on the system was determined by measuring the product $\mathcal{E}It$ of potential difference, $\mathcal{E}$, current, I, and time, t. Yet another arrangement,

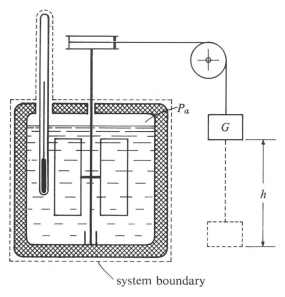

FIGURE 5.1. *Joule's experiment.*

† In his *Natural Philosophy of Cause and Chance* (Oxford: Clarendon Press, 1949), M. Born states on p. 38: "I discussed the problem [the unsatisfactory exposition of thermodynamics prevalent at the time] with my mathematical friend, Carathéodory, with the result that he analyzed it and produced a much more satisfactory solution."

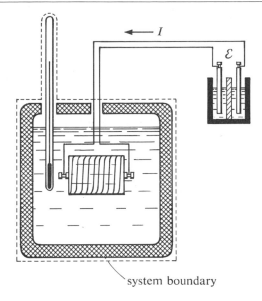

FIGURE 5.2. *Joule's experiment performed with the aid of an immersion heater.*

shown in Figure 5.2, consisted of an immersion heater supplied with an electric current which thus performed the work $W_{\mathrm{ad}} = \mathcal{E}It$ during the adiabatic process under consideration directly. Conversely, if the initial and final state of the system were to be prescribed, it would be found that the amount of work performed on it adiabatically to produce such a change of state would be independent of the details of the process.

5.3 Primary formulation of the First Law of thermodynamics for closed systems

It is clear from the preceding description that each of the different variants of Joule's experiment involves an irreversible process which occurs between an initial and a final state of equilibrium in a closed system. The process, in each case, occurs when some constraint is removed, such as, for example, the slide shown in Figure 4.16. When the paddle wheel churns the water, whether driven by the weight or by the electric motor, or when the water is heated by the immersion heater, the system ceases to be in equilibrium. The pressure and shearing forces exerted by the paddle wheel on the water establish temperature, pressure, and velocity gradients throughout the system, and during the time when the process occurs, the state of the system cannot be described by indicating the values of the two variables which are sufficient for the description of its state in equilibrium. Furthermore, it is easy to observe that given an initial state, it is possible to reach only such final states as are described by a temperature θ_2 which exceeds the initial temperature θ_1, it being impossible *adiabatically* to reduce the temperature, that is, to render $\theta_2 < \theta_1$, and so to raise the weight or to cause the electric current to flow against the potential difference $\mathcal{E}$. Thus, the processes have all the characteristics of an irreversible process described in Section 4.6. State 2 *can* be reached from state 1, but state 1 *cannot* be reached from state 2 in an adiabatic process, that is, one involving the performance of work only. State 1 can, however, be reached from state 2 by an entirely different sequence of processes, brought about with the aid of such other types of interactions as take place through diathermal walls.

We shall now center our attention on two features of such processes, and assert that they are present in all irreversible adiabatic processes, in any system, however complex.

> First,   *Given two arbitrary states of equilibrium 1 and 2 of any **closed***
> *   **system**, it is either possible to reach state 2 from state 1 or state 1*
> *   from state 2, but not both, by an adiabatic process involving the*
> *   performance of work only.*
>
> Secondly,   *The work performed is independent of the details of the process.*

These two assertions will provide the basis for our formulation of the First Law of thermodynamics, and we shall, thus, regard the above as its primary formulation. However, as far as the first assertion is concerned, we shall, at present, concentrate on the fact that between two given states 1, 2 *it is possible* to perform one irreversible process. The fact that one of the two directions $1 \rightarrow 2$ or $2 \rightarrow 1$ *cannot* occur adiabatically will provide the basis of the formulation of another bold generalization of thermodynamics — its Second Law. In particular, the statement will be amplified and conclusions will be drawn from it in Chapters 9 and 10.

5.4   Mathematical formulation of the First law of thermodynamics for closed systems. Energy of a system

In order to translate the verbal statement of the First Law of thermodynamics given in the preceding section into precise, mathematical terms, we shall attempt to classify all states 2 which can be reached from a given state 1 of a system, according to the amount of adiabatic work W_{ad} required during the respective processes $1 \rightarrow 2$. As a result, as will be seen presently, it will prove possible to define a particular potential for each system which will be given the designation of the *energy* of the system. We shall perform this classification in relation to a gas, because the required measurements, and the details of the processes involved, are simple to describe. We shall assert that analogous procedures can be adopted for any closed system whatsoever.

Accordingly, we imagine a gas enclosed in a compartment of volume V_1, at pressure P_1, and at a temperature θ_1 whose value is determined by the equation of state $\theta(P, V)$, as shown in Figure 5.3(a). The cylinder enclosing the gas is adiabatic and its total volume is V_2. The remainder of the cylinder (of volume $V_2 - V_1$) is evacuated, and provided with a series of ideal slides, the arrangement being familiar to the reader from Figure 4.16(c) in Section 4.6. By removing the slides one-by-one it is possible to reach a series of states of equilibrium $2'$, $2''$, $2'''$, ... , characterized by the volumes V_2', V_2'', . . . , without performing any work at all. This series of states can be represented in the form of the series of discrete points in the state-diagram P, V shown in Figure 5.3(b). The volume V_2 can be chosen larger and larger, and the experiment can be continued as long as desired even if, as will become clear in Section 7.4, the gas will either liquefy or solidify, eventually. It is noticed that all states $2'$, $2''$, $2'''$, ... , 2 have one feature in common, namely that they can all be reached from state 1 adiabatically without the need to perform work. Since the volume increments can be chosen, at least in

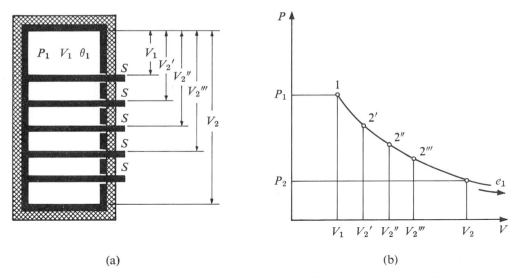

FIGURE 5.3. *States 2 which can be reached from state 1 adiabatically without the performance work.*

principle, as small as we please, it is clear that all final points 2 will trace some locus, shown as curve e_1, in Figure 4.15(b).

In order to vary state 1, we can imagine that the top of the cylinder has been replaced by a piston and a mechanism suitable for the performance of reversible adiabatic work, as shown in Figure 5.4(a). By performing varying positive or negative amounts of adiabatic and reversible work W_{ad}, it is possible to reach a continuum of states 1, shown as states 1_1, 1_2, 1_3, and then, by removing the slides S, it is possible to determine all states $2_1'$, $2_1''$, ..., $2_2'$, $2_2''$, ..., which have the property that they can be reached from the respective states 1_1, 1_2, 1_3, 1_4, ... without the performance of any additional work. In this manner it will prove possible to trace the loci e_2', e_2'', e_2''', e_2'''', and so on in Figure 5.4(b). The latter have the property that they can be reached from state 1 by an irreversible process,† for example, $1 \to 1_1 \to 2_1'$, at the expense of a predetermined amount of positive or negative adiabatic work W_{ad}. The statement of the First Law made previously provides the assurance that any state 2, for example, $2_3'''$ or $2_2''$, first, can be reached from state 1 directly, and not necessarily in the manner described, and secondly, that the adiabatic work required for the process is the same as before. Thus, all states of the system have been classified according to the results of such irreversible experiments into a continuous family of loci e_1, e_2', e_2'', and so on.

Just as was the case with the isotherms in Section 2.4, it is possible, and very useful, to say that all states along one locus e have a common property, and to designate this property as the *energy of the closed system*. The respective locus is usually referred to as an *isoenergetic*. At this stage, the term "energy" is accepted only provisionally, because its use would not be justified unless it can be shown that the new concept is identical with that known as energy in mechanics. To accept the term under any other conditions would lead to confusion.

---

† It is clear that a process consisting of a reversible portion followed by an irreversible portion is irreversible.

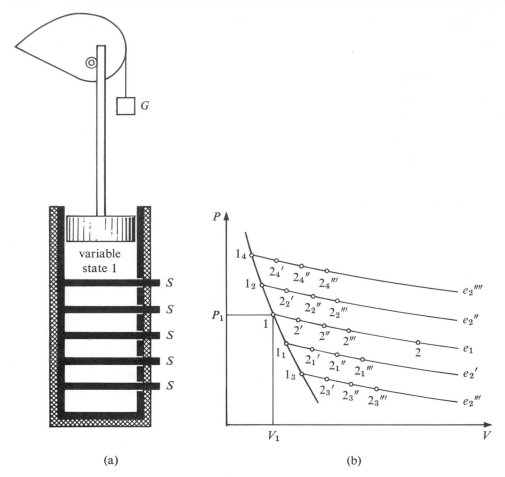

FIGURE 5.4. *Tracing loci of equal adiabatic work.*

Carrying the analogy with temperature one step further, it is clearly perceived that it is necessary to provide a conventional measure for the energy of the system, and that this can be done in relation to the adiabatic work, since the adiabatic work needed to reach all states on one isoenergetic which *can* be reached from all the states on another isoenergetic is a constant. When this is done, it is clear that the family of isoenergetics will define a *potential* for which the symbol E will be used. Thus the difference in the potentials between *any* two states 1 and 2 will be equal to the adiabatic work W_{ad} required to reach state 2 from state 1 or state 1 from state 2, whichever is applicable. In actual fact, for reasons of convenience, this difference is set equal to the *negative* of the work W_{ad}, and we shall write

$$E_2 - E_1 = -W_{ad}. \tag{5.1}$$

This convention corresponds to our intuitive understanding of energy, and leads to the statement that upon performing adiabatic work on a system ($W_{ad} < 0$), the energy of the system is increased ($E_2 > E_1$), and conversely, when the system performs work adiabatically on its surroundings ($W_{ad} > 0$), its energy is thereby decreased ($E_2 < E_1$). It is emphasized that this statement is a consequence of the sign convention embodied in equation (5.1).

Once a potential E has been introduced, and its *existence* demonstrated, the manner in which this has been achieved becomes of secondary importance only, since a value of the potential can now be associated with any *state of the system*. Consequently, if a reversible process is considered, the change in energy dE during an "infinitesimal" step in the process will become a *perfect differential*. More precisely, since the energy of a system can be expressed in terms of the independent variables in the form of an equation of state, for example,

$$E = E(P, V),$$ (5.2)

we can write

$$dE = \left(\frac{\partial E}{\partial P}\right)_V dP + \left(\frac{\partial E}{\partial V}\right)_P dV,$$ (5.2a)

and the line integral

$$\int_1^2 dE = \int_1^2 \left\{ \left(\frac{\partial E}{\partial P}\right)_V dP + \left(\frac{\partial E}{\partial V}\right)_P dV \right\} = E(P_2, V_2) - E(P_1, V_1)$$ (5.2b)

becomes equal to the difference in the values of the potential at the end points, regardless of whether state 2 has been reached from state 1 by a reversible or by an irreversible process, adiabatically or in any other manner, and regardless of whether $E_2 > E_1$, or $E_2 < E_1$. It follows that for any cycle, reversible or irreversible, the total change in energy is zero, and in particular, for a reversible cycle

$$\oint dE = 0.$$ (5.2c)
$$\text{any curve } C$$

It must be stressed that the verbal statements of the First Law adduced in Section 5.3 are valid for closed systems only, hence, the mathematical consequences derived from them are equally restricted in their validity to closed systems.

It is instructive to try to visualize the manner in which some of the states 2 other than the states along the isoenergetic e_1, displayed in Figure 5.4(b), can be reached from the initial state 1 directly. This can be done most easily by the scheme shown in Figure 5.5 in which additional work W'_{ad} is performed on the system by a paddle wheel, similar to the one employed by Joule. By allowing the weight G to rise or to fall and by adding a suitable amount of work W'_{ad} it is possible to reach any of the states 2 from state 1. Alternatively, the piston itself may be provided with an appropriate amount of friction. In the first case, the additional work W'_{ad} is always positive. The addition of friction has the effect of either decreasing the positive work $W_{ad} = Gh$ done by the system on the weight, or of increasing the absolute value of the negative work done on the system by the weight G for a given change in volume. The preceding remarks constitute, evidently, results of observations and are made here in preparation for the time when we shall revert to this topic in connection with the formulation of the Second Law of thermodynamics in Chapter 9.

It might appear to the reader that the experimental evidence cited so far in support of the primary formulation of the First Law of thermodynamics is meager and uncon-

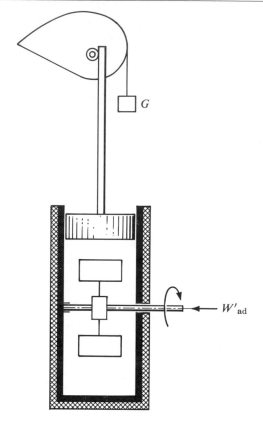

FIGURE 5.5. *Reaching states 2 from state 1 directly.*

vincing. This, actually, must be conceded. Furthermore, it is interesting to note that no systematic, precise experiments to verify this generalization directly have ever been attempted. Such measurements would prove extremely taxing, if at all possible, even only in view of the very large number of types of systems one would have to consider. Rather, the generalizations should at this stage be treated as plausible hypotheses, or postulates, whose truth or falsity will later be tested by comparing conclusions drawn from them with experimental facts. Indeed, no conclusions have ever been derived from the First Law which could be contradicted by experiment. Thus, the truth of our hypotheses is accepted by inference. The belief in the truth of the First Law is now so strong in science that any experiment contradicting it would itself be questioned. Although not absolutely excluded, contradictory experiments are highly unlikely. On reflection, it will be seen that all great generalizations in physics, Newton's laws of motion, Maxwell's equations of electromagnetic theory, relativity, and so on are accepted in a similar way, that is, on circumstantial evidence. Incidentally, it should be clear that the theory of relativity introduces a constraint on the formulation of the First Law of thermodynamics without "abolishing" it, the constraint being that the observer and system must not move with respect to each other with a velocity comparable to that of light.

It might appear strange to the reader that equation (5.2c) was not written down immediately on the strength of the fact that "adiabatic work is independent of the path." If we were to *define*

$$dE = -dW_{ad},\qquad(5.3)$$

it would seem that the preceding statement leads to

$$\oint dW_{ad} = 0,\qquad(5.3a)$$

and hence to

$$\oint dE = 0.\qquad(5.3b)$$

Although the conclusion in equation (5.3b) is perfectly correct, it would have been arrived at on the strength of an unsound line of reasoning. It will be remembered from Section 4.3 that the vanishing of the circular integral of a Pfaffian expression for some special curves C does not prove that the Pfaffian is a perfect differential. The circular path implied in equation (5.3a) is a special one, in that only adiabatic cycles are admitted. Secondly, a Pfaffian expression for work can only be written for reversible or at least quasistatic processes, and it is not at all clear that a reversible adiabatic cycle can always be devised. In fact, as further study will reveal, reversible adiabatic cycles can only be devised for systems with more than two independent variables. Furthermore, it is not always possible to link an arbitrarily prescribed pair of states of a system, say 1 and 2, by a *reversible* adiabatic process, whether $1 \to 2$ or $2 \to 1$. This particular fact is intrinsically linked with the Second Law of thermodynamics.

There is no difficulty in realizing that for more complex systems the isoenergetics will become hypersurfaces of $n - 1$ dimensions, in the manner of all potentials. For example, they will be surfaces for systems with three independent variables.

5.5   The nature of energy

In thinking about energy we are instinctively inclined to regard it as a kind of weightless fluid whose total quantity is preserved when different systems are made to interact with each other or to perform work one upon another. Such a view is only partly consistent with physical facts. Actually, a large portion of the picture conjured in the imagination by the above feeling is false, and, being contradicted by what we already know about energy, may on occasion become conducive to grave errors. It is, therefore, necessary to re-examine the concept of the energy of a system in this light.

The concept of energy is connected with *two different states of a single closed system* and a numerical value can only be ascribed to the difference $E_2 - E_1$ between the energies in the two states, because only this difference, or its negative, can be measured by means of an adiabatic, irreversible process. In the day-to-day working with this concept it is convenient to select one arbitrary state, known as a *reference state*, for every system and to assign an arbitrary absolute value E_0 to the energy of the system at that state. It is customary, but not necessary, to assume that $E_0 = 0$, for ease of handling. In this manner, an absolute, but conventional value of energy is assigned to any other state

$$E = E_0 + \Delta E, \tag{5.4}$$

where

$$\Delta E = -W_{ad}. \tag{5.5}$$

Here, the symbol ΔE denotes the energy difference $E - E_0$, and W_{ad} or $-W_{ad}$ is the adiabatic work performed along any of the irreversible paths which can be used to join the arbitrary state to the reference state. Exceptionally, this path can be a reversible one. This has the advantage of conferring upon energy the mathematical characteristics of a property. Conventions of this kind are adopted in all sets of tables used in practical calculations, such as, for example, in the Steam Tables, Tables IX to XII or the Gas Tables, Table XVI. In the case of homogeneous systems it is evidently more convenient to tabulate the *specific energy*

$$e = e_0 + \Delta e \tag{5.6}$$

or the equivalent molar energy, by putting

$$\frac{E}{e} = \frac{E_0}{e_0} = \frac{\Delta E}{\Delta e} = m \quad \text{or} \quad = n. \tag{5.7}$$

It is clear that the energy of a system is an extensive property, because the adiabatic work W_{ad} for a homogeneous closed system is proportional to its mass, as is known from experiment.

It is natural to attempt to compare the energy of a homogeneous system with that of a portion of it. Suppose that the mass of the system is m and that we wish to compare its energy with that of a subsystem of mass m'. One might write down the difference in the energies

$$E - E' = me - m'e, \tag{5.8}$$

since the specific properties of a subsystem of a homogeneous system have the same values as those of the whole system. In doing so one would have yielded to the impulse of treating energy as a weightless fluid which fills the system and a portion of which is contained in the subsystem. A moment's reflection should convince us that no physical meaning can be attached to such an operation. In the first place, we have assigned absolute values to individual states only by an artifice, and the symbols E, E', e, e' in equation (5.8) actually refer to *two* states, the arbitrary state with no subscript, and the reference state with subscript $_0$. Hence, in view of equation (5.6), equation (5.8) is really equivalent to

$$E - E' = (m - m')e_0 + (m - m')\Delta e. \tag{5.9}$$

In this expression, the term $(m - m')\Delta e$ represents a measurable physical quantity — the difference between the adiabatic work needed to bring system m from an arbitrary state to a reference state or vice versa, and that required to do the same with system m'. The first term, however, namely the term $(m - m')e_0$, does not represent a real physical quantity. Since e_0 is arbitrary, we can assign to it any value we please, and so the difference $E - E'$ will acquire any value we please, and cannot be the result of any measurement. We conclude, therefore, that no physical meaning can be attached to the difference between the energies of two *different* systems, even if the two systems merely represent different masses of the same homogeneous substance. The idea that energy can be likened to a weightless mass permeating uniformly a homogeneous system has led us astray.[†]

It is interesting to note, however, that the energy ratio E/E' for a system of mass m and a subsystem of mass m' composed by the same homogeneous substance and considered between two states which are identical with respect to intensive and specific properties, does possess physical significance. Indeed

$$\frac{E}{E'} = \frac{m(e_0 + \Delta e)}{m'(e_0 + \Delta e)} = \frac{m}{m'},$$

on condition that the arbitrary constant E_0' for system m' is chosen to be proportional to E_0, namely $E_0 = me_0$ and $E_0' = m'e_0$.

The reader can easily verify that the same argument applies to the concept of potential energy in mechanics, Figure 5.6. Assigning an arbitrary value e_0 to the potential energy of a unit mass at an arbitrary reference level, we write

$$E = E_0 + mgz \qquad E' = E_0' + m'gz,$$

whence

$$\frac{E}{E'} = \frac{m}{m'} \qquad \text{if } E_0 = me_0 \quad \text{and} \quad E_0' = m'e_0,$$

but the difference

$$E - E' = (m - m')e_0 + (m - m')gz$$

can assume any value which we please to assign to it, and so is devoid of physical meaning. It should be clear to the reader that the same can be said about any potential.

The preceding argument provides the justification for the stress laid in this book on the distinction between a property and a pseudoproperty, like energy, which consti-

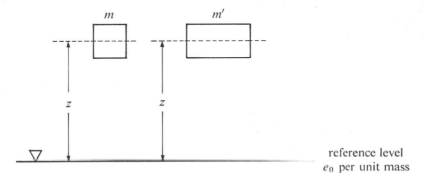

FIGURE 5.6. *Potential energy in mechanics.*

[†] It is remarkable that even so great a physicist as Arnold Sommerfeld yielded to this impulse in Vol. V of his monumental *Lectures on Theoretical Physics.* See Sommerfeld, A., *Thermodynamics and Statistical Mechanics*, translated by J. Kestin (Academic Press, 1956), Solution to Problem 1.2 on p. 356.

tutes a potential. The distinction is not very important as long as all processes studied are discussed in terms of closed systems only, since then, so to say automatically, only different states of a single system are ever considered. Under such circumstances the arbitrary constant E_0 will always cancel, because only *differences* in energy will occur. However, in modern times, and in this book, it is found convenient to analyze many problems in terms of open systems. When this is done, due care must be exercised not to fall into the trap again, as will be pointed out once more in Section 6.13.

We conclude our remarks on the nature of energy by pointing out that occasionally two apparently different systems do form two states of a single system, and one can properly inquire as to the difference in the energies between them. This occurs in the case of systems which undergo chemical, or, for that matter, nuclear reactions. For example, two units of mass of hydrogen (H_2) and sixteen units of mass of oxygen (O_2) mixed together on the one hand, and eighteen units of mass of steam (H_2O) on the other, constitute two different states of a single system. When a mixture of oxygen and hydrogen in the above proportions is enclosed in a rigid adiabatic bomb at temperature θ_1 and pressure P_1 and is ignited, the contents will transform explosively and irreversibly into an equal mass of steam at temperature θ_2 and pressure P_2 which can be determined by experiment. Since the adiabatic work involved in this process is zero, we come to the conclusion that the difference in energy between 18 units of mass of steam at P_2, θ_2 and a stoichiometric mixture of oxygen and hydrogen of equal mass at P_1, θ_1 is zero. The two energies are equal but they are different at the same values of pressure and temperature. We shall discuss this point again in Section 6.13.2, and we shall learn to calculate this energy difference in Volume II. The same can be said about the reactants and products in any chemical reaction.

5.6   Justification for the use of the term "energy." Internal energy

When the definition of the concept of the energy of a system was discussed in Section 5.4, it was pointed out that the term "energy" given to this new concept would have to be justified by an argument that it represented an extension of the concept used in other branches of physics, notably in mechanics. That this is so must not be assumed without further consideration, otherwise, the terminology in thermodynamics might conflict with that in mechanics, electromagnetic theory, and so on and would be devoid of the precision essential to it.

We shall now show, as was the case with the concept of work in Chapter 4, that the thermodynamic concept of energy is a natural extension of that in mechanics, and that it includes it as a special case, leaving it to the reader to do the same for the other branches of physics. In order to calculate the change in the potential energy of a mass m raised very slowly, that is, reversibly, in a uniform gravitational field of strength g, it is necessary to calculate the adiabatic work done on the system, Figure 5.7. The process is adiabatic, and the work is

$$dW_{ad} = -mg \, dz,$$

the negative sign appearing owing to the fact that the force $F = mg$, external to our system, performs work on it. Thus,

$$dE = mg \, dz \qquad (5.10)$$

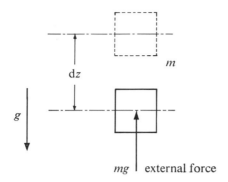

FIGURE 5.7. *Potential energy in mechanics.*

and the energy increases as the mass is lifted, in accordance with the usual convention. Since the more general concept of potential energy in mechanics constitutes a consistent elaboration of the preceding simple concept, it is evident that potential energy in mechanics is a special case of the thermodynamic concept of energy.

The same can be done for kinetic energy, Figure 5.8. Considering a mass m moving along a straight line with velocity $\mathcal{V}$ and being accelerated by an external force $F = m\,d\mathcal{V}/dt$, we can calculate the adiabatic work dW_{ad} required to change the velocity by an amount $d\mathcal{V}$, for which a distance $\mathcal{V}dt$ is required. This is

$$dW_{ad} = -m\frac{d\mathcal{V}}{dt}\mathcal{V}\,dt = -m\mathcal{V}\,d\mathcal{V}.$$

Consequently, the change in energy is

$$dE = m\mathcal{V}\,d\mathcal{V} = d(\tfrac{1}{2}\,m\mathcal{V}^2). \tag{5.11}$$

Once again, an increase in energy ($dE > 0$) is associated with an increase in velocity ($d\mathcal{V} > 0$) and an increase in the quantity $\tfrac{1}{2}m\mathcal{V}^2$, known in mechanics as the kinetic energy of the mass. The concept of kinetic energy for more complex systems performing more complex motions constitutes a generalization of the preceding elementary concept which changes nothing in our line of reasoning. Kinetic energy, too, proves to be a special case of the energy of a system. The arbitrary constant which arises from the integration of equation (5.11) is usually suppressed in that it is assumed that at $\mathcal{V} = 0$, that is, with respect to the chosen system of coordinates, the energy $E_0 = 0$. The fact that in the preceding two examples the change in potential or kinetic energy was cal-

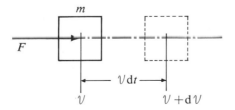

FIGURE 5.8. *Kinetic energy in mechanics.*

culated by means of reversible processes, the slow raising of a weight in a gravitational field or the acceleration of a mass in a conservative field of forces, need not disturb us here. Once the potential E has been defined, and once its existence has been ascertained, there is no objection to calculating it along a reversible path if the two states in question happen to be such that a reversible adiabatic path joining them *can* be found. Thus, with reference to Figure 5.4(b) we could have written

$$dE = -dW_{ad}$$

for any step along the reversible adiabatic path $1 \rightarrow 1_4$ or $1 \rightarrow 1_3$.

The object in any thermodynamic analysis is to provide an accurate description of some process or phenomenon. The state of the system is described in terms of parameters which change during the process, there being no point in including those which remain constant. For example, when we discuss a reversible expansion or compression of a given mass of a gas, we shall exclude its velocity V and its elevation z in a gravitational field, if these quantities remain constant or if the effect of changing them is negligible. However, if they change and if the change produces important effects, we shall include them, and the same will apply to parameters describing a possible electrical field, magnetic field, and so on.

In general, the change in the energy of a system between two states will depend on all independent *properties* of the system. However, it is clear that in many cases the change in energy will be simply the sum of the changes each due to a particular phenomenon. For example, if we consider a simple chemical system at rest which is subjected to a process as a result of which its state is changed from P_1, θ_1 to P_2, θ_2, it will undergo a change in energy which we shall denote by

$$E_2 - E_1 = U_2 - U_1. \tag{5.12}$$

If in addition the system is accelerated and changes its velocity from V_1 to V_2 and is displaced in a gravitational field of strength g from elevation z_1 to z_2 the total change in energy will become

$$E_2 - E_1 = (U_2 - U_1) + (\tfrac{1}{2}mV_2^2 - \tfrac{1}{2}mV_1^2) + (mgz_2 - mgz_1). \tag{5.13}$$

Equation (5.13) can be written as a result of experience, because it is known that in most cases accelerating the system (not too violently) and lifting it (extremely slowly and over a reasonable height) in a gravitational field will not change its pressure and temperature. When this is the case, we say that the different processes are superimposed on and do not interact with each other, or that the processes are *not coupled*. Whether processes in any particular case do or do not interact must be decided with reference to experiment, but when it is established that no coupling exists, the change in energy can be represented as a sum of changes, each associated with a single process. In cases like this it is customary, and convenient, to coin a name for each term. The energy associated with processes occurring in simple systems at rest, at a constant elevation, in the absence of electric or magnetic fields, and in the absence of surface tension or capillary effects and so on, is given the name of *internal energy U*. The other possible terms are given their usual names of kinetic, potential, electrical, . . . energy. Using appropriate subscripts, we can write for any process

$$\Delta E = \Delta U + \Delta E_{kin} + \Delta E_{pot} + \Delta E_{el} + \cdots \tag{5.14}$$

or for reversible and irreversible quasistatic processes

$$dE = dU + dE_{kin} + dE_{pot} + dE_{el} + \cdots , \tag{5.14a}$$

on condition that the processes are not coupled.

The term *internal energy* is not always exclusively reserved for processes occurring in simple chemical systems involving changes in volume, pressure and temperature together with changes of phase or chemical reactions. In the case of the electrical cell discussed in Sections 4.6 and 4.8.1, it is often customary to apply the designation "internal energy" to the potential $E(\mathcal{E}, \theta)$. Hence, the term is not unambiguous.

5.7   The First Law for nonadiabatic processes in closed systems.
The concept of heat

From the consideration of adiabatic processes, we now turn to processes taking place within diathermal walls. During the former, the system is prevented from interacting with its surroundings other than by a flow of work. Observation teaches that in the absence of adiabatic walls, the interaction between a system and its surroundings becomes more complex. As a consequence, the simple relation expressed in equation (5.1) ceases to apply.

We can assume that the energy differences $E - E_0$ between all possible states of all possible systems and suitably chosen reference states have been measured by measuring adiabatic work. If now measurements are performed on such systems under conditions when the processes are *not* adiabatic, it will be found that the work $W_{1,2}$ will no longer be equal to the change in energy $E_2 - E_1$. Thus, we must write

$$W_{1,2} \neq E_1 - E_2 \tag{5.15}$$

for any process, or

$$dW \neq -dE \tag{5.16}$$

for quasistatic processes.

Observation shows that this is the case, for example, when a system at a temperature θ is allowed to interact with surroundings at a different temperature θ'. Even if no work is performed ($W_{1,2} = 0$ or $dW = 0$), it is found that the state of the system changes. An interaction of this type is called the *transfer of heat*. More precisely, the algebraic differences

$$Q_{1,2} = (E_2 - E_1) - (-W_{1,2})$$

and

$$dQ = dE - (-dW) \tag{5.17}$$

will be called the *quantities of heat transferred during the respective processes*. The reasons for choosing the above differences rather than their negatives $(-W_{1,2}) - (E_2 - E_1)$ or $(-dW) - (dE)$ are purely conventional and of the same nature as the arbitrary designation of work done *by* a system as positive, or as the designation of *negative* adiabatic work as the *increase* in energy. In each of these cases we could have accepted the opposite convention with equal justification.

The definition in equation (5.17) undoubtedly appears arbitrary, or *formal*, to the reader, as indeed it is at this stage. Actually, no objection can be raised against the definition itself, at most one might take exception to the name "heat" given to this quantity on the ground that the term is reserved for another, "known" concept. As far as our exposition of thermodynamics is concerned, the term is not "known," as it has appeared for the first time in a precise form. It is true that human beings have an intuitive understanding of the concept of heat and that this concept is based on everyday experience. In this the position is similar to that which existed with respect to temperature before the reader studied Chapter 2. At first, a formal definition of the concept was given and later it was shown, but certainly not *proved*, that the formal concept agreed with the intuitive one, being superior to it in precision and rigor. We shall follow the same path with the new concept of *heat*.

Equations (5.17), written

$$Q_{1,2} = E_2 - E_1 + W_{1,2} \tag{5.18}$$

for any process performed by a closed system, or

$$dQ = dE + dW \tag{5.18a}$$

for a reversible or irreversible, quasistatic process performed by a closed system, constitute a generalization of the First Law of thermodynamics to include all processes performed between some initial and some final state of equilibrium: in the case of reversible processes, every state is one of equilibrium, and in the case of irreversible quasistatic processes, a sequence of near-equilibrium states is implied. The equations certainly provide a definition of heat, but they are more than merely definitions. They express the fact, already known and adequately discussed, that the energy difference $E_2 - E_1$ is independent of the details of the process or that dE is a perfect differential. It has been shown in Chapter 4 that work $W_{1,2}$ does not possess that characteristic and that dW is an imperfect differential. If we now consider any process $1 \rightarrow 2$, we find in equation (5.18) that one term $W_{1,2}$ does, but another term $E_2 - E_1$, does not depend upon the details of the process. Similarly, in equation (5.18a) one term, dE, is, but another, dW, is not a perfect differential. It follows that the third, balancing, term $Q_{1,2}$ must depend on the details of the process and that dQ is not a perfect differential for a reversible process. This distinction constitutes an important physical truth which transcends the fact that $Q_{1,2}$ and dQ have been introduced to balance the equations.

Equations (5.18) and (5.18a) constitute operational definitions of heat and indicate that heat is measured in a process by measuring the work $W_{1,2}$ performed during the process under consideration and by measuring the adiabatic work $W_{ad} = E_1 - E_2$ or $-W_{ad} = E_2 - E_1$ during *another* process, namely during an adiabatic process between the same states.

5.8 Justification of the use of the term "heat"; equivalence with intuitive concept of heat

It has been mentioned in the preceding section that an exchange of heat produces a change in state in the absence of work; this is certainly one of the intuitive characteristics ascribed to the everyday concept of heat. Secondly, the *addition of heat* to the system ($Q_{1,2} > 0$; $dQ > 0$) in the absence of work, causes the energy of the system to increase ($E_2 > E_1$; $dE > 0$) which is also one of the attributes normally ascribed to heat.

The final justification can best be provided by considering the following *calorimetric* experiment. When two systems are allowed to interact without performing work in an adiabatic enclosure, we expect the total quantity of *heat* to be *conserved*, meaning that the positive quantity of heat gained by one system should exactly balance the quantity of negative heat given up by the other.

The experiment is illustrated in Figure 5.9 in which the two systems A and B, enclosed in an adiabatic container are separated by an adiabatic slide, state 1. The slide is withdrawn, and both systems are allowed to reach equilibrium, state 2. Initially, the temperatures $\theta_1^{(A)}$ and $\theta_1^{(B)}$ were different, but ultimately $\theta_2^{(A)} = \theta_2^{(B)}$. By means which have already been discussed, we have measured the energy differences

$$-W_{\mathrm{ad}}^{(A)} = E_2^{(A)} - E_1^{(A)} \quad \text{and} \quad -W_{\mathrm{ad}}^{(B)} = E_2^{(B)} - E_1^{(B)},$$

both corresponding to the adiabatic work which would be necessary to effect the changes of state. It is known from experiment that if, say, $\theta_1^{(A)} > \theta_1^{(B)}$, then the natural process $1 \rightarrow 2$ for system B would be irreversible, and the change in state could just as well have been produced by the performance of stirring or electrical work. In the case of system A, the process $1 \rightarrow 2$ could not be performed adiabatically, but the opposite process $2 \rightarrow 1$ could, again by the performance of stirring or electrical work. This is due to the fact that

$$\theta_1^{(A)} > \theta_2^{(A)} = \theta_2^{(B)} > \theta_1^{(B)}.$$

By applying equation (5.18) to the process $1 \rightarrow 2$ for systems A and B *separately*, we obtain

$$\left. \begin{aligned} Q_{1,2}^{(A)} &= E_2^{(A)} - E_1^{(A)} = -W_{\mathrm{ad}}^{(A)}, \\ Q_{1,2}^{(B)} &= E_2^{(B)} - E_1^{(B)} = -W_{\mathrm{ad}}^{(B)}. \end{aligned} \right\} \tag{5.19}$$

Work being additive, it is clear that energies are additive and that, consequently,

$$Q_{1,2}^{(A)} + Q_{1,2}^{(B)} = (E_2^{(A)} - E_1^{(A)}) + (E_2^{(B)} - E_1^{(B)}) = -(W_{\mathrm{ad}}^{(A)} + W_{\mathrm{ad}}^{(B)}). \tag{5.20}$$

Applying equation (5.18) to the *combined* system $A + B$, we find

$$Q_{1,2} = W_{1,2} = 0.$$

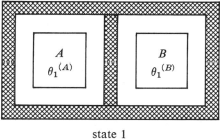

state 1

state 2

FIGURE 5.9. *Calorimetric experiment.*

This proves that the right-hand side of equation (5.20) vanishes or that

$$Q_{1,2}^{(A)} + Q_{1,2}^{(B)} = 0, \tag{5.20a}$$

which we have set out to demonstrate. More explicitly, we find that

$$Q_{1,2}^{(A)} = -Q_{1,2}^{(B)}. \tag{5.20b}$$

Thus, the new concept has all the normal, but admittedly vague, attributes associated with our intuitive understanding of "heat."

5.9   Principle of energy conservation. Isolated system

We emphasize that heat, like work, is not a characteristic of the state of the system, and the colloquial phrase "a body contains much (or little) heat" is meaningless. Equally, a statement that the "heat content" of a body, or system has changed during a process is devoid of meaning. The *energy* of the system *has changed* because this change (or difference) is independent of the details of the process. Heat, like work, can be said to constitute *an exchange of energy* ("energy in transition" in many textbooks) and the quantity of heat *exchanged* (transferred or transmitted) is associated with a process between two equilibrium states, it being dependent on all details of the process as well as on the end states.

If the preceding terminology is adopted, and if all terms are employed in their exact meanings, it is possible to state that the First Law of thermodynamics contained in equations (5.18) and (5.18a) expresses the *principle of energy conservation*. The *change* in the energy of a system during any process whatsoever is exactly balanced by the energy *exchanged* with the surroundings in the form of *heat transferred to* the system and in the form of *work done by* the system.

The preceding statement provides a justification for the three sign conventions regarding heat, work, and energy, adopted in thermodynamics and illustrated in Figure 5.10.

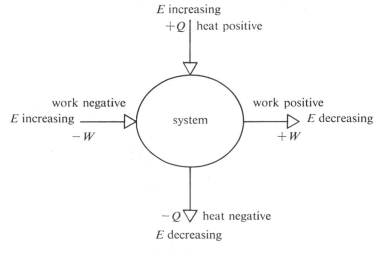

FIGURE 5.10. *Sign conventions.*

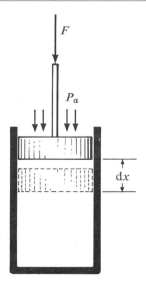

FIGURE 5.11. *Work of the atmosphere.*

A system which exchanges neither heat nor work with its surroundings is often referred to as an *isolated system*. During any process in such a system $Q_{1,2} = W_{1,2} = 0$. Consequently,

$$E_2 = E_1 \qquad\qquad (5.21)$$

for any process, or

$$dE = 0 \qquad\qquad (5.21a)$$

for a reversible or an irreversible quasistatic process. These equations contain an alternative expression of the *principle of energy conservation:*

> *The energy in an isolated system is conserved*

during any process whatsoever. If it increases in any part of the isolated system, it must decrease by an equal amount in another.

In practice, as has been pointed out earlier in Section 1.4, any system taken together with its immediate surroundings can often be regarded as an isolated system. In this connection, however, it must be remembered that if the system changes its volume during a process, the boundary of the immediate surroundings can be chosen far enough from it to allow us to neglect the transfer of heat across it, but a change in the volume of the system will cause this boundary to deform. In such cases the system with its immediate surrounding does not constitute an isolated system. For example, when a piston is forced into a cylinder compressing a gas contained in it, Figure 5.11, the total amount of work done on the system will be

$$dW = -F\,dx - P_a\,dV. \qquad\qquad (5.22)$$

where P_a is the "atmospheric" pressure (not necessarily equal to 1 atm) in the immediate surroundings. Irrespectively of how far the boundary is selected, it will deform to provide this work, known as the *work of the atmosphere*. If it is assumed that $P_a = $ const, then

$$P_a \, dV = d(P_a V).$$

The general term PV, first encountered in Section 4.7, plays an important part in the operation of some devices, such as reciprocating engines, pneumatic shock-absorbers and so on, and is frequently unappreciated by the beginner. It will play an essential part in the derivation of the expression of the First Law for open systems. Thus, we can establish the rule that any system combined with its immediate surroundings constitutes an adiabatic system. When the system itself is rigid, then the system together with its immediate surroundings constitutes an isolated system. A deforming system immersed in an atmosphere can be transformed into an isolated system together with its immediate surrounding by the device shown illustrated in Figure 5.12. The atmosphere can be imagined removed, and replaced by a cam mechanism raising weight G and exerting an equivalent pressure on the system through the piston. When this is done, $P_a = 0$ and $d(P_a V) = 0$. Thus, the system becomes isolated on condition that the weight G is included with it. In this manner, work done on or by the original system will appear as a change in the potential energy of weight G.

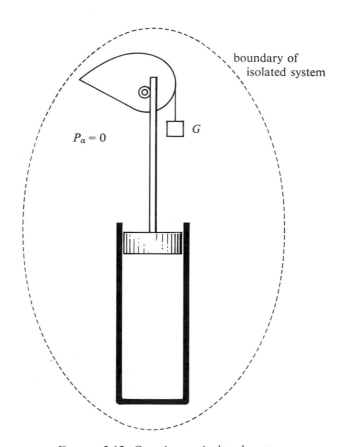

boundary of
isolated system

$P_a = 0$

G

FIGURE 5.12. *Creating an isolated system.*

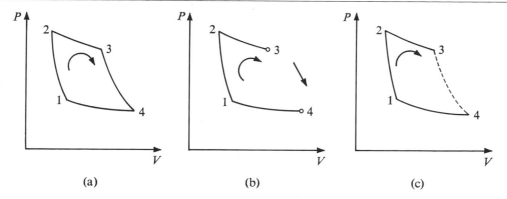

FIGURE 5.13. *Cycles. (a) Reversible cycle. (b) Process 3–4 is irreversible.*
(c) Process 3–4 is quasistatic and irreversible.

The preceding method of transforming a deformable system together with its immediate surroundings into an isolated system rests on the implied assumption that the
work $P_a\,dV$ is transferred wholly to the system. In other words, the change in the state
of the surroundings produced by the deformation of the boundary of the system is
neglected.

In connection with the enunciation of the principle of energy conservation, just as
on p. 23, the reader must contain his impulse to consider the "whole universe" as
an isolated system and to state the First Law of thermodynamics in the sweeping form
that the *energy of the universe is constant*. In order to give a precise meaning to such a
statement it would be necessary to analyze in detail the nature of our universe, a task
which transcends the resources of present-day science. Otherwise, the assertion
becomes a mere emotional, oratorical exclamation.

5.10   Conservation of energy in a cycle.
Perpetual motion engine of the first kind

In the preceding section we have enunciated the principle of energy conservation
for any process. Among the many processes studied in thermodynamics, the *cycle*,
first introduced in Section 4.2, plays a crucial part, particularly in its application to
engineering problems. It will be recalled that a cycle is a sequence of processes, reversible or irreversible, which restores the system to its initial state of equilibrium. If
the cycle is reversible, it can be represented by a closed curve in a state diagram. The
curve will be continuous, but it need not possess a continuously turning tangent, as
shown in Figure 5.13. Many cycles considered in thermodynamics are of this latter
type.

In the case of a reversible cycle, it is instructive to take line integrals of all the terms
in equation (5.18a) around the closed path in the sense indicated. The fact that the
path may have discontinuous derivatives has no influence on the mathematical process
of computing the circular integrals.

In this manner we obtain

$$\oint_C dQ = \oint_C dE + \oint_C dW. \tag{5.23}$$

However, since energy is a potential, the circular integral of energy vanishes, and equation (5.23) can be simplified to

$$\oint_C dQ = \oint_C dW.$$ (5.23a)

Equation (5.23) expresses the fact that *the algebraic sum of all quantities of work, positive and negative, performed around a reversible cycle is equal to the algebraic sum of all the quantities of heat* exchanged around the cycle.

When the cycle is irreversible, or when it contains irreversible segments, equation (5.18) yields

$$Q = W,$$ (5.24)

since $E_1 = E_2$ for a cycle. In equation (5.24) the subscript 1, 2 has been dropped in recognition of the fact that now states 1 and 2 are identical. If we put

$$Q = \oint_C dQ, \qquad W = \oint_C dW,$$ (5.25)

equation (5.23a) will reduce to equation (5.24), as it obviously should, since equation (5.18) applies to any cycle whatsoever.

It is clear that in the summation implied in equations (5.25) some terms will be positive and some negative, and an *algebraic sum* is implied. Very often it is convenient to add all positive quantities and all negative quantities of heat separately. We shall denote these by Q^+ for the sum of the positive quantities and by Q^- for the negative quantities, respectively. Furthermore, in order to attain flexibility of notation, we shall consider that the symbol Q^- is taken to represent the numerical value together with its sign, and we shall introduce the symbol $|Q^-|$ for the absolute (positive) value of Q^-. In this notation equation (5.24) can be written

$$Q^+ + Q^- = W$$

or, more conveniently,

$$Q^+ - |Q^-| = W$$ (5.26)

in order to display the negative character of Q^-. This notation is justified on the ground that in cycles which produce work, that is, in cycles for which $W > 0$ so that $Q^+ > |Q^-|$, the positive quantity of heat Q^+ must be supplied at some expense in fuel and so on, whereas the negative quantity of heat $-|Q^-|$ is simply rejected to the atmosphere at no cost. A similar distinction for work is not found necessary. It is clear that the same distinction can be introduced in the case of irreversible cycles, and that then equation (5.26) still applies, except that Q^+, Q^- and W must be *measured*. They cannot be calculated, as for a reversible cycle, when the process is prescribed.

A fictitious machine which would produce work continuously or periodically *without some other form of energy disappearing simultaneously* is called a *perpetual motion engine of the first kind*. A perpetual motion engine of the first kind, or, for that matter, any machine which could convert heat into work continuously or periodically, must operate on a cycle. If it did not, its state would change continually, and this could not go on indefinitely; it would be necessary to arrest it when its state were to reach an impracticable condition. The First Law, expressed in its form (5.24) or (5.26) asserts that

A perpetual motion engine of the first kind is impossible.

The following cases can be discerned. First, $W > 0$, when $Q > 0$, and work is done at the expense of heat. Secondly, $Q = 0$, and $W = 0$, which means that either no work is performed, or else, that a positive quantity of work is performed by the engine with an equal (negative) quantity of work being performed on the engine. In any case, a perpetual motion engine of the first kind cannot be constructed.

Equation (5.24) suggests that it might be possible to supply a quantity of heat Q to a system performing a cycle and to convert it *all* into work. Unfortunately this is impossible, but in order to understand the reasons for it, it will be necessary to study the Second Law of thermodynamics, Chapters 9 and 10.

In many engineering applications, work is performed solely by the expansion and compression of a fluid, the *working fluid*, contained in a cylinder provided with a piston, the processes, at least in *idealized engines*, being reversible. Such a cycle is represented in Figure 5.14, the curve 1*a*2*b* enclosing a finite area. The work $dW = P\,dV$ along an element of curve is represented by the shaded strip. It is either supplied by the system to the surroundings or absorbed by it, depending on whether $dV > 0$ or $dV < 0$. Simultaneously a quantity of heat $dQ = dU + P\,dV$ is exchanged. When the work performed by the system during the expansion process 1*a*2 (area 1*a*2*dc*) exceeds the quantity of work which must be performed on the system during the compression process 2*b*1 (area 2*b*1*cd*), a net quantity of work

$$W = \oint_{ab} P\,dV$$

is performed by the system on the surroundings. This quantity of work is represented by the positive area encircled by the closed path of the cycle. It is positive when the

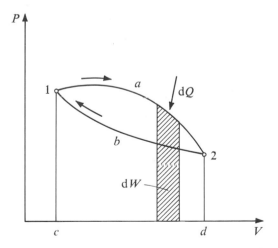

FIGURE 5.14. *A thermodynamic cycle in P, V coordinates.*

cycle is performed in the clockwise or *forward direction*. It changes sign when the operation is *reversed*. The area enclosed by the path of the cycle is also equal to the net heat $Q^+ - |Q^-|$, as seen from equation (5.26). Since $dW = P\,dV$ only for reversible processes, the area enclosed by the curve of the cycle will represent positive work for a forward or *power cycle* or negative work for a *reversed cycle* on condition that the whole cycle is reversible.

5.11 Units of heat and energy. Mechanical equivalent of heat

Since energy, equation (5.1), and later heat, equation (5.18), have been defined in terms of specified quantities of work, it is natural to employ the same units for their measurement as for the measurement of work. Thus, energy and heat can be measured in identical units

$$\{E\} = \{Q\} = \text{kpm}, \quad \text{ft lbf}, \quad \text{or} \quad \text{J}.$$

Frequently, the Joule proves to be too small a unit for practical use, and its 10^3 multiple, the kilo-Joule (kJ) is preferred. The units

$$\text{erg} = \frac{\text{g cm}^2}{\text{sec}^2} \quad \text{and} \quad \frac{\text{lbm ft}^2}{\text{sec}^2}$$

of the CGS system and the absolute English system, respectively, are no longer in use. The specific energy e is, consequently, measured in

$$\{e\} = \frac{\text{kpm}}{\text{kg}}, \quad \frac{\text{ft lbf}}{\text{lbm}}, \quad \frac{\text{J}}{\text{kg}}, \quad \text{or} \quad \frac{\text{kJ}}{\text{kg}}.$$

It is noteworthy that specific energy is never expressed per unit mass kp sec²/m or lbf sec²/ft of the gravitational systems as already stated in Section 1.3.3. The Ninth International Conference on Weights and Measures (Paris, 1948), and the Fifth International Conference on Properties of Steam (London, 1956) both adopted the Joule as the fundamental unit of work, energy, and heat. It is hoped that all tables of thermodynamic properties will be converted to give effect to the preceding resolutions eventually. However, at the present time there exist several alternative units which are frequently employed in tables and in computations, and note must be taken of their existence.

In principle there is no objection to the selection of an *independent unit* for heat and energy, that is, for the selection of a unit whose definition is not related to the unit of work. Although such a choice is very inconvenient, it is the one which has been made originally, and which still persists in practice. According to the original definition, the unit of heat and energy in the metric system is called one kilocalorie (kcal); it was defined as that energy change which is produced in 1 kg of water at atmospheric pressure when its temperature is raised by 1°C. Precise measurements show that the same *change* in temperature produces different changes in energy, depending on the temperature at which the process occurs. Consequently, the preceding definition was refined by appending the specification that the increase in temperature must be produced from 14.5°C to 15.5°C precisely. The resulting unit was called the fifteen-degree kilocalorie, abbreviated to 15°-kcal or $\text{kcal}_{15°}$.

The corresponding unit in the English system, the British thermal unit (Btu), was originally defined as 1/180th part of the change in energy accompanying the heating of 1 lbm of water from the ice point to the steam point. However, in modern times a conventional fraction of the kilocalorie is defined as 1 Btu. The fraction chosen is a combination of the ratio of 1 lbm to 1 kg and of 1°F to 1°C, namely

$$1 \text{ Btu} = 1 \frac{\text{lbm}}{\text{kg}} \cdot \frac{°\text{F}}{°\text{C}} \text{ kcal}$$
$$= \frac{0.45359237}{1.8} \text{ kcal} = 0.251996 \text{ kcal}.$$

The conversion factor is so chosen that the change in energy per unit mass and degree of temperature, or the so-called specific heat (Sections 5.4 and 7.2) of water at 15°C should be equal to unity in both systems. Hence,

$$1 \frac{\text{Btu}}{\text{lbm °F}} = 1 \frac{\text{kcal}}{\text{kg °C}}. \tag{5.27}$$

When two independently defined units for the same physical quantity exist side by side, it becomes necessary to compare them with the aid of very precise measurements and to determine the so-called mechanical equivalent of heat $\mathbf{J}$ which expresses the mechanical equivalent (in kpm, ft lbf, or J) of one "heat" unit (kcal or Btu). Early measurements of this kind have been performed in the same apparatus as those described under the heading of Joule's experiment in Section 5.2. In fact, Joule designed the experiment for this purpose and discovered that this ratio was constant. This discovery formed the basis of the formulation of the First Law of thermodynamics, and it is instructive to digress for a moment, and to attempt to understand his reasoning.

In order to produce a given change in state, in this case a given change in temperature in water at atmospheric pressure, it is possible either to add heat without work, or to perform work without exchanging heat, that is, adiabatically. In the former case

$$Q_{1,2} = E_2 - E_1 \tag{5.28}$$

and in the latter

$$W_{1,2} = -(E_2 - E_1). \tag{5.28a}$$

Since the unit of heat has been defined in terms of a change in state in water, no actual heat measurements are required. When measuring work, either of two cases is possible: If a potential E exists, then

$$Q_{1,2} = -W_{1,2}$$

and since heat and work are expressed in independent units, the ratio

$$\mathbf{J} = \frac{-W_{1,2}}{Q_{1,2}} \tag{5.29}$$

must be a constant between *any* pair of states, as discovered by Joule. If the potential E were not to exist, the right-hand sides of equations (5.28) and (5.28a) would depend on the respective paths, and the ratio (5.29) would *not* be a constant. Thus, Joule's discovery makes it possible to assert that the adiabatic work W_{ad} is independent of the path of the process.

Measurements performed during the first decades of the present century† established the numerical values

$$
\begin{aligned}
1 \text{ kcal}_{15°} &= (4185.5 \pm 0.4)\text{J} \\
&= (426.80 \pm 0.04)\text{kpm} \\
1 \text{ Btu} &= 777.94 \text{ ft lbf,}
\end{aligned} \right\} \tag{5.30}
$$

that is,

$$
\mathbf{J} \approx 427 \, \frac{\text{kpm}}{\text{kcal}} \approx 778 \, \frac{\text{ft lbf}}{\text{Btu}} \tag{5.30a}
$$

approximately. Some authors prefer to use the reciprocal of the preceding quantity, namely

$$
\mathbf{A} \approx \frac{1}{427} \, \frac{\text{kcal}}{\text{kpm}} \approx \frac{1}{778} \, \frac{\text{Btu}}{\text{ft lbf}}, \tag{5.30b}
$$

that is, the heat equivalent of mechanical energy.

It will be remembered from the discussion in Section 1.3.6 that the adoption of two different units for two physical quantities which appear side by side in a single equation, the First Law of thermodynamics in equation (5.18) in the present case, poses a problem in the practical handling of computations which can be solved in one of two ways. One way is to insert the conversion factor $\mathbf{J}$ or $\mathbf{A}$, according to preference, into the equation, and to write

$$
\mathbf{J}Q_{1,2} = \mathbf{J}(E_2 - E_1) + W_{1,2} \quad \text{or} \quad Q_{1,2} = E_2 - E_1 + \mathbf{A}W_{1,2}.
$$

If this is done, the conversion factor $\mathbf{A}$ or $\mathbf{J}$, like k in Newton's Second Law, equation (1.13), will subsequently appear in all the equations which are derived from the fundamental one in the development of the subject. In order to avoid the need to carry an additional constant, it is possible, and in our opinion preferable, to postulate that

$$
\mathbf{A} \equiv \mathbf{J} \equiv 1,
$$

which has the effect of suppressing these constants in all equations, as was done consistently in this chapter. When this is done, all quantities can be expressed in terms of one unit, or alternatively, in numerical work, use may be made of the *conversion equations* (5.30). The latter are equivalent to the conversion equations (1.16) for Newton's Second Law.

Present-day practice more or less forces us to use both units simultaneously because work is measured or computed most easily in mechanical units, whereas the energy of systems is tabulated in heat units. The Fifth International Conference on Properties of Steam adopted a resolution favoring the abolition of the heat unit and, as a temporary measure, related the heat unit to the mechanical unit of energy by the adoption of conventional factors in the conversion equation. This slightly affected the size of the previous units of heat—the 15°-kcal and the corresponding Btu—and it was felt necessary to adopt distinctive names and symbols for the modified units. These are known as the International Steam Tables kilocalorie and British thermal unit, respectively, and are

† By Jaeger, W., and von Steinwehr, H. (1921); Laby, T. H., and Hercus, E. O. (1927, 1935); and Osborne, N. S., Stimson, H. F., and Ginnings, D. C. (1939). See Cohen, E. R., Crowe, K. M., and Dumond, J. W., *The Fundamental Constants of Physics* (Interscience, 1957), p. 20.

abbreviated to

1 IT-kcal   and   1 IT-Btu   or   1 kcal$_{IT}$ and   1 Btu$_{IT}$.

The conversion factors are:

$$1 \text{ kcal}_{IT} = 4186.8 \text{ J}$$
$$1 \frac{\text{Btu}_{IT}}{\text{kg}} = 2.326 \times 10^3 \frac{\text{J}}{\text{kg}},$$

so that

$$1 \text{ Btu}_{IT} = 0.251996 \text{ kcal}_{IT}$$

and

$$J = 426.935 \frac{\text{kpm}}{\text{kcal}_{IT}} = 778.169 \frac{\text{ft lbf}}{\text{Btu}_{IT}}.$$

(5.30c)

A similar convention used by chemists follows a recommendation made by F. D. Rossini in 1949. It defines a unit known as the thermochemical kilocalorie by the convention

$$1 \text{ thermochemical kcal} = 4184.0 \text{ J}.$$

This is equivalent to

$$1 \text{ kcal}_{15°} = (1.000034 \pm 0.00010) \text{ thermochem kcal}.$$

We shall refrain from using this unit in the course of our present study.

The procedure of defining the conversion factor is more rational than that of defining an entirely separate unit. The only effect now is that the specific heat of water at 15°C must be measured in units of J/kg°C. This measurement replaces the earlier determinations of the mechanical equivalent of heat.

The most important units of energy and their conversion factors can be found listed in Table IV.† The specific heat of water is seen listed in Table IX.

5.12   Distinction between the flow of heat and work

The distinction made between the concepts of energy, work, and heat permits us to set up an important working rule for the efficient analysis of processes requiring the application of the First Law of thermodynamics. Since changes in the energy of a system during a process are characteristic of changes of state, they can be detected by examining the whole volume contained within the boundary of the system. On the other hand, the performance of work and the transference of heat are associated with the interaction between the system and its surroundings which take place across the boundary. Thus, their occurrence will be judged by examining the boundary rather than the volume of the system. For example, if it is found that (a) the boundary deforms, or that (b) the boundary is pierced by a rotating shaft, or, finally, that (c) the boundary is crossed by wires carrying an electric current, it will be concluded that work has been done on or by the system. If the system is accelerated, the boundary will be subjected to strains or concentrated forces at the boundary, or, if other phenomena

† See Volume II.

are important, it will be necessary to take into account other characteristics, but it is essential to note that in all cases the boundary itself, and not the system must be examined. The three mechanisms for the performance of work enumerated above, constitute the three most important modes of its transference encountered in this book, as already stated in Section 4.9.

The transference of heat is also detected by examining the boundary. In analyzing the example of the exchange of heat between two bodies of different temperature in a calorimeter in Section 5.8, it was noticed that it is conditioned by the existence of such a temperature difference. At the boundary it will manifest itself as the appearance of a temperature gradient causing the system to depart from equilibrium and suggesting that the transfer of heat is an irreversible phenomenon. The amount of heat crossing the boundary can be determined from a knowledge of this gradient by the methods developed in the branch of science known as heat transfer. A detailed study of heat transfer is outside the scope of this book, but it can be stated that it is possible to discern three *modes of heat transfer:* conduction through a material medium in which a temperature gradient exists; convection through a fluid in a state of motion where the temperature gradient is confined to a thin layer near the solid body; and radiation between two systems of different temperatures which consists in the exchange of electromagnetic energy without the intervention of any material bodies between the systems. When radiant heat is absorbed by a surface, it will cause the appearance of a temperature gradient within the system, near its surface. It is important to note that the presence of a transfer of heat is detected at the boundary by the existence of a temperature gradient.†

Since the boundary is drawn arbitrarily for every process, it must be expected that a change in boundary, even if it is an inessential one from the point of view of the description of the process, may cause a change in the nature of the interaction across it. What appears as the transfer of work with respect to one boundary may often continue as the transfer of heat with respect to another. This is always the case in phenomena loosely described as the "transformation of mechanical energy into heat" in resistors or in the presence of friction. For example, in the system shown in Figure 5.15 which represents the second variant of Joule's experiment first discussed in Section 5.2, and in which an electric current is supplied to a resistor, we say that (electrical) *work* is supplied to the system within boundary *a* which includes the resistor, but that heat is supplied to the system within boundary *b* which excludes it. We also maintain that the resistor "transforms electrical energy into so-called Joule heat," but it must be clearly perceived that the preceding statement implies a change in the reference system, that is, a change in the boundary.

The definition of heat given in Section 5.7 implies that any interaction between a system and its surroundings other than that involving the performance of work results in the transference of heat. It is, therefore, necessary to analyze whether such a distinction between heat and work can always be made. It is certain, from experience, that it can be made unambiguously in a large number of cases but it is possible to indicate phenomena for which this is not true.

---

† The transfer of heat by radiation into a gas is determined by examining the whole system, and not only its boundary. Similarly, the transfer of work by an electrostatic or electromagnetic field (Section 8.5) is also determined by examining the whole system. However, in most engineering problems only transfers through the boundaries occur.

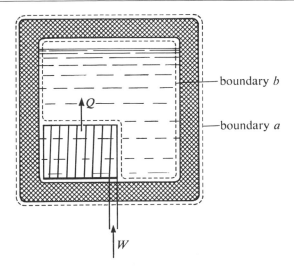

FIGURE 5.15. *Influence of choice of boundary on the distinction between heat and work.*

The difficulties in making an unambiguous distinction between heat and work may be simply connected with the complexity of the phenomenon. In analyzing Joule's paddle-wheel experiment in Section 5.2, Figure 5.1 the boundary was drawn in a way which made such a distinction simple. However, if the boundary were drawn around the water only and to the exclusion of the paddle, it would become impossible to do so. Readers familiar with the phenomenon of turbulence in fluid mechanics will appreciate that a system containing within its boundaries a highly turbulent quantity of fluid will be of a type for which the distinction cannot be made, particularly if the boundary is a ficti-tious one, drawn across an eddying mass of fluid. Here the difficulty is an inherent one.

In this connection the study of dry friction poses some problems which it is useful to resolve.†

5.12.1   Solid friction

An excellent illustration of the ambiguity between heat and work which sometimes exists can be obtained by examining the very simple process of pushing a block over a rough surface. Accordingly, we consider a block M which rests on a rough surface S and which is dragged along this "pavement" by the action of a force F *external* to the block, Figure 5.16. It is known from experience that temperature gradients will be set up in the block and in the pavement, as the former is moved along the latter from posi-tion (state) 1 to position (state) 2 over a distance x. We shall now analyze this process in terms of the system delineated by the boundary B_1, taken so that it cuts through the block. The combined action of the force F and the friction forces will strain the body and produce stresses, normal, σ, as well as tangential, τ, along the cut. From mechanics it is known that the resultant of all stresses must possess a horizontal component of magnitude $-F$. Examining the boundary of the system it will be concluded, as sug-

† The following argument is based on P. W. Bridgman's perceptive analysis in *The Nature of Thermody-namics*, (Harvard Univ. Press, 1943).

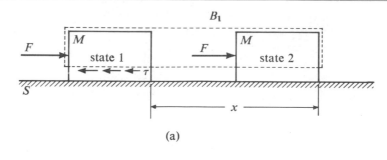

(a)

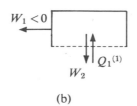

(b)

FIGURE 5.16. *Block on a rough surface. System (1).*

gested by Figure 5.16(b), that at the point of application of force F work W_1 will flow *into* the system; hence, W_1 is negative and

$$W_1 = -Fx.$$

Along the cut, positive work

$$W_2 = Fx$$

will flow out of the system, and the net work

$$W = W_1 + W_2 = 0.$$

In addition, a flow of heat $Q_1^{(1)}$ across the cut will be observed. During the process the system will not be in thermal equilibrium, and hence, the process is an irreversible one. If equilibrium is allowed to set in after state 2 has been reached, for example, by surrounding the block by an adiabatic enclosure which is imagined stretched over the cut as well, it will be possible to assert that

$$E_2^{(1)} - E_1^{(1)} = Q_1^{(1)}, \tag{5.31}$$

where the superscript (1) refers to the system as shown in the sketch. The unfamiliar feature of this analysis lies in the appearance of an observable heat flux without the presence of a *heat source*, that is, of another system of higher temperature.

The same process can be analyzed in terms of the system enclosed by boundary B_2 in Figure 5.17 which is now drawn so that it cuts through the pavement, but includes the block. A similar analysis to the one just outlined will reveal a flux of work $W_1 = -Fx$ and a flux of heat $Q_2^{(2)}$ *out of* the system, so that $Q_2^{(2)}$ is now negative. Denoting the absolute value of $Q_2^{(2)}$ by the symbol $|Q_2^{(2)}|$ and assuming, as before, that the addition of an adiabatic pad around the boundary inclusive of the cut has allowed the system to attain equilibrium, we can write

$$E_2^{(2)} - E_1^{(2)} = -|Q_2^{(2)}| + Fx. \tag{5.32}$$

As the boundary B_1 is made to include more and more of the block, and boundary B_2 is made to include less and less of the pavement, we shall have

$$(E_2^{(2)} - E_1^{(2)}) \rightarrow (E_2^{(1)} - E_1^{(1)}),$$

since the mass included will be closer and closer to that of the block alone. In the limit,

$$E_2^{(2)} - E_1^{(2)} = E_2^{(1)} - E_1^{(1)} = E_2 - E_1,$$

and equations (5.31) and (5.32) must be written

$$E_2 - E_1 = Q_1 \tag{5.31a}$$

and

$$E_2 - E_1 = Fx - |Q_2|, \tag{5.32a}$$

respectively. It is seen that the limits are *not* identical.

In order to investigate the matter somewhat more closely, it is useful to analyze the same process in terms of yet another system, system (3) shown sketched in Figure 5.18. The boundary B_3 now includes the lower part of the block M and part of the pavement. The external shearing stresses τ perform the negative work $W_1 = -Fx$ on the system, causing work W_1 to flow out of it, and two fluxes of heat $Q_1^{(3)}$ into the remainder of the block, and $Q_2^{(3)}$ into the pavement, both negative, are observed. The First Law must now be written

$$E_2^{(3)} - E_1^{(3)} = Fx - (|Q_1^{(3)}| + |Q_2^{(3)}|). \tag{5.33}$$

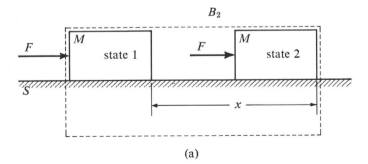

(a)

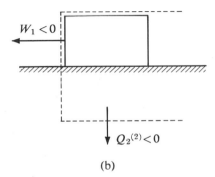

(b)

FIGURE 5.17. *Block on a rough surface. System (2).*

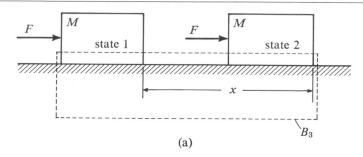

(a)

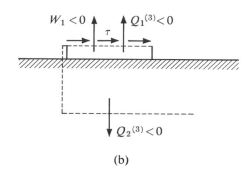

(b)

FIGURE 5.18. *Block on a rough surface. System (3).*

If the boundary B_3 is allowed to shrink to zero, it will contain less and less mass and, consequently, the change in its energy must vanish in the limit. Hence, equation (5.33) will transform to

$$Fx = |Q_1| + |Q_2|, \qquad (5.33a)$$

where Q_1 and Q_2 are the quantities of heat observed to have entered the block and the pavement, respectively. This is a surprising result because it indicates that a flux of work Fx has entered the imaginary surface between the block and the pavement which contains no matter, and has been "transformed" in it into two heat fluxes, Q_1 and Q_2. The latter thus emerged from empty space, that between the block and the pavement, and entered into the block and into the pavement, respectively.

The strangeness of the preceding statement is a result of our excessive idealization of the problem. Two rough surfaces do not glide over each other with friction, as has been tacitly assumed in Figures 5.16 to 5.18, and cannot be separated from each other by a surface drawn through space and never crossed by matter. In actual fact the contact surface between two rough bodies presents an appearance similar to that drawn schematically in Figure 5.19 in which protrusions from both are intermeshed in a complex manner. As one surface is made to slide over the other, protrusions are abraded, and no clear demarcation of a closed system in the strict sense can be achieved. The so-called dissipation of energy, that is the appearance of fluxes of heat at the cost of the disappearance of a flux of work, is much more complex than the above, superficial analysis has been able to reveal. If all details of the process are taken into account, it becomes impossible clearly to distinguish between a flux of work and a flux of heat *at the surface* itself. Protrusions undergo plastic deformations and rupture, and even the description of the state of the systems becomes questionable.

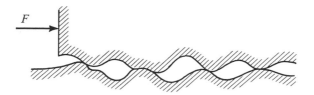

FIGURE 5.19. *Two rough surfaces.*

Similar difficulties present themselves in connection with Joule's experiment as already mentioned. An attempt to analyze the process in terms of the fluid alone, to the exclusion of the paddle, would present difficulties of the same nature. Similar difficulties occur in the presence of turbulence in flow fields (Section 6.12.2), or in the detailed analysis of the phenomena which accompany the evolution of Joule heat in a resistor. A fuller understanding of such phenomena can be acquired only with the aid of the Second Law of thermodynamics, and in terms of continuous systems. These concepts will also be necessary to understand the processes which occur in thin layers of viscous lubricant which often exist between two solid surfaces sliding one upon another.

In spite of all these conceptual difficulties, the analysis of the problem represented by the preceding equations is appropriate and consistent. The only question which cannot be answered by it is the determination of the ratio of Q_1 to Q_2 in equation (5.33a). The division of the flux of work Fx into the two heat fluxes Q_1 and Q_2 depends on the properties of the materials of which the block and the pavement are made, namely on the ratio of their thermal conductivities.†

The examples just considered provide the answer to the question as to whether a clear distinction between a heat flux and a flux of work can always be made. It appears that the answer is negative. In some cases, as in Joule's experiment, the distinction can be made possible by a judicious change in the boundary chosen for the analysis, but in other cases this may fail. However, if it is possible to cause the same change in the state of the system by another process, the change in internal energy accompanying it can be determined, and hence, the difference

$$Q - W = E_2 - E_1$$

between the two fluxes is known. It may be possible to achieve this by an adiabatic process ($Q = 0$), by a process involving no work ($W = 0$), or by a process in which both the heat flux Q and the work flux W can be determined separately. The advantages of concentrating one's attention on the change in energy are now clear, and it might be stated that in most problems encountered in practice, only the difference $Q - W$, that is, *the change in energy $E_2 - E_1$ is of real consequence.*

5.13   The reversible transfer of heat. Heat reservoirs

The examples illustrating the concept of heat considered so far demonstrated that the transfer of heat is irreversible. At the boundary of two systems of different temperature, the transition from temperature θ_1, of system 1, Figure 5.20, to temperature θ_2 of

---

† For a more complete understanding of these statements, the reader must wait until he has studied the phenomenon of conduction in heat transfer.

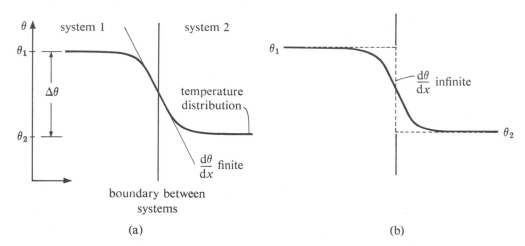

FIGURE 5.20. *Conditions at a boundary.*

system 2 is usually continuous, but it takes place in comparatively narrow regions adjacent to the boundary. The details of such transitions as well as the study of the thicknesses of these so-called *thermal boundary layers* form the object of study of the discipline known under the name of *heat transfer* or *heat transmission*. For our present purposes it is possible to neglect the existence of thermal boundary layers and to use the expression that the flow of heat is due to the temperature difference $\Delta\theta = \theta_1 - \theta_2$. Thus the finite temperature gradient $d\theta/dx$ at the boundary is replaced by an infinite one, implying an infinite *rate* of heat flow dQ/dt.

When the temperature difference decreases, the rate at which heat crosses the boundary decreases, other things being equal, and in the limit when $\theta_1 = \theta_2$ the two systems are in equilibrium, the flow of heat ceases. However, when we idealize the process by disregarding the existence of thermal boundary layers, the rate of heat flow is "infinite." The idealization implies that passing to the limit $\Delta\theta = 0$ does not necessarily mean that the rate of heat transfer dQ/dt tends to zero. Very frequently it is profitable, and indeed necessary, to make this second idealization. In such cases it will be asserted that a quantity of heat Q can be exchanged between two systems even when $\Delta\theta = 0$. Causing $\Delta\theta$ to increase slightly in the positive direction ($\Delta\theta > 0$) will cause a real flow of heat from system 1 to system 2. The reverse change ($\Delta\theta < 0$) will cause heat to flow from system 2 to system 1. This observation convinces us that the limiting case of heat transference at $\Delta\theta = 0$ constitutes an idealization of the process which renders it reversible. In this, the argument is completely analogous, and equivalent, to the idealization considered in Section 4.5 when the reversible work of compression or expansion $dW = PdV$ was calculated at a boundary across which the pressure difference ΔP vanished.

In the development of our subject it will be necessary frequently to assume that heat is exchanged reversibly, that is, at $\Delta\theta = 0$, and in such cases the direction of heat flow can be prescribed in either sense in accordance with the requirements at the time.

In addition to the idealization to reversible heat transfer it will be often convenient as well as necessary to make one further abstraction. When two systems exchange a quantity of heat, Q, without the performance of work, in the manner of the calorimeter experiment discussed in Section 5.8, the quantity of heat is conserved, equation (5.20), or

$$Q_{1,2} + Q_{2,1} = 0.$$

Denoting the parameters of systems 1 and 2 by suitable superscripts, we can write down the First Law for them in the following forms

$$Q_{1,2} = E_2^{(1)} - E_1^{(1)}; \qquad -Q_{1,2} = E_2^{(2)} - E_1^{(2)}$$

or

$$E_2^{(1)} - E_1^{(1)} = -(E_2^{(2)} - E_1^{(2)}).$$

The change in energy is connected with a change in temperature, and if one of the systems, say system 2, is very large in mass compared with the other, its temperature will change very little compared with the change in system 1. Consequently, we shall have

$$\theta_2^{(2)} - \theta_1^{(2)} \ll \theta_2^{(1)} - \theta_1^{(1)}.$$

In the limit it will be possible to postulate that the temperature of system 2 does not change, $\theta_2^{(2)} = \theta_1^{(2)}$, while the temperature of the other undergoes a considerable change, implying $m^{(2)} \to \infty$ with $m^{(1)}$ finite. A system whose change in temperature is negligible when it exchanges heat with another system will be referred to as a *heat reservoir* and frequently a distinction between a *heat source* and a *heat sink* will be made. A *heat source* supplies heat to a system of finite mass under consideration, whereas a *heat sink* extracts heat from the system under consideration without changing its own temperature.

If it is necessary to analyze a reversible process undergone by a system whose temperature changes continuously, we shall sometimes use the fiction of "an infinite number" of sources or sinks. At every step of the process the system is made to interact with a source or sink, as the case may be, whose temperature is equal to the instantaneous temperature of the system. As a result the temperature of the system increases or decreases, leaving the temperature of the heat reservoir unchanged. At the next step, a new reservoir is made to interact with the system, once again causing a reversible exchange of a quantity of heat dQ and so on.

It is necessary for the student to convince himself that the preceding abstractions constitute idealizations of real processes in nature because we shall frequently resort to them in this book.

5.14 Analysis of some elementary processes.
Definition of specific heats and enthalpy

In order to illustrate more systematically the application of the concepts connected with the First Law of thermodynamics, we shall discuss several elementary processes. In every case we shall consider two processes, a reversible process possessing some characteristic and an irreversible process which changes the same initial state into the same final state. We shall confine our remarks to pure substances or to mixtures of pure substances in a single phase.

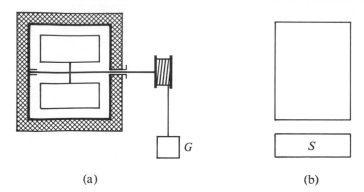

(a)   (b)

FIGURE 5.21. *Constant-volume processes.*

5.14.1 Constant-volume process. Specific heat at constant volume

Two constant-volume (also known as *isochoric*) processes are illustrated in Figure 5.21. In both, the system is confined in a rigid container of volume V which does not change or deform. In Figure 5.21 the initial state of equilibrium 1 is changed by an interaction involving the performance of work by a weight G through the intermediary of a paddle wheel, the cylinder being insulated adiabatically. The performance of electrical work could be employed to the same effect. The process is illustrated in the P, V diagram of Figure 5.22 which shows the initial state 1 as well as the final state 2 for which $V_2 = V_1 = V$. The intermediate states are not states of equilibrium and cannot be represented by points in the diagram. By arresting the process at intermediate stages and by allowing the system to reach equilibrium at every stage, it would be possible to realize intermediate states, all lying along the vertical line 1–2 in the diagram and between points 1 and 2, but it would be impossible to attain them in a continuous way.

Applying the First Law, equation (5.18), we can write

$$Q_{1,2} = 0$$

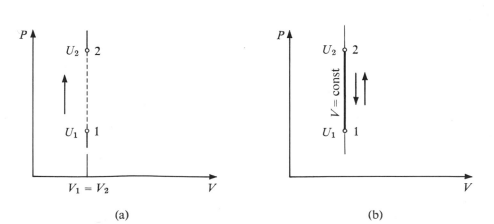

(a)   (b)

FIGURE 5.22. *Diagrams for constant-volume processes.*

and

$$U_2 - U_1 = -W_{1,2}. \tag{5.34}$$

It is noted that $W_{1,2}$ will always be negative, it being evident from experience that a system of this kind will never reduce its own internal energy and raise a weight G simultaneously.

During the second process, Figures 5.21(b) and 5.22(b), the system is put in contact with a heat reservoir S so that it exchanges heat reversibly at every step. If at each step a suitable new reservoir is chosen, the process becomes reversible, and every state of equilibrium between states 1 and 2 for which the value is equal to V is traversed in a continuous way. At every step

$$dW = 0$$

so that, by the First Law, equation (5.18a),

$$dU = dQ$$

and for the whole process, by integration, we obtain

$$U_2 - U_1 = Q_{1,2}.$$

It is seen that the same change in state from (V, U_1) to (V, U_2) can be achieved either by performing adiabatic work, or by adding heat, on condition that both are equal,

$$Q_{1,2} = -W_{1,2}.$$

There is, however, one important difference. The reversible process can take place in either direction, $1 \rightarrow 2$ or $2 \rightarrow 1$, whereas the irreversible process can take place in direction $1 \rightarrow 2$ only. If the temperature of the heat reservoir were not kept equal to that of the system at every step in the process, the change in state would also become irreversible. The system would perform a process in the direction of equalizing its temperature with that of the reservoir, that is, either increasing or decreasing its temperature as the case may be.

The fact that the same change of state, that is, the same effect, can be brought about either by the addition of heat or by the performance of negative work (equivalent to the lowering of a weight in the surroundings) explains the reasons for adopting the seemingly complex definition of negative work given in Section 4.4.

It is clear that a process which occurs at constant volume in a simple system is completely described by indicating its initial and final internal energy U_1 and U_2 as well as the constant volume. Alternatively, it is completely described by indicating the quantity of heat $Q_{1,2}$ or work $W_{1,2}$, as the case may be, in addition to specifying the initial state. The change in state is, in general, accompanied by a change in temperature, which is different for different processes and for different substances. In order to form a numerical measure of the extent of the change in temperature, it is customary to define an average change in energy per unit change in temperature. Thus, the ratio

$$\overline{C}_v = \frac{U_2 - U_1}{\theta_2 - \theta_1}, \tag{5.35}$$

called the *heat capacity* of the system at volume V and between temperatures θ_1 and θ_2, is formed. For homogeneous systems, it is convenient to refer this quantity to a unit of mass, and to introduce the *mean specific heat* at specific volume v and between the temperature limits θ_1, θ_2, defined as

$$\bar{c}_v = \frac{\overline{C_v}}{m} = \frac{u_2 - u_1}{\theta_2 - \theta_1}. \tag{5.35a}$$

The limit of this expression

$$c_v = \lim_{\theta_2 \to \theta_1} \frac{u_2 - u_1}{\theta_2 - \theta_1} \tag{5.35b}$$

as θ_2 tends to θ_1 is called the *specific heat at constant volume, c_v,* of the substance. Thus, the specific heat, c_v, is measured by performing a series of processes at constant volume during which the change in energy is measured and by extrapolating the values to zero temperature difference, as shown in Figure 5.23. In practice it is preferable to measure the change in internal energy by performing a process involving the exchange of heat in the absence of work, rather than the reverse. For this reason, in the elementary study of the subject, the specific heat is defined as

$$c_v = \lim \frac{dQ}{d\theta} \quad \text{as} \quad d\theta \to 0,$$

but the reader will appreciate that the definition is misleading to the extent that dQ is not the differential of a property and that it is, therefore, necessary carefully to describe the details of the process to which the definition is meant to refer.

The process of extrapolation which leads to the concept of specific heat at constant volume is equivalent to forming the partial derivative

$$c_v = \left(\frac{\partial u}{\partial \theta}\right)_v \tag{5.36}$$

of the function of state $u(\theta, v)$ with respect to θ keeping v constant. Thus, the symbol used in equation (5.36) is consistent with the notation discussed in Section 3.4. This is

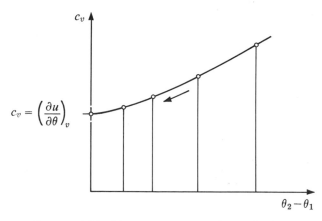

FIGURE 5.23. *The measurement of specific heat.*

consequent upon the fact that the limit in equation (5.35b) is a property of the substance at the given state, since it refers to the variation of one property, the internal energy u, with respect to another, the temperature θ. If the equation of state $u(\theta, v)$ is known, the specific heat is obtained by simple differentiation which results in another function of the same independent variables,

$$c_v(\theta, v). \tag{5.37}$$

The inverse procedure of calculating the internal energy from a known function (5.37) would require the determination of an additional function of volume, because we can write

$$u(\theta, v) - u(\theta_0, v) = \int_{\theta_0}^{\theta} \left(\frac{\partial u}{\partial \theta}\right)_v d\theta + \psi(v), \tag{5.38}$$

where $\psi(v)$ is a "constant of integration." This function would have to be determined with reference to additional data of an experimental nature. Hence, the equation of state (5.37) is not a fundamental one with respect to internal energy in the sense defined in Section 3.8.

The average value $\bar{c}_v$ can also be represented by the equation

$$\bar{c}_v = \frac{\displaystyle\int_{\theta_1}^{\theta_2} c_v(\theta, v) d\theta}{\theta_2 - \theta_1}, \tag{5.39}$$

which follows directly from the *mean value theorem* of calculus. It is, therefore, given the name of *mean specific heat at constant volume*, between the temperatures θ_1 and θ_2.

In the preferred MKS system the unit of specific heat is

$$\{c_v\} = \frac{J}{kg°K}.$$

In the systems in common use, specific heats are measured in

$$\{c_v\} = \frac{Btu}{lbm°R} \quad \text{or} \quad \frac{kcal}{kg°K}. \tag{5.40}$$

The definition of the British thermal unit given in Section 5.12 is equivalent to *assuming* that the average specific heat of water between steam point and ice point is unity. The definition of the 15-degree kilocalorie discussed in the same section is equivalent to *assuming* that the mean specific heat of water between 14.5°C and 15.5°C is unity. Since the temperature interval is so small, it is sufficiently accurate to state that *the specific heat of water at 15°C is assumed to be equal to unity*. Consequently, the two units in (5.40) are nearly equal; they can be assumed to be equal in practical calculations. Conversely, the British thermal unit can be redefined by postulating the equality of the units in equation (5.40), as stated in Section 5.11.

The specific heat at constant volume can be considered to be a function of temperature and pressure

$$c_v(\theta, P)$$

by a simple change in variables. It has been emphasized several times that the actual choice of independent variables in an equation of state is immaterial, as long as the requisite number of them is included. The variation of the specific heat c_v with pressure is quite small for water. Table IX gives values of c for water in the range 0°C to 100°C at a pressure of 1 atm. The same table can be used up to quite high pressures because the dependence of the specific heat c_v of any liquid on pressure is extremely weak, as attested by many measurements. It is noteworthy that the specific heat of water passes through a minimum at +34°C.

Values of the specific heats of other substances can be found in Tables V, XIV, and XVI.

It should be noted that the heat capacity

$$C_v = \left(\frac{\partial U}{\partial \theta}\right)_V$$

is an extensive property, whereas the specific heat c_v from equation (5.36) is a specific property as it refers to a unit of mass of a homogeneous system. In books on chemical thermodynamics the term "heat capacity" is used for the quantity c_v, here called "specific heat," and this may lead to confusion. Semantically, the latter term is preferable because the work "capacity" implies a reference to the complete system. In this book we shall favor the more rational nomenclature.

Strictly speaking, the process of differentiation in the definition of specific heat at constant volume, equation (5.36), can be performed only along a reversible path. However, once the equation of state $u(\theta, v)$ has been established, it is immaterial whether we calculate the specific heat in conjunction with a reversible or an irreversible process. Specific heat is a property itself and assumes a fixed value at any state of equilibrium, irrespective of how the latter has been reached.

The reader should note how the value of the derivative has been obtained by a process of extrapolation, equation (5.35b), on the basis of measurements on systems undergoing real, that is, irreversible processes. Since no reversible processes occur in nature, the same problem will recur when other properties are to be measured. The advantage of making a clear distinction between properties, potentials, and quantities which are neither, is here apparent.

The mathematically trained reader might wish to ask at this point whether the limit c_v always exists. A full answer to this question can only be given after further study, but it might be of interest to state here that for simple systems existing in a single phase this is usually the case. Exceptions occur at the so-called *critical point* discussed in Section 7.4.3 and when changes of phase occur. Thus, to be meticulously precise, it might be necessary to rephrase the definition and to state that the limit in equation (5.34b), *if it exists*, is called the specific heat at constant volume.

Very frequently it is preferable to refer the change in internal energy per degree of temperature of a homogeneous system to one mol of the substance and to use molar specific heats at constant volume measured in

$$\{c_v\} = \frac{J}{kmol°K}, \quad \frac{kcal}{kmol°K}, \quad \text{or} \quad \frac{Btu}{lbmol°R}. \tag{5.40a}$$

The last two units are, obviously, identical for the same reasons that the two units in equation (5.40) were identical.

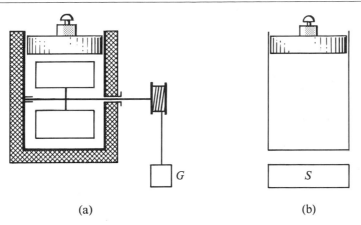

(a)   (b)

FIGURE 5.24. *Constant-pressure processes.*

5.14.2 *Constant-pressure process. Enthalpy. Specific heat at constant pressure*

The preceding processes can be made to occur at constant pressure by providing the cylinder with a piston and loading it with a constant weight, as shown in Figure 5.24. A process which occurs at constant pressure is often called an *isobaric process*. The analysis can proceed in exactly the same terms as before except that it is now necessary to include the work done by or against the weight on the piston. We called this the *work of the atmosphere* in Section 5.9. Assuming that the piston moves very slowly, irrespective of whether the process is reversible or irreversible, we can apply equation (4.20) and write

$$W_P = \int_{V_1}^{V_2} P \, dV = P(V_2 - V_1) \qquad (P = \text{const}). \qquad (5.41)$$

In the irreversible process shown in Figures 5.24(a) and 5.25(a), the piston will always be raised, consequently, $W_p > 0$. For the irreversible process we have

$$Q_{1,2} = 0, \qquad W = W_{1,2} + P(V_2 - V_1),$$

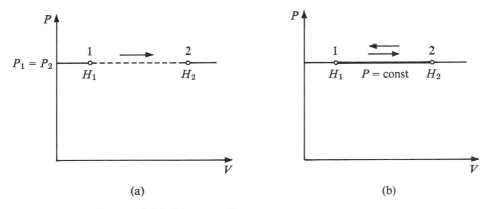

(a)   (b)

FIGURE 5.25. *Diagrams for constant-pressure processes.*

where $W_{1,2}$ denotes the work done on the system by the weight driving the paddle. Hence,

$$U_2 - U_1 = -W_{1,2} - P(V_2 - V_1)$$

or

$$(U_2 + P_2 V_2) - (U_1 + P_1 V_1) = -W_{1,2}, \qquad \text{since } P_1 = P_2 = P.$$

For the reversible process, we have

$$dQ \neq 0, \qquad dW = P\, dV,$$

and

$$dU = dQ - P\, dV,$$

or

$$d(U + PV) = dQ.$$

For the whole process we obtain

$$(U_2 + P_2 V_2) - (U_1 + P_1 V_1) = Q_{1,2} \qquad \text{on condition that } P = \text{const.}$$

The combination of properties

$$H = U + PV, \tag{5.42}$$

which is itself a property, occurs so frequently in thermodynamics that it is given a separate name — *enthalpy*.† The specific enthalpy is

$$h = \frac{H}{m} = u + Pv. \tag{5.42a}$$

It is measured in the same units as specific energy, that is,

$$\{h\} = \frac{\text{J}}{\text{kg}}, \quad \frac{\text{kcal}}{\text{kg}}, \quad \frac{\text{Btu}}{\text{lbm}}.$$

We can now repeat the remainder of the analysis of the preceding section and assert that the same change in state from H_2, P to H_1, P can be brought about by the performance of work $W_{1,2}$ or by the addition of an equivalent quantity of heat $Q_{1,2}$, *excluding in either case the work of the atmosphere*. It is also possible to repeat all the remarks concerning the distinction between a reversible and an irreversible process, including the statement about the *natural direction* of the process. Finally, the accompanying change in temperature can be described by the *heat capacity at constant pressure*

$$C_p = \left(\frac{\partial H}{\partial \theta} \right)_P$$

or by its specific counterpart, the *specific heat at constant pressure*

$$c_p = \left(\frac{\partial h}{\partial \theta} \right)_P. \tag{5.43}$$

† Pronounced en-thăl′-py and not ĕn′-thăl-py; from the Greek meaning "heat function."

The latter, being a specific property, can be described in terms of two equivalent equations of state

$$c_p\,(\theta,\,P) \quad \text{or} \quad c_p\,(\theta,\,v)$$

none of them being fundamental with respect to enthalpy. The units of specific heat, c_p, are identical with those for c_v.

Since for all substances an increase in temperature at $P = \text{const}$ causes the volume to increase, the system must perform a positive quantity of atmospheric work

$$P\mathrm{d}v = \mathrm{d}(Pv) \qquad \text{since } P = \text{const.}$$

It is *plausible* that, therefore,

$$c_p \geq c_v,$$

where the sign of equality has been added to guard against special cases. In fact, this is always the case as will be proved quite generally in Section 12.5.

The ratio of the specific heats

$$\gamma = \frac{c_p}{c_v} \tag{5.44}$$

is, therefore, always greater than unity; in limiting cases it may become equal to unity. This ratio, which unfortunately has no established name, is also a property and can be represented by the alternative equations of state

$$\gamma(\theta,\,P) \quad \text{or} \quad \gamma(\theta,\,v).$$

It is sometimes given the designation "*isentropic index.*" This designation is justified only for perfect gases.

It might be worth noting that for all substances, *heating* ($Q > 0$) at constant volume causes the pressure as well as the temperature to increase ($\mathrm{d}P > 0$, $\mathrm{d}\theta > 0$ for reversible steps). Similarly, heating at constant pressure causes the volume and the temperature to increase ($\mathrm{d}V > 0$, $\mathrm{d}\theta > 0$ for reversible steps). These circumstances will be discussed in general terms in Volume II.

Values of the specific heat c_p and the ratio γ for gases can be found in Tables V, XIII, and XIV.

5.14.3   *Process at constant internal energy*

Referring to the First Law of thermodynamics in the form

$$Q_{1,2} = U_2 - U_1 + W_{1,2}, \tag{5.45}$$

it is seen that during a process for which the energy at the final state 2 is equal to that at the initial state 1, the work performed must exactly balance the heat absorbed, or

$$Q_{1,2} = W_{1,2}. \tag{5.46}$$

Thus, two cases are possible, the first one being the case when

$$Q_{1,2} = W_{1,2} = 0. \tag{5.46a}$$

It is recalled that a system which undergoes a process without exchanging heat or work is known as an *isolated system*, Section 5.19, and that in any process in an isolated system the energy remains constant. An example of such a process was first given in Section 4.6 when we considered the adiabatic, unresisted expansion of a gas; the same process was examined somewhat more closely in Section 5.4, Figure 5.3. It is sufficient to note here that the process is an irreversible one, and that it is represented by two discrete points on a horizontal line in the U, V diagram shown in Figure 5.26(a). The process can take place in one direction only, namely in the direction of *increasing* volume, the reverse process being impossible. By subdividing the volume V_0 into small compartments ΔV it is possible to reach any discrete number of states intermediate between 1 and 2 and to determine experimentally, by interpolation, the locus of points of constant energy between the states 1 and 2, as we already know. It is also known from experience that at every state of higher volume, the pressure is lower, as shown in the P, V diagram of Figure 5.26(b). This property is quite general, as will be shown in detail in Volume II. As the state changes along the line $U = $ const from 1 to 2, the temperature also changes, and the nature of this change will be investigated later, when we shall study the properties of particular systems.

Having established by experimental means involving irreversible processes the variation of pressure P with volume V along the line $U = $ const, we shall have no difficulty in devising a system capable of performing a reversible process which occurs at constant internal energy and which, therefore, causes the system to pass through *every* state of equilibrium between the initial state 1 and the final state 2. In order to achieve this, the system is enclosed in a cylinder fitted with an ideal piston. Considering a small step in the process, it is possible to evaluate the work done

$$dW = P \, dV, \qquad (5.47)$$

since the relation between P and V is now known from the preceding experiment. Thus, it is possible to design the cam in Figure 5.27 in such a way that there is a balance between the moment PAr of the pressure force, and that of the weight, GR. By choosing a suitable shape for the cam this balance can be maintained at every volume, that is, at every step in the process.

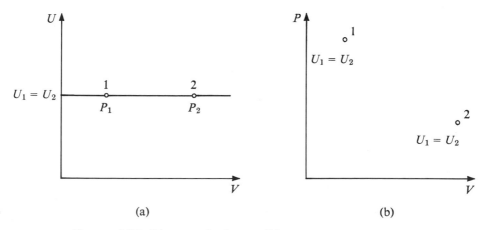

FIGURE 5.26. *Diagrams for irreversible constant-energy process.*

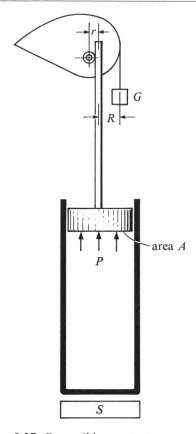

FIGURE 5.27. *Reversible constant-energy process.*

In order to ensure that the internal energy remains constant, it is necessary and sufficient to satisfy condition (5.47) at every step, or to ensure that

$$dQ = dW \tag{5.48}$$

at all times. This can be done by providing a series of heat reservoirs (an "infinite" series, to be sure), each at the instantaneous temperature at every step and to allow it to exchange a quantity of heat dQ exactly equal to dW from equation (5.47). It is clear that the resulting highly idealized process is reversible.

The *P, V* and *U, V* diagrams for such a reversible process are shown sketched in Figure 5.28. By adding to the weight G or subtracting from it an arbitrarily small weight ΔG, the phenomenon can be made to proceed in either direction, as desired.

It is interesting, and important, to note that during a reversible constant-energy process, like in any cycle, Section 5.10, heat is completely converted into mechanical work when both are positive ($Q_{1,2} > 0$, $W_{1,2} > 0$). Conversely, when work is performed on the system ($W_{1,2} < 0$), the energy will remain constant only on condition that its equivalent is extracted from it completely, at every step in a reversible process, or over the whole process, when it is irreversible. On superficial examination it might appear that a process at constant energy is completely equivalent to a cycle when the

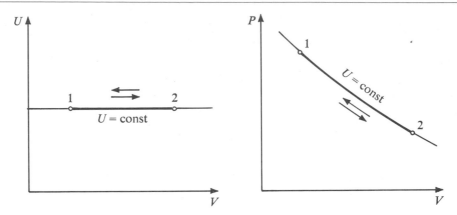

FIGURE 5.28. *Diagrams for a reversible constant-energy process.*

conversion of heat into mechanical energy is undertaken. Both effect a *complete* conversion of heat into mechanical energy. From this point of view, however, the difference between the two phenomena is much more important than their similarity, and should be noted for future reference. Whereas a cycle can be repeated an arbitrary number of times, a process at constant energy cannot be kept in operation indefinitely. In a cycle, the system reverts to its initial state periodically and this makes it possible for it to repeat itself as many times as desired. During a process at constant energy, the state of the system changes continually and succeeding states are further and further removed from the initial state. Thus, some parameter, say the volume in the preceding example, must change without limit, which is obviously impossible; the process must come to an end at some stage. Thus, only a cycle offers a ready means for the conversion of heat into work.

The important question as to what are the best conditions for such a continuous conversion of heat into mechanical energy, as well as to what its limitations are, can only be answered on the basis of the Second Law of thermodynamics, and the matter will be discussed thoroughly in Section 8.4. This is, as it is easy to appreciate, the problem of the large-scale production of power.

Comparing reversible expansion with irreversible expansion between the same end states 1 and 2, it is noteworthy that during the irreversible process

$$W_{\text{irr}} = 0,$$

whereas during the reversible process

$$W_{\text{rev}} > 0,$$

and hence,

$$W_{\text{rev}} > W_{\text{irr}} \tag{5.49}$$

for a constant-energy process between the same end states. At the same time

$$Q_{\text{rev}} > Q_{\text{irr}}, \tag{5.50}$$

since

$$W_{\text{rev}} - Q_{\text{rev}} = W_{\text{irr}} - Q_{\text{irr}}.$$

The inequalities (5.49) and (5.50) are general, as we shall see in Section 13.7 in connection with a systematic discussion of irreversible processes and the Second Law of thermodynamics.

5.14.4 *Processes at constant temperature*

The preceding two processes can be easily performed in a manner to ensure that the temperature of the system remains constant. For this purpose it is sufficient to allow the system to interact with a heat reservoir at constant temperature θ_0, as shown in Figure 5.29, and to absorb or reject heat, as the case may be. A process at constant temperature is often referred to as an *isothermal process*. The state diagrams which illustrate

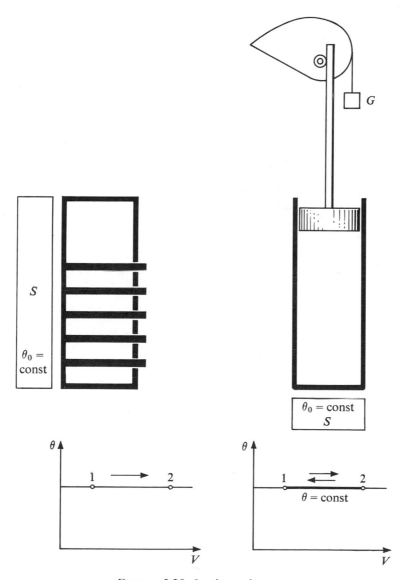

FIGURE 5.29. *Isothermal process.*

these processes are shown in Figure 5.29 and require no further comment. At this stage it is impossible to continue the analysis because nothing has yet been said about the relation between the internal energy u and the independent properties of various systems. It is evident that the analysis cannot progress without information of this kind. Since the equations of state $u(\theta, P)$ or $u(\theta, v)$ are different for different substances, the characteristics of isothermal processes will be discussed for different classes of substances separately. For example, the isothermal process in a perfect gas is represented by the hyperbola $Pv = R\theta_0 = $ const, as we know from Figure 3.3 in Section 3.3. It will, however, be stressed once more that an irreversible isothermal process allows the system to reach only a discrete set of states of equilibrium which lie on the θ_0 isotherm of the system. The reversible process causes the system to trace this isotherm in a continuous way.

5.14.5   Adiabatic processes

A process which occurs without the exchange of heat with the surroundings, that is, within an adiabatic enclosure is called *adiabatic*. The irreversible process at constant internal energy analyzed in Section 5.14.3, or the irreversible processes at constant volume and pressure discussed in Sections 5.14.1 and 5.14.2, constitute examples of *irreversible adiabatic processes* since in all cases we had

$$Q_{1,2} = 0. \tag{5.51}$$

When an adiabatic process is also *reversible*, it is known as an *isentropic process*. The justification for the term "isentropic," meaning "at constant entropy" cannot be given here. The property known as *entropy* and its significance for reversible processes in thermodynamics can be understood only together with the Second Law of thermodynamics. For the present, the term "isentropic" can be regarded as an abbreviation for "adiabatic *and* reversible."

The First Law, equation (5.18), shows that in any adiabatic process whether reversible or not, we must have

$$U_2 - U_1 = -W_{1,2}, \tag{5.52}$$

if we assume that $\Delta E \equiv \Delta U$. This can be expressed by stating that in an adiabatic process work is done by the system ($W_{1,2} > 0$) at the expense of internal energy ($U_2 < U_1$) or, conversely, that work done on the system ($W_{1,2} < 0$) is "stored" in it in the form of internal energy ($U_2 > U_1$).

A *reversible adiabatic* process, that is, an *isentropic process*, can be performed with the aid of the arrangement shown in Figure 5.30 and already familiar to the reader. During an isentropic process there is no exchange of heat at every step in the process, so that

$$dQ = 0.$$

Moreover, since the process is reversible, we can write

$$dW = P\,dV$$

and the application of the First Law leads to the condition

$$dU + P\,dV = 0. \tag{5.53}$$

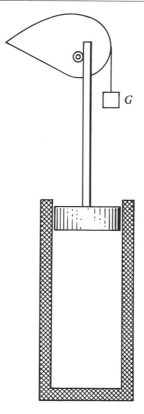

FIGURE 5.30. *Isentropic process.*

When written

$$\mathrm{d}U = -P\,\mathrm{d}V \tag{5.54}$$

the equation implies the same statement as that attached to equation (5.52) earlier, except that now, as is usual with reversible processes, the condition must be satisfied at every step.

It will be recognized that condition (5.53) represents a *differential equation* for the two independent properties of the system, and that its integration would lead to a relation between them, that is to a curve in a state diagram. This curve is known as an *isentrope* or an *isentropic*. In order to see this more clearly we shall suppose that pressure P and volume V have been chosen as independent variables. Consequently, the internal energy is expressed as a function of these two variables, that is, in the form

$$U(P, V).$$

Since internal energy is a potential, $\mathrm{d}U$ in equation (5.53) is a perfect differential and can be written

$$\mathrm{d}U = \left(\frac{\partial U}{\partial P}\right)_V \mathrm{d}P + \left(\frac{\partial U}{\partial V}\right)_P \mathrm{d}V, \tag{5.55}$$

where the partial derivatives

$$\left(\frac{\partial U}{\partial P}\right)_V \quad \text{and} \quad \left(\frac{\partial U}{\partial V}\right)_P$$

are now *known functions* of pressure and volume. Consequently, on substituting equation (5.55) into (5.53), we obtain

$$\left(\frac{\partial U}{\partial P}\right)_V dP + \left[\left(\frac{\partial U}{\partial V}\right)_P + P\right] dV = 0$$

or an equation of the form

$$\frac{dP}{dV} = -\frac{\left(\frac{\partial U}{\partial V}\right)_P + P}{\left(\frac{\partial U}{\partial P}\right)_V}.$$

By introducing the abbreviations

$$\left.\begin{aligned}
\left(\frac{\partial U}{\partial V}\right)_P + P &= M(P, V), \\
\left(\frac{\partial U}{\partial P}\right)_V &= N(P, V),
\end{aligned}\right\} \tag{5.55a}$$

it can be seen that the preceding equation is equivalent to

$$\frac{dP}{dV} = -\frac{M(P, V)}{N(P, V)}, \tag{5.56}$$

where M and N are known functions. Regarding P as the dependent variable (in the above equation only) and V as the independent variable, it can be recognized that equation (5.56) is a nonlinear ordinary differential equation of the type

$$\frac{dy}{dx} = -\frac{M(x, y)}{N(x, y)}, \tag{5.56a}$$

whose solution is a family of curves $F(x, y, c)$ with c denoting a parameter which arises from the process of integration. In the present case, the solution of equation (5.56), if it could be obtained, would give a similar relation, except that the constant of integration would be determined by the initial state 1. It would therefore amount to a relation $P(V)$, as asserted earlier.

Equations of the type (5.56a) play an important part in thermodynamics as well as in other branches of science. When written in the equivalent form

$$dz = M(x, y)dx + N(x, y)dy = 0, \tag{5.57}$$

they are known as Pfaff's *differential equations*, because in them a Pfaffian form is equated to zero. They have been discussed in a preliminary way in Section 4.2 and we shall return to them in Section 10.2.

For the time being, it is sufficient to note that the equation can easily be integrated by a step-by-step procedure if no closed analytic solution can be found, which is often the case. Reverting to the notation of equation (5.56), we observe that the slope

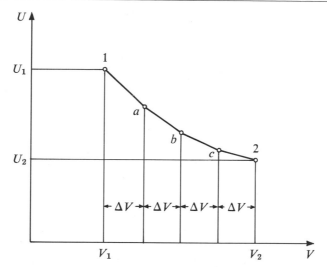

FIGURE 5.31. *The step-by-step tracing of an isentropic. Method of isoclines.*

dP/dV can be calculated for any state for which the pressure and volume are given. Starting with the initial state 1, Figure 5.31, it is possible to calculate the slope at that point

$$\left(\frac{dP}{dV}\right)_1 = -\frac{M(P_1, V_1)}{N(P_1, V_1)},$$

and to replace a length of curve from V_1 to $V_1 + \Delta V$ by a portion of the tangent to the curve, as shown in the drawing. At the intersection of this tangent and the vertical through $V_1 + \Delta V$ a point a can be found which constitutes an approximation to the state which will be reached by the system at volume $V_a = V_1 + \Delta V$. Hence, P_a can be found and the slope

$$\left(\frac{dP}{dV}\right)_a = -\frac{M(P_a, V_a)}{N(P_a, V_a)}$$

can be determined. By a repetition of the previous step it is possible to progress from volume V_1 to volume V_2 in steps of ΔV and to trace the broken line $1ab \ldots 2$ which constitutes an approximation to the isentropic representing the process.[†]

The reader will have noticed that only negative slopes dP/dV have been drawn in Figure 5.31. This circumstance is not accidental and its general validity will be proved and discussed in Volume II.

Owing to its importance in further applications, we shall quote here without proof[‡] a fundamental mathematical theorem concerning Pfaff's equation (5.57), or its equivalent, the general, nonlinear first-order ordinary differential equation (5.56a). In order to appreciate the theorem, it is necessary to notice that the preceding method of solving

[†] For a more detailed description of the step-by-step method and for a description of the equivalent method of isoclines, see Courant, R., *Differential and Integral Calculus*, translated by J. E. McShane (London: Blackie, 1936), II, p. 454.

[‡] For a proof, see Goursat, E., *A Course in Mathematical Analysis*, translated by E. R. Hedrick and O. Dunkel (Ginn, 1917 or Dover, 1959) Vol. II, Part II, "Differential Equations," pp. 45 ff.

the equation step-by-step breaks down at points in the plane, denoted by x_i^*, y_i^*, for which the two functions M and N vanish simultaneously. Thus, points whose co-ordinates are solutions of the two simultaneous algebraic equations

$$\left.\begin{array}{l} M(x_i^*, y_i^*) = 0 \\ N(x_i^*, y_i^*) = 0 \end{array}\right\} \tag{5.58}$$

will be called *singular*, all other points being called *regular*. At such points both components of the vector (M, N) vanish, and the vector itself is identically zero. Consequently, equation (5.57) which expresses the orthogonality condition between the vector (M, N) and the element of the curve which is its solution and whose components are (dx, dy), becomes an identity, and the slope

$$\frac{\mathrm{d}y}{\mathrm{d}x} = -\frac{M(x_i^*, y_i^*)}{N(x_i^*, y_i^*)}$$

is undetermined at any one of the singular points of the equation.

The so-called existence and uniqueness theorem for the type of equation under consideration states that through *every regular point x_1, y_1 in the plane there passes one and only one curve which is a solution of equation (5.56a)*. Hence, there exists a relation $y = y(x)$ which is satisfied by x_1, y_1 and which, when substituted into equation (5.57) transforms it into an identity.

In terms of our original problem, this signifies that from any state of a simple system it is always possible to start an isentropic process and that no two isentropic curves can intersect at one state point. The latter statement follows from the fact that the two expressions in equation (5.55a) cannot vanish simultaneously. That this is so cannot be proved at this stage, but it is useful to remember that the preceding statements have been established in relation to systems possessing two independent variables only.

5.14.6 *Alternative forms of First Law*

In many practical problems, it is frequently preferable to describe states by means of enthalpy rather than internal energy. Since

$$H = U + PV,$$

and since the product PV is a property, it is possible to eliminate the energy U from equations (5.18) and (5.18a) for the case of a reversible process performed by a simple system. Under these restrictions, $E = U$ and $W_{1,2} = \int_1^2 P\mathrm{d}V$. Hence,

$$Q_{1,2} = U_2 - U_1 + \int_1^2 P\,\mathrm{d}V \tag{5.59}$$

or

$$\mathrm{d}Q = \mathrm{d}U + P\,\mathrm{d}V, \tag{5.59a}$$

and we can put

$$U_2 - U_1 = (H_2 - H_1) - (P_2 V_2 - P_1 V_1)$$

or

$$dU = dH - d(PV),$$

and consequently,

$$Q_{1,2} = H_2 - H_1 - \int_1^2 V\,dP \tag{5.60}$$

or

$$dQ = dH - V\,dP. \tag{5.60a}$$

The pairs of equations, (5.59) and (5.60), and (5.59a) together with (5.60a) are entirely equivalent. They differ merely by the variables used in them. Equation (5.60) contains the integral $W_t = - \int V\,dP$ which is sometimes called *technical work*; the Pfaffian $dW_t = -V\,dP$ is the element of technical work, and its mathematical properties are those of the integrand of a line integral. Geometrically, technical work can be interpreted as the line integral of vector $\mathbf{F}_t\ (0, -P)$ or as the area contained between the diagram of the reversible process and the axis of ordinates. Referring to Figure 5.32, it is easy to see that

$$\text{area } a21b = - \int_1^2 V\,dP,$$

whereas

$$\text{area } c12d = + \int_1^2 P\,dV.$$

It is clear that instead of a chemical system which performs work by compression or expansion, any one of the simple systems discussed in Section 4.8 could become of interest. In such cases it is sufficient to regard P as the generalized force Y and V as the generalized displacement Z.

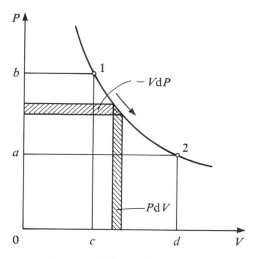

FIGURE 5.32. *Technical work.*

We would then write

$$Q_{1,2} = H_2 - H_1 - \int_1^2 Z\, dY \qquad (5.61)$$

$$dQ = dH - Z\, dY \qquad (5.61a)$$

for any reversible process in a closed system. Clearly, the enthalpy is here treated as a function of the variables Y and Z.

5.14.7   *Quasistatic, irreversible processes*

The individual processes discussed earlier can also be imagined performed quasistatically and irreversibly. In each case, the equation of the process, $V = $ const, $P = $ const, $U = $ const, and so on, will be the same as for the corresponding reversible process. The difference, we emphasize again, consists in the fact that the system finds itself in a state of near-equilibrium at each stage instead of being in equilibrium. Consequently, the state point which describes the near-equilibrium state of the system on a diagram represents that equilibrium state which would set in if the system were enclosed in an adiabatic envelope and allowed to reach a true state of equilibrium. It follows that a state point represents a near-equilibrium state only approximately.

The second difference consists in the fact that the work performed during the process can no longer be described in terms of the properties of the system and in the form of a Pfaffian expression. In particular, for a simple chemical system

$$dW \neq P\, dV, \qquad (5.62)$$

and in general

$$dW \neq Y\, dZ. \qquad (5.62a)$$

In all cases, and at every step in the process

$$dE = dQ - dW \qquad (5.63)$$

or

$$dU = dQ - dW, \qquad (5.63a)$$

if $E = U$. Whereas the perfect differentials dE and dU can be computed from the known equation of the process and the known properties of the system, the heat dQ and work dW cannot be computed without the knowledge of further details concerning each process.

5.15   The principle of energy conservation and the statistical interpretation of thermal processes

The microscopic description of the state of a system enables us to study its thermodynamic properties in terms of the averages of certain quantities associated with the chaotic movement of the molecules of matter. The possibility of doing so rests on the hypothesis that matter consists of discrete particles, and as a consequence, all problems concerned with the behavior of substances under different conditions are reduced to a statistical study of the motion of the particular mechanical model under consideration in each case. This motion is studied in terms of Newtonian mechanics in classical statistical mechanics or in terms of quantum mechanics in quantum statistical mechanics. In the light of this hypothesis, the First Law of thermodynamics reduces to a statement that the energy of an isolated system is conserved, that is, that no dissipative forces are present in a system in equilibrium. Hence, the energy of a system, the sum of the kinetic and potential energies of all the elementary particles, is associated with the state of the system, and constitutes a potential. It is not a property in the strict sense of the word, because energies of particles can only be measured with respect to an arbitrary reference state. For example, the molecule of a gas whose instantaneous velocity is zero need not necessarily have zero energy, because the atoms in the molecule may vibrate with respect to each other or the atoms may rotate in a complex manner about the center of mass of the molecule and so on.

In other words, the mechanical, microscopic model of a thermodynamic system must be conservative.

When the system interacts with its surroundings so that work and heat cross its boundary, it is postulated that an exchange of energy takes place between the molecules of the system and the molecules of the surroundings owing to mechanical interactions taking place between them. Thus both work and heat affect the motion of the molecules, and so also the energy of the system. The First Law of thermodynamics, in the extended form given in equation (5.18), merely expresses the fact that the change in the energy of the system is balanced by a flux of energy which arises at its boundary as a result of interactions with the molecules of the surroundings.

This view also explains the fact that the performance of work or the addition of heat must necessarily occur irreversibly in nature. The molecular interaction will usually commence after the removal of some constraint, and will first occur at the boundary. Thus, at the boundary the statistical averages will differ from those at the interior, because the latter will change only later, owing to subsequent interactions between the molecules in the system. Hence, microscopically, the system will appear to have departed from equilibrium. Another state of equilibrium will set in after the lapse of a sufficient period of time after the interaction with the surroundings has ended. Then, once again, the statistical averages throughout the system will have assumed equilibrium values.

Similar considerations apply to long-range interactions through fields or through radiation; these will be mentioned in Chapter 8, but a more detailed discussion of such problems would exceed the scope of this course.

List of Symbols for Chapter 5

Latin letters

A	Heat equivalent of mechanical energy, $= 1/J$
C	Parameter
C_p	Heat capacity at constant pressure P
c_p	Specific heat at constant pressure P
C_v	Heat capacity at constant volume V
c_v	Specific heat at constant volume v
$\overline{C_v}$	Mean heat capacity at constant volume V between two specified temperatures

$\bar{c}_v$	Mean specific heat at constant volume v between two specified temperatures
E	Electric potential; energy
e	Specific energy
$\mathcal{E}$	Electromotive force
F	Force
G	Weight
g	Gravitational acceleration
H	Enthalpy
h	Specific enthalpy; linear displacement
I	Electric current
$\mathbf{J}$	Mechanical equivalent at heat, $= 1/\mathbf{A}$
M	Function defined by equation (5.55a)
m	Mass
N	Function defined by equation (5.55a)
P	Pressure
P_a	Atmospheric pressure
Q	Heat
R	Radius, Figure 5.14; gas constant
r	Radius, Figure 5.14
t	Time
U	Internal energy
u	Specific internal energy
V	Volume
v	Specific volume
$\mathcal{V}$	Velocity
W	Work
W_{ad}	Adiabatic work
W_t	Technical work
z	Coordinate

Greek letters

γ	Isentropic index or ratio of specific heats ($= c_p/c_v$)
θ	Temperature, specifically when measured on an empirical temperature scale
ψ	Constant of integration in equation (5.38)

CHAPTER 6

Introduction to the Analysis of
Continuous Systems and the First Law
of Thermodynamics for Open Systems

6.1 Continuous systems

So far, we have established the existence of equations of state only in relation to macroscopic systems whose state could be described by indicating a small number of measurable, macroscopic independent variables. In particular, when employing intensive or specific variables, we have restricted our attention to systems in which their values were the same for whole homogeneous regions of the system. A moment's reflection convinces us that such relatively simple systems constitute the exception rather than the rule. For example, when a system performs an irreversible process, it is observed that certain intensive or specific properties seem to vary in them from point to point. Similarly, when certain systems are placed in gravitational or centrifugal fields, the intensive and specific properties are observed to vary throughout them even in cases when the system can be said to be in equilibrium.

We shall describe such systems by calling them *continuous systems*, conforming to the observation that certain of their measurable properties vary in them *continuously* from point to point in space. Since such systems occur very frequently in applications, the problem of describing their state naturally forces itself upon our attention.

6.2 Examples of continuous systems

We shall first consider in some detail a number of examples of continuous systems in order to obtain an observational basis for their subsequent classification.

6.2.1 Column of gas in gravitational field

As our first example, we propose to discuss a large column of gas of cross-sectional area A, say a column of air several miles high, placed in the terrestrial, gravitational field, and shown sketched in Figure 6.1. The column of gas is assumed contained in a tall, adiabatic cylinder closed by a piston at the top, and it is clear from elementary considerations of mechanics that the pressure P must vary with elevation throughout

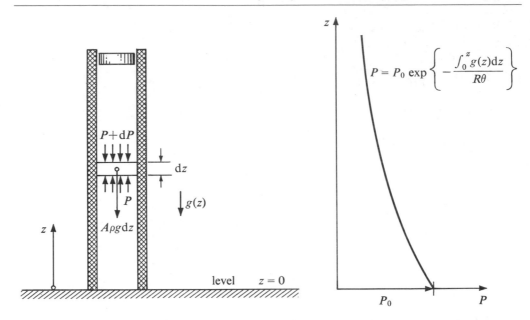

FIGURE 6.1. *Column of air in gravitational field.*

the column even in cases when there is no motion. In fact, concentrating on the balance of forces acting on an element of thickness dz, we shall find that it will be at rest if the net pressure force

$$-A\,dP$$

balances its weight†

$$-A\rho g\,dz.$$

Here, $\rho = 1/v$ denotes the density of the gas, and $g(z)$ is the variable acceleration due to gravity. Thus,

$$dP = -\rho g(z)dz. \tag{6.1}$$

If the properties of the gas can be approximated by those of its perfect counterpart, it is possible to determine its density, ρ, from the perfect-gas law

$$\rho = \frac{P}{R\theta}.$$

Substitution of this relation into equation (6.1) leads to the differential equation

$$\frac{dP}{P} = -\frac{g(z)dz}{R\theta} \tag{6.2}$$

for pressure. This equation can be integrated for a uniform temperature θ to yield

$$P = P_0 \exp\left\{-\frac{\displaystyle\int_0^z g(z)dz}{R\theta}\right\}, \tag{6.3}$$

† Their *sum* must be zero.

where P_0 denotes the pressure at $z = 0$. If the column is not excessively high, we may assume that $g = g_0$ is constant, when

$$P = P_0 \exp \left\{ -\frac{g_0 z}{R\theta} \right\}. \tag{6.3a}$$

Equations (6.3) and (6.3a) are known under the name of the *barometric formula* and express the variation in pressure P with altitude z which must exist in the absence of motion, that is, when mechanical equilibrium is preserved. Since for $\theta = \text{const}$, we have $P/P_0 = \rho/\rho_0$ for a perfect gas, the density variation is given by similar expressions, namely,

$$\rho = \rho_0 \exp \left\{ -\frac{\int_0^z g(z)\,dz}{R\theta} \right\} \tag{6.4}$$

or

$$\rho = \rho_0 \exp \left\{ -\frac{g_0 z}{R\theta} \right\}. \tag{6.4a}$$

It is seen that both the pressure P, and the density ρ, must vary continuously over the system, even if the temperature is constant, and in the absence of any motion. Similar conditions will prevail in a strong centrifugal field.

6.2.2   Fluid motion

When a gas expands behind a piston at a finite rate, Figure 6.2, the piston accelerates and acquires a finite velocity $\mathcal{V}_p$ at a given instant. The particles of the gas adjacent to the piston move with its velocity, whereas those adjacent to the closed end of the piston are at rest. Thus, along the cylinder, there will establish itself a continuous velocity distribution, as shown in the sketch. In actual fact, the velocity field established behind the piston will be more complex, because the particles adjacent to the vertical walls will be at rest too. In addition, as students familiar with fluid mechanics will appreciate, the flow of the gas behind the piston may become turbulent and much more complex than

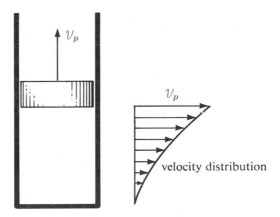

FIGURE 6.2. *Acceleration of piston by expanding gas.*

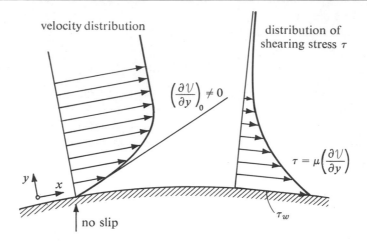

FIGURE 6.3. *The no-slip condition; velocity distribution near a wall.*

that suggested in the diagram, because at any point in the flow, the velocity will fluctuate in a random manner about a constant, or varying smooth mean value.

A so-called perfect fluid, that is, one which has no viscosity, can only transmit normal stresses. Thus, at a solid boundary in such a fluid, the forces acting on it will be normal to the boundary, and it must be assumed that perfect fluids slide along solid walls at rest. Although such a drastic idealization is often acceptable for the purposes of rough analysis, it must be realized that it is contrary to observation which reveals that all fluids, even those whose viscosity is very small, adhere to solid walls. Thus, at a solid wall, the relative velocity of the fluid is zero, Figure 6.3, and is said to satisfy the *no-slip condition*. On a microscopic scale, the existence of the no-slip condition is attributed to the presence of strong attractive intermolecular forces acting between the molecules of the fluid and those of the solid wall. Some slip does appear, however, when the fluid has extremely low density, such as would exist in a gas at pressures very much below atmospheric. We shall exclude this case from further consideration, because under such conditions, the fluid can no longer be treated as a continuum, and statistical methods must be used to analyze the flow.[†] In continuum flow, near a solid wall there appears a very large transverse velocity gradient $\partial \mathcal{V}/\partial y$. The product of this large velocity gradient and even a very small viscosity, μ, gives rise to a significant shearing stress

$$\tau = \mu \frac{\partial \mathcal{V}}{\partial y} \tag{6.5}$$

which decreases from

$$\tau_w = \mu \left(\frac{\partial \mathcal{V}}{\partial y} \right)_0 \tag{6.5a}$$

at the wall to a very small value further inside the stream, Figure 6.3. Here, $(\partial \mathcal{V}/\partial y)_0$ denotes the velocity gradient at the wall itself, and a partial derivative has been used because the velocity $\mathcal{V}$ may vary downstream with x as well as across it, with y.

[†] See, for example, Hayes, W. D., and Probstein, R. F., *Hypersonic Flow Theory* (Academic, 1959).

As a rule, the large velocity gradient is confined to a narrow zone near the wall, known as the *boundary layer*.† Throughout the boundary layer, the velocity varies continuously with position, and is represented by a *velocity field*.

6.2.3   The transfer of heat

A continuous system is also created when heat is transferred into it at a finite rate $\dot{Q}$ from a source of a different temperature, say θ_1, as shown in Figure 6.4. The parts of the system adjacent to the source acquire a temperature which is very close to θ_1, whereas those at larger distances will have different, say lower temperatures. Throughout the system we shall observe a continuous temperature field, analogous to the velocity field in Figure 6.2. When the system is at rest, as is the case with a solid body or a very thin layer of fluid, we say that heat is transferred through the continuous system by *conduction*.

In the gravitational field of the earth, differences in temperature in a fluid—liquid or gas—produce differences in density and very frequently motion is created within the continuous system, so that a velocity field is superimposed on the temperature field. Sometimes, as in the example sketched in Figure 6.5, the fluid is induced to flow over a solid wall with a *forced* motion. In both cases it is said that heat is transferred by *convection*, natural or free convection in the first case, and forced convection in the latter case.

In convection, the change in temperature also usually occurs across a very thin *thermal boundary layer*.

Heat may also be transferred by *radiation* from one system to another when the two are not in contact. Heat is then transmitted by action at a distance in the form of electromagnetic waves which do not require the presence of a material medium for their propagation.

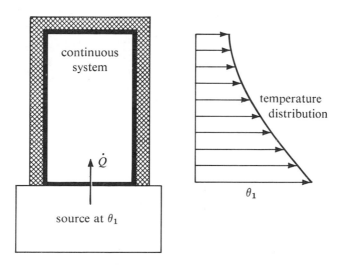

FIGURE 6.4. *Transfer of heat at a finite rate.*

---

† See Schlichting, H., *Boundary Layer Theory*, translated by J. Kestin (4th ed.; McGraw-Hill, 1960).

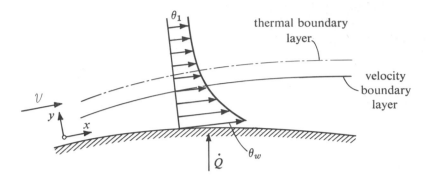

FIGURE 6.5. *Thermal boundary layer.*

A temperature field can be created in a fluid stream by the action of internal shearing stresses even when there exists no imposed temperature difference between the fluid and a wall. The process, described as the dissipation of energy by shear forces, is analogous to that which was discussed in Section 5.12 in connection with dry friction.

The detailed relations which exist between the rate of heat transferred, Q, the temperature difference $\theta_w - \theta_1$, the characteristics of the motion, and the properties of the fluid are studied as a separate subject—that of *heat transfer*.

6.3   The state of a continuous system

The preceding examples show that the state of a continuous system requires the specification of several *functions* rather than of several variables, as was the case with the simpler systems treated so far. For ease of expression, we shall refer to the latter as to *uniform systems*. In other words, in order to extend our earlier concepts and results, we proceed in a manner undoubtedly known to the reader from his study of the other branches of engineering science and applied without explanation in Section 6.2.1 in the course of the derivation of the barometric formula.

Faced with a continuous system, Figure 6.6, we focus our attention on a small element of volume ΔV centered on an internal point i and imagine that the small system has been isolated from the rest by an adiabatic enclosure. At first let us assume that the system is at rest and that it is not exposed to the action of a gravitational, electric, or magnetic field of varying intensity, and that it is chemically homogeneous. Under these conditions, the element ΔV will reach thermodynamic equilibrium and its pressure, temperature, and so on will reach the equilibrium values $\overline{\theta}_i, \overline{P}_i, \ldots$. In general, these values will differ from element to element. Passing to the limit $\Delta V \to 0$ so as to shrink the volume to point i, that is, extrapolating the values of the parameters $\overline{\theta}_i, \overline{P}_i, \ldots$ to zero volume, we shall observe that they tend to definite limits

$$\theta_i = \lim_{\Delta V \to 0} \overline{\theta}_i, \; P_i = \lim_{\Delta V \to 0} \overline{P}_i, \ldots .$$

These values are then ascribed to the point i to which the volume ΔV has been contracted, and the procedure is identical with that discussed in Section 1.7. As before, complications which arise from the particulate structure of matter are ignored.

In this manner it is concluded that the state of a *continuous system* is described by a number of *continuous functions*. In the general case the local or point values will vary with the spatial coordinates x, y, z at any given instant. Thus, the *state* is described by a number of functions of position x, y, z or by a number of fields, for example $\theta = \theta(x, y, z)$; $P = P(x, y, z)$; and so on, *at instant t*. When time is included in the fields as a variable

$$\theta = \theta(x, y, z, t); \qquad P = P(x, y, z, t),$$

a *process* undergone by the continuous system is described.

It is worth noting that an analogous method of description is used when the principles of point dynamics are extended to include continua.†

When a chemical reaction is in progress within the system, we shall imagine that upon isolating an element ΔV an *anticatalyst* is introduced so that the chemical composition is *frozen*, or inhibited, instantaneously. When the system is immersed in a gravitational, electric, or magnetic field of varying intensity, as was the case with the air column in Section 6.2.1, we shall imagine that it has been replaced by one of constant intensity upon isolation, namely, that intensity which corresponds to point i. Finally, in the presence of motion, we shall stipulate that equilibrium is attained in the elementary system while it moves with a uniform velocity, representative of the point i to which the volume ΔV is contracted.

When all these possibilities are taken into account, it will be concluded that the description of the state of a continuous system involves the specification of a number of scalar fields, vector fields, and even tensor fields, particularly if distributed stresses come into play.

6.4 Principle of local state

Having obtained a satisfactory description of the state of a continuous system, it is clearly necessary to answer a number of important questions before a mathematical analysis of the system can be undertaken.

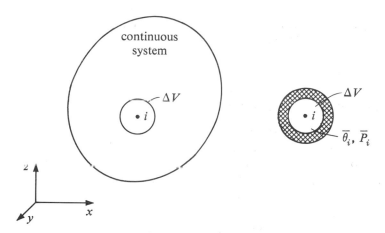

FIGURE 6.6. *State of a continuous system.*

† See, for example, Prager, W., *Introduction to Mechanics of Continua* (Ginn, 1961).

The first question which poses itself is whether the description by means of fields is adequate. More precisely, it is noted that at any point and at any instant, there will exist throughout the field *gradients* of every property in question. In the example shown in Figure 6.1 there exist the gradients dP/dx and $d\rho/dx$ of pressure and density. In Figure 6.2 there exists a velocity gradient dV/dx which may be accompanied by pressure, temperature, and density gradients . . . . It is, therefore, necessary to inquire whether these gradients are also needed to complete the description. This question is evidently related to the existence of equations of state which link the local and instantaneous values of the thermodynamic properties of a continuous system. Specifically, does a relation of this kind depend on the local and instantaneous *values* of the thermodynamic parameters, or is it necessary to include the rates, or gradients, with which they vary locally?

Clearly, questions of this kind can only be answered with reference to experiment, if the macroscopic view of classical thermodynamics is adopted. In this matter, experience seems to lead to the realization that the *local and instantaneous relations between the thermodynamic properties of a continuous system*, that is, the relations which tie together the values of the properties observed simultaneously at a point in space at a particular instant of time *are the same as for a uniform system in equilibrium*; they are, therefore, independent of the values of the local gradients. In other words, any equation of state of a uniform system in equilibrium applies to the local and instantaneous state of a continuous system. In the future, we shall refer to the preceding statement as the *principle of local state*.

The principle of local state is certainly true when the gradients are not very large. The question as to *how* large these gradients must become for departures to arise cannot be completely answered other than by experiment. The problem can be studied theoretically in more detail with the aid of statistical mechanics, but even there, at the present state of our knowledge, no unequivocal answer can be given. Instead, we accept the validity of the principle of local state by inference, as usual. For our purposes, it is sufficient to say that the study of fluid mechanics, heat transfer, elasticity, electromagnetic theory, and of many other branches of engineering science is based on the acceptance of its validity. The circumstance that all these studies lead to results which agree with experiment leads us to accept the truth of this hypothesis, recognizing that it represents an acceptable approximation even though its universal validity cannot be asserted.

6.5   The mass and energy of a continuous system

Since the mass and energy of a collection of systems is equal to the sum of the masses and energies of them all, the mass and energy of a continuous system must be evaluated by integration over the volume of the system for a particular instant. The same is, of course, true about all the *extensive* properties of a continuous system.

If $\rho(x, y, z, t)$ is the density distribution, then the mass of the system is given by

$$m = \int_V \rho(x, y, z, t) \, dV, \qquad (6.6)$$

where the integral is taken over the whole volume. Similarly, if E denotes any extensive property, in particular the energy, and if $e(x, y, z, t)$ denotes the distribution of this property over the system in terms of the specific property per unit mass, $e = dE/dm$, then

$$E = \int_V \rho(x, y, z, t) \cdot e(x, y, z, t)\, dV. \tag{6.7}$$

It should be noted that the time t plays the part of a parameter during the evaluation of this integral, because the state is determined at an instant, the passage of time being associated with a thermodynamic *process*.

6.6 The First Law of thermodynamics

The last question which we must answer in relation to continuous system concerns the validity of the First Law of thermodynamics, and, indeed, of the other laws of thermodynamics which are usually formulated for uniform systems. Here, too, the simplest answer, namely, that the laws of thermodynamics retain their validity, seems to fit the experimental facts.

Explicitly, we assert that *the First Law of thermodynamics applies to any continuous system as well as to any part of it, however small.*

6.7 The First Law of thermodynamics for a closed, continuous system at rest

We shall now apply the First Law of thermodynamics to a closed, continuous system at rest. A process in a continuous system is studied in terms of time elapsed, as already stated. Accordingly, we envisage two infinitely close states, state 1 which prevails at time t, and state 2 which prevails at time $t + dt$, and consider a reversible or irreversible, quasistatic process $1 \to 2$. During this time, the energy E of the system will change by dE, and the rate of change of energy with time must be computed as an integral extended over the volume V of the system; evidently, the volume V need not remain constant. Referring to equation (6.7), we can write

$$dE = \left\{ \frac{d}{dt} \int_V \rho e\, dV \right\} dt. \tag{6.8}$$

The terms dQ and dW in the equation of the First Law denote the total amounts of heat and work, respectively, which have been absorbed by the continuous system. In this connection it is useful to amplify the remark made in Section 4.9 relative to uniform systems, and to recognize the existence of a greater variety of cases when continuous systems are included.

When a continuous system interacts with its surroundings, or when the interaction between an elementary continuous system and the whole system is considered, it is useful to make a distinction between short-range and long-range interactions.

Short-range interactions take place across the boundary of the system. As far as the transfer of heat is concerned, either conduction or convection may be involved. Work can be transferred by forces distributed around the boundary, or by the flow of an electric current across it. It must be recognized that the rate at which heat or work crosses the boundary per unit time and area may vary continuously around the boundary. Thus, the heat dQ and the work dW absorbed by the system during a time interval dt must be computed with the aid of surface integrals extended over the instantaneous surface of the boundary. It follows that in any particular problem we shall be faced with the task of determining the distribution of the flux of heat $\dot{\mathbf{q}}$ throughout the system, and particularly around a deforming boundary. This is the general problem of heat transfer which will not be treated in this book. At this stage we shall confine our remarks to the statement that the heat flux $\dot{\mathbf{q}}$, that is, the rate of heat transferred per unit time and area, is a vector quantity, as will be proved in Volume II; consequently, the short-range interaction in the mode of heat is fully described by a vector field

$$\dot{\mathbf{q}} = \dot{\mathbf{q}}(x, y, z, t).$$

The heat flux $\dot{\mathbf{q}}$ is measured in the following, alternative units

$$\{\dot{\mathbf{q}}\} = \frac{\text{kJ}}{\text{m}^2\text{sec}}; \quad \frac{\text{kcal}}{\text{m}^2\text{sec}}; \quad \frac{\text{lbf ft}}{\text{ft}^2\text{sec}}; \quad \frac{\text{Btu}}{\text{ft}^2\text{sec}};$$

frequently,

$$1 \text{ h} = 3600 \text{ sec}$$

is employed as the unit of time in preference to the second, in order to obtain a more convenient unit of heat flux.

The short-range interaction in the manner of work will be discussed in more detail in Sections 6.11 and 6.15 for some simple cases, and in more general terms in Volume II. At this stage, we shall merely remark that a full description of this interaction requires the specification of a *tensor field* of stress, $\boldsymbol{\sigma}(x, y, z, t)$ together with a *vector field* of displacements.

The long-range interaction in the manner of heat occurs through radiation. The long-range interaction in the manner of work occurs through the intervention of body forces created throughout a continuous system by the application of external fields. These may include gravitational fields, electrostatic fields, magnetostatic and electromagnetic fields, and so on. In all these cases, the quantities dQ and dW are obtained by volume integrals.

Introducing the preceding expression for dE into the equation $dQ - dW = dE$, and dividing through by dt, we obtain

$$\frac{dQ}{dt} - \frac{dW}{dt} = \frac{d}{dt} \int_V \rho e \, dV. \tag{6.9}$$

The left-hand side of the equation contains the difference between the total rate of heat flow

$$\dot{Q} = \frac{dQ}{dt} \tag{6.10}$$

and that of the total rate of flow of work

$$\dot{W} = \frac{dW}{dt}, \tag{6.10a}$$

and the equation expresses the balance between these two rates of flow and the time-rate of change of energy throughout the volume of the system. Thus, equation (6.9) can also be written

$$\dot{Q} - \dot{W} = \frac{d}{dt} \int_V \rho e \, dV. \tag{6.11}$$

Since the mass of the closed system remains constant, we can perform the differentiation, noting that

$$\frac{d}{dt} \int_V e(\rho \, dV) = \int_V \frac{de}{dt} (\rho \, dV) + \int_V e \frac{d}{dt} (\rho \, dV).$$

The second integral vanishes,† and the preceding equation can be simplified to

$$\dot{Q} - \dot{W} = \int_V \dot{e} \rho \, dV, \tag{6.12}$$

where

$$\dot{e} = \frac{de}{dt}. \tag{6.12a}$$

This equation indicates that the difference between the time-rate of flow of heat and work is equal to the integral of the product of local density into the local rate of change of specific energy, the integral being evaluated over the instantaneous volume V. The specific energy $e(x, y, z, t)$, its rate of change with time $\dot{e}(x, y, z, t)$, and the density $\rho(x, y, z, t)$ are all represented by time-dependent scalar fields.

The changes which must be introduced in the preceding considerations in the presence of motion will be discussed in Volume II, it being clear that no changes are required if the continuous system moves like a rigid body. In the latter case, however, the energy must include the kinetic and potential energy terms $\frac{1}{2}m\mathcal{V}^2$ and mgz.

6.8   Extension of the concept of equilibrium; steady state

Continuous systems are seldom studied in all their generality. Most frequently, attention is centered on processes in continuous systems during which the *local state* at every point throughout the system is *independent of time*. A system of this kind,

---

† The above derivation is not rigorous. By remembering that the volume, V, of the system is treated here as a function of time, use can be made of the general formula

$$\frac{d}{dt} \int_{V(t)} f(x, y, z, t) \, dV = \int_{V(t)} \frac{\partial f}{\partial t} \, dV + \int_{A(t)} f \times (\mathbf{v} \cdot \mathbf{n}) \, dA, \tag{a}$$

where A denotes the surface of the simply connected three-dimensional region V, $\mathbf{v}$ is the velocity of a point on A, and $\mathbf{n}$ denotes the outward normal at that point.

In our problem $f(x, y, z, t) = e(x, y, z, t)\rho(x, y, z, t)$, and

$$\frac{d}{dt} \int_{V(t)} \rho(x, y, z, t) \, dV = 0$$

for a closed system owing to mass conservation.

For a more rigorous proof see Prager, W., *Introduction to Mechanics of Continua* (Ginn, 1961), p. 75. An elementary proof in one dimension (easily extended to three) is given in Courant, R., *Differential and Integral Calculus* (London: Blackie, 1936), Vol. II, p. 220.

regardless of whether it is open or closed, is said to be in *steady state*. Steady-state systems play a very important part in engineering applications, and the reader is certainly aware of the fact that the majority of systems studied in elementary fluid mechanics, electromagnetic theory, elasticity, and so on are, in fact, steady-state systems.

In steady-state systems, the local rate of change of specific energy is zero, so that

$$\frac{\mathrm{d}}{\mathrm{d}t} \int_V \rho e \, \mathrm{d}V = \int_V \rho \dot{e} \, \mathrm{d}V = 0. \qquad (6.12b)$$

Hence, in steady state

$$\dot{Q} - \dot{W} = 0 \qquad \text{(steady state).} \qquad (6.13)$$

In order to maintain a steady state it is, therefore, necessary to balance the rate of heat flow with that of the performance of work. More specifically, if work is done on the system ($\dot{W} < 0$), its equivalent must be extracted in the form of heat by cooling ($\dot{Q} < 0$). Conversely, if the system performs work ($\dot{W} > 0$), the equivalent in heat must be supplied to it ($\dot{Q} > 0$). We can summarize these statements by asserting that a system in steady state transforms heat into work or vice versa in the same way as a cycle.

It is useful explicitly to remember that the volume of a closed system in steady-state must be maintained constant. Thus, a closed system in steady state cannot perform work by deforming its boundary. It follows also that equation (6.13) constitutes a necessary condition for the system to be in steady state, but the condition is not a sufficient one, for it is easy to visualize systems in which the rate of performing work balances the rate of heat exchange thus conserving the energy of the system, without the rate of change of specific energy $\dot{e}$ being constant and independent of time at every point within the system. For example, this will occur in a system which changes its volume at a given rate, the work of expansion or compression being completely balanced by an exchange of heat.

A special case of steady state occurs when the system exchanges neither heat ($\dot{Q} = 0$) nor work ($\dot{W} = 0$) with the surroundings. As we already know from the considerations of Chapter 2, a system will reach a state of equilibrium under such conditions. In the presence of external fields, as was the case with the column of air discussed in Section 6.2.1, the system will remain a continuous one, and will not be classed as a system in equilibrium by our previous definitions. Nevertheless, it is useful to extend the concept of equilibrium to such cases also, and to *say* that an isolated continuous system in steady state is in equilibrium. The pressure and density are no longer constant throughout a chemically homogeneous portion of the system, but are said to have reached an *equilibrium distribution*.

Since equation (6.12) provides a relation between the *rate* of heat flow, $\dot{Q}$, the *rate* of work flow, $\dot{W}$, and the local *rate* of change of energy, it is often referred to as a *rate equation*.

6.9   Reversible and irreversible processes in continuous systems

When a continuous system undergoes a process, the process is described as a reversible one if the process undergone by every subsystem, however small, is reversible; otherwise it is irreversible.

The case of a reversible process in a *uniform system* is, evidently, contained in equation (6.12) as a special one. When the system is in equilibrium at every step during the process, the rate of change of energy, $\dot{e}$, is constant throughout every homogeneous part of the system, and the same applies to density. Hence,

$$\int_V \rho \dot{e} \, dV = \rho \dot{e} V = m\dot{e},$$

since $\rho V = m$. In this manner, equation (6.12) assumes the trivial form

$$\dot{Q} - \dot{W} = m \frac{de}{dt},$$

which is identical with

$$dQ - dW = dE$$

for every homogeneous part, as must have been expected. Here, dW may be replaced by the appropriate expression for reversible work in terms of the properties of the system.

6.10   Formulation of the First Law for open systems

In the preceding chapter and in Section 6.7, we have concentrated on an exhaustive formulation and discussion of the First Law in terms of a closed system. In principle this should be adequate for all applications of thermodynamics because, as pointed out repeatedly before, any process can be discussed in terms of a closed system by a suitable choice of the boundary. Nevertheless, an examination of most prime movers and thermal machines used in engineering reveals that the need for continually providing fictitious membranes or fictitious cylinders and pistons is awkward and cumbersome in practice. It is clearly advantageous to attempt to do it once and for all by recasting the First Law into a form which would contain exclusively parameters relating to an open system. This we shall now proceed to do in general terms, carefully noting the additional, restrictive assumptions which are required for the purpose.

We shall formulate the First Law for open systems in two steps. First we shall discuss the less general case of a steady-state open system, and then we shall consider the case of nonsteady processes. Thus, we shall proceed from the particular to the more general case for ease of comprehension. In principle, it would be sufficient to concentrate on the second, treating the first one as a special case.

6.11   Steady-state open systems

In line with the general concept of steadiness in fluid mechanics and in other branches of physics, we have described a system as being in a steady state when all its properties were invariant with respect to time. Very frequently open systems encountered in applications are continuous systems admitting different fluids through several channels and discharging mixtures or products of reactions with them through others. In such cases, a system will be classed as being in steady state when all local properties are time independent, that is, when all the fields discussed in Section 6.3 depend on the

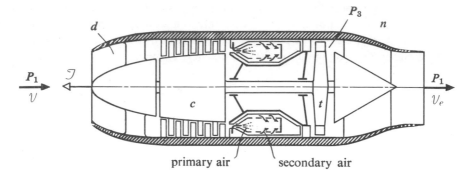

FIGURE 6.7. *Cross section of gas-turbine jet engine.*

coordinates *x, y, z* only but not on time, in complete analogy with a closed continuous system.

The gas-turbine jet engine, depicted in simplified cross section in Figure 6.7 and schematically in Figure 6.8, affords an example of such an open system in steady state. The engine consists of a turbocompressor *c* which ingests air from the atmosphere at pressure P_1 through a diffuser *d* and compresses it to a higher pressure P_2. The compressed air passes into the combustion chamber *C*, where it is divided into two streams, a primary and a secondary. The primary stream is used to provide oxygen to burn the liquid fuel injected into the combustion chamber through channel *f*. This is done to ensure good combustion, because too high an air-fuel ratio would adversely affect the flame. The temperature of the resulting combustion gases is too high for the material of the turbine blades, and in order to reduce the temperature, the combustion gases are mixed with the secondary air, and the mixture of air and combustion gases is then discharged to the turbine *t*. The gases expand in the turbine from a pressure somewhat lower than P_2, owing to losses, to a pressure P_3 which is higher than the atmospheric pressure P_1. The operation is so arranged that the net power output $\dot{W}_t$ of the turbine is equal to the power $\dot{W}_c$ required to operate the turbocompressor. The mixture of air and combustion gases which had been previously expanded to pressure P_3 in the turbine is now passed through the nozzle *n*, where it is finally expanded to a pressure

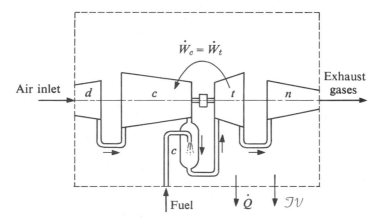

FIGURE 6.8. *Schematic diagram of gas-turbine jet engine.*

which is close to the atmospheric pressure P_1. In the nozzle, the working fluid acquires a high exit velocity V_e (usually expressed as a relative velocity with respect to the aircraft) directed towards the rear of the engine and thus provides the thrust $\mathcal{J}$ which drives the aircraft.

If, as shown in the schematic diagram of Figure 6.8, the boundary of the open system is drawn to include the diffuser d, the turbocompressor c, the combustion chamber C, the turbine t, and nozzle n, an open system is obtained. This open system is crossed by matter at the diffuser inlet, where air is admitted; at the fuel line, where kerosene is admitted; and at the nozzle exit, where the mixture of combustion gases and air is discharged. Further, the boundary transmits heat at a rate $\dot{Q}$ to the surroundings. The rate of heat transmission is usually not very large and may often be neglected in a first analysis. Finally, the nozzle supplies the thrust $\mathcal{J}$, and if the aircraft moves at an "absolute" velocity of flight V, work at the rate $\mathcal{J}V$ crosses the boundary of the system. No work crosses if the engine is at rest, for example on a test stand.

It should be clear to the reader that an open system in steady state must be provided with at least two channels, one through which a fluid enters the system and another through which it leaves it. For, otherwise, mass would accumulate inside it, or be discharged from it, and the local states would necessarily vary with time. It is also clear that a steady-state open system contains a constant mass.

Very frequently, the flow velocities at entry and exit as well as throughout the system are so small that the kinetic energy associated with them can be disregarded entirely. We shall begin our analysis by considering the simplest open steady-state system, Figure 6.9, that is, one provided with an entrance at 1, an exit at 2, and one in which the flow into and out of it is "infinitely slow" and yet occurs at a finite mass-rate $\dot{m}$ (lbm/sec or kg/sec). The system is assumed to perform (electrical and shaft) work at a rate $\dot{W}$ and to exchange heat at a rate $\dot{Q}$, both rates being constant, as required by the condition of steadiness.

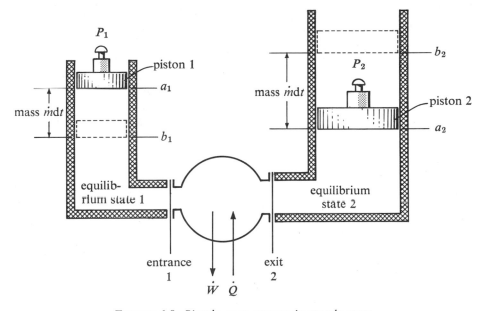

FIGURE 6.9. *Simple open system in steady state.*

In order to write the First Law for this system, it is first necessary to close it, because so far the First Law has been formulated for closed systems only. The system can be converted into a closed one in one of two ways. It can be closed by adding to it fictitious adiabatic cylinders and pistons, as shown in Figure 6.9, where it has been assumed that inside each cylinder the fluid between the entrance section 1 and piston 1 is at equilibrium at state 1 which corresponds to that of the inflowing fluid. A similar assumption is, evidently, made about the state of the fluid between the exit 2 and the fictitious piston 2. This mode of closing the system corresponds to the use of Euler's method of description in fluid mechanics. The second possibility which corresponds to Lagrange's method of description, consists in selecting an arbitrary mass of fluid, say a unit mass, at equilibrium at state 1, and in analyzing the processes undergone by it as it passes through the system and emerges at equilibrium state 2 at exit. The work W done and the heat Q exchanged by a unit mass are then

$$W = \frac{\dot{W}}{\dot{m}} \quad \text{and} \quad Q = \frac{\dot{Q}}{\dot{m}}. \tag{6.14}$$

Concentrating on the Eulerian description, we suppose that we observe the system during an interval of time dt during which a mass $\dot{m}\, dt$ of fluid at state 1 enters the system at 1, an equal mass leaving it at state 2. During this interval the left-hand fictitious piston will move from a_1 to b_1, and the right-hand piston will move, likewise, from a_2 to b_2. Thus, the closed system is observed from an initial state a to a final state b. During the process from state a to state b of the closed system, a mass $\dot{m}\, dt$ of fluid at state 1 has been forced into the open system, a mass $\dot{m}\, dt$ of fluid at state 2 has been forced out of the open system, and the open system exchanged a quantity of heat $\dot{Q}\, dt$, performed a quantity of work $\dot{W}\, dt$ at its own boundary and two quantities of work

$$- \dot{m}\, dt\, P_1 v_1 \quad \text{and} \quad + \dot{m}\, dt\, P_2 v_2 \tag{6.15}$$

at the fictitious pistons. In writing these last expressions it is assumed that the fictitious pistons are displaced infinitely slowly, so that at each piston

$$W_p = \dot{m}\, dt \int P\, dv.$$

Since the state does not change at either end, the two pressures, P_1 and P_2 remain constant, and the expressions in equation (6.15) result. The work of the left-hand piston is done *on* the system, and is negative, the opposite being true about the right-hand piston.

Substituting these values into the First Law in the form

$$Q = E_2 - E_1 + W_{1,2}, \tag{6.16}$$

we obtain, after dividing by dt, that

$$\dot{Q} - \dot{W} = \dot{m} \left\{ (u_2 + P_2 v_2) - (u_1 + P_1 v_1) \right\}, \tag{6.16a}$$

because the energy of the continuous system contained between b_1 and a_2 remains constant. The change in energy is equal to

$$\frac{d}{dt} \int_V \rho \cdot u(x, y, z)\, dV = 0$$

as shown in equation (6.12b), where the integration extends over a volume — that enclosed by the boundary and surfaces b_1 and a_1 — within which nothing changes during the process $a \rightarrow b$, that is, during time dt.

Remembering that the specific enthalpy, equation (5.42a), has been defined as

$$h = u + Pv,$$

we have

$$\dot{Q} - \dot{W} = \dot{m}(h_2 - h_1). \tag{6.17}$$

This is one of the most important equations in engineering thermodynamics. For obvious reasons it is sometimes referred to as the *enthalpy theorem*, or as the *steady-flow energy equation*. In this connection many authors prefer to describe the open system by referring to it as the contents within a *control volume*.

6.12   Finite entrance velocity and large change in elevation

The enthalpy theorem in equation (6.17) has been derived under the drastic simplifying assumption that the entrance as well as the exit velocity are "infinitely small," and that the transfer of the fluid from equilibrium state 1 to equilibrium state 2 does not involve a change in elevation in the terrestrial gravitational field. Furthermore, it has been assumed, also by way of simplification, that the fictitious systems contained between piston 1 and entrance at 1, as well as between exit at 2 and piston 2, were uniform, whereas the actual open system between entrance 1 and exit 2 was a continuous one, the process occurring within it being reversible or irreversible. In actual applications real fluids will enter and leave the system with finite velocities, as explained on the example of the jet engine in Figures 6.7 and 6.8. Furthermore, in hydraulic turbines or in water pumps the entrance and exit sections may be located at widely differing elevations, and it is necessary to examine the effect of such complications on the form of equation (6.17).

First, we examine the effect of finite velocities at entrance and exit bearing in mind the remarks made about real fluids and their idealization to perfect fluids in Section 6.2.2. The problem consists in examining the means whereby the open system can be turned into a closed one, and of the form of the expression for the work performed by the fictitious boundaries which corresponds to our previous equation (6.15).

6.12.1   Perfect-fluid assumption

The simplest case occurs when the perfect-fluid assumption is adequate, and when the no-slip condition can be ignored. In this case, as intimated in Figure 6.10, the system can still be closed by the introduction of two fictitious pistons, each moving with the respective velocity — $\mathcal{V}_1$ at inlet and $\mathcal{V}_2$ at exit. Since the fluid slides along the fictitious walls, its velocity will be uniform over the cross sections; it moves in the manner of a slug sliding along the walls of the ducts.

In such idealized circumstances the fluid will enter at a rate†

$$\dot{m}_1 = \rho_1 \mathcal{V}_1 A_1$$

† For a more detailed derivation see Section 6.17.4, equation (6.72).

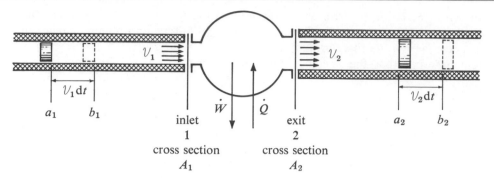

FIGURE 6.10. *Enthalpy theorem for perfect fluid flowing with finite velocity.*

and will leave at a rate

$$\dot{m}_2 = \rho_2 V_2 A_2,$$

where ρ_1, ρ_2 is the density at inlet and exit, and A_1, A_2 are the two cross-sectional areas. In steady state $\dot{m}_1 = \dot{m}_2 = \dot{m}$, and

$$\rho_1 V_1 A_1 = \rho_2 V_2 A_2 \qquad (= \dot{m}). \tag{6.18}$$

The pistons are displaced over the respective distances $V_1 \, dt$ and $V_2 \, dt$ in time dt, and work is performed at rates

$$-A_1 P_1 V_1 \quad \text{and} \quad +A_2 P_2 V_2,$$

respectively. This is due to the fact that a perfect fluid can only exert a normal, uniform pressure on each piston. Thus, the work performed from state a to state b in time dt is

$$-A_1 P_1 V_1 \, dt = -(A_1 \rho_1 V_1)(P_1 v_1) \, dt = -\dot{m} \, dt \cdot P_1 v_1 \qquad \text{(at inlet)}$$

(since $\rho_1 v_1 = 1$); its form is identical with that in equation (6.15). We can show similarly that the expression for work at exit has not changed, and that, therefore, equation (6.17) retains its validity, except for the circumstance that the fluid now carries the kinetic energy $-\frac{1}{2}\dot{m}V_1^2$ per unit time at inlet, and $+\frac{1}{2}\dot{m}V_2^2$ per unit time at exit. If, in addition, the level of the inlet is at z_1 and that of the exit is z_2, the fluid will also carry potential energy, $-\dot{m}gz_1$ per unit time at inlet, and $+\dot{m}gz_2$ at exit.

It follows that instead of the internal energy u in equation (6.16a), we must insert the energy

$$e_1 = u_1 + \tfrac{1}{2}V_1^2 + gz_1 \quad \text{and} \quad e_2 = u_2 + \tfrac{1}{2}V_2^2 + gz_2$$

for u_1 and u_2, respectively. Hence, we obtain

$$\dot{Q} - \dot{W} = \dot{m}\{(h_2 + \tfrac{1}{2}V_2^2 + gz_2) - (h_1 + \tfrac{1}{2}V_1^2 + gz_1)\}. \tag{6.19}$$

In the study of compressible fluid flow[†] it is found that the quantity

$$h_0 = h + \tfrac{1}{2}V^2 \tag{6.20}$$

[†] See Liepmann, H. W., and Roshko, A., *Elements of Gas Dynamics* (Wiley, 1957). Also Shapiro, A. H., *The Dynamics and Thermodynamics of Compressible Fluid Flow* (Ronald, 1953, 1954) I, II. A most elementary introduction to this subject is contained in Section 6.17.4 later in this book.

often recurs in equations and it is considered useful to reserve a symbol for it and to give it the name of *total* or, preferably, *stagnation enthalpy*. It appears useful to do the same for the quantity

$$H^\circ = E + PV = U + \tfrac{1}{2}mV^2 + mgz + PV \tag{6.20a}$$

and its specific counterpart

$$h^\circ = e + Pv = u + \tfrac{1}{2}V^2 + gz + Pv. \tag{6.20b}$$

The name *methalpy*† will be proposed for it. Thus the First Law for open systems in steady-state can be contracted to read

$$\dot{Q} - \dot{W} = \dot{m}(h_2^\circ - h_1^\circ). \tag{6.21}$$

In more complex cases the open system may be provided with several channels. It is then convenient to adopt the convention that the rate of flow *into* the system is positive and that it is negative *out* of the system. In Figure 6.9 we would put $\dot{m}_1 = +\dot{m}$ at 1 and $\dot{m}_2 = -\dot{m}$ at 2, so that equation (6.19) could be contracted to

$$\dot{Q} - \dot{W} = -\dot{m}_2 h_2^\circ - \dot{m}_1 h_1^\circ. \tag{6.21a}$$

It is immediately apparent that a fictitious piston associated with any stream $\dot{m}_i$ of a perfect fluid flowing into or out of an open system contributes a term of work $-\dot{m}_i P_i v_i$ which combined with the respective energy term will give rise to a term $-\dot{m}_i h_i^\circ$. Thus, for an arbitrary number n of channels, equation (6.21a) can be generalized to

$$\dot{Q} - \dot{W} = -\underset{n}{\Sigma}\, \dot{m}_i h_i^\circ$$

$$= -\underset{n}{\Sigma}\, \dot{m}_i (h_i + \tfrac{1}{2}V_i^2 + gz_i). \tag{6.22}$$

If no sign convention for the rates of flow is adopted, the equation can be given the alternative, but entirely equivalent form

$$\dot{Q} - \dot{W} = \underset{\text{out}}{\Sigma}\, \dot{m}_i h_i^\circ - \underset{\text{in}}{\Sigma}\, \dot{m}_i h_i^\circ$$

$$= \underset{\text{out}}{\Sigma}\, \dot{m}_i (h_i + \tfrac{1}{2}V_i^2 + gz_i) - \underset{\text{in}}{\Sigma}\, \dot{m}_i (h_i + \tfrac{1}{2}V_i^2 + gz_i), \tag{6.22a}$$

often preferred by some authors.

When the number of channels exceeds two, the condition that the mass within the open system must remain constant can be written

$$\underset{n}{\Sigma}\, \dot{m}_i = 0 \tag{6.23}‡$$

which is a form of the *law of mass conservation* applicable to systems of this kind.

A glance at equation (6.22) shows that it does, as intended, contain only parameters which describe the open system, namely the rate of heat transmission $\dot{Q}$, and the rate

---

† The name is coined by combining the Greek work *meta*, meaning beyond, or transcending, and *enthalpy*.
‡ The counterpart of this equation when no sign convention is used is

$$\underset{\text{in}}{\Sigma}\, \dot{m}_i = \underset{\text{out}}{\Sigma}\, \dot{m}_i. \tag{6.23a}$$

of work transfer, or power, $\dot{W}$, both measured at the boundary of the open system. The two quantities are related to the change in state in the working fluid entering or leaving the system, also measured at its boundary.

6.12.2   Viscous fluids and the no-slip condition

Owing to the fact that the fluid crossing the boundary of an open system was assumed to be perfect, it proved possible to convert the open system into a closed one by the addition of fictitious pistons. This, in turn, has enabled us to compute, by means of a simple expression, the work performed by the surroundings in forcing a fluid into an open system or in allowing its discharge. In attempting to modify these expressions to include the case of real fluids which can sustain shearing stresses in flow and which adhere to solid boundaries, it must be emphasized at the outset that the limitations of the preceding equations are not serious in the analysis of the performance of engines. Thus, for all such applications, the form of equation (6.22) is adequate; it becomes inadequate in the detailed study of fluid flow, when a general *energy equation* for continuous systems supporting a flow field will be derived.† At present, we shall be satisfied with an analysis which will reveal the inadequacy of equation (6.22) for the study of the flow of real fluids without, that is, providing a more general form for it.

When a real fluid flows through a channel, it must adhere to its walls. Consequently, at any cross section, the velocity must vary from zero at the wall to some maximum value in the center of the channel, Figure 6.11. In such circumstances, it is impossible to close the system by means of a moving piston. If this were done, no closed system could be obtained because the piston would sweep before it the fluid adhering to the walls. Instead, it would be necessary to imagine a flexible membrane b rather than a rigid piston. At time $t = 0$ the membrane can be imagined flat and spanning the cross section. After a time $\mathrm{d}t$, every fluid particle will move by a distance $\mathcal{V}\,\mathrm{d}t$, where $\mathcal{V} = \mathcal{V}(r)$ varies over the cross section, and the membrane would assume the shape b', its profile being proportional to the velocity profile.

Conditions become even more involved in the case of turbulent flow. In a turbulent stream, the local velocity at every point in the stream fluctuates in a random manner with time, even if the mean profile $\bar{\mathcal{V}}(r)$ is time independent. Thus, no truly steady state

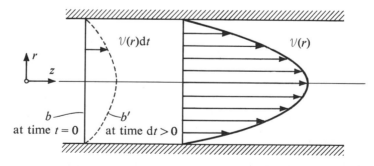

FIGURE 6.11. *Viscous fluid in a channel.*

† See also H. Schlichting, *Boundary Layer Theory*, translated by J. Kestin (4th ed.; McGraw-Hill, 1960), p. 288.

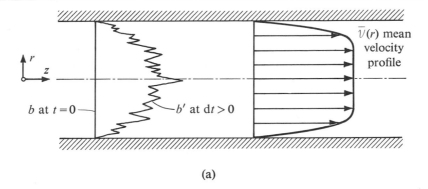

(a)

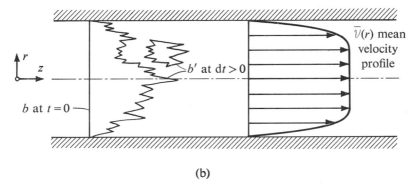

(b)

FIGURE 6.12. *Turbulent flow*.

can be achieved and only a quasisteady regime can be produced. If this circumstance is taken into account, Figure 6.12, it is seen that an initially flat, fictitious membrane *b* will assume a ragged, complex form at a later instant d*t* > 0; it may even become disconnected, the original fluid mass separating into several connected regions, as intimated in Figure 6.12(b). If the deforming membrane is drawn with respect to the *average* flow, the system will cease to be a closed one, since fluid particles will move across it with the oscillating components of the local velocities.

In either case the force transmitted along the imaginary boundary ceases to be normal to it, as was the case with a perfect fluid, and the expression for work must take this circumstance into account.

It is now clear that equation (6.22) is restricted to cases when the fluid enters and leaves the open system *without shear* or with a velocity small enough for the effects of shear to be negligible. Nevertheless, the restriction applies to the boundary only and not to the interior of the open system. Thus, the equation can be successfully applied to cases when the flows within the boundary are viscous and even turbulent, because nothing has been stipulated with regard to the nature of the process performed by the open system, except that a steady state must have been attained; the process may, therefore, be *irreversible inside the open system*.

The accuracy with which equation (6.22) applies to the analysis of a particular open system in steady state can, evidently, be increased by a judicious choice of the boundary which ensures that fluids cross it with small velocity and negligible shear.

6.13   Significance of the additive constant in the definition of energy and enthalpy; heat of a transformation

The perceptive reader may have noticed that equation (6.22) contains algebraic sums of products $\dot{m}_i h_i^\circ$ and may have wondered about the effect of the free additive constant inherent in the internal energy u_i and hence, also in the enthalpy $h_i = u_i + Pv_i$, in the light of the remarks made in Section 5.5. In particular, it is necessary to ascertain whether the addition of arbitrary constants h_{0i} to the enthalpies of the different substances affects the difference $\dot{Q} - \dot{W}$. Clearly, it should not affect it, because this difference constitutes a measurable quantity in each particular case and as such, it cannot depend on the arbitrary level of energy chosen for the description. Since equation (6.22) has been derived from equation (6.16) which has been shown to be independent of such a choice, the resultant equation must also be independent of it. However, it is instructive to discuss this matter in complete detail in order to avoid the possibility of committing a common, but avoidable error.

It will be recalled from Section 5.5 that it is possible to measure only *differences in energy between two states of a single closed system*. The same, of course, is true about enthalpy, as is easily verified if it is noted that

$$H_2 - H_1 = (U_2 - U_1) + (P_2 V_2 - P_1 V_1).$$

When the incoming and outgoing streams consist of fluids of the same chemical nature, the values of all specific enthalpies h_i will be derived from a single table of thermodynamic properties and will be measured with respect to a single reference state. Consequently, on forming the algebraic sum, the arbitrary constant assigned to this common reference state will cancel.

The case when different chemical substances are mixed or dissolved, or when a chemical reaction occurs inside the open system is more complex and requires further attention. In general, the different streams will consist of substances of different chemical composition, as shown by the example of the gas-turbine jet engine which admits a stream of air and fuel and ejects a stream of combustion gases mixed with air. Consequently, it is erroneous to substitute into equation (6.22) values of the enthalpies derived from unrelated sets of tables, each based on an arbitrary choice of the reference state. If this were done, the computed value of the difference $\dot{Q} - \dot{W}$ would bear no relation to the actual process. Thus, for every combination of streams it is necessary carefully to examine the processes which transform the fluids in some of the streams into different fluids in the others.

6.13.1   Heat of a transformation. Hess' law

In order to see this point clearly, it is necessary to identify the various equilibrium states which set in as substances are allowed to mix, dissolve or diffuse through each other, and then to react chemically. This is best done by imagining that constraints are progressively removed, and that after every step, the system is allowed to reach equilibrium. We assume, therefore, that several substances, let us say two for ease of expression, are contained in two separate compartments of an adiabatic cylinder, and that they are separated within it by a diathermal, infinitely thin slide p, Figure 6.13.

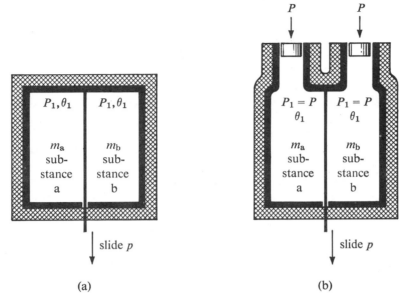

FIGURE 6.13. *Mixing and chemical reaction carried out step-by-step in a rigid cylinder or under a constant pressure. (a) Rigid cylinder, V = const. (b) Fixed pressure, P = const.*

As shown in the diagram, the process can be studied with a variety of overall constraints; the diagram in Figure 6.13(a) shows a system for which $V =$ const, whereas that in Figure 6.13(b) refers to a system with $P =$ const. Naturally, additional, overall constraints (such as $\theta =$ const) could be imagined, but the preceding two constitute the ones which are important in practice. We shall pursue the two examples in turn, choosing V and θ as our independent variables in the first case, and P and θ in the second.

In the diagram of Figure 6.13(a), the substances are assumed to be at a common pressure P_1 and at a common temperature θ_1. The two substances existing side by side in mechanical and thermal equilibrium together constitute state 1 of the system enclosed by the adiabatic cylinder. When the diathermal slide is removed, the substances will mix, diffuse through each other, or dissolve in each other. In an actual experiment, we may observe one of three cases. First, the two substances may mix or dissolve completely, forming a single phase. Secondly, they may remain separate, or they may dissolve in each other partially, the latter two cases leading to the appearance of at least two phases. We shall concentrate on the case when a single, homogeneous phase results. When equilibrium will have been reached, state 2, Figure 6.14, the pressure and temperature have, in general, assumed different values from those at state 1, say P_2 and θ_2. In some exceptional cases, notably when dilute gases, that is gases at very low density, are mixed, there may be no change in temperature or pressure. The process $1 \rightarrow 2$ is evidently irreversible and adiabatic, and the (adiabatic) work performed during the process is zero. Hence,

$$U_1 = U_2 \tag{6.24}$$

for the system treated as a whole. The several (in our example two) substances being mixed may be chemically inert with respect to each other, or they may be chemically active. Often, as is the case with hydrogen and oxygen mixtures, an apparent state of equilibrium will prevail, and no chemical reaction will occur unless a catalyst is added, or the potential reaction is released by a spark. A state, like state 2 in the example, which involves a potentially reactive mixture is known as a state of *retarded equilibrium*. The addition of a catalyst or the creation of a spark is equivalent to the removal of a constraint which is here of a chemical nature. Retarded equilibrium will persist when the system is cooled (or heated, as the case may be) in a way to restore its initial temperature θ_1. In order to ensure that this is the case, we can imagine that an ideal *anticatalyst* has been added. In this manner, the system will reach state 3, and its pressure will assume a value P_3 which is, in general, different from P_1 and P_2. During this process, $W_{2,3} = 0$, but $Q_{2,3}^v \neq 0$. Here, the superscript v has been added to distinguish the present case from that in which the pressure will be kept constant.

Applying the First Law of thermodynamics to process $2 \rightarrow 3$, we obtain

$$U_3 = U_1 + Q_{2,3}^v. \tag{6.25a}$$

The *negative* of the quantity of heat $Q_{2,3}^v$ required to restore the original temperature θ_1 at constant volume is known as the *heat of mixing* (diffusion or solution) of the system of substances $a + b$; it depends evidently on the reference temperature θ_1 as well as on the volume V_1. We shall use the symbol

$$Q_{\theta_1}^v = -Q_{2,3}^v$$

for this quantity, replacing θ_1 by its numerical value in particular cases. In most handbooks of chemistry, the *standard temperature* $25°C = 298.15°K$ is employed. Frequently, the dependence of the heat of mixing $Q_{298.15}$ on the volume V_1 is unimportant; mention of it in the symbol has been omitted for this reason. In general, this quantity is quite small, and becomes equal to zero asymptotically when gases are mixed at very low density. In such cases, states 2 and 3 become identical.

We now imagine that at state 3 the chemical reaction between the mixed reactants has been started, for example, by a spark or by the addition of a perfect catalyst. This will give rise to an adiabatic, irreversible process during which the chemical reaction

$$a + b \rightarrow c$$

will occur. We have chosen one symbol, c, for the products of reaction for the sake of brevity, realizing that the chemical nature of the products is inessential for our argument.

When equilibrium is reached at state 4, yet another pressure, P_4, and yet another temperature, θ_4, will be measured. The adiabatic work flux during the process $3 \rightarrow 4$ is again zero, and we can write

$$U_4 = U_3. \tag{6.25b}$$

Let us, finally, imagine that a process is instituted, process $4 \rightarrow 5$ in Figure 6.14, as a result of which the temperature of the system is restored to its initial value θ_1 without the performance of work. This can only be achieved by an exchange of heat $Q_{4,5}^v$, cooling for a so-called *exothermic reaction* $(\theta_4 > \theta_1)$, or heating for a so-called *endothermic reaction* $(\theta_4 < \theta_1)$. By an exchange of heat alone, it is possible to restore the parameter θ_1, and the total as well as the specific volume remain the same as for

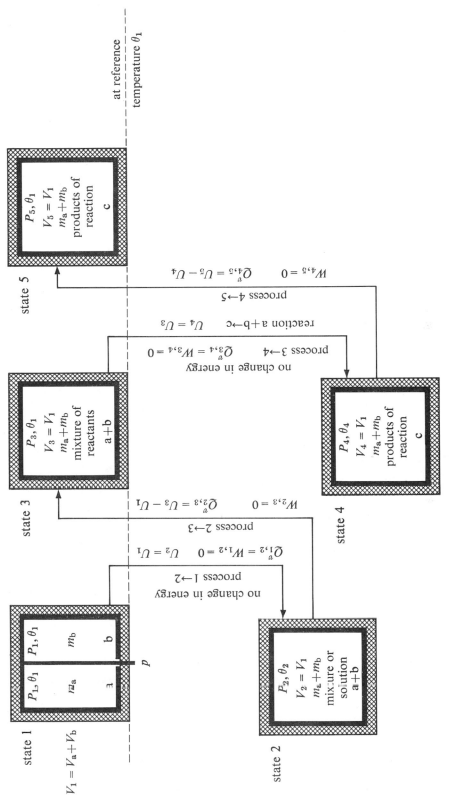

FIGURE 6.14. *Sequence of states at V = const.*

states 2, 3, 4, since mass is conserved. State 5 is characterized by the fact that the temperature and volume are the same as in states 1 and 3, but is different from them in that the *chemical nature* of the system (and, incidentally, also the pressure) has changed. The system now obeys a different equation of state from that valid for states 2 and 3, though the latter is the same as for state 4.

The *negative* of the quantity of heat $Q_{4,5}^{v}$ required to restore the original temperature θ_1 at constant volume is known as the *heat of reaction*

$$Q_{\theta_1}^{v} = -Q_{4,5}^{v} \tag{6.25c}$$

at temperature θ_1 and volume V_1. The heat of reaction is usually orders of magnitude larger than the heat of mixing, even if chemical reactions are conducted at very low densities.

By the First Law, we can write

$$U_5 = U_4 + Q_{4,5}^{v} \quad \text{or} \quad U_5 = U_4 - Q_{\theta_1}^{v}. \tag{6.25d}$$

It is noted that all states considered, namely, 1, 2, 3, 4, and 5 represent *different equilibrium states of the same system*. The energy is the same for the pairs of states 1, 2 and 3, 4, but these are described by different values of the intensive parameters, pressure P and temperature θ, even though the volume is the same for all. It may come as a surprise to realize that the energies of the three states 1, 3, and 5, which are described by the *same* values of volume, V, and temperature, θ, are *not* equal. The reason for this resides in the different chemical constitutions, separate components at state 1, mixed components at state 3, and the products of a reaction at state 5.

The various states shown in Figure 6.15 form an analogous sequence, except that now the pressure is the same for all; by contrast, the volume as well as the specific volume change their values. When the various processes are performed, the adiabatic work ceases to be zero, because some of it is supplied by the two pistons. However, no *additional* work is required, and the only difference with the preceding case consists in the fact that the quantities of heat exchanged have become equal to the differences in the enthalpy of the final and initial state, respectively, for each process. Thus, equations (6.24) and (6.25a, b, c, d) are replaced by the sequence

$$H_1 = H_2 \tag{6.26}$$

$$H_3 = H_1 + Q_{2,3}^{p} \tag{6.26a}$$

$$H_4 = H_3 \tag{6.26b}$$

$$Q_{\theta_1}^{p} = -Q_{4,5}^{p} \tag{6.26c}$$

$$H_5 = H_4 + Q_{4,5}^{p} \quad \text{or} \quad H_5 = H_4 - Q_{\theta_1}^{p}. \tag{6.26d}$$

We note again that a mixture a + b of two substances a and b has the same enthalpy as the separated components at a different temperature but the same pressure. At the same temperature *and* pressure, the enthalpies differ by a quantity of heat $Q_{2,3}^{p}$. Similarly, the products c of a reaction a + b → c have the same enthalpy as the reactants when the temperatures are different for the same pressure. When the temperature *and* pressure are the same, the enthalpies differ by a quantity of heat $Q_{4,5}^{p}$.

The negatives of the quantities of heat $Q_{2,3}^{p}$ and $Q_{4,5}^{p}$ are also called the heats of mixing or reaction, respectively, both now at constant pressure. They depend on the reference temperature θ_1 and, much less strongly, on the pressure P_1. All these quanti-

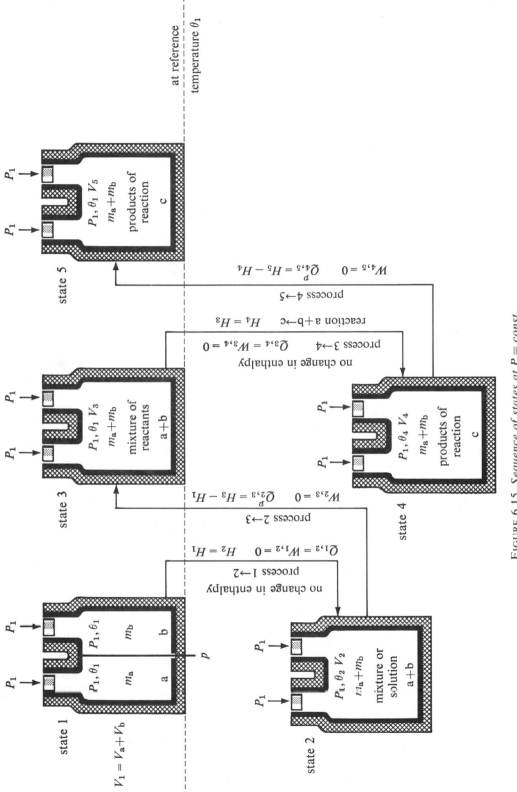

FIGURE 6.15. *Sequence of states at P = const.*

ties are given the generic name of *heat of transformation* or *heat tone*. The latent heat of a phase transformation to be discussed in Sections 7.4.2 and 7.4.4 belongs to the same class of quantities.

The heats of mixing and reaction at constant pressure are encountered more frequently than those at constant volume because, in practice, most processes of mixing and most reactions are performed under conditions when the pressure is constant. They are also frequently conducted in open-flow systems at a steady state and without the performance of additional work when the quantities of heat exchanged are equal to the changes in enthalpy, equation (6.17). In some treatises no clear distinction is made between the heat tones at constant pressure and at constant volume, and some cautions should be exercised when the unqualified terms "heat of mixing" or "heat of reaction" are encountered.

The numerical values of heat tones are quoted for a specified quantity of matter in the system. Since the reactants and products can occur in different ratios of masses, depending on the details of the chemical reaction, this quantity must be specified. In relation to combustion reactions, it is customary to refer these quantities to one mol or a unit of mass of the fuel rather than the oxydant. Frequently, the heat tone is given for a chemical reaction "as written." For example, the heat of the reaction

$$CO + \tfrac{1}{2}O_2 = CO_2 \tag{6.27}$$

is

$$^bQ^\circ_{298.15^\circ} = 67,636 \text{ kcal/kmol}$$

the superscript $^\circ$ denoting the extrapolated limit when $P \to 0$. Here, $^bQ^\circ_{298.15}$ is quoted per 1 kmol of the fuel—carbon monoxide. If the reaction were written

$$2CO + O_2 = 2CO_2, \tag{6.27a}$$

we would have

$$Q^\circ_{298.15^\circ} = 135,272 \text{ kcal/kmol},$$

and referred to 2 kmol of carbon monoxide, 1 kmol of oxygen, and 2 kmol of carbon dioxide.

Many reactions can be carried out in successive steps. For example, graphite can be burned directly to produce carbon dioxide, when

$$C_{\text{graph}} + O_2 = CO_2 \quad \text{with} \quad {}^cQ^\circ_{298.15^\circ} = 94,052 \text{ kcal/kmol}. \tag{6.28}$$

It can also be first burned to carbon monoxide according to the reaction

$$C_{\text{graph}} + \tfrac{1}{2}O_2 = CO \quad \text{with} \quad {}^aQ^\circ_{298.15^\circ} = 26,416 \text{ kcal/kmol}, \tag{6.29}$$

the carbon monoxide being subsequently burned to carbon dioxide in accordance with equation (6.27). Since the heats of reaction are equal to differences in enthalpy, their values must be independent of the details of the process. Consequently, the sum of the heats of the two intermediate reactions (6.29) and (6.27) must be equal to the heat of the complete reaction (6.28). Thus,

$$^aQ^\circ_{298.15^\circ} + {}^bQ^\circ_{298.15^\circ} = {}^cQ^\circ_{298.15^\circ}, \tag{6.30}$$

as the reader may verify directly. The rule represented by equation (6.30) was discovered empirically by H. Hess in 1840. It is now referred to as *Hess' law* and we can formulate it as follows:

> *The heat tone of a chemical reaction is equal to the sum of the heat tones of a sequence of chemical reactions, all referred to a common temperature and a common volume or pressure, on condition that the initial reactants and that the final products are the same.*

An analogous rule applies to mixing.

There exist two additional conventions for recording heats of reaction. In one, the heat of reaction is written as part of the chemical formula. In the preceding examples, we would write equations (6.27), (6.28), and (6.29) as

$$C_{graph} + \tfrac{1}{2}O_2 = CO + 26{,}416 \text{ kcal/kmol}, \tag{a}$$

$$CO + \tfrac{1}{2}O_2 = CO_2 + 67{,}636 \text{ kcal/kmol}, \tag{b}$$

$$C_{graph} + O_2 = CO_2 + 94{,}052 \text{ kcal/kmol}. \tag{c}$$

The symbol kcal/kmol signifies that the heat of reaction is measured per that number of mols of a substance as appears in the equation (for example, 1 kmol of C_{graph} or $\tfrac{1}{2}$ kmol of O_2 in reaction (a)). Furthermore, the heat quantity is written with a positive sign, because the enthalpy of the mixture of the reactants (for example, 1 kmol C_{graph} and $\tfrac{1}{2}$ kmol O_2 in reaction (a)) *exceeds* that of the products (1 kmol of CO in this example). The values of the reference temperature and pressure (or volume) must be indicated separately, but the resulting equations can be manipulated according to the rules of algebra.

An alternative notation utilizes the form of equations (6.26d) or equation (6.25d). Since

$$Q^v_{\theta_1} = -(U_5 - U_4) \quad \text{or} \quad Q^p_{\theta_1} = -(H_5 - H_4)$$

(state 5 for products and state 4 for reactants), we may write

$$\Delta U^v_{\theta_1} = -Q^v_{\theta_1} \quad \text{or} \quad \Delta H^v_{\theta_1} = -Q^p_{\theta_1}. \tag{6.31}$$

For example, for reaction (a), (b), and (c), we would write

(a) $\Delta H^\circ_{298.15^\circ} = -26{,}416$ kcal/kmol,
(b) $\Delta H^\circ_{298.15^\circ} = -67{,}636$ kcal/kmol,
(c) $\Delta H^\circ_{298.15^\circ} = -94{,}052$ kcal/kmol.

Tables of heats of reaction will be included in Volume II.

6.13.2   *Normalization of additive constants*

When tables of the thermodynamic properties of substances are prepared, it is customary, and economical of effort, to restrict them to chemically pure substances, because rules can be established for the computation of the properties of mixtures from those of the components (see Sections 7.5 and 13.5), or even of the properties of compounds from those of the elements (see Volume II). Naturally, each set of tables is based on an arbitrary reference state, and there is no assurance that the relations stipulated, for example, in equations (6.25d) and (6.26d) will be satisfied.

Let us suppose that state 1 in Figures 6.14 and 6.15 is the reference state, and that at that reference state the tables list the specific values u_a^*, h_a^*, u_b^*, h_b^* for the specific properties of the two substances a and b. Then, for the whole system we would write

$$U_1 = m_a u_a^* + m_b u_b^*,$$

$$H_1 = m_a h_a^* + m_b h_b^*.$$

Similarly, for substance c in state 5 the values u_c^* and h_c^* would be listed; hence,

$$U_5 = (m_a + m_b)\, u_c^*$$

and

$$H_5 = (m_a + m_b)\, h_c^*.$$

Now, from equations (6.25a, d) and (6.26a, d), we find that we must have

$$U_5 - U_1 = Q_{2,3}^v + Q_{4,5}^v$$

and

$$H_5 - H_1 = Q_{2,3}^p + Q_{4,5}^p.$$

It follows that

and that

$$\left.\begin{aligned}
(m_a + m_b) u_c^* - (m_a u_a^* + m_b u_b^*) &= Q_{2,3}^v + Q_{4,5}^v \\
(m_a + m_b) h_c^* - (m_a h_a^* + m_b h_b^*) &= Q_{2,3}^p + Q_{4,5}^p.
\end{aligned}\right\} \qquad (6.32a, b)$$

It is thus clear that the necessary relations (6.32a, b) will not normally be satisfied, and that the tables for substances a, b, and c must be *normalized* to take this requirement into account. This is done specifically and separately for each particular case, and the adjustment must not be overlooked when problems are solved numerically.

The need for normalization can be easily appreciated, if it is realized that habitually, either

$$u_a^* = u_b^* = u_c^* = 0$$

or

$$h_a^* = h_b^* = h_c^* = 0$$

is stipulated. Obviously both assumptions cannot be made simultaneously, since by definition

$$u_a^* = h_a^* - P^* v_a^*, \quad u_b^* = h_b^* - P^* v_b^*, \quad \text{and} \quad u_c^* = h_c^* - P^* v_c^*,$$

where P^* is the reference pressure and v_a^*, v_b^*, v_c^* denote the specific volumes at the reference pressure P^* and the reference temperature θ^*. In either case, the left-hand side of one of the necessary relations (6.32a, b) would vanish, instead of assuming the required value.

It is evident that the concepts of heat of mixing or reaction are unaffected by the number of subsystems considered in each state and by the fact that some of the subsystems may themselves be mixtures or chemical compounds. The heats of mixing or reaction are usually quoted per one mol of one of the substances involved, as already stated. In the case of the heat of reaction, it is usually assumed that the reaction is completed, and that the reactants are present in their stoichiometric ratios. From such data all other cases can be computed by simple proportions. In this, it should be remembered that energies should be normalized when the heats of mixing and reaction at *constant volume* are given. When heats of mixing and reaction at *constant pressure* are available, enthalpies should be normalized.

Assuming, therefore, that in equations (6.32a, b) the quantities $Q_{2,3}^{v}$, $Q_{4,5}^{v}$, $Q_{2,3}^{p}$, and $Q_{4,5}^{p}$ are given per unit mass in the form of heats of mixing $Q_{\text{mix},\theta}^{v}$ or $Q_{\text{mix},\theta}^{p}$ and in the form of heats of reaction $Q_{\text{reac},\theta}^{v}$ and $Q_{\text{reac},\theta}^{p}$, we must introduce the products $(m_{a} + m_{b})(Q_{\text{mix},\theta}^{v} + Q_{\text{reac},\theta}^{v})$ and $(m_{a} + m_{b})(Q_{\text{mix},\theta}^{p} + Q_{\text{reac},\theta}^{p})$ on the right-hand sides of the equations. In this manner, we obtain

and

$$
\left.
\begin{aligned}
u_{c}^{*} &= \frac{m_{a}}{m_{a} + m_{b}} u_{a}^{*} + \frac{m_{b}}{m_{a} + m_{b}} u_{b}^{*} - Q_{\text{mix},\theta}^{v} - Q_{\text{reac},\theta}^{v} \\[2ex]
h_{c}^{*} &= \frac{m_{a}}{m_{a} + m_{b}} h_{a}^{*} + \frac{m_{b}}{m_{a} + m_{b}} h_{b}^{*} - Q_{\text{mix},\theta}^{p} - Q_{\text{reac},\theta}^{p}
\end{aligned}
\right\} \qquad (6.32\text{c, d})
$$

6.13.3 Separate channels

In some applications, such as in heat exchangers, several streams are guided through channels which exchange heat but do not exchange matter. A schematic diagram of such a heat exchanger used for the transfer of heat between a fluid and a gas is shown in Figure 6.16. In such cases the tables for the gas and for the fluid need not be normalized. For a heat exchanger performing no work and losing heat at a rate $\dot{Q}$ to the surrounding, we can write

$$
\dot{Q} = \dot{m}_{g}(h_{2} - h_{1}) + \dot{m}_{f}(h_{4} - h_{3}) \qquad (6.33)
$$

because states 1 and 2 as well as states 3 and 4 constitute two sets of states of two interacting systems each of which preserves its chemical identity.

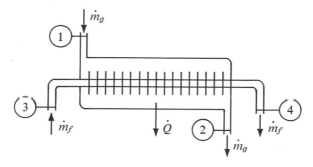

FIGURE 6.16. *Schematic diagram of heat exchanger between a gaseous and a liquid stream.*

6.14 Remarks concerning the energy-balance equation.
Eulerian and Lagrangian description

The equations derived in Section 6.10 are very useful in the solution of engineering problems ranging from the analysis of performance data taken on actual engines, when they lead to so-called heat balances (Section 6.17.2), to preliminary design analyses. Their application is not restricted to heat engines, such as steam or gas turbines or compressors, but extends to hydraulic engines, water pumps, heat exchangers, and many others. These equations represent the *energy balance* of all devices which operate in a steady-state regime. The most serious limitation of the usefulness of these equations, as already mentioned earlier, is a consequence of the assumption that the working fluids enter or leave the system with uniform velocities, and slide along the inlet and outlet channels. Thus, on entering or leaving, the fluids are assumed to be perfect, and any effects caused by viscosity and by the absence of slip along solid walls are neglected. This deficiency can be remedied to a certain extent by drawing the boundaries in a manner which will include only cross sections through which fluids move with negligible velocity and shear, as already stated.

The manner of deriving these equations was very closely related to the Eulerian description used in fluid mechanics. It is instructive to examine at this point the difference which would result if the Lagrangian method of description had been adopted. In the Lagrangian description attention would be centered on a closed system consisting of a fixed mass m of fluid entering. In the case of several feeder streams this mass would be composed of all the fluids entering, Figure 6.17, and taken in proportion to their respective (constant) mass rates of flow. In the example sketched, with two streams, these would be

$$\frac{\dot{m}_1}{\dot{m}_1 + \dot{m}_2}m \quad \text{and} \quad \frac{\dot{m}_2}{\dot{m}_1 + \dot{m}_2}m, \tag{6.34}$$

respectively. The phenomena would then be traced as this system passes through its sequence of reversible or irreversible processes including, in some cases, the mixing and separation of different substances. For the sake of simplicity, the sketch in Figure 6.17 includes only one, homogeneous stream at exit 3. It is clear that such a description would be much more detailed than the Eulerian description of Section 6.10, as every process taking place in the interior of the open system would have to be taken into account. Since this would be based on the same fundamental form of the First Law,

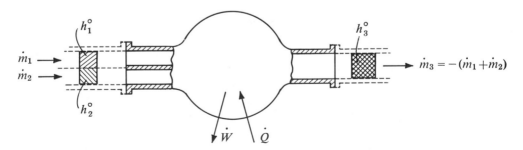

FIGURE 6.17. *Lagrangian description of open system in steady flow.*

equation (6.16), it would be entirely equivalent to the Eulerian description insofar as the quantities observed at the boundaries are concerned. When designing engines of different kinds, an attempt is made to perform a Lagrangian analysis as far as it is possible. Such a set of calculations takes the form of a so-called *design analysis*. In this manner it is possible to arrive at a close approximation to the whole sequence of processes performed by the mass of fluid under consideration.

For the Lagrangian representation it is more convenient to introduce the quantities Q and W per unit mass from equation (6.14). Dividing all terms in equation (6.22) by the rate of flow in, that is, by the sum of all positive quantities $\dot{m}_i$, say $\dot{m}$, we obtain the equivalent equation in the form

$$Q - W = h_2^{\circ} - h_1^{\circ}, \tag{6.34a}$$

where h_2° and h_1° refer to a unit mass entering or leaving, and composed of suitable proportions of the different substances, as given in equation (6.31). Thus,

$$h_2^{\circ} = \sum_{\text{out}} \frac{\dot{m}_i}{\dot{m}}(h_i + \tfrac{1}{2}V_i^2 + gz_i),$$

the summation being extended over all streams leaving the system, and

$$h_1^{\circ} = \sum_{\text{in}} \frac{\dot{m}_i}{\dot{m}}(h_i + \tfrac{1}{2}V_i^2 + gz_i),$$

where the summation extends over all streams entering the system. It is evident that the sum of all rates of flow out of the system is also equal to $\dot{m}$ owing to the conservation of mass. In this form the equation constitutes merely an energy balance equation which links the initial equilibrium state 1 with the final equilibrium state 2, when both are known. The task of calculating exit states from a knowledge of inlet states and of the characteristics of the system constitutes one of the central problems of design analysis in engineering thermodynamics.

6.15   Nonsteady open systems

The considerations of the preceding section are easily generalized to the case when the process in an open system is not steady, that is, to the case when all local quantities, including those which describe the various streams, are functions of time. It will be sufficient to consider one stream through which matter flows into or out of the system ("control volume") enclosed within the surface C, as sketched in Figure 6.18.

At first, for the sake of simplicity, we shall suppose that the boundary of the open system is rigid, and that it is filled with a homogeneous substance whose state is uniform inside the boundary. In other words, we shall suppose that the boundary contains a uniform system, and we shall use symbols without subscripts for the description of its state. Observing the system during a period of time dt, it will be assumed that a mass dm, whose properties will be described by symbols with the subscript ξ, is forced into it or discharged from it. The convention that $dm > 0$ for flow into the system and that $dm < 0$ for flow out of the system is a natural one to adopt, since at any instant the rate of change of mass within the boundary C is then simply

$$\dot{m} = \frac{dm}{dt}, \tag{6.35}$$

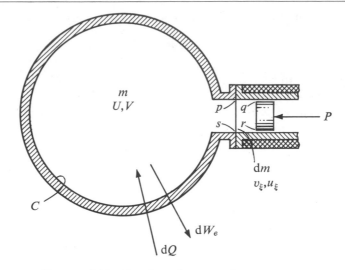

FIGURE 6.18. *First Law for general open system.*

and the mass itself is

$$m = \int_{t_1}^{t} \dot{m}(t)\,dt + m_1, \tag{6.35a}$$

where m_1 is a constant of integration. This equation is an expression of the principle of conservation of mass. With the assumption that the contents of the system form a uniform system, the specific properties and specific values of the potentials of the mass dm will be the same as those within the system for the process of discharge. However, when a mass dm is forced into the system, this need not be the case; it is for this reason that we have added the subscript ξ to the symbols describing the state of mass dm. We are not yet in a position to discuss the case when the chemical nature of the mass dm differs from that within the system. In order to do so it is necessary to study first the process of *mixing* substances of different chemical composition in greater detail than in Section 6.12. This will be deferred to Sections 7.5 and 13.5. Thus, the only difference between the mass dm and the masses within the system may consist of a difference in temperature (and hence, specific volume, and so on), it being further stipulated that their pressures are also equal. Thus, there is a possibility that masses of different temperature will at first be in contact across surface p–s in Figure 6.18 and then mixed inside surface C. The process will be idealized by neglecting the flow of heat between masses dm and m and by assuming that the state of mass $m + dm$ is instantly uniform upon the completion of the process.

   In order to write down the First Law it is necessary, as was done before, to draw a boundary including mass dm and so to analyze the process in terms of a *closed system*, as evidenced by the fictitious closing ideal piston moving along a fictitious, adiabatic cylinder shown in Figure 6.18. Thus, two states will be considered. At state *a* the small mass is still outside boundary C and the boundary of the closed system includes the surface $pqrs$. At state *b*, the mass has been *slowly and quasistatically* driven into the system. At the same time the system exchanged a quantity of heat dQ with the surroundings and performed a quantity of work dW_e. The energy of the closed system at state a is thus

$$E + e_\xi \, dm$$

and at state b it is

$$E + dE,$$

where dE denotes the change in energy within the boundary C. The closed system exchanged heat dQ and performed external work dW_e at the boundary C and work $-Pv_\xi \, dm$ at the piston, since there, the *change* in volume is equal to the *volume* $v_\xi \, dm$ of mass dm. Hence, the First Law can be written

$$dQ = dE - e_\xi \, dm + dW_e - Pv_\xi \, dm.$$

The terms E and e_ξ can now be expressed as sums of the internal, potential and other energies, in the same way, and under the same restrictions as in Sections 6.11 and 6.12. Assuming that only the internal energy of mass m is of importance and that regarding mass dm it is necessary to take into account only its potential (gravitational) and kinetic energy, in addition to its internal energy, the preceding equation can be transformed to

$$dQ = dU - (h_\xi + \tfrac{1}{2}V_\xi^2 + gz_\xi)\,dm + dW_e, \qquad (6.36)$$

where the obvious substitution

$$u_\xi + Pv_\xi = h_\xi$$

has been made. It can be verified that the equation contains only parameters which describe the open system and the instantaneous state of the mass flowing across its boundary. This, as stated earlier, was precisely the aim of the present derivation. For a rigid boundary and a homogeneous system ($U = mu$), the equation simplifies to

$$dQ = d(mu) - (h_\xi + \tfrac{1}{2}V_\xi^2 + gz_\xi)\,dm + dW_e. \qquad (6.36a)$$

As already stated, it is sometimes convenient to introduce the rates of performing work and exchanging heat $dQ/dt = \dot{Q}$ and $dW_e/dt = \dot{W}_e$ and to write

$$\dot{Q} = \frac{d}{dt}(mu) - \sum_n (h_\xi + \tfrac{1}{2}V_\xi^2 + gz_\xi)_i \dot{m}_i + \dot{W}_e, \qquad (6.36b)$$

where the summation sign $\sum_n$ has been added to generalize the equation to include n streams i; it could have been added to any one of the preceding equations for the same purpose.

In problems of charging or discharging rigid vessels through one duct, the abbreviated forms

$$\dot{Q} = \frac{d}{dt}(mu) - h_\xi \frac{dm}{dt} \qquad (6.37)$$

or

$$dQ = d(mu) - h_\xi \, dm \qquad (6.37a)$$

will be found very useful. The implications following the omission of the terms $\tfrac{1}{2}V_\xi^2$ and gz_ξ should be noted and remembered. In particular, for discharge, the state ξ is identical with that inside the system, and equation (6.37a) can be written in the two alternative forms

$$dQ = d(mu) - h\,dm$$

or, since $d(mu) = udm + mdu$, we can also write

$$dQ = m\,du - Pv\,dm \tag{6.37b}$$

which could be written down at once from first principles.

The preceding equations transform immediately into those of Section 6.11. If it is noted that for a steady-state system

$$\frac{dm}{dt} = 0,$$

equation (6.35a) assumes the form

$$\sum_n \dot{m}_i = 0$$

for n channels, which is identical with equation (6.23). It is now clear formally that the existence of one channel in a steady-state system would imply no flow ($\dot{m} = 0$), and at least two channels must be provided. In a steady-state system the state within is invariant with time

$$\frac{d(mu)}{dt} = 0$$

and equation (6.36) becomes identical with equation (6.22).

The equations quoted in this section and in Section 6.11 are extremely useful in many applications, particularly in engineering. We shall have frequent occasion to refer to them. However, they must be used only very cautiously owing to the large number of conditions which must be satisfied for them to apply; these should always be kept vividly in one's memory. In particular, it must be remembered that the work of shearing stresses has been consistently omitted. Consequently, the preceding equations *cannot* be used in a rigorous development of an analytic theory of the flow of a viscous fluid.

In the present case, the problem of normalization of states, discussed in the preceding section, should also be considered. It will become of real importance when the mixing of dissimilar substances will be included.

To conclude this section, it may be useful to write down the equations in a form which makes allowances for the fact that the system may be a continuous one, its specific properties varying with position and time. In agreement with equations (6.6) and (6.7), it should be evident that the only modifications required are to change $\frac{d}{dt}(mu)$ to

$$\frac{d}{dt}\int_V u(x, y, z, t)\rho(x, y, z, t)\,dV, \tag{6.38}$$

where ρ denotes the local density and the time plays the part of a parameter in the process of integration. The equation of conservation of mass is then

$$\sum_n \dot{m}_i = \frac{d}{dt}\int_V \rho(x, y, z, t)\,dV. \tag{6.39}$$

It is worth noting here that the method used in formulating the First Law for open systems by reducing the problem to one involving a closed system is analogous to the formulation of Newton's Second Law for systems of variable mass. In both cases, the fundamental laws of nature, the First Law of thermodynamics as well as Newton's Second Law of motion apply only to closed systems. It should, therefore, be realized that the above equations for open systems are *not more general*, because a consequence cannot be more general than the premiss. They are certainly more *convenient*, but the appearance of generality is misleading. The First Law of thermodynamics (just as Newton's Second Law) cannot be written for an open system which is not *reducible* to a closed system.

At this stage it may be puzzling to discover that the steady-state energy balance equation derived in the preceding section is valid under less stringent limitations, being applicable to cases when both mixing of different chemical species or reactions between them take place within it, on condition only that the end states are states of equilibrium. In the present, apparently more general case, these processes have been excluded from consideration. This is entirely due to the fact that in a steady-state system the energy within it remains constant between inlet and exhaust, irrespective of the nature of the process taking place. Hence, there is no need to analyze the process at all. In the more general case the change in energy dE within the open system must be known and we are not yet in a position to complete the analysis for the excluded processes. This will be achieved in Section 13.6 when we shall resume the whole problem anew.

6.16 Summary of equations

The need to familiarize oneself with the rather large number of different forms of the First Law together with the specific assumptions under which each of them applies is found taxing by the beginner. For this reason it might be useful to provide here a concise summary for ease of future reference.

Closed systems
General form, applicable to reversible as well as irreversible processes

$$Q_{1,2} = E_2 - E_1 + W_{1,2}. \tag{6.40}$$

General form, applicable to quasistatic (reversible and irreversible) processes only

$$dQ = dE + dW. \tag{6.41}$$

Specialized to processes in which only internal energy need be taken into account

$$Q_{1,2} = U_2 - U_1 + W_{1,2}. \tag{6.42}$$

Specialized to reversible processes in which only internal energy and work of compression or expansion need be taken into account

$$dQ = dU + PdV \tag{6.43}$$

or

$$dQ = dH - VdP. \tag{6.44}$$

The forms in equations (6.43) and (6.44) are entirely equivalent and interchangeable.

Open systems

Steady-flow system. Quasistatic charging and discharging of perfect fluids; arbitrary process within system, reversible or irreversible, including chemical reaction on condition that specific properties are normalized; work of shearing stresses at boundaries neglected.

Conservation of energy

$$\dot{Q} - \dot{W} = -\underset{n}{\Sigma} \, \dot{m}_i (h + \tfrac{1}{2} V^2 + gz), \tag{6.45}$$

Conservation of mass

$$\underset{n}{\Sigma} \, \dot{m}_i = 0. \tag{6.46}$$

Nonsteady system. Homogeneous state throughout control volume; reversible charging or discharging of perfect fluids; streams and contents of identical chemical compositions; quasistatic expansion or compression at boundaries;† only internal, potential, and kinetic energies included; reversible or irreversible shaft work; work of shearing stresses at boundaries excluded.

Conservation of energy

$$dQ = d(mu) - \underset{n}{\Sigma} \, (h_\xi + \tfrac{1}{2} V_\xi^2 + gz_\xi) dm + dW_e + P \, dV, \tag{6.47}$$

or

$$\dot{Q} = \frac{d}{dt}(mu) - \underset{n}{\Sigma} \, (h_\xi + \tfrac{1}{2} V_\xi^2 + gz_\xi) \dot{m}_i + \dot{W}_e + P\dot{V}, \tag{6.47a}$$

where $\dot{V} = dV/dt$;

Conservation of mass

$$\frac{dm}{dt} = \underset{n}{\Sigma} \, \dot{m}_i. \tag{6.48}$$

Nonsteady rigid system. Continuous distribution of states, otherwise identical with preceding restrictions; pressure at each inlet equal to local pressure at point of discharge or inlet.

Conservation of energy

$$dQ = d \left(\int_V u\rho \, dV \right) - \underset{n}{\Sigma} \, (h_\xi + \tfrac{1}{2} V_\xi^2 + gz_\xi) dm + dW_e, \tag{6.49}$$

or

$$\dot{Q} = \frac{d}{dt} \int_V u\rho \, dV - \underset{n}{\Sigma} \, (h_\xi + \tfrac{1}{2} V_\xi^2 + gz_\xi) \dot{m}_i + \dot{W}_e; \tag{6.49a}$$

Conservation of mass

$$\frac{d}{dt} \int_V \rho \, dV = \underset{n}{\Sigma} \, \dot{m}_i. \tag{6.50}$$

† The term $P \, dV$ has been added here to achieve somewhat greater generality.

Quasistatic filling of rigid vessels. Through single channel; remaining restrictions as before; kinetic and potential energies neglected; uniform state within.

Conservation of energy

$$dQ = d(mu) - h_\xi \, dm, \qquad (6.51)$$

Conservation of mass

$$\dot{m} = \frac{dm}{dt}. \qquad (6.52)$$

Quasistatic discharge from vessels. All restrictions as in preceding case; conservation of mass equation (6.52).

Conservation of energy

$$dQ = m \, du - Pv \, dm \qquad (6.53)$$

or

$$dQ = d(mu) - h \, dm. \qquad (6.54)$$

It is impossible to foresee and to write all feasible forms which may occur in applications, but with the preceding equations as examples, the reader should have no difficulty in writing them if and when required. It is necessary to emphasize again that the existence of shearing stresses along the streams and around boundaries has been neglected. Consequently, the preceding equations cannot be applied to the derivation of the energy equation in fluid mechanics without modification.

6.17 Examples of simple, open, steady-state systems

In this section we propose to study several simple but important examples of open systems concentrating on steady-state phenomena.

6.17.1 Supply line

When a fluid flows through a supply line, Figure 6.19, and its state is known at two cross sections, the rate at which heat is lost can be calculated by the immediate application of equation (6.45), whence we obtain

$$\dot{Q} = \dot{m}\{(h_2 - h_1) + \tfrac{1}{2}(V_2^2 - V_1^2) + g(z_2 - z_1)\}. \qquad (6.55)$$

The equation is applicable to cases when the cross section is constant as well as when it is variable, on condition that the rate of variation of area along the axis is not too great. If the cross-sectional area were to vary at a considerable rate it would no longer be permissible to assume that the velocity is uniform across a section and that it is unidirectional, as was done here. Strictly speaking, the presence of shear near the cross sections 1 and 2 invalidates equation (6.55) because the existence of shearing stresses is incompatible with the underlying assumption that the fluid entering and leaving is perfect, and that its properties as well as its velocity are uniform over the cross section. Nevertheless, equation (6.55) is used in applications as an adequate approximation, and the velocity, temperature, and enthalpy assigned to cross sections 1 and 2 are sometimes obtained by forming integral averages. If the cross section is circular, and if a quantity α varies with the radius r, so that $\alpha = \alpha(r)$, the average

$$\bar{\alpha} = \frac{1}{\pi R^2} \int_0^R \alpha(r) \times 2\pi r \, \mathrm{d}r = \frac{2}{R^2} \int_0^R r \cdot \alpha(r) \mathrm{d}r \qquad (6.55a)$$

may be used. For example, for velocity

$$\bar{\mathcal{V}} = \frac{2}{R^2} \int_0^R r \cdot \mathcal{V}(r) \mathrm{d}r.$$

The mean value $\bar{\alpha}$ can be found by graphical integration, that is, by measuring the area under the plot of $r \cdot \alpha(r)$ against r, Figure 6.20.

The form of equation (6.55) immediately suggests its relation to Bernoulli's equation known from hydraulics. In problems in hydraulics, the flow is assumed adiabatic ($\dot{Q} = 0$), and equation (6.55) can be written in the simpler form

$$h + \tfrac{1}{2}\mathcal{V}^2 + gz = \text{const}, \qquad (6.56)$$

which is very useful in applications. In order to show its relation to Bernoulli's equation, it is necessary to recall that

$$h = u + Pv = u + \frac{P}{\rho} \qquad (6.57)$$

and to realize that most flows discussed in hydraulics are isothermal and that under

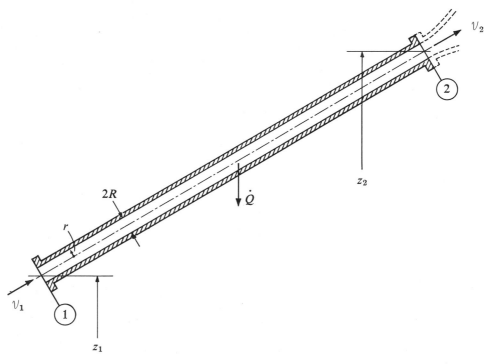

FIGURE 6.19. *Supply line.*

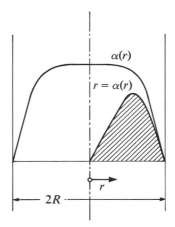

FIGURE 6.20. *Computation of average quantity in a channel.*

such conditions, they are also isoenergetic, provided that shearing forces at the walls are neglected, as will be shown more precisely in Section 11.1. With these assumptions, Bernoulli's equation

$$\frac{P}{\rho} + \tfrac{1}{2}\mathcal{V}^2 + gz = \text{const} \tag{6.58}$$

is immediately obtained.

The application of the preceding equations to heat exchangers was already mentioned in Section 6.13.3, Figure 6.16.

6.17.2   *Heat balance for prime mover*

Most modern prime movers, that is, machines built for the purpose of providing mechanical power on a large scale operate on the steady-state principle. The example of a gas-turbine jet engine was already mentioned in Section 6.11. In many cases the prime mover admits the *working fluid* through one duct and discharges it through another. An idealized system of this kind is shown in Figure 6.21. The First Law provides the so-called heat balance for a prime mover, and can be written

$$\dot{Q} = \dot{m}\left\{ (h_2 - h_1) + \tfrac{1}{2}(\mathcal{V}_2^2 - \mathcal{V}_1^2) + g(z_2 - z_1) \right\} + \dot{W} \tag{6.59}$$

as an immediate application of equation (6.45). The term $g(z_2 - z_1)$ is important only in hydraulic turbines and can be neglected in prime movers operating with steam or gases. In all cases, the prime mover is so designed that the change in kinetic energy from inlet to exit, but not necessarily between points within the engine casing, is negligible, which makes the term $\tfrac{1}{2}(\mathcal{V}_2^2 - \mathcal{V}_1^2)$ small compared with the others in the equation. The rate of heat transferred, $\dot{Q}$, is termed *heat lost to surroundings*, and is also small in a well-designed and properly maintained engine. Thus, the power developed is given by the very simple relation

$$\dot{W} = \dot{m}(h_1 - h_2) \tag{6.60}$$

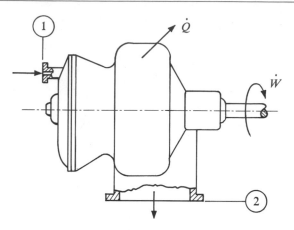

FIGURE 6.21. *Schematic diagram of prime mover.*

in which the difference $h_1 - h_2$ is known as the *enthalpy drop*, or heat drop in older textbooks. However, the term heat drop is misleading and will not be used in this book.

When a reciprocating engine is provided with large receiver spaces at inlet and exit in order to damp out the fluctuations in the state, as shown in Figure 6.22, and if the state is measured at sections 1 and 2, equation (6.60) can still be applied.

In many applications, an engine is built for the sole purpose of changing the state of some fluid from a given state 1 to a desired state 2. This is done, for example, in compressors which can be rotary or reciprocating. The change in state usually requires

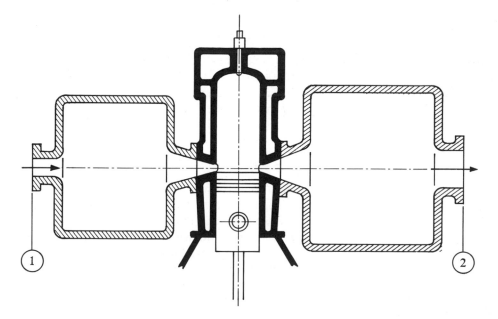

FIGURE 6.22. *Reciprocating engine with receivers.*

the expenditure of power $(W < 0)$ and equation (6.60) is written

$$-\dot{W} = \dot{m}(h_2 - h_1) \tag{6.60a}$$

for adiabatic engines, or

$$-\dot{W} = \dot{m}(h_2 - h_1) - (-\dot{Q}) \tag{6.60b}$$

for cooled engines, or engines losing heat to the surroundings $(-\dot{Q} > 0)$.

In particular, it should be noted that a knowledge of the rate of flow $\dot{m}$ and of the enthalpy at inlet, h_1, and at exit, h_2, is sufficient to determine the power consumed or produced, if the engine operates *adiabatically*, and regardless of whether its operation is reversible or not. The calculation of the enthalpy drop for different types of engines including the effects of irreversibility forms one of the central problems of engineering thermodynamics, as already mentioned in Section 6.14. Since most modern engines operate on the rotary principle and use fluids as their working media, a thorough knowledge of fluid mechanics is also essential for the purpose.

It should be apparent that in a complete heat balance for an engine, more details than those discussed here will normally be included.

6.17.3   *The porous plug experiment. Throttling. Inversion*

James Prescott Joule, whose name has already been mentioned in connection with the crucial experiment (Section 5.2) which led to the formulation of the First Law of thermodynamics, carried out an extensive investigation into the properties of gases. In this connection he performed experiments in which gases were subjected to unresisted adiabatic expansions, as described in Section 5.14.3. Since, for his purposes, such experiments proved to be of insufficient accuracy, he devised, together with Lord Kelvin (then Sir William Thomson), the famous porous plug experiment which will now serve as a further illustration of the application of the equation of the First Law for open systems in steady flow. In this experiment, Figure 6.23, the gas at a constant pressure P_1 and temperature θ_1 was forced in a well-lagged pipe through a plug p made of a porous material, such as cotton wool for low pressures or a ceramic for higher pressures. The gas emerged from the plug at state 2 (P_2, θ_2) after suffering a pressure drop $P_1 - P_2$. A similar effect occurs when the gas is allowed to pass through a con-

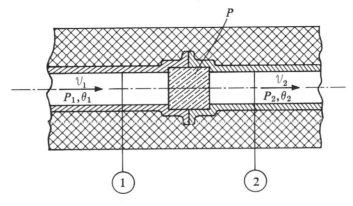

FIGURE 6.23. *The porous plug experiment or the Joule-Thomson experiment.*

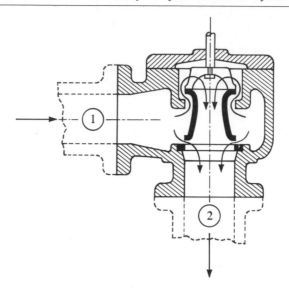

FIGURE 6.24. *Throttling in a valve.*

striction in a pipe, such as a slightly opened valve, Figure 6.24, or through a very long and narrow capillary. In general, a process in which a gas is made to suffer a loss of pressure on passing a constriction is referred to as throttling. During throttling, the gas acquires a certain velocity in the narrow passages, but at a certain distance behind it, the velocity decreases to a small value. Throttling can be performed in a continuous manner by providing a compressor C, Figure 6.25, which restores the original pressure P_1 to the gas at the expense of work W. By applying the First Law to the closed system shown in Figure 6.25, it is noted that the system absorbs work at a rate $\dot{W}$, and since its energy must remain constant in steady-state operation, heat must be withdrawn in cooler C_1 at a rate

$$\dot{Q} = \dot{W}$$

in order to restore the gas to state 1.

It is easy to see that the process is an irreversible one because the gas passing through the plug or throttle is not in equilibrium and because the process cannot be reversed by the application of an infinitely small cause. It is further noted that it is impossible to increase the pressure by means of adiabatic throttling, and $P_2 < P_1$ for all gases.

Applying the First Law to the open system in Figure 6.23, it is possible to assert that

$$h_1 = h_2 \qquad (\dot{m} = \text{const}) \tag{6.61}$$

or that the specific enthalpy at state 2 is equal to that at state 1. When the gas moves with finite velocities $\mathcal{V}_1$ and $\mathcal{V}_2$ before and after the throttle, the equation can be written

$$h_1 + \tfrac{1}{2}\mathcal{V}_1^2 = h_2 + \tfrac{1}{2}\mathcal{V}_2^2 \tag{6.62}$$

which asserts that the stagnation enthalpy has not changed upon throttling, assuming, as we have in equation (6.62), that the gas behaves like a perfect fluid and slides along the wall. For the time being, however, we shall neglect both velocities, stipulating that $V_1 = V_2 = 0$.

Throttling experiments are very important in the investigation of the properties of fluids. It is clear that, in the same way as we have done it with Joule's unresisted expansion discussed in Section 5.14.3, it is now possible to determine the sequence of states along a line of constant enthalpy, that is, along an isenthalpic. By varying the opening of the throttle, the length of the plug or of the capillary, it is possible to attain a number of equilibrium states 2 from a fixed state 1, the two states differing from one another by the pressure P_2. During such measurements it is observed that the final temperature θ_2 is sometimes higher and sometimes lower than the initial temperature θ_1. A typical result of such a throttling experiment performed on a gas is shown in Figure 6.26 in the form of a plot of temperature *versus* pressure. The plot shows that the locus of all states 2 which can be attained by throttling from a given state 1, all of which, as will be recalled, have the same value of specific enthalpy, is represented by a curve which passes through a very flat maxium for certain ranges of enthalpy. With the results of such experiments to hand it is easy to devise a *reversible* isenthalpic process, at least in principle, it being merely necessary to arrange for the gas to traverse the states along the curve $h = \text{const}$ in a continuous way. This can be achieved, for example, by means of a cylinder provided with a piston and cam in the same way as was done for the processes considered in Sections 5.14.3 and 5.14.4.

The change in temperature $\theta_1 - \theta_2$ associated with throttling is referred to as the *Joule-Thomson effect*. When the pressure drop $P_1 - P_2$ is large, it is customary to speak of the *integral* Joule-Thomson effect, whereas the *differential* Joule-Thomson effect is said to occur when this difference is extrapolated to a value zero. In the latter case,

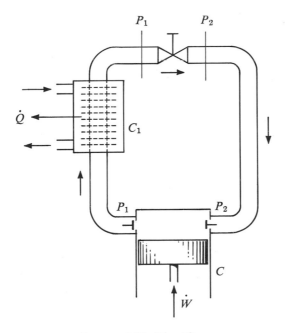

FIGURE 6.25. *Throttling.*

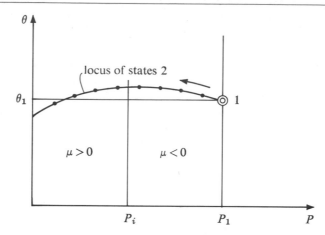

FIGURE 6.26. *Experimental determination of an isenthalpic.*

the magnitude and the direction of the effect is described by the *Joule-Thomson coefficient*

$$\mu = \left(\frac{\partial \theta}{\partial P}\right)_h = \lim_{P_1 \to P_2} \frac{\theta_1 - \theta_2}{P_1 - P_2} \qquad (h_1 = h_2). \tag{6.63}$$

The numerical value of the Joule-Thomson coefficient is equal to the inclination of the tangent to the isenthalpic curve in the P, θ diagram at a given state. It is, of course, a thermodynamic property of the gas.

In the case of all gases, except near the range when they condense, the value of the Joule-Thomson coefficient is small, indicating that

$$\theta_1 \approx \theta_2 \tag{6.64}$$

approximately. Furthermore, as already mentioned, the isenthalpic curve exhibits a characteristic maximum, shown in Figure 6.26. The state which corresponds to this maximum is known as the *inversion point*, because at that point the sign of the Joule-Thomson coefficient undergoes an inversion. For initial pressures which are lower than that at the inversion point, P_i, $(P_1 < P_i)$, the temperature of the gas always decreases $(\theta_2 < \theta_1, \mu > 0)$ on throttling, it being remembered that the pressure must always decrease. For initial pressures $P_1 > P_i$, the gas always emerges hotter $(\theta_2 > \theta_1, \mu < 0)$ in a differential Joule-Thomson experiment. The integral Joule-Thomson effect depends, in addition, on the total pressure loss $P_1 - P_2$.

When the initial state 1 is changed, it is possible to obtain a series of isenthalpic curves, shown sketched in Figure 6.27. It is then found that above a certain value of specific enthalpy h_i, the isenthalpic curves all ascend in the direction of decreasing pressure, so that $\mu < 0$ for $h > h_i$. For lower values of enthalpy, $h < h_i$, the curves exhibit the characteristic maximum, all maxima forming a locus, shown dotted in Figure 6.27, and known as the *inversion curve* for the gas. The inversion curve is described by an empirical relation

$$\theta_i(P_i)$$

between the *inversion temperature*, θ_i, and the inversion pressure, P_i. In the range

$h < h_i$, the differential Joule-Thomson effect is positive ($\mu < 0$) for states outside the area enclosed by the inversion curve, being negative ($\mu > 0$) inside it. Thus, there exists a maximum inversion temperature $\theta_{i,\max}$ at $P = 0$ which is obtained by extrapolation to zero pressure. The inversion pressure, on the other hand, passes through a maximum $P_{i,\max}$ for a temperature which depends on the nature of the gas. At pressures $P > P_{i,\max}$, the differential Joule-Thomson effect is always positive ($\mu < 0$). At pressures $0 < P < P_{i,\max}$ the effect is negative for temperatures contained between two inversion temperatures, an upper inversion temperature θ_i' and a lower inversion temperature θ_i''. When throttling is performed near the inversion curve, the approximate equality (6.64) is satisfied quite accurately for comparatively large pressure drops $P_1 - P_2$. In particular, at low pressures this occurs near the maximum inversion temperature $\theta_{i,\max}$.

Values of the maximum inversion temperatures, $\theta_{i,\max}$, for several gases are contained in Table XXVI from which it is seen that the maximum inversion temperature is higher than the ordinary temperature of our surroundings for most gases. It becomes smaller only in the case of hydrogen and helium. This circumstance is particularly important for hydrogen supply lines, owing to the explosive nature of mixtures of hydrogen and atmospheric oxygen. When a leak occurs in a supply line, the gas is subjected to throttling, and in the case of hydrogen this leads to a discharge of heated gas into the atmosphere, thus creating favorable conditions for an explosion.

A set of isenthalpic lines for carbon dioxide is shown in Figure 6.28. It is seen that the course of the isenthalpic curves becomes quite steep near the curve marked "vapor pressure curve" where the gas liquefies. We shall study the properties of gases near this range of states in more detail in Section 7.4. The Joule-Thomson effect can be used to liquefy gases as is done in the gas liquefaction machine invented by Carl von Linde.

Applying the general relation between three properties (h, θ, and P in this case) given in equation (3.34), we find that

$$\left(\frac{\partial h}{\partial \theta}\right)_P \left(\frac{\partial \theta}{\partial P}\right)_h \left(\frac{\partial P}{\partial h}\right)_\theta = -1. \tag{6.65}$$

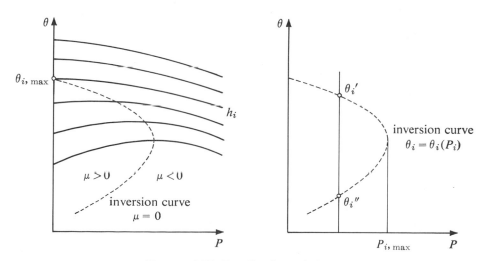

FIGURE 6.27. *Family of isenthalpics.*

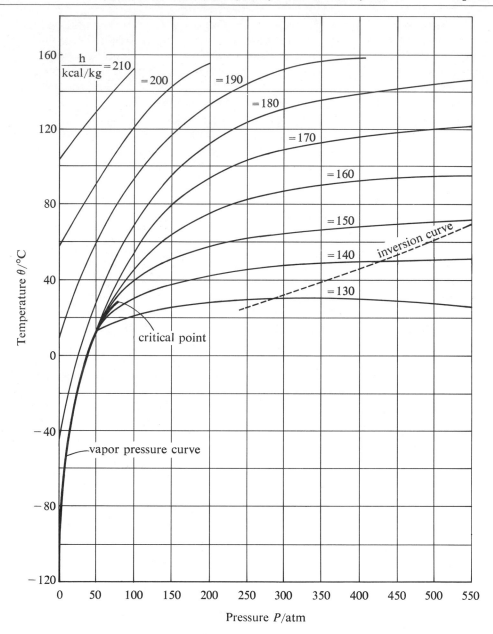

FIGURE 6.28. *Isenthalpic curves for carbon dioxide, after F. Din.* (Thermodynamic Functions of Gases, *Butterworth, Vols. 1, 2, 1956, Vol. 3, 1961.*)

Here, the first term is the specific heat c_p known from Section 5.14.2, whereas the second term is the inverse of the Joule-Thomson coefficient. Thus,

$$\left(\frac{\partial h}{\partial P}\right)_\theta = -\mu c_p. \tag{6.66}$$

The property $(\partial h/\partial P)_\theta$, which is known as the *isothermal* Joule-Thomson coefficient, can be measured by performing throttling at constant temperature, Figure 6.29. It is evident that this process must involve an exchange of heat Q, and applying the First Law, equation (6.45), we can write

$$Q = h_2 - h_1. \tag{6.67}$$

Thus, by measuring the heat Q calorimetrically, it is possible to determine the change in enthalpy, to perform the extrapolation

$$\lim_{P_1 \to P_2} \frac{h_2 - h_1}{P_2 - P_1} = \left(\frac{\partial h}{\partial P}\right)_\theta, \tag{6.68}$$

and so to evaluate the partial derivative $(\partial h/\partial P)_\theta$ as a function of pressure and temperature. Frequently, as shown in Figure 6.29(b), the gas is first throttled adiabatically to state 2 and subsequently heated electrically. The heater is adjusted to restore the initial temperature $(\theta_3 = \theta_1)$, and the electrical input provides an accurate measure of the heat Q. A typical plot of the isotherms of a gas in an h, P diagram is given in Figure 6.30. Since c_p is always positive, equation (6.66) shows that $(\partial h/\partial P)_\theta$ has the opposite sign to the Joule-Thomson coefficient μ and vanishes along the inversion curve, as shown in the diagram.

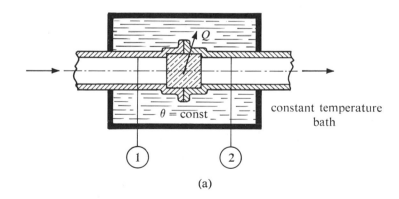

(a)

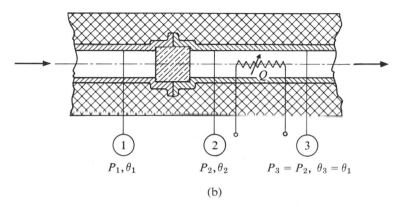

(b)

FIGURE 6.29. *Constant temperature throttling.*

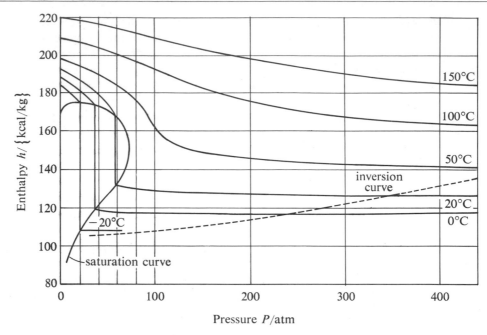

FIGURE 6.30. *Isotherms of carbon dioxide and helium in an h, P diagram, after F. Din.* (Thermodynamic Functions of Gases, *Butterworth, Vols. 1, 2, 1956, Vol. 3, 1961.*)

It is necessary to note for future reference that

$$\lim_{P \to 0} \left(\frac{\partial h}{\partial P} \right)_\theta \neq 0 \qquad (6.69)$$

so that

$$\lim_{P \to 0} \left(\frac{\partial \theta}{\partial P} \right)_h \neq 0 \qquad (6.70)$$

for a real gas, except at the maximum inversion temperature $\theta_{i,\max}$. The above partial derivatives vanish *only along the inversion curve.*

6.17.4   *Flow of fluids. Hydraulic approximation*

A further example of the application of the First Law of thermodynamics in its formulation for open, continuous systems presents itself in the study of fluid flow. For the present, we shall limit ourselves to cases of steady flow through channels of slowly varying cross section, Figure 6.31, *on the assumption that the fluid is perfect.* From the short discussion already given (Section 6.2.2), it can be surmised that the preceding assumptions are equivalent to postulating that at every cross section in a channel the velocity is uniform across it. Thus, as an approximation, the no-slip condition at the solid wall is neglected and the fluid is presumed to slide along it. The fact that the cross-sectional area varies slowly in the direction of flow means, for example, that in a channel of circular cross section, the axial velocity component by far exceeds the radial

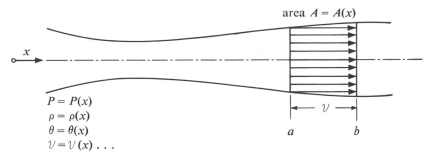

FIGURE 6.31. *Channel of slowly varying cross section.*

component so that the latter can be neglected compared with the former. In cross sections of other shapes it is still assumed that the axial component of velocity is the only one that needs to be taken into account. The system under consideration is a continuous one, and its state is described by indicating the variation of velocity $V(x)$, pressure $P(x)$, and so on, along the flow axis in terms of a single coordinate x as shown in Figure 6.31. When the axis of the channel is curved, as shown in Figure 6.32, the same assumptions can be retained, on condition that the radius of curvature $R = R(x)$ is large compared with the linear dimensions of the cross section. The coordinate x is then measured along the curved axis of the channel. When the flow of a fluid is analyzed, by way of approximation, under the preceding set of assumptions, it is said that the flow is *one-dimensional* or that the *hydraulic* or *engineering approximation* is employed.

When the variation in velocity and pressure along the flow axis is small, it is possible to introduce a further simplification and to assume that the fluid is *incompressible*, or that its specific volume v is constant. In the study of fluid flow it is customary to prefer to use the density $\rho = 1/v$ instead of the specific volume. Hence, the assumption that the fluid is incompressible is equivalent to assuming that the equation of state has the singular form

$$\rho = \text{const} \qquad \text{implying} \qquad \left(\frac{\partial \rho}{\partial \theta}\right)_P = 0, \qquad \left(\frac{\partial \rho}{\partial P}\right)_\theta = 0. \qquad (6.71)$$

Actually, when it was shown in Section 6.17.1 that the energy equation (6.55) was

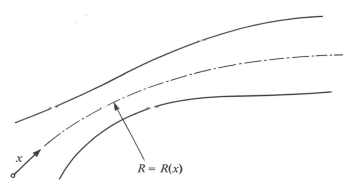

FIGURE 6.32. *Curved channel.*

equivalent to Bernoulli's equation (6.58), implicit use was made of this assumption. The complete study of the flow of fluids which obey the equation of state (6.71) habitually belongs to fluid mechanics.

When a more general form of the equation of state is assumed, such as, for example, the equation of state of a perfect gas, the flow, as well as the fluid, are said to be *compressible*. In order to describe the properties of the flow in mathematical terms, it is necessary to write down the three conservation laws of physics which must be satisfied in this case. These must express the *conservation of mass, momentum, and energy*.

The equation which expresses the conservation of mass, as already shown in Section 6.10, assumes the form $\dot{m} = $ const at every cross section. If we concentrate our attention on any cross section a and follow in our mind's eye the path of the particles during a unit of time, Figure 6.31, we shall notice that all the fluid particles which have crossed it are contained within a cylinder of base A extending as far as section b at a distance $\mathcal{V}$, so that its volume is $A\mathcal{V}$. In actual fact, the particles will spread or contract, depending on the change in the shape of the channel, as the fluid must fill it entirely in all cross sections between a and b. This demonstrates that the particles away from the center line must possess a velocity component at right angles to the axis, but, as already mentioned, this component is neglected in our present approximation. Consequently, the rate at which fluid passes any cross section, expressed in units of mass per unit time is

$$\dot{m} = A\rho\mathcal{V} \qquad (\dot{m} = \text{const}). \tag{6.72}$$

The above equation, known as the *continuity equation*, can be expressed in differential form (preferably by differentiating logarithmically) as follows:

$$\frac{dA}{A} + \frac{d\rho}{\rho} + \frac{d\mathcal{V}}{\mathcal{V}} = 0, \tag{6.72a}$$

where all quantities are functions of the parameter x.

The law of momentum, or Newton's Second Law of motion, can be derived with reference to Figure 6.33 in which the channel is shown divergent in order to render

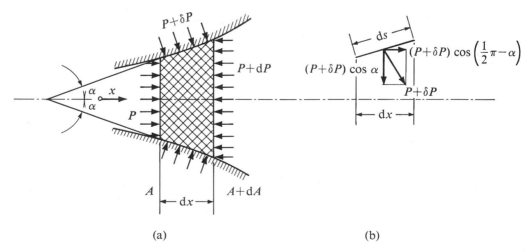

(a)   (b)

FIGURE 6.33. *Equation of motion.*

$\mathrm{d}A/\mathrm{d}x > 0$ and so to preserve a consistent sign convention. Considering an element of fluid of length $\mathrm{d}x$, we can write its mass as

$$A\rho\,\mathrm{d}x,$$

its acceleration as

$$\frac{\mathrm{d}\mathcal{V}}{\mathrm{d}t} = \frac{\mathrm{d}\mathcal{V}}{\mathrm{d}x}\cdot\frac{\mathrm{d}x}{\mathrm{d}t} = \mathcal{V}\,\frac{\mathrm{d}\mathcal{V}}{\mathrm{d}x}.$$

The forces acting on it consist of pressures acting on the faces at A and $A + \mathrm{d}A$, and yield a net force

$$AP - \{AP + \mathrm{d}(AP)\} = -P\,\mathrm{d}A - A\,\mathrm{d}P.$$

In addition, the divergent channel exerts a pressure, which by the mean value theorem of mathematics can be put at $P + \delta P$, with $\delta P < \mathrm{d}P$, acting at an angle $\tfrac{1}{2}\pi - \alpha$ to the axis. It is known from hydrostatics that the resultant of this pressure acting on the circumferential area is axial and equal to the product of the pressure itself and the *projection* of the area on a plane normal to the axis, that is, $\mathrm{d}A$.[†] Thus, the sum of all the pressure forces is

$$-P\,\mathrm{d}A - A\,\mathrm{d}P + (P + \delta P)\,\mathrm{d}A = -A\,\mathrm{d}P.$$

Sometimes, in the engineering approximation, the absence of slip is disregarded and it is quite arbitrarily assumed that the sliding fluid is acted upon by the wall with a frictional shearing stress τ. We shall disregard such forces as being inconsistent with the assumption that the fluid is perfect.

Combining all the forces and equating them to the product of mass and acceleration, it is possible to obtain the *equation of motion*

$$\frac{1}{\rho}\,\mathrm{d}P + \mathcal{V}\,\mathrm{d}\mathcal{V} = 0 \tag{6.73}$$

in which the parameter x does not occur explicitly; it is, evidently, implicit in both terms.

The law of the *conservation of energy*, that is, the First Law of thermodynamics, can be written at once with reference to equation (6.45), whence we obtain

$$\mathrm{d}Q = \mathrm{d}h + \mathcal{V}\,\mathrm{d}\mathcal{V}. \tag{6.74}$$

On subtracting equation (6.73) from equation (6.74) and remembering that $\mathrm{d}P/\rho - v\,\mathrm{d}P$, we obtain

$$\mathrm{d}Q = \mathrm{d}h - v\,\mathrm{d}P. \tag{6.75}$$

It is easy to recognize that this is the equation which would be obtained if the First

---

[†] If the reader does not remember this result he can easily derive it by decomposing the pressure into an axial component $(P + \delta P)\cdot\cos(\tfrac{1}{2}\pi - \alpha)$ and a radial component $(P + \delta P)\cos\alpha$. The radial components cancel around the circumference, and the axial resultant is

$$C\,\mathrm{d}s\,(P + \delta P)\cos(\tfrac{1}{2}\pi - \alpha),$$

where $\mathrm{d}s$ denotes the length of the element of surface, as shown in the Figure 6.33(a), and C is the perimeter. The term $C\,\mathrm{d}s\,\cos(\tfrac{1}{2}\pi - \alpha)$ is the projection of the area $C\,\mathrm{d}s$ on a plane normal to the axis and equals $\mathrm{d}A$.

Law were written for a Lagrangian system consisting of a mass of fluid contained in a lamina of thickness $\mathrm{d}x$ and moving over a distance $\mathrm{d}x$ in time $\mathrm{d}t$. Upon comparing this equation with equation (6.44) which expresses the formulation of the First Law for a reversible process performed by such a system, namely,

$$\mathrm{d}Q = \mathrm{d}h - v\,\mathrm{d}P,$$

it is immediately apparent that the flow is *reversible* when viscous shear is absent, and the fluid is perfect. This result could, evidently, have been arrived at on physical grounds as well. The term *reversible* means that an element of fluid (a continuous system) performs a reversible process when viewed in a Lagrangian frame of reference.

In many problems of fluid flow, no heat is added across the boundary, or the amount of heat added is small compared with the change in enthalpy and kinetic energy. When this is the case, the flow is termed *adiabatic*. As usual, when the flow is both adiabatic and reversible, it is termed *isentropic* (see Section 5.14.5);† it is then governed by the simpler equations:

equation of motion (also known as Euler's equation in this case)

$$\frac{\mathrm{d}P}{\rho} + \mathcal{V}\,\mathrm{d}\mathcal{V} = 0 \tag{6.76}$$

energy equation (also known as the *compressible Bernoulli equation* in this case)

$$\mathrm{d}h + \mathcal{V}\,\mathrm{d}\mathcal{V} = 0. \tag{6.77}$$

On subtracting the former from the latter it will then be confirmed that the process performed by a Lagrangian system is, indeed, isentropic. In addition, since the heat flux $\mathrm{d}Q$ has disappeared from them, both equations become identical if it is realized that a reversible process is performed by a fluid particle. This is consistent with what is known from mechanics when it is proved that for *conservative systems* the energy equation is simply an integral of the equation of motion, the addition of heat being consistently disregarded in mechanics. A conservative system in mechanics constitutes a particular case of a closed system subjected to a reversible process. Thus, the two equations (6.76) and (6.77) can be used interchangeably, one providing no more information than the other. For incompressible flow, $\rho = \mathrm{const}$, and the equation of motion (6.77) integrates to

$$\frac{P}{\rho} + \tfrac{1}{2}\mathcal{V}^2 = \mathrm{const},$$

which is the Bernoulli equation known from incompressible fluid mechanics. The Bernoulli equation has already been derived from the First Law of thermodynamics in Section 6.17.1 on the assumption that the flow was adiabatic and the preceding remarks explain why this should be expected in the circumstances of ideal, adiabatic flow. The Bernoulli equation for incompressible flow no longer contains any param-

---

† In this book we consistently reserve the term *isentropic* for *reversible*, adiabatic processes. Nonadiabatic, quasistatic, irreversible processes which follow the same sequence of states (each of them a near-equilibrium state), are not called isentropic; we shall use the term *quasi-isentropic* for them.

eters which depend on temperature, and this is the reason for our ability to study such flows in hydraulics without any prior knowledge of thermodynamics.

It should be noted here that in the presence of a boundary layer $(\tau \neq 0)$, or of heat addition $(\mathrm{d}Q \neq 0)$, the equation of motion and the energy equation would no longer be equivalent, and both would have to be used in order to obtain explicit solutions.

Summarizing the preceding investigation, it is noted that the flow is determined completely when the variation of pressure, density, velocity, and enthalpy is known along the flow axis. In other words, a problem in compressible fluid flow is considered solved when the four functions, $P(x)$, $\rho(x)$, $V(x)$, and $h(x)$ have been determined. These four functions are determined by the three conservation equations: the continuity equation (6.72a), the equation of motion (6.73), and the energy equation (6.74). The fourth equation required for the solution is provided by the equation which describes the properties of the fluid, that is, the equation of state in the form

$$F(P, \rho, h) = 0.$$

The applicability of the equation of state derived from experiments on uniform systems in equilibrium to the present continuous system has already been justified in Section 6.4.

The four equations, or more precisely the three former equations, contain, in addition, the function $A(x)$ which is considered given when the shape of the channel is known. The heat transferred $Q(x)$ must be calculated with the aid of the laws governing the transfer of heat.

It has already been stressed that the most important characteristic of the flow of a real fluid lies in the fact that its relative velocity with respect to any solid boundary is zero, and that it develops a boundary layer near it. Thus, on the one hand, the velocity varies across the flow and cannot remain constant in a cross section. On the other hand, in the presence of shear, the pumping work at the open boundaries of the system is no longer properly accounted for by the energy equation (6.74), and the hydraulic, one-dimensional approximation ceases to be consistent with the physical features of the problem, and must be abandoned. A more extensive study of compressible fluid flow belongs to the subject of gas dynamics.†

6.18 The filling and discharging of rigid vessels

The processes of filling or discharging of rigid vessels occur very frequently in engineering applications. These processes are essentially nonsteady, and their study is greatly facilitated by the use of the formulation of the First Law of thermodynamics for open systems given in Section 6.15. Owing to the limitations imposed in the course of the derivation, we shall confine ourselves to processes which do not involve the mixing of different chemical species or chemical reactions. Furthermore, it will be necessary to continue to assume that the fluids are perfect and slide along walls instead of adhering to them, as they do in actual fact. In many cases, the approximation is sufficient for practical applications. Finally, we shall assume that the processes are slow enough for

† Liepmann, H. W., and Roshko, A., *Elements of Gas Dynamics* (Wiley, 1957); Shapiro, A. H., *The Dynamics and Thermodynamics of Compressible Fluid Flow* (Ronald, 1953, 1954) I, II; Oswatitsch, K., *Gas Dynamics*, translated by G. Kuerti (Academic, 1956); Owczarek, J. A., *Fundamentals of Gas Dynamics* (International Textbook, 1964).

the state in the vessel to be homogeneous. Thus, the fact that the system within the vessel is a continuous one is ignored, and the fluid is treated like a uniform system whose properties have been averaged over those of the real, continuous system. Mathematically, this is equivalent to replacing the integral (6.38) by an average value, thus

$$\frac{d}{dt} \int_V u(x, y, z, t) \, \rho(x, y, z, t) \, dV = \frac{d}{dt} \{ V \bar{u}(t) \bar{\rho}(t) \},$$

where

$$\bar{u}(t) \, \bar{\rho}(t) = \frac{1}{V} \int_V u(x, y, z, t) \, \rho(x, y, z, t) \, dV,$$

and similarly for all other quantities.

The equation which governs the process in all cases has already been derived in Section 6.15 as equation (6.37a); it is

$$dQ = d(mu) - h_\xi \, dm, \tag{6.78}$$

for a single flow channel.

6.18.1   Discharge

We shall now consider the case when the fluid is discharged from a vessel inside which the pressure is high through a throttling valve to an atmosphere at lower pressure, Figure 6.34. In this case the subscript ξ can be dropped, as the fluid emerging at $A-A$ has the same enthalpy as that inside the vessel, because there is no change in enthalpy across the throttle. Consequently, the terms $d(mu)$ and $h \, dm$ can be combined, and equation (6.37a) can be transformed as in equation (6.37b). Thus,

$$dQ = m \, du - Pv \, dm, \tag{6.79}$$

in which m is variable. Since the volume of the vessel V is assumed constant, and since

$$V = mv = \text{const},$$

we must have

$$m \, dv = -v \, dm,$$

so that equation (6.79) can be transformed to

$$dQ = m(du + P \, dv). \tag{6.80}$$

This is the First Law written for a closed system consisting of m units of mass of fluid and for a reversible process. Thus, the process of slow discharge is *reversible* as far as the change in the state of fluid particles *remaining* in the vessel is concerned. That this is so can be seen at once by choosing a closed system of mass m inside the vessel and confining it to the left of the fictitious membrane $B-B$ shown in the sketch. It is clear that the fluid to the left expands quasistatically and performs work Pdv per unit mass on forcing the fluid to the right out of the vessel. However, the whole process is irreversible, because the flow across the throttle is irreversible.

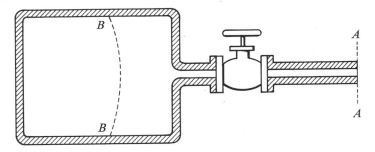

FIGURE 6.34. *Discharge.*

When the fluid leaving the vessel acquires a velocity $\mathcal{V}$ at exit which cannot be neglected, the enthalpy h in equation (6.78) must be replaced by the stagnation enthalpy

$$h_0 = h + \tfrac{1}{2}\mathcal{V}^2.$$

In general the preceding equations cannot be integrated without more specific information concerning the equation of state of the fluid. However, when the flow of heat is so arranged that the process is isothermal and the temperature of the fluid emerging at A–A is constant, the enthalpy h_ξ in equation (6.78) remains constant, the integration can be completed in the general case. This fact was utilized in an important experiment to be discussed in the next section.

6.18.2   The Washburn experiment

It was shown in Section 6.17.3 that throttling experiments can be used to advantage to study the properties of real gases. A variant of these experiments, first devised by E. W. Washburn[†] and then performed by F. D. Rossini and M. Frandsen[‡] can be used to a similar purpose. It has the advantage that it can be performed with a relatively high degree of precision.

The instrument used for the purpose is depicted schematically in Figure 6.35(a). It consists of a high pressure vessel A filled with a gas at an initial pressure P. The latter is discharged slowly through a long coiled capillary C into the atmosphere at B–B until the pressure in the vessel A becomes equal to that outside it. The instrument is immersed in a large adiabatic calorimeter D in which the temperature is maintained constant by the provision of an electric heater H as shown.

During the experiment the gas is made to perform an irreversible process which is best analyzed with the aid of equation (6.78) as applied to the open system shown in outline in Figure 6.26(b). Thus, at any step

$$\mathrm{d}Q = \mathrm{d}(mu) - h_0\,\mathrm{d}m. \tag{6.81}$$

Here h_0 denotes the constant enthalpy of the gas at the point of discharge where its pressure is equal to the back pressure P_0 (atmospheric) and its temperature is equal to the constant temperature of the bath. Thus, equation (6.81) can be integrated

† Bur. of Std. J. of Res., **9** (1932) 521.
‡ Bur. of Std. J. of Res., **9** (1932) 733.

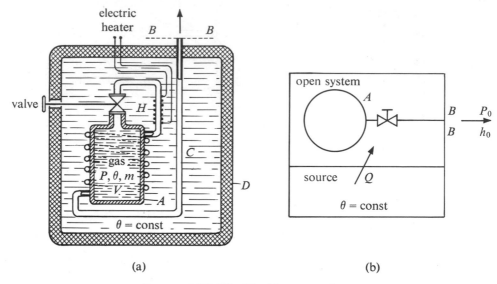

(a)   (b)

FIGURE 6.35. *The Washburn experiment.*

immediately to yield

$$Q = m_0 u_0 - mu - (u_0 + P_0 v_0)(m_0 - m),$$

where m_0 is the mass in vessel A of volume V at the end of the experiment when its pressure is equal to the back pressure P_0 and the temperature is θ. The initial mass, denoted by m, corresponds to a pressure P, temperature θ, and specific internal energy u in the vessel. Hence,

$$Q = m(u_0 - u) + P_0(m v_0 - V), \qquad (6.81a)$$

since $m_0 v_0 = V$. In the experiment it is possible to determine the heat supplied, Q, the initial mass, m, the specific volume, v_0, together with the back pressure, P_0, and volume V. Thus, the experiment serves to determine the difference in energy

$$u - u_0 = u(P, \theta) - u(P_0, \theta) = \frac{P_0(m v_0 - V) - Q}{m} \qquad (6.82)$$

at constant temperature θ, but for two different pressures, P and P_0.

The plot in Figure 6.36 displays the results obtained on air and oxygen. By extrapolating the experimental values to zero pressure difference, it is possible to compute the limit

$$\lim_{P \to P_0} \frac{u - u_0}{P - P_0} = \left(\frac{\partial u}{\partial P}\right)_\theta, \qquad (6.83)$$

that is, the partial derivative of internal energy with respect to pressure at constant temperature. The results shown in Figure 6.36 lead to the conclusion that in the modest range of pressures from 1 to 40 atm, the value of the derivative is constant and equal to the slope of the straight lines drawn in the figure. It is seen that

$$\left(\frac{\partial u}{\partial P}\right)_\theta \neq 0$$

even at the limit of very low pressure. More extensive experimental results would show this to be true at any temperature; this conclusion will turn out to be important in Section 12.3 in connection with the discussion on the thermodynamic temperature scale.

In general, the derivative $(\partial u/\partial P)_\theta$ conceived as a function of temperature and pressure, depends on both parameters; it becomes independent of pressure at low pressures, but even then its value continues to depend on temperature. This result can be recorded in the form of the statement that

$$\left(\frac{\partial u}{\partial P}\right)_\theta = \mathrm{f}(\theta); \quad \text{at low pressures, but } \mathrm{f}(\theta) \neq 0. \tag{6.84}$$

When experimental values of the function $\mathrm{f}(\theta)$ are available, it is possible to evaluate the specific internal energy by integration, on condition that the pressure range is not too large. Thus,

$$u(P,\theta) - u(P_0,\theta) = \mathrm{f}(\theta) \times (P - P_0) + \psi(\theta), \tag{6.84a}$$

where the constant of integration ψ depends on the value of θ held constant during the integration. In order to calculate the difference in energy for higher values of pressure P, terms of higher order than $(P - P_0)$ would have to be included because $(\partial u/\partial P)_\theta$ ceases to be constant, even at constant temperature.

The value of the constant of integration $\psi(\theta)$ cannot be obtained with the aid of this type of measurement, and additional, and different, measurements are needed for the purpose.

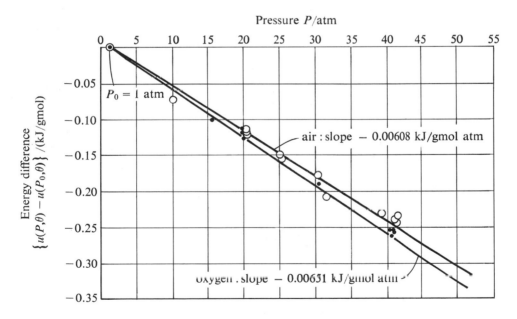

FIGURE 6.36. *Experimental results obtained in the course of a Washburn experiment; after F. D. Rossini and M. Frandsen.*
$\circ$ *air at 28°C; average slope −0.00608 kJ/gmol atm*
$\bullet$ *oxygen at 28°C; average slope −0.00651 kJ/gmol atm*

The measurements of the derivative $(\partial u/\partial P)_\theta$ are related to the measurements of the adiabatic and isothermal Joule-Thomson coefficients $\mu = (\partial\theta/\partial P)_h$ and $(\partial h/\partial P)_\theta$, to those of the specific heat c_p and to the equation of state $F(P, v, \theta) = 0$. The exact form of this relation can be derived only with the aid of certain equations which are consequences of the Second Law of thermodynamics, Section 12.1.

6.18.3 Filling

The discussion in Section 6.18.1 demonstrated that the fluid remaining in the vessel during discharge performs a reversible process. This was a consequence of the fact that the enthalpy h_ξ in equation (6.78) referred to the same state as the internal energy u. When the vessel is filled, this is no longer the case.

When the vessel is filled from a line, Figure 6.37, in which a constant state is maintained, h_ξ will be constant and equal to, say, h_1. As long as the flow in the line is ideal and at right angles to the connecting line a, the velocity of flow has no influence on the process, and h_1 is equal to the specific enthalpy at cross section A–A, and not to the stagnation enthalpy

$$h_0 = h_1 + \tfrac{1}{2}V_1^2.$$

Under these conditions the equation becomes identical with that in the preceding section and can be integrated in general terms.

It is easy to verify that in the case of filling

$$\mathrm{d}Q = m(\mathrm{d}u + P\,\mathrm{d}v) + (h - h_1)\,\mathrm{d}m$$

which reduces to the First Law for reversible processes only if $h = h_1$. Thus, for $h \neq h_1$ the process is irreversible as asserted before; it is interesting to note that during adiabatic filling $(\mathrm{d}Q = 0)$ from a vacuum $(m_0 = 0)$

$$mu = h_1 m \quad \text{or} \quad u = h_1. \tag{6.85}$$

Since the internal energy u of a substance is lower than its enthalpy at the same temperature $(u = h - Pv)$, it follows that the temperature in the cylinder (corresponding to

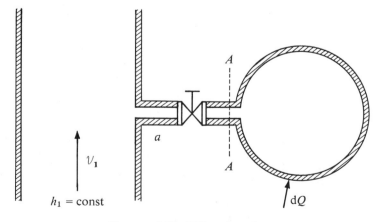

FIGURE 6.37. *Filling from line.*

u) is *higher* than that in the supply line (corresponding to h_1). This result can be understood on physical grounds if it is realized that work is done on the contents of the cylinder by the external atmosphere during the filling process.

The existence of boundary layers considerably complicates the preceding analysis. We are not in a position to discuss these complications beyond drawing the reader's attention to the limitations inherent in results like that contained in equation (6.85).

List of Symbols for Chapter 6

Latin letters

A	Area
c_p	Specific heat at constant pressure
E	Extensive property; energy
e	Specific property; specific energy
g	Gravitational acceleration
H	Enthalpy
h	Specific enthalpy
$H°$	Methalpy, defined on p. 223
$h°$	Specific methalpy, defined on p. 223
h_0	Stagnation enthalpy
m	Mass
P	Pressure
P_i	Inversion pressure
Q	Heat
$\mathcal{Q}$	Heat of mixing (diffusion or solution)
$\dot{\mathbf{q}}$	Heat flux vector
R	Gas constant; radius, Figures 6.19 and 6.20; radius of curvature, Figure 6.32
r	Radial coordinate
t	Time
$\mathcal{T}$	Thrust
U	Internal energy
u	Specific internal energy
V	Volume
v	Specific volume
$\mathcal{V}$	Velocity
W	Work
x	Coordinate
y	Coordinate
z	Coordinate

Greek letters

α	General quantity, equation (6.55a); angle, Figure 6.33
θ	Temperature
θ_i	Inversion temperature
μ	Dynamic viscosity; Joule-Thomson coefficient

ρ	Density
σ	Stress tensor
τ	Shearing stress
ψ	Constant of integration, equation (6.84a)

Superscripts and marks above symbols

*	Values at reference state, Section 6.13.3
—	Average value of respective quantity
.	Derivative with respect to time or time-rate of respective quantity

CHAPTER 7

Thermodynamic Systems I. The Pure
Substance and Simple Mixtures

In its primary form, the First Law of thermodynamics relates the difference between the heat exchanged and the work performed during any process which occurs *between* two states of equilibrium in a uniform system to the properties of the system *at* those two states of equilibrium. In a continuous system, the expressions for heat and work become surface integrals, and their difference is related to the volume integral of internal energy. Hence, whenever the principles of thermodynamics are applied to the solution of practical problems, it is necessary to possess data which describe the thermodynamic properties of various classes of systems as well as the relations between them. These data may be given in the form of empirical equations, diagrams, tables, or even computer programs, all of them representing various equations of state of systems. It has already been emphasized that in most cases such collections of properties must be compiled from direct, experimental determinations. In some cases the methods of statistical mechanics can be employed for the calculation of thermodynamic properties from a few microscopic constants which describe the mechanical model of the macroscopic system. At present, there is available a vast accumulation of such data, and in order to find one's way through them, it is necessary to discuss a number of typical systems in descriptive terms, but more systematically than has been done so far. We shall concentrate primarily on the properties of uniform systems, because their understanding is important in itself and, besides, contains the key to the understanding of the properties of continuous systems. We shall devote this chapter primarily to the descriptive study of pure substances. The next chapter will extend the discussion to various other systems including a brief mention of continuous systems, and this will compel us to consider a number of *fields*.

Before this is done, however, it is worth stating that our knowledge of the thermodynamic properties of systems always has, and still does lag behind the requirements encountered in practical applications. The determination of thermodynamic properties is a continuing task, measurements on new properties becoming available together with improved, and more reliable, values for properties which are known only imperfectly.

7.1 A material point

When a material point of mass m is displaced infinitely slowly in a uniform gravitational field $\mathbf{g}$, its state will depend on a single variable, the elevation z above an arbitrarily chosen reference level, Figure 7.1(a), that is, above an arbitrary equipotential

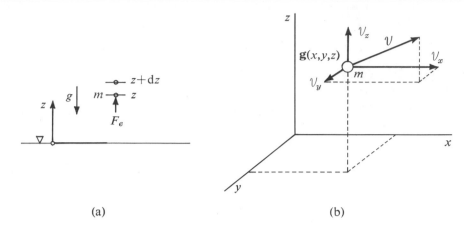

FIGURE 7.1. *Sketch of a material point in a uniform gravitational field.*

plane. Hence, z constitutes the single property which determines the state of a material point in a uniform gravitational field. Since the process of displacing the point infinitely slowly is an adiabatic one, the work $-mg\mathrm{d}z$ performed on the system by the force F_e must be equal to the negative of the change in its energy, or

$$\mathrm{d}E = mg\mathrm{d}z. \tag{7.1}$$

When the material point is free to move in the gravitational field, the description of the state must be supplemented by the indication of its velocity $\mathcal{V}$. When the gravitational field $\mathbf{g}(x, y, z)$ is not uniform, and the motion is in three dimensions, Figure 7.1(b), it is necessary to indicate six quantities in order to describe its state. These may be chosen as the three Cartesian coordinates x, y, z and the three components of velocity, $\mathcal{V}_x$, $\mathcal{V}_y$, and $\mathcal{V}_z$. This fact has already been noticed in Section 1.6 in connection with the discussion of the microstate of a complex system of material points. Instead of the components of velocity, it was then preferable to choose the momenta $p_x = m\mathcal{V}_x$, $p_y = m\mathcal{V}_y$, and $p_z = m\mathcal{V}_z$. Although different independent properties were chosen, their total number has turned out to be invariant; it is, of course, invariant for any thermodynamic system.

Since the process of accelerating a mass m in a gravitational field $\mathbf{g}(x, y, z)$ is also adiabatic, the principle of energy conservation in mechanics allows us to write

$$\mathrm{d}E = \mathrm{d}E_k + \mathrm{d}E_p = 0, \tag{7.2}$$

where

$$\mathrm{d}E_p = -m\mathbf{g} \cdot \mathbf{dr} \quad \text{and} \quad \mathrm{d}E_k = m\mathcal{V} \cdot \mathrm{d}\mathcal{V} \tag{7.2a} \dagger$$

represent the increments in potential and kinetic energy, respectively. The equation applies to the motion of a mass in a potential, gravitational field when no external forces act on it ($\mathrm{d}W = 0$), and when no heat is exchanged ($\mathrm{d}Q = 0$).

---

† Note that in equation (7.1) the vector $\mathbf{g}$ is opposite in direction to the positive vector $\mathbf{dr}$.

7.2   Incompressible fluid

Students conversant with fluid mechanics will know that often the assumption is made that a fluid, that is, a liquid *or a gas*, is incompressible during a certain flow process. In actual fact, all fluids, and even solids subjected to uniform pressure, change their specific volume, and hence also their density, when the pressure and temperature are changed. Depending on the properties of the system and on the range of variation of pressure and temperature in a particular flow process, the specific volume may undergo a greater or smaller change. Sometimes this change is so small that disregarding it does not lead to serious errors in the solution of the mechanical problem in hand. We then say that the fluid "is" incompressible because in this way our descriptive language becomes more flexible.

In the case of solids or liquids, it is necessary to apply very high changes in pressure to effect a significant change in specific volume; in the case of gases, negligible changes in specific volume result from *sufficiently small* pressure changes. Similarly, in many problems the temperature changes during a process are so small that their effect upon the specific volume can also be disregarded. In terms of thermodynamics, this is equivalent to replacing the thermal equation of state of the system by the very simple statement that

$$v = \text{const} \quad \text{or} \quad \rho = \text{const.} \tag{7.3}$$

The "constant" is selected as a suitable average in a particular mechanical problem; it is variable from problem to problem, and on changing problems, the new average is selected with reference to the true thermal equation of state

$$F(P, v, \theta) = 0. \tag{7.3a}$$

Geometrically, the assumption in equation (7.3) is equivalent to saying that the surface of states is a plane perpendicular to the v axis, Figure 7.2. In this manner, the real surface $F(P, v, \theta) = 0$ is replaced by the plane $v = \text{const}$; the latter is not tangent to the former and does not constitute a mathematical approximation in the same sense that a tangent surface would, and it is necessary to realize that we are dealing here with a physical approximation. Consequently, the relations between the thermodynamic properties of the approximation, or, as it is sometimes called, *the model*, need not be the same as those between the thermodynamic properties of the real substance.

Writing the total differential

$$dv = \left(\frac{\partial v}{\partial \theta}\right)_P d\theta + \left(\frac{\partial v}{\partial P}\right)_\theta dP, \tag{7.3b}$$

we notice that equation (7.3) implies $dv = 0$ for any values of the increments $d\theta$ and dP, so that

$$\left(\frac{\partial v}{\partial \theta}\right)_P = \left(\frac{\partial v}{\partial P}\right)_\theta = 0, \tag{7.4}$$

which is a mathematical way of saying that v remains constant regardless of the variation in pressure and temperature. It follows that for an incompressible fluid, the coeffi-

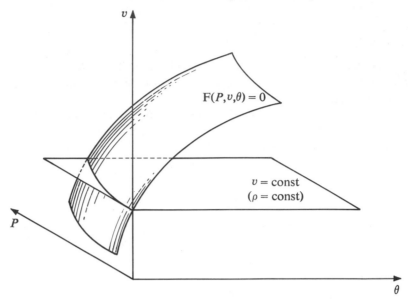

FIGURE 7.2. *Incompressible fluid.*

cients β, π, and κ defined in equations (3.16), (3.17), and (3.18) acquire the singular values

$$\left.\begin{aligned}
\beta &= \frac{1}{v}\left(\frac{\partial v}{\partial \theta}\right)_P = 0 \\[2mm]
\pi &= \frac{1}{P}\left(\frac{\partial P}{\partial \theta}\right)_v = \text{indeterminate} \\[2mm]
\kappa &= \frac{1}{v}\left(\frac{\partial v}{\partial P}\right)_\theta = 0.
\end{aligned}\right\} \tag{7.5}$$

In solving the mechanical problem, the values (7.5) must be used for consistency; on changing problems, the real values of these coefficients or the thermal equation (7.3a) must be used to establish the new constant, average value of specific volume.

Another consequence of the assumption of incompressibility is that the work in any reversible process,

$$W_{1,2} = \int_1^2 P \, dV = m \int_1^2 P \, dv = 0, \tag{7.6}$$

always vanishes because the integrand of the line integral is identically zero.

It will be shown later (Section 11.1.2), but it can now be accepted as an experimental fact, that the internal energy u of an incompressible fluid is a function of temperature alone. Hence,

$$u = u(\theta), \tag{7.7}$$

and the specific heat at constant volume from equation (5.36) becomes

$$c_v = \left(\frac{\partial u}{\partial \theta}\right)_v = \text{f}(\theta), \tag{7.8}$$

that is also a function of temperature alone; the form of the function must be obtained from experiments. In many cases, the variation with temperature of the specific heat c_v of an incompressible fluid can be disregarded. When the assumption $c_v = \text{const}$ is made, equation (7.8) can be integrated to give

$$u_2 - u_1 = c_v(\theta_2 - \theta_1) \qquad (v = \text{const}; c_v = \text{const}), \qquad (7.9)$$

otherwise

$$u_2 - u_1 = \int_{\theta_1}^{\theta_2} c_v(\theta)\,\mathrm{d}\theta \qquad (v = \text{const}; c_v = c_v(\theta)). \qquad (7.9a)$$

The enthalpy, however, is not independent of pressure, since

$$h = u + Pv.$$

It follows, therefore, that

$$h_2 - h_1 = u_2 - u_1 + v(P_2 - P_1) = \left\{ \int_{\theta_1}^{\theta_2} c_v(\theta)\,\mathrm{d}\theta \right\} + v(P_2 - P_1). \qquad (7.10)$$

The specific heat at constant pressure, c_p, can be calculated by direct differentiation

$$c_p = \left(\frac{\partial h}{\partial \theta}\right)_P = \left(\frac{\partial u}{\partial \theta}\right)_P,$$

because the product Pv in $h = u + Pv$ is independent of temperature. Since, however, the internal energy u is a function of temperature alone, we have

$$\left(\frac{\partial u}{\partial \theta}\right)_P = \left(\frac{\partial u}{\partial \theta}\right)_v = c_v,$$

and

$$c_p = c_v = c. \qquad (7.11)$$

Thus in the case of an incompressible fluid there is no distinction between the two specific heats c_p and c_v and the symbol c can be used to replace both. With this new symbol, we can rewrite equations (7.9a) and (7.10) in the form

$$u_2 - u_1 = \int_{\theta_1}^{\theta_2} c(\theta)\,\mathrm{d}\theta \qquad (7.12)$$

$$[= c(\theta_2 - \theta_1) \qquad \text{for } c = \text{const}] \qquad (7.12a)$$

and

$$h_2 - h_1 = \int_{\theta_1}^{\theta_2} c(\theta)\,\mathrm{d}\theta + v(P_2 - P_1) \qquad (7.13)$$

$$[= c(\theta_2 - \theta_1) + v(P_2 - P_1) \qquad \text{for } c = \text{const}]. \qquad (7.13a)$$

In the case of an incompressible fluid with a constant specific heat, the First Law for open systems with one inlet and exit channel in steady flow, equation (6.17), can be written in the specialized form

$$\dot{Q} - \dot{W} = \dot{m}\{c(\theta_2 - \theta_1) + v(P_2 - P_1) + g(z_2 - z_1)\}. \qquad (7.14)$$

Since equation (7.14) is often applied to problems in fluid mechanics when the use of density is preferred, an alternative form of this equation is

$$\dot{Q} - \dot{W} = \dot{m}\left\{c(\theta_2 - \theta_1) + \frac{P_2 - P_1}{\rho} + g(z_2 - z_1)\right\}. \tag{7.15}$$

In other problems in fluid mechanics it is found necessary to take into account the effect of a change in temperature, θ, on the specific volume, v, while the effect of a change in pressure may still be disregarded. This means that of the two assumptions in equation (7.4), the assumption

$$\left(\frac{\partial v}{\partial P}\right)_\theta = 0 \tag{7.16}$$

is retained, but it is stipulated that

$$\left(\frac{\partial v}{\partial \theta}\right)_P \neq 0. \tag{7.17}$$

Consequently,

$$\beta = \frac{1}{v}\left(\frac{\partial v}{\partial \theta}\right)_P \neq 0,$$

and since v is a function of temperature only, we must also assume

$$\beta = \beta(\theta). \tag{7.18}$$

In other words, the coefficient of thermal expansion, as well as the specific volume must be averaged with respect to the variation of pressure in the problem, but their dependence on temperature are accounted for. This fluid model has no special name and is also described as incompressible because semantically the word "compressibility" relates to effects of pressure, and not to the change in volume. The difference between this and the previous case is that now the effect of thermal expansion has been allowed for.

Geometrically, the equation $F(P, v, \theta) = 0$ of an incompressible but thermally expanding fluid is described by a cylindrical surface, since $v = $ const at $\theta = $ const, Figure 7.3(a). This surface averages, but does not approximate, the real P, v, θ surface. Constant-level lines, $v = $ const, on the cylindrical surface are parallel to the P axis, because

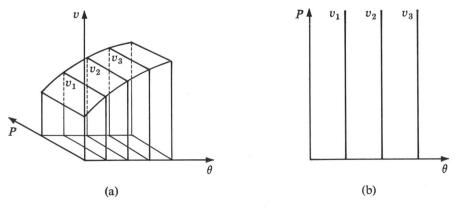

(a)   (b)

FIGURE 7.3. *Incompressible fluid with thermal expansion.*

the specific volume is independent of pressure; they project themselves as straight lines on the P, θ diagram of Figure 7.3(b).

The work in a reversible process ceases to be identically equal to zero, as was the case previously, except in the special case when the process is also isothermal. In terms of the coefficient of thermal expansion

$$\mathrm{d}W = P\,\mathrm{d}V = \beta PV\,\mathrm{d}\theta \qquad (7.19)$$

as seen also from equation (4.19).

7.3 Perfect gas

It has already been pointed out in Section 3.2 that the thermal equation of a perfect gas is

$$Pv = R\theta \qquad (7.20)$$

by virtue of the adoption of the perfect-gas temperature scale. Perfect gases do not exist in nature, but the properties of all known gases approach those of the respective perfect gas as the pressure is extrapolated to zero. We express this fact by saying that equation (7.20) constitutes the *asymptotic form* for all real gases. In spite of this, the perfect-gas law in equation (7.20) can be successfully used as an approximation to represent the properties of real gases even at comparatively high pressures. When used judiciously, equation (7.20) secures a sufficiently high degree of approximation, and many practical calculations, particularly those pertaining to power cycles in internal combustion engines, compressors, and gas-turbine cycles, or to the flow of an ideal, or real compressible fluid, are based on this model. Values of the gas constant, and several other properties of perfect gases have been collected in Table V to facilitate such calculations.

Frequently, use is made of the differential equivalent of equation (7.20),

$$\frac{\mathrm{d}P}{P} + \frac{\mathrm{d}v}{v} = \frac{\mathrm{d}\theta}{\theta} \qquad (7.20\mathrm{a})$$

which is obtained by logarithmic differentiation.† For m units of mass, the equation is

$$PV = m\,R\theta. \qquad (7.20\mathrm{b})$$

The equation shows that reversible constant-pressure, or isobaric, processes are represented by the linear relation

$$v = A\theta$$

between specific volume and temperature, when the constant A is given by

$$A = \frac{R}{P} \qquad (P = \mathrm{const}).$$

Similarly, reversible constant-volume or isochoric processes are represented by the linear relation

$$P = B\theta \quad \text{with} \quad B = \frac{R}{v} \qquad (v = \mathrm{const}).$$

† That is, by taking the natural logarithm first and then differentiating.

The corresponding isobars and isochores have been sketched in the v, θ and P, θ diagrams of Figure 3.3 in which the increasing direction in the property held constant should be noted.

Equally, reversible isothermal processes are represented by the equation

$$Pv = C \quad \text{with} \quad C = R\theta \qquad (\theta = \text{const}; R = \text{const})$$

which are represented by the hyperbolae of the P, v diagram in Figure 3.3, the value of the constant temperature increasing outwards.

The three diagrams in Figure 3.3 represent the respective constant level lines of the P, v, θ surface of a perfect gas shown in an isometric projection in Figure 3.2 which has been adequately discussed in Section 3.3.

In order to perform practical calculations, it can be assumed provisionally, say as a result of experiments, that the internal energy u as well as the enthalpy

$$h = u + Pv = u + R\theta \tag{7.21}$$

of a perfect gas are functions of temperature alone. In this respect a perfect gas differs markedly from an incompressible fluid, liquid or gas, whose internal energy is a function of temperature alone, but whose enthalpy is a function of both temperature *and* pressure. Later, in Sections 11.1 and 12.10, we shall demonstrate that *this is a necessary consequence of the laws of thermodynamics and the mathematical form of the perfect-gas law*. It follows that the specific heats

$$c_v = \left(\frac{\partial u}{\partial \theta}\right)_v \quad \text{and} \quad c_p = \left(\frac{\partial h}{\partial \theta}\right)_P,$$

being derivatives with respect to temperature of functions of temperature, are also functions of temperature alone. We can thus replace the partial derivatives by total derivatives, because only functions of the single variable θ are involved, and write

$$c_v = \frac{du}{d\theta} \quad \text{or} \quad du = c_v\, d\theta \tag{7.22a}$$

and

$$c_p = \frac{dh}{d\theta} \quad \text{or} \quad dh = c_p\, d\theta. \tag{7.22b}$$

The specific heats, c_p, of several perfect gases have been listed in Table XVI for reference. It can be verified by differentiating the definition (7.21) that

$$c_p - c_v = R. \tag{7.23}$$

Thus, only one specific heat needs to be tabulated. Similarly, it is sufficient to tabulate only the enthalpy $h(\theta)$, as was done in Table XVI, because the internal energy can be calculated from equation (7.21). Equations (7.22a, b) demonstrate that the internal energy and the enthalpy are simple integrals of the specific heats c_v and c_p, respectively,

$$u = \int_{\theta_0}^{\theta} c_v(\theta)\,d\theta + u_0, \tag{7.23a}$$

$$h = \int_{\theta_0}^{\theta} c_p(\theta)\,d\theta + h_0. \tag{7.23b}$$

The specific heats of perfect gases (or real gases at low pressures) are slowly increasing functions of temperature. Consequently, when the range of temperatures traversed in a particular process is not large, both specific heats can be assumed to be constant; the values given in Table V can then be used to work out examples based on this approximation. Alternatively, integral averages

$$\overline{c_v} = \frac{1}{\theta_2 - \theta_1} \int_{\theta_1}^{\theta_2} c_v(\theta)\,\mathrm{d}\theta \tag{7.24a}$$

$$\overline{c_p} = \frac{1}{\theta_2 - \theta_1} \int_{\theta_1}^{\theta_2} c_p(\theta)\,\mathrm{d}\theta \tag{7.24b}$$

can be worked out from Table XVI.

In order to create a more efficient terminology, it will be said that the model based on equation (7.22a) or (7.22b) refers to a perfect gas. If in addition, the specific heats, enthalpy, and internal energy are approximated by functions of temperature alone, we shall say that the gas is *semiperfect*. The model based on constant specific heats is referred to as an *ideally perfect* gas.

The internal energy and enthalpy of an ideally perfect gas can be obtained by direct integration from equations (7.22a, b). In this manner we obtain

$$u_2 - u_1 = c_v(\theta_2 - \theta_1) \tag{7.24c}$$

and

$$h_2 - h_1 = c_p(\theta_2 - \theta_1). \tag{7.24d}$$

7.4 Pure substance

Systems consisting of a given mass m of a substance of fixed chemical composition and undergoing compressions or expansions constitute a class which will be studied most frequently in this book. We shall refer to such systems as *pure substances* as opposed to systems composed of mixtures of substances, each of whose components constitutes a pure substance. Incompressible fluids and perfect gases represent simple examples of pure substances. Although the special terms "incompressible fluid" and "perfect gas" are used to simplify our descriptive language, in reality, each of them refers to a pure substance when the latter is considered over a restricted range of states. Thus, whether a pure substance can be regarded as an incompressible fluid or a perfect gas depends on the problem at hand, on the range of pressures and temperatures which is expected to appear in it, and on the required accuracy of the result.

In the present section we propose to examine the properties of pure substances in a descriptive way, as already stated. Later, in Volume II, we shall be able to cover much the same ground more systematically, making full use of the relations between properties which will be found to exist for every system by virtue of the Second Law of thermodynamics, or by virtue of equations which result from a combination of the First and Second Law.

In most cases, and particularly in this section, we shall be interested in systems which exert a uniform pressure on the vessel containing them. We shall, further, be interested in processes in which electric or magnetic fields are absent. In many cases we shall also exclude gravitational fields and motion either within the system or of the system as a whole. It is known from experiment that under such circumstances the *shape* of the system plays no part in its thermodynamic description under the additional restriction that capillary forces or forces of surface tension can be disregarded. Experience also shows that the thermodynamic state of such systems is entirely determined by *two independent variables*. It will be seen presently that the specific volume v together with either the temperature θ or pressure P can be chosen as the independent variables under any circumstances, whereas the two intensive properties, pressure P and temperature θ, cannot always be adjusted independently of each other. A given quantity of water, ice, or steam, or a mixture of water and ice provide examples of such pure substances.

7.4.1 Phase

A substance is classed as pure when it consists of a single chemical compound, not necessarily of a chemical element. The preceding simple example shows that pure substances can occur in different states of physical aggregation, ice and water being examples of the same pure substance — H_2O in this case — which can exist in the solid or liquid state. In fact all substances can exist in the liquid, solid or gaseous states, and solids can exist in different *allotropic modifications*. For example, at a temperature of just under 100°C and under atmospheric pressure, the chemical substance sulphur, S, can exist in two different forms, the lemon-yellow rhombic and the more orange-colored monoclinic variety. Upon close microscopic examination, it is found that allotropic modifications differ from each other by the symmetry of the arrangement of their atoms in the lattice, that is, by their crystalline structure. Details of these structures can be studied in relation to the characteristic diffraction patterns which are displayed when an electron or x-ray beam is reflected from the surface of the solid.

It is convenient to have a common term to describe each of the different forms in which a pure substance can exist, and the word *phase*, first coined by the famous American pioneer in thermodynamics, Josiah Willard Gibbs, is now used for this purpose. Any homogeneous region within a system is called a phase of the system. When a system consists of several coexisting phases, such as a mixture of water and ice at 0°C or a mixture of different allotropic forms of the same solid, it is discovered that each phase is separated from the others by a clearly defined boundary. Even though the intensive parameters, pressure P and temperature θ, are the same for two phases, the other properties, such as specific volume v, refractive index n, and so on, and sometimes even the color, change discontinuously on crossing the *phase boundary*.

The concept of phase is not restricted to pure substances. Mixtures or solutions of pure substances can also exist in several phases, the thermodynamic properties, including the composition, changing discontinuously across phase boundaries; they are uniform and homogeneous within a phase. A system consisting of several phases is called *heterogeneous*; when it consists of a single phase, it is called *homogeneous*. Frequently, as is the case with air which consists of a mixture of oxygen, nitrogen, argon, water vapor, and traces of the rare gases, Table XV, a homogeneous phase of a mixture of constant chemical composition can be treated as if it were a single phase of a pure substance. The essential difference between pure substances and mixtures manifests itself during processes which lead to *phase transitions*.

A system in equilibrium in which three phases coexist, for example, a mixture of liquid water, ice, and water vapor, is said to be at a *triple point*. We shall accept provisionally that experiments show that a pure substance can exist in equilibrium as a single phase, as a mixture of two phases, or, at most, as a mixture of three phases. In order to produce a heterogeneous system consisting of four or more phases, it is necessary to mix a number of pure substances. Later, in Volume II, it will be shown that there exists a direct relation between the number of pure components in a system and the maximum number of phases which can coexist in it. This relation is known as J. W. Gibbs' *phase rule*. It states that the number of independent *intensive* properties, f, which determine the state of a heterogeneous system is given by the relation

$$f = \alpha - \beta + 2, \tag{7.25}$$

where α denotes the *number* of pure components and β denotes the *number* of phases present in the system. Equation (7.25) will be derived rigorously in Volume II.

7.4.2 Evaporation

In order to appreciate the relations of phases to each other, and in order to discover the nature of the independent variables which can be chosen to describe the state of heterogeneous systems, it is best to study several simple experiments with the aid of which changes in phase can be brought about. We shall begin by discussing the process of reversible *evaporation*, that is, with the process of turning a liquid into a vapor in a reversible way.

To this end, we imagine a unit mass (1 lbm or 1 kg) of a pure liquid, say water, contained in a cylinder enclosed by a piston and so loaded as to maintain a constant pressure, say $P = 1$ atm (or 14.7 lbf/in²) inside our system, Figure 7.4. When heated with the aid of a series of sources to ensure the reversibility of the process, from 0°C (32°F) upwards, the volume of the unit mass of water will contract a little at first, as shown in the diagram of Figure 7.5, and familiar to the reader from Figure 3.1. The contraction will continue until a temperature of 4°C at point *b* will have been reached, when the density of the water attains a maximum. On further heating, the volume will continuously expand. In this, water shows *anomalous* behavior, most other substances exhibiting a *continuous increase* in volume. Bismuth, for example, constitutes another anomalous substance.

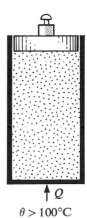

0°C $< \theta <$ 4°C $\theta = 4$°C $\theta = 100$°C $\theta > 100$°C

FIGURE 7.4. *Reversible evaporation (water).*

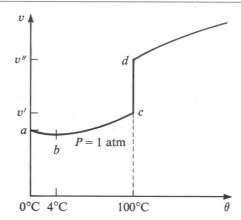

FIGURE 7.5. *Change in volume of water at atmospheric pressure.*

The decrease in the volume of water between 0°C and 4°C has been explained by the microscopic hypothesis of *molecular association* according to which water consists of a mixture of molecules, each constituting a multiple of the fundamental molecule H_2O. Thus, molecules $(H_2O)_2$, $(H_2O)_3$,[†] and so on are presumed to be present. At least in this region, it is supposed that water is not a pure substance, but a mixture of varying composition, and it is conjectured that every pure substance increases its volume upon heating. The net decrease in volume is thought to be due to the variation in composition with temperature in a manner generally characteristic of a chemical reaction between different chemical species. It is not known whether the same microscopic explanation applies to the other anomalous substances, such as bismuth.

When the system reaches a temperature of 100°C (212°F), the first bubble of steam appears in it, point *c* in the diagram; from this point onwards, the continued addition of heat has no further effect on the temperature of the system, and merely produces additional quantities of steam. The system has separated into two phases, and retains its characteristic temperature as long as both of them are present. Depending on conditions, the two phases may be separated into two distinct regions, the denser liquid resting at the bottom and the lighter steam being collected at the top in a manner sketched in the figure. Sometimes, as is the case when a boiling liquid flows through a duct, the liquid phase may be present in the form of a fine spray of droplets, or an array of steam bubbles may be distributed more or less evenly through the bulk of the liquid. There is, however, no essential difference between these possible arrangements of the two phases, except for the effects of surface tension, Section 7.5. In each case one phase is separated from the other by clearly discernible boundaries, and the temperature remains constant if the pressure is kept constant.

A system in which the liquid and vapor phases coexist in equilibrium is called *saturated.* The liquid at state *a* just before evaporation begins is also called saturated, and its specific volume will be denoted by the symbol v'. Upon heating at constant pressure, the state of the saturated liquid in the system does not change, there is only progressively less of it. When the last drop of liquid has become exhausted, the system

[†] These are described generically as polymers; double molecules, for example $(H_2O)_2$, are called dimers, the terms "trimer," "tetramer," and so on being sometimes used for the higher polymers.

consists of (dry) *saturated steam* only. The specific volume v'' of this saturated steam is much larger than that of the liquid, v', from which it originated. In the case of water substance at atmospheric pressure, v'' exceeds v' by a factor of 1603 which makes it impossible to draw the diagram in Figure 7.5 to scale. This will be appreciated if it is noted that

$$v_a = 0.0010002 \text{ m}^3/\text{kg}; \quad v_b = 0.0010000 \text{ m}^3/\text{kg}; \quad v' = v_c = 0.0010435 \text{ m}^3/\text{kg};$$
$$v'' = v_d = 1.673 \text{ m}^3/\text{kg}.$$

Although the pressure and temperature of the system remain constant as long as both phases exist together, its volume continues to increase from c to d in direct proportion to the amount evaporated. However, the *specific* volume of the saturated *steam* in the mixture, just as was the case with the *specific* volume of the saturated *liquid*, remains unaltered and equal to v'' during the whole process. The system consisting of a liquid and gaseous phase, particularly if the liquid is present in the form of a fine spray of droplets, is called *wet steam* or *wet vapor* in general.

As the process of evaporation is conducted at different pressures, the same sequence of events repeats itself qualitatively, except that to each pressure P there correspond a different saturation temperature θ, and different values of the specific volumes, v' for the liquid and v'' for the vapor. This is illustrated on the example of the 100 atm isobar for water in Figure 7.6, for which the saturation temperature has risen to 311.9°C, with a very slight increase in v' but a large decrease in v'' compared with 1 atm. The diagram in Figure 7.6 has been drawn more nearly to scale, but even so, the lines at small volumes have been drawn further apart than they are in reality.

When heating continues after the system has transformed into a single gaseous phase, the volume will continue to increase and the temperature will resume its upward course.

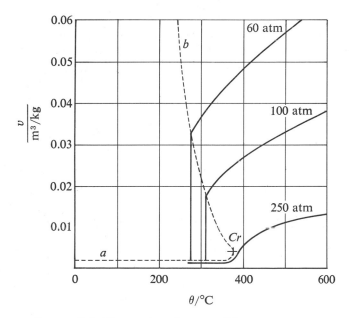

FIGURE 7.6. *Change in volume at different pressures.*

Thus, at a given pressure, it is possible to attain a wide range of temperatures, when only vapor is present, in contrast with the single temperature for the two-phase system of wet vapor. A vapor heated beyond its saturation temperature for a given pressure is called *superheated*.

From the preceding description of the process of evaporation, it is clear that the two intensive parameters, temperature, θ, and pressure, P, can be used as independent variables as long as only one phase exists. When two phases exist, the pressure is linked to the temperature (or vice versa) by a functional relation

$$\phi^{(e)}(P, \theta) = 0, \tag{7.26}$$

and the two are no longer independent. This is consistent with equation (7.25) of the phase rule in which $f = 1$ for $\alpha = 1$ and $\beta = 2$. The graphical representation of the function $\phi^{(e)}(P, \theta)$ is called the *vapor-pressure curve*. Thus, the volume V, an extensive quantity for m units of mass, or the *specific volume v of the whole system* must be used as one of the independent properties. Instead of specifying the volume V or the specific volume $v = V/m$ of a two-phase system, it is often customary to specify the mass x of saturated steam (or vapor, in general) present in a unit mass of wet steam. Denoting the mass of saturated water in a two-phase mixture by m' and that of saturated steam by m'', we have

$$m = m' + m'',$$

so that

$$x = \frac{m''}{m} \quad \text{and} \quad 1 - x = \frac{m'}{m}. \tag{7.27}$$

The ratio x — a dimensionless number — is called the *dryness fraction* of the equilibrium mixture of the two phases. Accordingly, for dry saturated steam $x = 1$, whereas for saturated water $x = 0$. The dryness fraction can be used as one of the independent variables of the system, replacing the specific volume, but the two cannot be used together, because they are related. Indeed, by simple proportions, it is found that

$$v = (1 - x)v' + xv'' = v' + x(v'' - v'), \tag{7.28a}$$

because the system consists of $1 - x$ units of mass of liquid, and x units of mass of vapor.

The values of the specific volumes of the liquid and vapor at saturation are usually tabulated for different substances. Tables X and XI contain these values for steam and water, whereas Tables XVII to XXIII list them for a range of other substances. Here, for convenience, Table X for H_2O contains the saturation temperature as the primary argument, whereas Table XI uses the saturation pressure in its stead, the other intensive property being listed for reference in both cases. Thus, the two first columns of Tables X and XI constitute a tabular representation of the vapor-pressure curve from equation (7.26) for water. Since the values of v' and v'' stem from experiment, they are approximate. Thus, equation (7.28a) represents the volume v as that of the liquid, v', with a correction $x(v'' - v')$ for the presence of the vapor. The equation will lead to accurate results if x is close to zero. In the opposite case, when its value is close to unity, it is preferable to use the algebraically equivalent equation

$$v = v'' - (1 - x)(v'' - v'), \tag{7.28b}$$

in which a correction $(1 - x)(v'' - v')$ has been made to the volume of the dry vapor; in this manner, a higher degree of accuracy is safeguarded in the calculation.

Since in a two-phase system in a state of equilibrium, the two phases merely exist side by side in their saturated states, it is clear that all specific properties of the whole system can be related to their values at saturation for the same pressure and temperature, and to the dryness fraction x. Thus for specific internal energy we can write by analogy

$$u = u' + x(u'' - u') = u'' - (1 - x)(u'' - u'). \tag{7.29}$$

Similarly, for specific enthalpy

$$h = h' + x(h'' - h') = h'' - (1 - x)(h'' - h'), \tag{7.29a}$$

and for *any* extensive specific property ϕ,

$$\phi = \phi' + x(\phi'' - \phi') = \phi'' - (1 - x)(\phi'' - \phi'). \tag{7.29b}$$

Here, as before, the primed symbols relate to the saturated liquid, and those with two primes refer to the saturated vapor.

The enthalpy difference

$$l = h'' - h', \tag{7.30}$$

or the heat required to evaporate a unit mass of liquid at constant pressure and temperature is given the name of *latent heat of evaporation*. Since $h = u + Pv$, we can replace equation (7.30) by the relation

$$l = u'' - u' + P(v'' - v'), \tag{7.30a}$$

remembering that a constant-pressure process is involved. This equation shows that the heat of evaporation is partly utilized to produce the required change in the internal energy of the system, $u'' - u'$, the balance serving to provide the work $P(v'' - v')$ which the system must perform against the surroundings. The work $P(v'' - v')$ usually constitutes only a small fraction of the latent heat l. Tables X and XI list the values of the latent heat of evaporation of water, as well as the saturation values u', h', u'', and h''. Similar entries are included in the tables for the other substances. In these tables the specific energy has not been listed because it can always be computed from the enthalpy $h = u + Pv$. The reader will do well to remember that the internal energy u and the enthalpy h are habitually given in heat units, whereas the product Pv appears in mechanical units, so that the conversion factors in equations (5.30), (5.30a), or (5.30b) must be used. The latent heat of evaporation constitutes a *heat tone* as defined in Section 6.13.1.

We note, parenthetically, that the work of the atmosphere

$$W_a = P(v_2 - v_1)$$

which is performed by liquid water when heated at constant pressure in the anomalous region of decreasing volume is *negative*. Thus, in this region, the energy increases by an amount which is equal to the *sum* of the heat added and the work performed by the atmosphere *on* the system. Owing to the fact that the changes in the volume of water when heated at constant pressure are very small, the work of the atmosphere is also very small compared with the change in enthalpy.

7.4.3   Critical point

As the pressure P under which a pure substance is evaporated reversibly is increased, the changes in specific volume $(v'' - v')$ produced by the phase transition decreases until it reaches a value zero at a particular pressure P_{cr}. This pressure is known as the *critical pressure* of the substance. A clear representation of the significance of the critical pressure can be obtained from the P, v diagram for steam, drawn approximately to scale in Figure 7.7. The line a has been drawn through the points which represent the specific volume v' of saturated water at different pressures, whereas line b has been drawn through the points which represent the specific volume v'' of saturated steam, so that a horizontal intercept represents the change in volume $v'' - v'$ produced by the phase transition at a given pressure. Line a is known as the *liquid line*, whereas line b is known as the *vapor line*. In chemical textbooks the terms bubble point and dew point are sometimes used for the points along lines a and b, respectively. At a pressure P_{cr} (equal to 218.2 atm or 3206.2 lbf/in² in the case of water), the two lines join, because the volume difference between the liquid and vapor has disappeared. Thus, when a liquid is heated at a pressure which exceeds the critical, it no longer separates into two phases, and at no time does its temperature remain constant at constant pressure. This behavior has been illustrated by the 250 atm isobar for water shown in Figure 7.6. The broken line in Figure 7.6 represents the *boundary curve a–b*, already familiar from Figure 7.7.

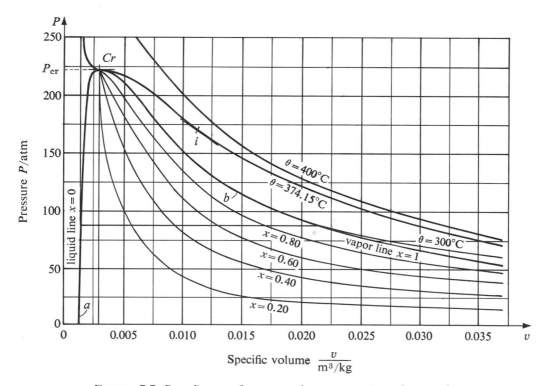

FIGURE 7.7. *P, v diagram for steam, drawn approximately to scale.*

The vertex of the boundary curve (or "dome"), denoted by Cr in the P, v diagram of Figure 7.7 as well as in the v, θ diagram of Figure 7.6, uniquely determines a definite state of the pure substance known as its *critical point*. The *critical data*, including the critical pressure P_{cr}, the critical (specific) volume v_{cr}, and the critical temperature θ_{cr}, have been determined by measurement for a large number of substances. They are seen listed in Table XXIV. It is remarkable that for all substances the critical volume is about three times larger than the volume v_0 of the liquid near the point where the pure substance solidifies. The critical pressure ranges from a low value of 1.15 atm for the isotope He^3 to a high value of 1040 atm for mercury. Similarly, the critical temperature ranges from a low of 3.33°K for He^3 to a high of 1373°K for mercury. Extensive measurements lead to the conclusion that all known pure substances possess a critical point.

The two diagrams shown in Figures 7.6 and 7.7 can be regarded as contour projections of the surface

$$\mathrm{F}(P, v, \theta) = 0$$

of a substance in which the region of coexistence of the vapor and the liquid has been included. The diagram in Figure 7.6 shows three typical isobars, whereas the diagram in Figure 7.7 includes several typical isotherms. The critical isotherm in the P, v diagram displays a horizontal point of inflection at the critical point which can be described analytically by the two simultaneous conditions

$$\left(\frac{\partial P}{\partial v}\right)_\theta = 0 \quad \text{and} \quad \left(\frac{\partial^2 P}{\partial v^2}\right)_\theta = 0. \tag{7.31a, b}$$

The course of the isotherms displayed in the diagram of Figure 7.7 permits us to examine the process of isothermal compression of a pure substance. When a superheated vapor is compressed isothermally at a supercritical temperature $\theta > \theta_{\mathrm{cr}}$, its volume decreases, the isotherms only slightly exceeding the critical showing two points of inflection. The critical isotherm itself possesses a nonhorizontal point of inflection at i which is of no particular significance, in addition to the horizontal point of inflection at the critical point. As the temperature is increased, the isotherms become progressively closer to the hyperbolic shape characteristic of a perfect gas.

When a superheated vapor is compressed at a temperature below the critical, its pressure increases approximately along a hyperbola, particularly when the temperature is considerably removed from the critical, and when the pressure is low. When the pressure attains the saturation value corresponding to the constant temperature under which compression is carried out, the vapor becomes saturated and further compression causes it to liquefy. The pressure now remains constant as long as both phases are present, and the isotherm acquires a horizontal portion in the diagram. During this phase of the process, the system is identical with that shown in Figure 7.4, except that now cooling must replace the heating discussed previously, the present process constituting an exact reversal of the former. Continued compression beyond the point of complete liquefaction causes a very rapid increase in pressure, the phenomenon being characterized by the statement that liquids, as opposed to gases, are nearly incompressible.

The P, v diagram, supplemented by the isotherms of the pure substance, shows that all pure substances progressively acquire the properties of a perfect gas as the pressure is decreased in comparison with the critical pressure. At pressures low enough, the

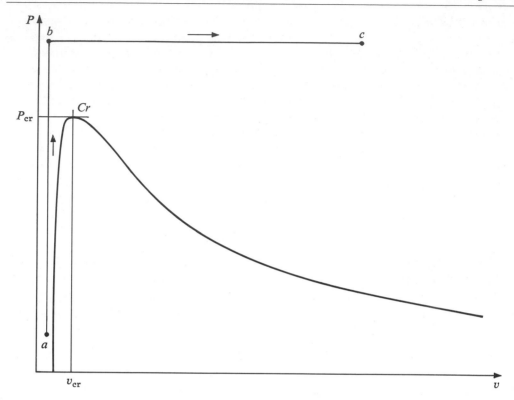

FIGURE 7.8. *Process in a supercritical boiler.*

properties of a superheated vapor differ very little from the properties of a perfect gas right up to the point at which it begins to liquefy. The diagram also shows the artificiality of the distinction between a vapor, a gas and a liquid. In fact, high-pressure and high-temperature steam can be produced by first compressing water to a supercritical pressure in a pump, approximately at constant volume, as shown by line *ab* in Figure 7.8. Further heating at constant pressure $P > P_{cr}$ will transform the water into highly superheated steam along *bc*, without the system ever having separated into two phases. Processes of this kind are carried out on a large scale in supercritical boilers, also known as Benson boilers.

The precise relations which a pure substance displays in the neighborhood of its critical point, and particularly the analytic conditions for the critical isotherm given in equations (7.31a, b) are, to a certain extent, in dispute. For example, some authors believe that the boundary curve does not attain a maximum at the critical point, but possesses there a horizontal segment of finite length. The uncertainties of our exact knowledge of the critical region are due to the fact that the performance of measurements near the critical point is difficult. Owing to the existence of the horizontal point of inflection, a very small change in pressure at the critical temperature causes a large change in specific volume, that is, in density. Hence, the fluid has a tendency to become stratified in a vessel in which conditions close to the critical point are maintained owing to the small changes in hydrostatic pressure in the terrestrial gravitational field, and it becomes exceedingly difficult to maintain all of it at a uniform thermodynamic state.†

The P, v diagram in Figure 7.7 has been supplemented with lines of constant dryness fraction x. Referring to equation (7.28a), it is noted that

$$x = \frac{v - v'}{v'' - v'}$$

which proves that a point of a given value of x divides the intercept $v'' - v'$ into two segments, ac and cb in Figure 7.9 which satisfy the relations

$$\frac{\overline{ac}}{\overline{ab}} = x \quad \text{and} \quad \frac{\overline{cb}}{\overline{ab}} = 1 - x.$$

Hence, point c divides the intercept in the ratio x to $1 - x$. The diagram in Figure 7.9 shows the lines of $x = 0.2, 0.4, 0.6, 0.8$, the two boundary curves corresponding to $x = 0$ and $x = 1$, as already stated. All these lines meet at the critical point.

A close examination of Figure 7.9 shows that the details of the process of heating wet steam or a two-phase water-dry vapor system at constant volume strongly depend on the dryness fraction and hence on the specific volume v of the system. When the specific volume exceeds the critical, point m in Figure 7.10, heating at constant volume leads to complete evaporation at n and subsequently to superheating at point p. For a given final temperature θ, the ultimate increase in pressure is not excessive. If the sys-

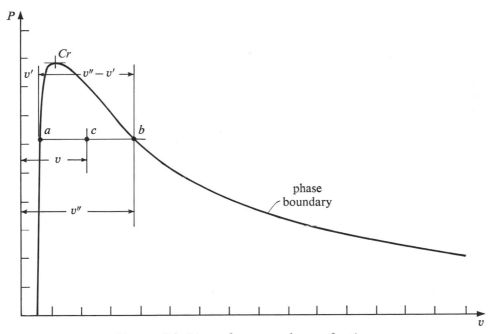

FIGURE 7.9. *Lines of constant-dryness fraction.*

† For additional details the reader is referred to an article by J. A. Beattie which constitutes Chapter VIII of *Argon, Helium and the Rare Gases*, ed., G. A. Cook (Interscience, 1961). See p. 269 ff.

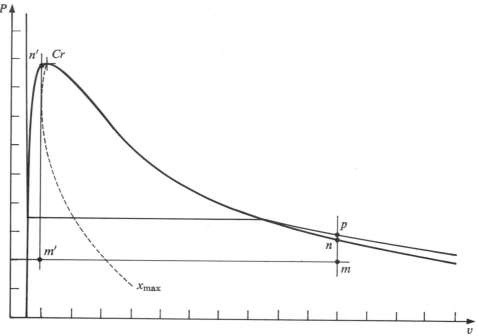

FIGURE 7.10. *Constant-volume heating.*

tem consists of a pool of liquid with vapor over it, as shown in Figure 7.11, the water level will move continuously downwards corresponding to the continuous increase in dryness fraction, until it disappears leaving dry saturated steam behind it.

When heating starts with a specific volume which is less than the critical, say at point m' in Figure 7.10, the process is entirely different. At first, the dryness fraction increases, reaching a maximum at x_{max}, but further heating causes it to decrease until the whole system is transformed into saturated water at n'. Continued heating causes a rapid and dangerous increase in pressure owing to the steep course of isotherms in this region. The corresponding movement of the water level is again illustrated by the sketches in Figure 7.11.

When a steam boiler is started up for operation, all exit valves from the drum are closed, and the two-phase system contained in it undergoes a process of isochoric heat-

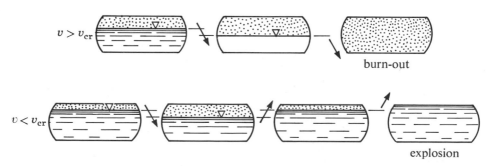

FIGURE 7.11. *Movement of water level.*

ing. Usually, the boiler drum is filled with a large quantity of water corresponding to a small value of x, so that $v < v_{cr}$ and there is a danger that the drum will explode owing to the high pressure of the water which might be created in it. If the quantity of water in the drum is small corresponding to a high value of x, there is danger of burn-out if all water is allowed to evaporate. For these reasons, it is essential to control the upper as well as the lower position of the water level, and to shut off, usually automatically, the burners when a predetermined maximum or minimum level is attained.

7.4.4   *Melting and sublimation*

The process of reversible melting, that is the process of reversibly transforming a solid into a liquid phase at constant pressure does not differ essentially from the process of evaporation. In this connection water substance also exhibits an anomaly, because at low pressures its solid has a larger volume than the liquid into which it turns, unlike the more normal substances. This fact introduces certain complications into the general discussion of melting, and will, therefore, be dealt with in the next section.

A normal substance increases its volume upon melting, and the temperature of a mixture of a solid and its liquid remains constant at constant pressure. The melting curve has the same appearance as that for evaporation, except that the change in volume $v'_i - v'''$ from saturated solid (v''') to saturated liquid in equilibrium with its solid (v'_i) is much smaller than the difference $v'' - v'$ for evaporation (excepting, of course, the critical region where the difference $v'' - v'$ becomes small and vanishes at the critical point itself).

The process of melting is illustrated with the aid of the θ, v and P, v diagrams in Figure 7.12 which have been drawn for a normal substance. On heating at constant pressure from state 1, the solid will increase its temperature θ as well as its volume v, the change in volume being described by the volumetric coefficient of thermal expansion β from equation (3.16). As soon as the saturation temperature has been reached at state 2, the first droplet of liquid appears in the system, and the temperature continues to remain constant as long as the two phases are present. When all of the solid has turned into liquid, the temperature increases from 3 to 4, and from then on the familiar phenomenon of evaporation will occur if heating is continued. Thus, in the two-phase region of coexistence between the solid and the liquid, the pressure P and temperature become related along the *melting curve*

$$\phi^{(m)}(P, \theta) = 0 \tag{7.32}$$

in complete analogy with equation (7.26) for evaporation. Once again, in equation (7.25) we obtain $f = 1$ for $\alpha = 1$ and $\beta = 2$. The heat required to melt a unit mass of solid at constant pressure and temperature is equal to the enthalpy difference

$$l_m = h'_i - h''' \tag{7.32a}$$

and is called the *latent heat of melting* or *fusion*; it also constitutes a heat tone. The subscript i in h'_i refers to the saturated liquid on the melting curve in contradistinction to that on the curve of evaporation.

At increased pressures, the specific volume v''' of the saturated solid as well as the specific volume v'_i of the saturated liquid decrease only very slightly, and consequently, the phase boundaries, that is, the loci of points 2 and 3 are nearly parallel to the θ and P axes, sloping slightly upwards and to the left.

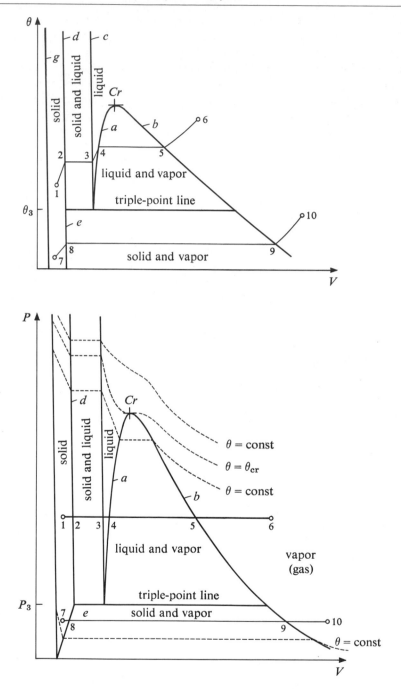

FIGURE 7.12. *Equilibrium between solid, liquid, and vapor for a normal substance.*

The similarity between the processes of melting and evaporation immediately suggests the question as to whether there exists a critical point for the transition from the solid to the liquid in the same way as for the further transition from the liquid to the vapor. At the present time no conclusive answer to this query can be given. All experiments aimed at discovering a critical point for melting have failed to uncover one. There are reasons to believe that such a critical point, if it exists at all, must occur at a pressure which should be lowest for helium, because the ordinary critical pressure is also lowest for helium. This would be a consequence of the principle of corresponding states discussed later in Volume II. Now, experiments on helium (substantially the isotope He[4]) have been carried out up to pressures of the order of 5630 atm,† and their result, as already stated, was negative, negative, that is, for a ratio $P/P_{cr} \approx 2500$, since $P_{cr} = 2.26$ atm. In addition, considerations of statistical mechanics which contrast the orderly, crystalline structure of the atoms in a solid with their more random arrangement in a liquid induce us to believe that the existence of a critical point for melting is highly unlikely.

7.4.5   Triple point

Upon decreasing the pressure at which the process of melting is performed, it is found that the specific volume v_i' of the saturated liquid which is in equilibrium with the solid differs progressively less from the specific volume v' of the liquid which is in equilibrium with its vapor. Ultimately, at a pressure P_3, different for every substance, to which there corresponds a temperature θ_3, also different for every substance, the two specific volumes become equal to each other

$$v_i' = v' = v_3'. \tag{7.33}$$

This signifies that at the pressure P_3 and temperature θ_3, the same liquid is in equilibrium with the solid as well as the vapor phases. The Second Law of thermodynamics leads to the conclusion that the vapor is also in equilibrium with the solid. It follows that under such conditions all three phases can coexist, their temperatures and pressures all being equal to P_3 and θ_3, respectively. The pure substance is then said to have formed a *triple point*. At the triple point, the intensive state is fixed, and in addition, the specific volume v_3''' of the solid, that of the liquid, v_3', as well as that of the vapor, v_3'', have fixed values. The triple point data for the coexistence of the three states of aggregation: the solid, liquid, and gaseous phases, are seen listed in Table XXV for a range of useful substances. This behavior is seen to be consistent with the phase rule, equation (7.25), which shows that for $\alpha = 1$ and $\beta = 3$, we have $f = 0$; in other words, at the triple point it is not possible to adjust independently even one intensive property.

When two phases coexist, it is possible to prescribe either the pressure or the temperature of the system, but not both. This set of circumstances is described by the statement that the intensive state of a two-phase system has one degree of freedom which is merely a different way of expressing the same idea. In general, the term *number of degrees of freedom*, borrowed from mechanics, specifies the number of independent variables under a given, or implied, set of circumstances. The reader will have noticed that a two-phase system has *two degrees of freedom* as far as its thermodynamic state is concerned. If, however, as is often convenient, attention is centered exclusively on its *intensive properties*, it can be asserted that it has only *one* degree of freedom; the symbol f in equation (7.25) denotes the number of degrees of freedom in a heterogeneous system, the term being interpreted in its narrower sense.

Employing the same terminology, it can be stated that a pure substance in its triple point has *zero* degrees of freedom, because its intensive state is described by a *unique*

† Keesom, W. H., *Helium* (Elsevier, 1942), p. 204.

pair of parameters P_3 and θ_3, their numerical values being determined by the chemical nature of the substance. For example, for water substance[†]

$$P_3 = (0.006108 \pm 0.000006) \text{ bar} = (0.006028 \pm 0.000006) \text{ atm}$$
$$\theta_3 = 0.01°C.$$

In addition, the specific volumes v_3', v_3'', and v_3''' of the liquid, vapor, and solid, respectively, assume particular values. In other words, whenever all three states of aggregation of a pure substance are observed in equilibrium in a single system, it is certain that the pressure is P_3 and, more importantly, that the temperature of the system is θ_3. This explains the unique utility of triple points in thermometry as well as the adoption of the triple point of water as the single fixed point, in addition to absolute zero, in the definition of the universal perfect-gas temperature scale. The addition or subtraction of heat to or from a triple-point system merely changes the relative masses of the three phases present, but not the temperature of the system, as long as all three of them are seen to exist. The only effect can come from the presence of impurities, or from the leakage of air into the system, because then the system ceases to be a pure substance. The triple point of a mixture, as seen from the phase rule, equation (7.25), and as will be shown in detail in Volume II, possesses more than zero degrees of freedom, depending on the number of pure components α in the system. For this reason, it is easier to create a well-controlled fixed thermometric point by producing a triple point in a pure substance than by producing a two-phase mixture such as the steam or ice point, when accurate control of the single degree of freedom of the system, in this case its pressure, is required. The triple point of a substance can also serve as a reproducible pressure standard. In fact the triple-point pressure[‡] of carbon dioxide which has been measured very accurately and is

$$P_3 = 5.112 \text{ atm}$$

is often used in this capacity. The triple-point temperature[†] for carbon dioxide is $-56.60°C$.

Circumstances are different when attention is centered on the whole thermodynamic state of a triple-point system. From this point of view, the system, like all systems containing a single pure substance, possesses two independent properties, and two ratios of the three masses, the mass m' of the liquid, mass m'' of the vapor and mass m''' of the solid can be chosen as independent variables. Since the total mass

$$m = m' + m'' + m''',$$

and since two replicas of a system which merely differ by their total masses are not, habitually, considered to be different, only two ratios suffice for the complete description of the state. For example, the specific volume can be written

$$v = \frac{m'}{m}v_3' + \frac{m''}{m}v_3'' + \frac{m'''}{m}v_3''', \tag{7.34a}$$

the internal energy is

$$u = \frac{m'}{m}u_3' + \frac{m''}{m}u_3'' + \frac{m'''}{m}u_3''', \tag{7.34b}$$

[†] As determined by the Sixth International Conference on the Properties of Steam, New York 1963.
[‡] Din, F., ed., *Thermodynamic Functions of Gases* (Butterworth, 1956), I, p. 121.

and the enthalpy is

$$h = \frac{m'}{m}h_3' + \frac{m''}{m}h_3'' + \frac{m'''}{m}h_3''', \tag{7.34c}$$

the three relations being the analogs of equations (7.29), (7.29a) and (7.29b) for a two-phase system. The ratios m'/m, m''/m and m'''/m, whose sum

$$\frac{m'}{m} + \frac{m''}{m} + \frac{m'''}{m} = 1 \tag{7.34d}$$

is equal to unity, are called *mass fractions*. It is clear, of course, that any two extensive or specific parameters, such as u and v, can be employed to describe the state of the triple-point system instead of two of the three ratios in equation (7.34d).

The triple point is represented by a horizontal line, labeled accordingly in the θ, v and P, v diagrams of Figure 7.12, since in both of them one of the independent variables is an intensive property which remains unchanged when the two mass ratios are varied. Consequently, the specific volume can range from that of the solid, when $m'/m = m''/m = 0$, to that of the vapor, when $m'/m = m'''/m = 0$, and a prescribed value of specific volume in that range can be obtained with different pairs of values of the ratios.

The diagram in Figure 7.13 has been plotted in terms of the two specific, extensive properties, the internal energy u and the specific volume v. It is now clear that the triple point must be represented by an area, the triangle abc, corresponding to the fact that the complete state of a triple-point system is determined by two extensive, specific properties. Since the sum of all three mass ratios must be equal to unity — equation (7.34d) — it is possible to choose only two of them arbitrarily. Hence, as seen from equations (7.34a) and (7.34b), prescribing two such values fixes the corresponding

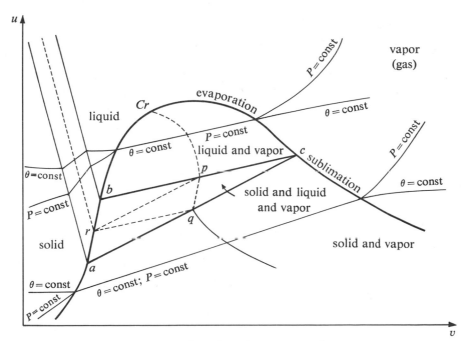

FIGURE 7.13. *Phase boundaries in u, v diagram.*

values of internal energy u and specific volume v. Conversely, owing to the linear nature of the relations, prescribing the values of u and v simultaneously in the range delimited by triangle abc determines the ratios m'/m, m''/m, as well as m'''/m.

The diagram in Figure 7.13 shows several lines of constant pressure P and constant temperature θ; these run concurrently in the two-phase regions; the triangle abc corresponds to a single value of both quantities, since $\theta = \theta_3$ and $P = P_3$ at any point within it. The broken straight lines represent loci of constant values of the mass ratios. For example, the line Cr–p corresponds to $m'/m = m''/m = 0.5$, line pr corresponds to $m'/m = 0.5$, and line pq corresponds to $m''/m = 0.5$. Each vertex corresponds to a value of unity for one of these ratios ($m''/m = 1$ at c, $m'/m = 1$ at b, and $m'''/m = 1$ at a). The side of the triangle opposite to the vertex corresponds to a zero value of this ratio ($m'/m = 0$ along ac, $m''/m = 0$ along ab, and so on), and the loci for values between zero and unity are straight lines owing to the linear nature of the relations, and are parallel to that side of the triangle along which the respective ratio assumes a value of zero.

Triple points can be formed with any three phases of a pure substance, and not only with the three different states of aggregation. For example, three allotropic modifications of a solid, or two allotropic modifications in equilibrium with the liquid can also form a triple point. At this stage it is useful to remind the reader that a single pure substance can develop at most one triple point involving all three states of aggregation; other triple points may include two solid phases and one liquid phase or three solid phases.

Finally, it might be interesting to note that all known substances form a triple point in which the three states of aggregation are in equilibrium, with the exception of helium. The peculiar properties of helium will be discussed in more detail in Section 7.4.12.

7.4.6   Sublimation

When a solid is heated at a constant pressure which is lower than that of the triple point, it does not melt, but gives off its vapor directly. This process is known as *sublimation*. During sublimation, the system consists of two phases, the solid and the vapor. The resulting two-phase system behaves essentially identically with the other two types of two-phase systems. The intensive state of the system has one degree of freedom, the pressure and temperature being related to each other along the *sublimation curve*

$$\phi^{(s)}(P, \theta) = 0, \qquad (7.35)$$

for which $\alpha = 1$, $\beta = 2$, and $f = 1$ in equation (7.25). The complete state requires at least one extensive property (or one mass ratio) for its specification, in addition to one intensive property. The process of sublimation at constant pressure and temperature, like the process of melting or evaporation, requires the addition of the *latent heat of sublimation*

$$l_s = h'' - h'''. \qquad (7.35a)$$

The areas which correspond to sublimation have been clearly marked in the three diagrams of Figures 7.12 and 7.13. It is noteworthy that sublimation occurs in a range of pressures (and therefore temperatures) which is lower than the corresponding range for evaporation, and that the two are separated by the triple point. In the neighborhood of zero pressure and absolute zero of temperature all substances, with the exception of helium, sublimate. The sublimation curve for carbon dioxide can be inferred from Table XVII.

7.4.7 *General characteristics of phase transitions; lines of constant quality*

All phase transitions described so far have it in common that they occur in systems with one degree of freedom and require the addition of a latent heat (heat tone) for their completion. Allotropic changes are usually of the same kind and also require the addition of a latent heat. In all two-phase systems, the extensive parameters are linear functions of the mass fractions of one phase. When represented graphically, lines of constant mass fraction are called *lines of constant quality*, the lines of constant dryness fraction in Figure 7.7 providing one such example. Finally, in all transitions of this type, the extensive parameters show a jump-like, discontinuous change from phase to phase, with the exception of the limiting, critical point. Phase transitions which possess the preceding characteristics are said to be *first-order transitions*. Later, we shall become acquainted with so-called *second-order* phase transitions, the λ point of helium discussed in Section 7.4.12 serving as a first example.

The phase of lower enthalpy is usually called the lower phase, the other being called the higher phase. Thus, the latent heat for a transition from a lower to a higher phase is positive by definition; it is negative for a transition from a higher to a lower phase. According to this convention

$$l^{(1,2)} = h^{(2)} - h^{(1)}, \tag{7.36}$$

where the superscripts in parentheses refer to the individual phases, and

$$l^{(1,2)} = -l^{(2,1)}. \tag{7.36a}$$

At a triple point there exist three phases. Just above the triple point there will occur two transitions, say from phase 1 to 2 and from 2 to 3, both characterized by the latent heats $l^{(1,2)}$ and $l^{(2,3)}$. We can now perform a cycle around the triple point in a manner illustrated in Figure 7.14. The cycle *abcd* consists of the transition *ab* from a state very close to state 1 through a state which is very close to state 2 to state *b*, selected to be

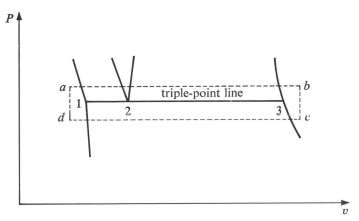

FIGURE 7.14. *Latent heat at the triple point.*

very close to state 3. The reverse path *cd* is very close to the transition from state 3 directly to state 1. In the limit of the triple point

$$l_3^{(1,2)} + l_3^{(2,3)} + l_3^{(3,1)} = (h_3^{(2)} - h_3^{(1)}) + (h_3^{(3)} - h_3^{(2)}) + (h_3^{(1)} - h_3^{(3)}) = 0.$$

Here, the superscripts refer to the phases, and the subscript $_3$ refers to the triple point. Hence, the algebraic sum of the three latent heats at a triple point is zero:

$$l_3^{(1,2)} + l_3^{(2,3)} + l_3^{(3,1)} = 0. \tag{7.37}$$

In the particular case of a triple point between the three states of aggregation

$$l_3^{(m)} + l_3^{(e)} = l_3^{(s)}, \tag{7.37a}$$

since the latent heat of sublimation is the negative of the latent heat of solidification from the vapor.

The preceding relation can, of course, be also inferred by applying the First Law of thermodynamics to the cycle *abcd* in the limit when it becomes coincident with the triple-point line, and by noticing that the net work of the atmosphere around the cycle is zero.

The u, v diagram of Figure 7.13 could be supplemented with lines of constant pressure and temperature. The two networks of lines would be distinct in the single-phase regions but would merge in the two-phase regions where the line of constant pressure would become identical with the saturation isotherm corresponding to it. Moreover, such lines would be straight; this can be inferred from equation (7.29b), an analog of which applies in any two-phase region, as already stated. For example, in the vapor-liquid region, a line of constant pressure and temperature is given by the two equations (7.28a) and (7.29) in which v', v'', u', and u'' are constants. The relation between u and v results from an elimination of the dryness fraction from these two equations; since both are linear, the resulting relation is also linear. The same can be said about the two remaining two-phase regions.

The lines P_3 and θ_3, distinct in the single-phase region, include the triangle *abc* in the locus.

The diagram also shows one line of constant quality, $x = m''/m$ in the liquid-vapor region, one line of constant m''/m in the solid-vapor region. Owing to the linearity of the relations between the extensive parameters u and v and the mass ratios, equation (7.29b), the lines of constant quality divide the intercepts on the lines of constant pressure and temperature into proportional parts in the same way as was explained in Section 7.4.3 when the drawing of lines of constant dryness fractions was discussed. The triple-point area *abc* can be imagined covered with three networks of lines, those of constant m'/m, m''/m, and m'''/m, one of which has been drawn in the diagram as explained in Section 7.4.5. They are all straight lines which are parallel to sides of the triangle *abc*. The equation of one such line, say that of $m'/m = $ const is obtained by eliminating m''/m and m'''/m from equations (7.34a) and (7.34b). Since both equations are linear, the resulting relation between u and v must also be linear, in analogy with the two-phase regions, as already mentioned. Evidently, at any point in the diagram, the labels on the lines $m'/m = $ const, $m''/m = $ const, and $m'''/m = $ const passing through it must add up to unity.

Diagrams in which the internal energy and specific volume are employed as coordinates are not normally used in practice. However, in Section 11.2 we shall become acquainted with the Mollier, enthalpy-entropy diagram in which both coordinates are extensive, specific properties. It can be, therefore, foreseen that the geometric relations in such diagrams will be identical with those described here.

7.4.8   State surfaces; the P, θ diagram

The relations which exist between the thermodynamic variables of pure substances and their different phases can be clearly understood and visualized with the aid of three-dimensional diagrams of the surfaces which represent the equation of state, in a manner similar to that used in connection with the perfect gas in Section 7.3. The isometric drawings shown in Figures 7.15 and 7.16 represent the state surface in P, v, θ and P, u, v coordinates, respectively. The present surfaces are considerably more complex than the hyperbolic paraboloid of Figure 3.2, but it is clear that the P, v, θ surface of any substance must tend to the shape of a hyperbolic paraboloid as the temperature increases and the pressure decreases. On the other hand, it must be realized that no portion of the P, v, θ surface of a pure substance or of a mixture of pure substances, for that matter, tend to the plane or cylindrical surface, Figures 7.2 and 7.3, characteristic of an incompressible fluid, either in the gaseous or in the liquid phases. Whereas the perfect-gas model represents the asymptotic properties of real substances,

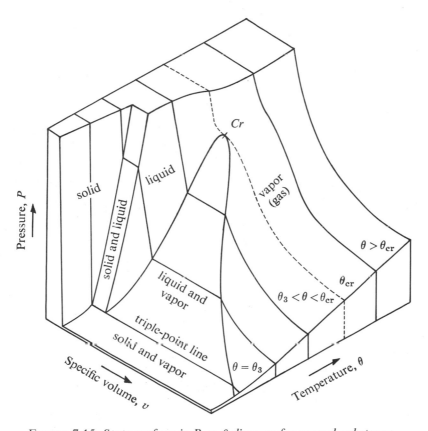

FIGURE 7.15. *State surface in P, v, θ diagram for normal substance.*

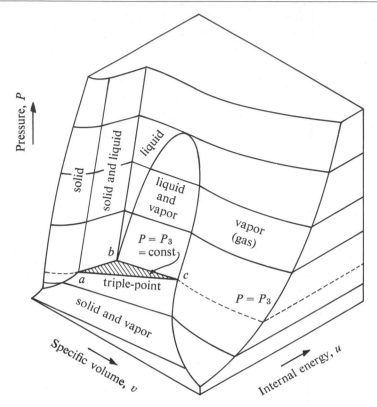

FIGURE 7.16. *P, u, v diagram for a normal substance.*

at least with respect to the thermal equation of state, the incompressible-fluid model used in fluid mechanics does not; it merely *averages* the properties over a suitably selected, narrow range of states.

The diagram in Figure 7.15 shows the traces left on the surface by intersecting it with typical isothermal planes, $\theta = \theta_3$, $\theta_3 < \theta < \theta_{cr}$, $\theta = \theta_{cr}$, and $\theta > \theta_{cr}$. These give an idea of the curvature of the surface at each point. The single-phase regions show double curvature at each point, whereas the two-phase regions which join the former along distinct "creases" are formed by a family of straight lines. Each of these straight lines is the intersection of a plane of constant pressure with a plane of constant temperature, so that, consequently, these portions of the surface are curved in one direction only. Whereas not all *ruled surfaces*, that is surfaces which are traced by a moving straight line, for example, a hyperboloid of revolution, are *developable*, the two-phase portions are developable. If each of them were cut out along the "creases," it could be straightened into a plane in the same way as a cylindrical surface.

The P, u, v surface of Figure 7.16 shows that the triangle *abc* of the triple region is wholly confined to a portion of the plane $P = P_3 = \text{const}$.

The P, v; θ, v diagrams familiar from Figures 7.6, 7.7 and 7.12 constitute topographical projections of the state surface in the direction θ for a P, v diagram, and in the P-direction for a θ, v diagram. It is instructive now to sketch a projection of the state surface P, v, θ in the direction of v and to represent it in terms of the two intensive parameters P and θ. This has been done in Figure 7.17 for a normal substance. Owing to the fact that the two-phase and three-phase portions of the surface are ruled by lines $P = \text{const}$, $\theta = \text{const}$, the respective areas project themselves as the lines $\phi^{(e)}$, $\phi^{(m)}$, and $\phi^{(s)}$ for the two-phase regions, and as point Tr for the triple-point region. The vapor-pressure line $\phi^{(e)}(P, \theta) = 0$ ends abruptly at the critical point, Cr, allowing the liquid and gaseous regions to merge continuously into each other. The vapor-pressure line $\phi^{(e)}$, the sublimation line $\phi^{(s)}$, and the melting line $\phi^{(m)}$, intersect in one point, the triple point Tr. The sublimation curve extends from the origin at $P = \theta = 0$ to the triple point, and the slopes

$$\left(\frac{\mathrm{d}P}{\mathrm{d}\theta}\right)_s > 0 \quad \text{and} \quad \left(\frac{\mathrm{d}P}{\mathrm{d}\theta}\right)_e > 0$$

for the vapor-pressure curves for sublimation and evaporation are positive. We shall discover in Volume II that this is a necessary consequence of the fact that the specific volume of the vapor of any substance is larger than that of the solid or liquid in equilibrium with it (except for the critical point, of course). Accordingly, for a normal substance for which $v''' < v_i'$, the slope

$$\left(\frac{\mathrm{d}P}{\mathrm{d}\theta}\right)_m > 0$$

of the melting curve is also positive. It will turn out to be negative for anomalous substances. It follows that all substances sublimate and evaporate at higher temperatures when the processes are conducted at higher pressures. Conversely, the higher the temperature, the higher the vapor pressure. On the other hand, normal substances melt at higher temperatures as the pressure is increased, whereas the melting point of an

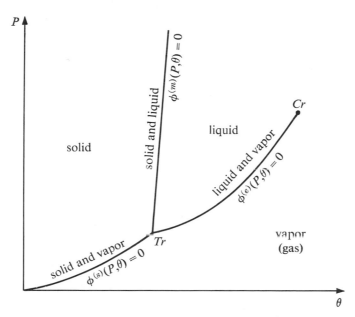

FIGURE 7.17. *Pressure-temperature diagram for a normal substance.*

anomalous substance, like water, is shifted towards a *lower* temperature as the pressure is *increased*, the phenomenon being known as the *depression of the melting point*.

On comparing the two diagrams in Figure 7.12 with the isometric drawing in Figure 7.15, it will be realized that the specific volume of a pure substance can never be reduced to zero. Accordingly, line g in the θ, v diagram of Figure 7.12 represents the variation of the volume of the solid with temperature at a very high, "infinite," pressure. Similarly, line f in the P, v diagram of the same figure represents the variation with pressure of the volume of the solid at absolute zero of temperature.

7.4.9   *The anomalous properties of water substance*

We have mentioned earlier that water substance is anomalous in that its liquid attains a maximum in density along an isobar. This occurs in the pressure range from 0.008 atm up to about 270 atm. The temperature at which this maximum occurs depends on pressure and ranges from 4.004°C at 0.008 atm to −2.07°C at 270 atm, being equal to +3.98°C at atmospheric pressure. At the low end of this temperature range, the maximum in density coincides with the beginning of evaporation whereas at the upper end of the range it coincides with the end of melting. Thus, the locus of the minima in specific volume joins the melting curve with the vapor-pressure line for evaporation. In addition, along the melting curve, the specific volume of the solid ice is larger than that of the liquid water which is in equilibrium with it, the difference in density between water and ice increasing with saturation pressure and temperature.† The variation of the specific volume of water substance in the range from absolute zero of temperature to evaporation at four different pressures is shown graphically, but not to scale, in Figure 7.18.‡ The diagram demonstrates that the density maximum occurs at lower temperatures for higher pressures, but this variation is relatively small.§ The melting point itself also shifts slightly, and anomalously, in the

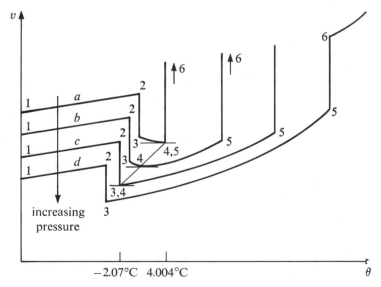

FIGURE 7.18. *Change in volume with temperature at different pressures for water substance. Not to scale.*

---

† The increase is from 0.09 cm³/g at 0°C and 1 atm to 0.1352 cm³/g at −22°C and 2045 atm.
‡ Measurements due to E. H. Amagat as reported in Dorsey, N. E., *Properties of Ordinary Water-Substance* (Reinhold, 1940).
§ It occurs at 3.98°C for 1 atm decreasing linearly by 0.0225°C/atm to 1.75°C at 100 atm.

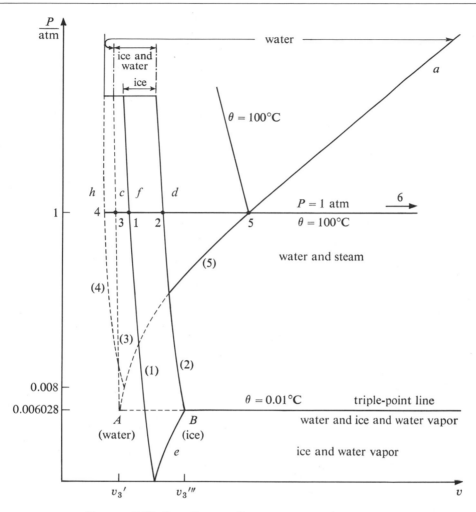

FIGURE 7.19. *P, v diagram for water; anomalous region.*

direction of lower temperatures as the pressure is increased. Curve *a* corresponds to the pressure of 0.008 atm, whereas curve *c* corresponds to 270 atm; line 4-4-4 traces the locus of maximum density. On each curve, the segment 1, 2 represents the heating of ice, 2, 3 describes the decrease in specific volume during melting, the equilibrium temperature for melting decreasing with pressure. The segments 3, 4, 5 represent the isobaric heating of the liquid with the density maximum at point 4. Finally, the segment 5, 6 represents the change in specific volume produced by evaporation which occurs at higher temperatures for higher pressures in the same way as in a normal substance.

The preceding anomalies considerably complicate the appearance of the P, v diagram for water and are also reflected in a more complex shape of the P, v, θ surface. The P, v diagram is shown in Figure 7.19 which is restricted to the region of low pressures and temperatures, its scale having been distorted in order to display the anomalies in a clear manner. The line of the triple point occurs at a pressure of 0.006028 atm (0.006228 kp/cm²) and at a temperature of 0.01°C, as we already know from Section 2.8 on the International Practical Temperature Scale and p. 290. On this line, point *A* corresponds to the liquid, volume v_3', whereas point *B* corresponds to the ice whose volume v_3''' exceeds that of the liquid. Below this pressure, water cannot exist. Line *e* sloping downwards from point *B* (ice at triple point) represents the change in the volume of sublimating ice. Line *f* represents the variation of the volume of ice at absolute zero of temperature with pressure; hence, line *f* is the locus of points 1 from Figure 7.18 and represents the lowest volume which *ice* can assume at different pressures. Nevertheless, and anomalously, water can assume even lower volumes.

Line *d* emanating from point *B* represents the volumes v''' of melting ice at varying pressures and so constitutes the locus of points 2 from Figure 7.18. These volumes are larger than those along line *f*. Line *c* represents the variation of the volume of saturated water v_i' in equilibrium with its ice; it emanates from point *A* on the triple line, which is the only point for water on that line. Line *h* represents the decreasing minimum specific volume of liquid water with pressure, and hence constitutes the locus of points 4 from Figure 7.18; as already stated, such minima exist in the pressure interval 0.008 atm $< P <$ 270 atm. At any pressure in that range this line represents the lowest volume which can be attained by water substance, regardless of temperature. It is clear that line *h* must terminate at line *c* at a pressure of 270 atm. Finally, line *a*, which must also start at point *A* for water on the triple line, traces the locus of points 5 from Figure 7.18, and represents the variation with pressure of the volume v' of saturated water in equilibrium with its vapor. Line *h* terminates on it at a pressure $P = 0.008$ atm.

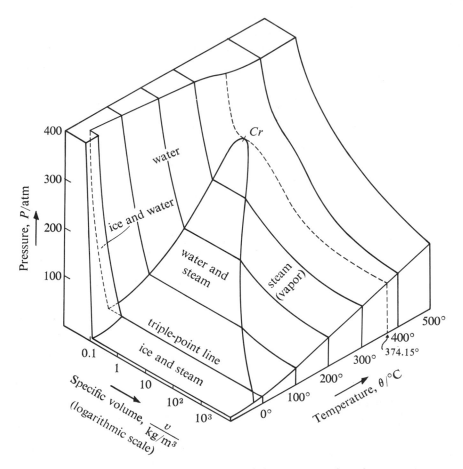

FIGURE 7.20. *Isometric projection of the P, v, θ surface for water.*

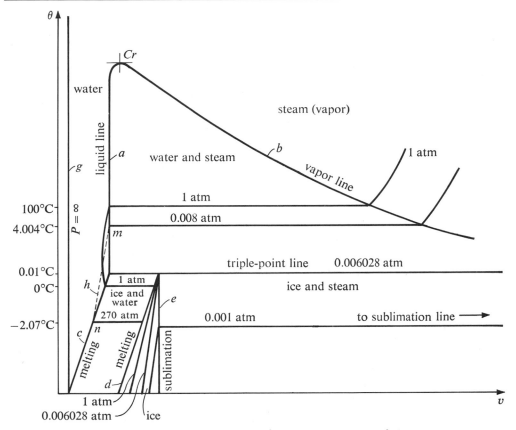

FIGURE 7.21. *θ, v diagram for water. (Not to scale.)*

An isometric projection of the P, v, θ surface is shown in Figure 7.20. On confronting this diagram with the P, v diagram from Figure 7.19 it becomes clear that the ruled surface of solid-liquid equilibrium projects itself so that it becomes superimposed on a portion of the ruled surface of liquid-vapor equilibrium. Equally, the doubly curved portion of the surface which corresponds to the solid projects itself on the developable surface of solid-liquid equilibrium. Finally, the curved surface for the liquid turns upon itself at the density maximum and covers the projection plane twice between curves h and c in Figure 7.19. This explains the reason for tracing curves h and c in broken lines; they would be hidden from view to an eye looking on the surface in the direction of positive temperatures, whereas lines e, f, and d would be visible.

The diagram in Figure 7.19 contains a sketch of the atmospheric isobar with points 1, 2, 3, 4, 5, and 6 from Figure 7.18 marked on it. The segment 1, 2 is visible, but the segment 2, 3, 4 is hidden from view. The segment 4, 5 is only partly visible, because the portion contained between point 4 and the point on the curved surface of liquid water which projects under point 2 is obscured from view. The 100°C isotherm is also shown sketched. This isotherm can never reach the area of solid-liquid equilibrium because the highest melting point is at the triple point, an increase in pressure causing a decrease in the temperature of melting.

A projection on the θ, v plane, partly contained in Figure 7.18, is given in Figure 7.21; it gives a qualitative picture of the P, v, θ surface over a wide range of states. The broken line h represents the locus of density maxima and extends from the liquid line a to the melting line c. The region of ice lies below the triple-point line and consists of a triangular area confined between the sublimation line e and the second melting line d.

Perhaps the clearest view of the relation between the various phases can be gleaned from Figure 7.22 which contains a P, θ diagram. In contrast with Figure 7.17 for a normal substance, the melting line exhibits a negative slope. The diagram shows clearly that water cannot be solidified by applying pressure at constant temperature, regardless of how low its temperature may be, and that the highest melting temperature occurs at the triple point. In fact, applying very high pressures to ice at constant temperature will always cause it to melt, in marked contrast with normal substances whose liquids can be solidified by applying sufficiently high pressures at constant temperature, and whose solids will never melt under such conditions. Saturated water in equilibrium with its vapor cannot exist at temperatures below that of the triple point which is at $\theta_3 = 0.01°C$. In particular, it cannot exist at 0°C, the contrary being sometimes stated in the literature.

The diagram also shows the locus of density maxima as a broken straight line extending from point m on the saturation line for liquid-vapor equilibrium to point n on the melting curve.

The simplicity of the P, θ diagram of Figure 7.22 is entirely due to the fact that lines of constant volume have not been drawn in it. The reader may wish to cross-plot some such lines from Figure 7.21 into Figure 7.22.

Of the three phase boundaries, the vapor-pressure curve for evaporation is by far the most important one in practical applications. In most cases, the pressure at the triple point is so low compared with the critical pressure that the latter is barely visible in a diagram drawn to scale. The graphs in Figure 7.23 contain vapor-pressure curves for several substances which are important in applications. All curves show a nearly exponential course, and the reasons for it will be understood in Volume II. It is interesting to note that the vapor-pressure curves of the different substances do not intersect; this means that, with very few exceptions, it is impossible to find two substances which

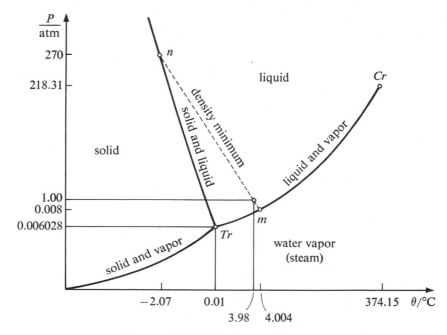

FIGURE 7.22. *P*, *θ* diagram for water.

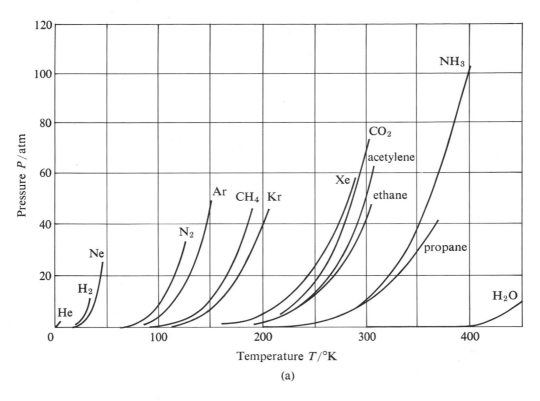

(a)

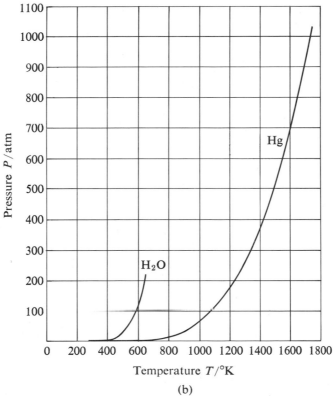

(b)

FIGURE 7.23. *Vapor-pressure curves for several substances.*

boil at the same temperature *and* pressure. It is also noteworthy that water substance occupies a middle position between the cold-boiling substances like carbon dioxide, ammonia, or the noble gases on the one hand, and mercury on the other. Mercury boils at a very high temperature for a given pressure. These circumstances are important in the selection of working fluids for refrigerators, which must be low-boiling, and for power generation (in liquid-vapor cycles), which must be high-boiling. The vapor-pressure curve of water substance makes it very suitable as a working fluid for power generation, not only on account of its abundance and cheapness, but also on account of its thermodynamic properties.

In order to gain a clear idea of the properties of liquid water and steam, it is useful to examine the three diagrams in Figures 7.24, 7.25, and 7.26; they have been drawn to scale, and the anomalous regions as well as the regions in which the solid exists have shrunk to such small proportions that displaying them would be impracticable. It is noteworthy that in the P, v diagram of Figure 7.24, the isotherms progressively tend to the hyperbolic shape of a perfect gas as the state is moved further away from the critical region and into the low-pressure range. Similarly, the isobars in the θ, v diagram of Figure 7.25 as well as the isochores in Figure 7.26 tend to become straight lines passing through the origin under the same conditions, in line with Figure 3.3 for a perfect gas. It is also noteworthy that the course of isochores in the liquid region strongly resembles that typical for an incompressible fluid, Figure 7.3. This signifies that in this region the properties of liquid water approximate those of an incompressible fluid very closely. This does not mean, however, that the use of the incompressible fluid model in fluid mechanics is necessarily restricted to regions like this one, as we already know from previous remarks.

The anomalous properties of water are responsible for several curious phenomena which we tend to accept as normal owing to our great familiarity with water substance which is so abundant in nature and which plays such an important part in our lives.

The increase in the volume of water substance upon melting or, in other words, the lower density of ice compared with its saturated water at atmospheric pressure is responsible for the preservation of life in rivers and lakes throughout the winter season. Ice, unlike the solid phases of normal substances, floats above water, so that water, unlike other substances, freezes from the top downwards. Thus, rivers and lakes form layers of ice in winter at their surfaces, providing thermal insulation for the water underneath them. As the temperature decreases, the layer of ice thickens, but sufficient quantities of air-saturated liquid water remain to allow the living organisms to survive the winter at temperatures which are close to the 4°C at maximum density. If water were not anomalous, survival would be impossible. It is possible to go even further and to state that life, as we know it on earth, would be impossible, because the evolution of terrestrial life started in water. On the other hand, however, the same property is responsible for the bursting of uninsulated water pipes in freezing weather.

The decrease in the melting point of water with pressure is responsible for our ability to skate on ice and to glide on packed snow. At the line of contact between the skate and the surface of the ice, there is exerted a very high pressure; it is produced owing to the very small area of contact. Thus, the pressure is increased to a very high value at constant temperature, and the ice melts under the skate. The thin layer of water created in this manner provides an excellent lubricant, reduces friction, and makes skating possible. If ice had normal properties, the high pressure under the skate would cause the

[Text continued on page 308]

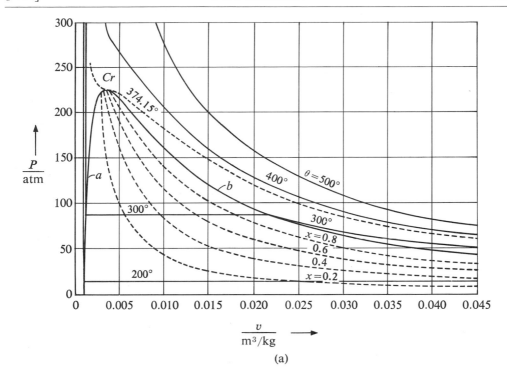

(a)

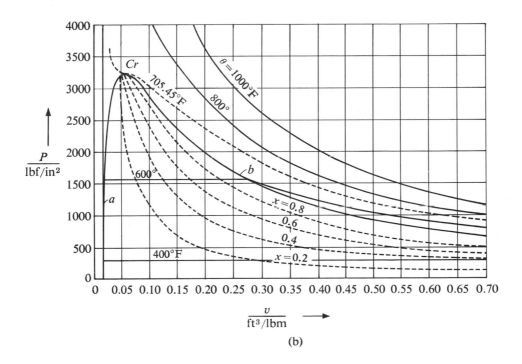

(b)

FIGURE 7.24. *P, v diagram for water and steam. (a) Metric units. (b) British units.*

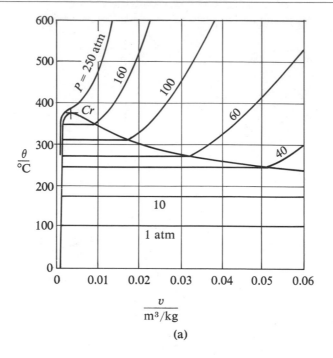

(a)

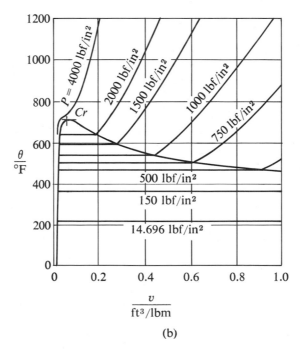

(b)

FIGURE 7.25. *θ, v diagram for water and steam. (a) Metric units. (b) British units.*

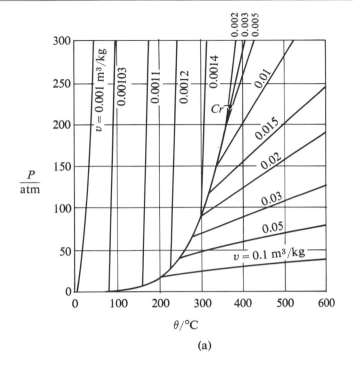

(a)

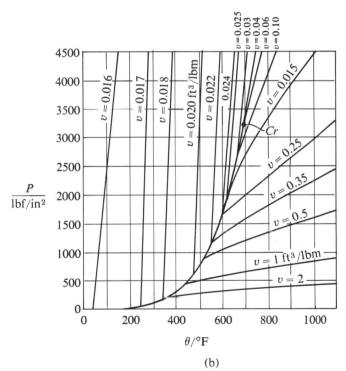

(b)

FIGURE 7.26. *P, θ diagram for water and steam. (a) Metric units. (b) British units.*

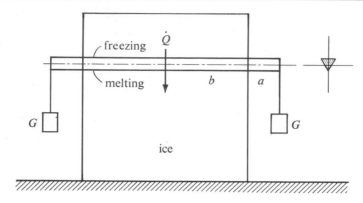

FIGURE 7.27. *Regelation.*

skater to freeze to the surface. A similar phenomenon occurs under a glacier and is responsible for its mobility. The deeper layers of a glacier move under the pressure of the masses above them owing to the lubricating action of melted ice which freezes again when the pressure decreases, the process being known in geophysics as *regelation.*

Regelation can be demonstrated by a simple experiment sketched in Figure 7.27. A steel rod *a* placed on a block of ice *b* and loaded with weights *G* will melt the ice under it since the increased pressure depresses the melting point. In this manner the bar will begin to penetrate into the ice, albeit very slowly, but the water above it will freeze, because its pressure has returned to atmospheric. The melting ice under the bar must be provided with its latent heat of fusion; this is supplied by the water freezing above it so that there is a constant flux of heat $\dot{Q}$ conducted through the steel bar. If the steel bar were replaced by a poor thermal conductor, the process of penetration would become very slow. The speed of the process can be increased by giving the bar a prismatic shape, as shown in Figure 7.27.

Another interesting, climatic consequence follows from the fact that the temperature of the triple point of water, $\theta_3 = 0.01°C$, is very close to the melting temperature $\theta_m = 0°C$ of ice under atmospheric pressure. This property accounts for the fact that the large masses of ice and snow deposited at the end of a spell of cold weather do not first melt and only subsequently evaporate. This would be the case if the triple-point temperature were much higher than it is thus leading to flooding. In actual fact, a large proportion of the snow or ice sublimates at the triple point because the atmosphere above it contains relatively little water vapor. The so-called *partial pressure* (Section 7.7.9)† of the water vapor immediately above the ice is approximately equal to the very low triple-point pressure of $P_3 = 0.006028$ atm, and solar radiation causes vigorous sublimation.

Apart from the common variety of ice, known as ice I, water can freeze into five more stable (II, III, V, VI, VII) and two unstable (IV and VIII) varieties of ice, each of which constitutes a different allotropic modification. The existence of these allotropic modifications further complicates the appearance of the *P, v, θ* surface for water substance and gives rise to six more triple points, all at pressures of the order of several thousand atmospheres.

7.4.10   *The problem of single-valuedness*

The appearance of the diagram in Figure 7.19 shows that the equation of state for water substance in which the pressure *P* has been chosen as one of the independent variables does not seem to be single-valued, contrary to what has been stated in Sec-

---

† That is, the imaginary pressure which would be exerted by the vapor if the air were removed.

tion 3.3. In fact, given a value of volume and pressure, it is sometimes possible to find as many as *three* values of temperature θ which satisfy the equation of state, together with the given values of volume and pressure. A case of this type is shown in Figure 7.28 which reproduces in schematic form one of the heating curves from Figure 7.18. It is seen here that the ice at point a, the mixture of ice and water at point b, and the liquid water at point c, have the same pressure *and* specific volume. However, this is only an apparent contradiction because in relation to physically significant problems it is always known which one of the phases or which particular mixture of phases is involved in each particular case. This is similar to the mathematical idea of dealing with a multivalued function. For example, when the function $y^2 = x$ is to be rendered single-valued, it is sufficient to *specify* which of the two branches of the parabola $y = \pm\sqrt{x}$ is meant in a particular case. Choosing specific volume, v, and temperature, θ, as the independent variables eliminates the need for such an additional specification.

7.4.11 *Undercooling of vapor and supersaturation of liquid; metastable states*

The process of evaporation and the reverse process of condensation does not always occur in the manner described in Section 7.4.2. When a vapor is cooled with some agitation and when foreign particles, such as specks of dust, ionized particles, or minute droplets of liquid are present in it, it will begin to condense when the pressure P and temperature θ simultaneously reach values which lie on the vapor-pressure curve. When the process is examined in more detail, it is found that condensation begins at the foreign particles which are said to serve as *nuclei of condensation*. In this connection it is immaterial whether the vapor-pressure curve is approached at constant pressure, at constant temperature, or in some other way, for example, by adiabatic expansion, the only criterion being the *combination* of values of pressure and temperature.

When great care is taken to remove the nuclei of condensation, and when the process occurs rapidly, but without undue agitation, the system appears to develop a certain internal resistance to condensation and remains in the gaseous state under conditions when it would otherwise separate into a gaseous and liquid phase. For example, when a vapor is compressed at a constant temperature θ, Figure 7.29, it would normally begin to condense upon reaching the saturation pressure P_a at state a on the vapor curve; upon further compression its volume would decrease owing to condensation at the constant pressure and temperature corresponding to line ab. However, in the present case, the vapor does not condense, but continues to be compressed uninter-

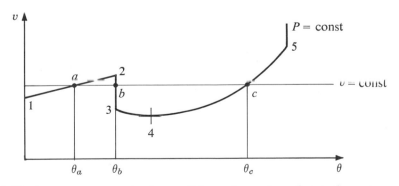

FIGURE 7.28. *Apparent many-valuedness of thermal equation of state for water substance.*

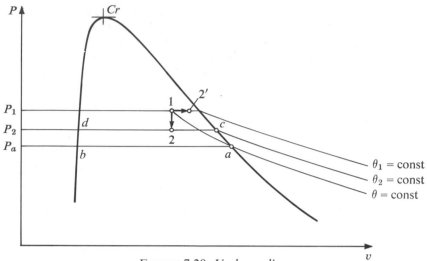

FIGURE 7.29. *Undercooling.*

ruptedly, say to pressure P_1 at state 1. At that state, the vapor exists at a temperature θ which is lower than the saturation temperature θ_1 for pressure P_1. For this reason, the *vapor* at state 1 is said to be *undercooled*. An undercooled vapor can also be said to exist at a pressure which exceeds the saturation pressure for its temperature.

If no disturbances are introduced, the vapor can persist in this condition for a long time. However, vigorous agitation, or the introduction of a nucleus of condensation causes the vapor spontaneously to condense in part and to assume a state of equilibrium, say, state 2, in which the pressure and temperature together lie on the vapor-pressure curve. This process is essentially irreversible because the opposite transition is never observed.† If the process is adiabatic and is allowed to occur in a closed, perfectly insulated vessel ($v = $ const), the new state of equilibrium can be determined with reference to the First Law of thermodynamics. Since agitation or the addition of a nucleus of condensation requires practically no work, we can put $W_{1,2} = 0$, and for an adiabatic process $Q_{1,2} = 0$. Thus, per unit mass

$$u_1 = u_2. \tag{7.38}$$

The internal energy u_1 of undercooled vapor at pressure P_1 and temperature θ_1 cannot be found in normal tables of properties, such as the steam tables, Tables X, XI, and XII, or similar compilations; they must be tabulated separately. State 2, however, is fully described in the tables, and in accordance with equation (7.28a) we can write

$$u_1 = u_2'' - (1 - x_2)(u_2'' - u_2'). \tag{7.39}$$

Here u_2'' is the internal energy of the saturated vapor, point c, at the unknown pressure P_2, u_2' is the corresponding value for the saturated liquid at point d, and x_2 denotes the dryness fraction at state 2. Similarly, for the volumes we can write

$$v_1 = v_2'' - (1 - x_2)(v_2'' - v_2'). \tag{7.40}$$

The two equations (7.39) and (7.40) in which v_1 and u_1 must be taken from tables for undercooled vapor, and are known, fully determine the final equilibrium state 2. That

† However, as is the case with all irreversible processes, the initial state can be retrieved by a suitably conceived *reversible* process.

this is so is not immediately clear, but it should be realized that the two equations will be satisfied *simultaneously* only if the appropriate saturation pressure P_2 together with the proper saturation temperature θ_2 have been chosen. This can be achieved by trial and error.

It does not require much imagination to recognize the similarity between the behavior of undercooled vapor subjected to disturbances and certain mechanical systems. For example, the sphere in Figure 7.30(a) is said to be in stable mechanical equilibrium because it will always revert to it after having been disturbed, no matter how vigorously. The sketch in Figure 7.30(b) depicts a mechanical system in neutral equilibrium, because a disturbance will change the position of the sphere to one in which it will remain indefinitely. Similarly, Figure 7.30(c) shows a sphere in unstable equilibrium which it will leave under the influence of a disturbance no matter how small. The system in Figure 7.30(d) is said to be in *metastable equilibrium*, because it is stable with respect to small disturbances, but when the disturbance exceeds a certain magnitude, the system seeks a new state of equilibrium.[†] By analogy, the single-phase undercooled vapor in state 1 is also said to be in *metastable* equilibrium, whereas the two-phase system in state 2 is said to be in *stable* equilibrium. So far in this book, only stable equilibrium states have been considered.

Although the state which involves the two phases of a system is colloquially referred to as the stable state, a cylinder containing such a two-phase system will not necessarily be in a stable state. Let us suppose that such a system is contained in a cylinder closed with a piston, thus securing a constant pressure, and remains in thermal contact with a heat reservoir. If the piston is displaced upwards or downwards, it will not revert to its original position but will remain in the displaced position. During the process some heat will be exchanged, and some vapor will condense or some liquid will evapo-

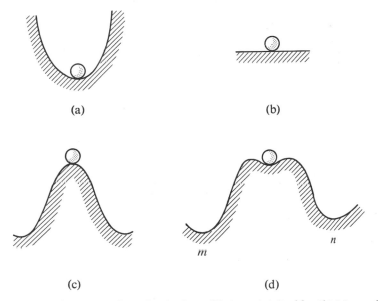

FIGURE 7.30. *Types of mechanical equilibrium. (a) Stable. (b) Neutral.*
(c) Unstable. (d) Metastable.

[†] A more detailed discussion of metastable equilibrium will be given in Chapter 14 (Vol. II). See also Reiss, H., *Methods of Thermodynamics* (Blaisdell, 1965).

rate (assuming the two-phase system to consist of a quantity saturated liquid and vapor). Thus, the system will be in neutral equilibrium with respect to such a disturbance. Conversely, the addition or extraction of a small quantity of heat will cause the piston to displace, and the system will continue to be in neutral equilibrium. By contrast, if a small weight is placed on the piston increasing the pressure from saturation pressure P_s to $P_s + \Delta P$ by a small amount, equilibrium will be disturbed. The two phases cannot coexist under such conditions, and the vapor will condense completely. Similarly, the subtraction of a small weight from the piston will cause the pressure to decrease to $P_s - \Delta P_s$, and all of the liquid must necessarily evaporate. Thus, the system will be in unstable equilibrium with respect to this type of disturbance. Nevertheless, the two-phase system constitutes the stable state with respect to a disturbed metastable state.

Metastable states exist also near the liquid line. When, for example, a liquid is expanded rapidly but without undue stirring at a constant temperature θ, Figure 7.31, it can reach a state, denoted by 1 in the sketch, without evaporating. Hence, it is seen to exist at a temperature θ and at a pressure P_1 which is lower than the saturation pressure P_a for temperature θ. Conversely, the liquid at state 1 can be said to exist at a pressure P_1 and at a temperature θ which is higher than the saturation temperature θ_1 for pressure P_1. The liquid in the metastable state 1 is, therefore, said to be *supersaturated*. Upon sufficiently vigorous stirring, the system can be induced to reach a state of stable equilibrium, the details of which depend on the external constraints.

Metastable states exist along both branches of the melting and sublimation lines as well as along the phase boundaries for allotropic transformations. The metastable states in solids can be particularly durable and insensitive even to large disturbances. In fact, certain alloys or glasses exist in their metastable states for practically indefinite periods of time. For example, objects made of iron in Egypt about 6000 years ago contain cementite—a metastable phase of iron and carbon—when uncovered by archeological expeditions, and show no traces of graphite which would appear in them in

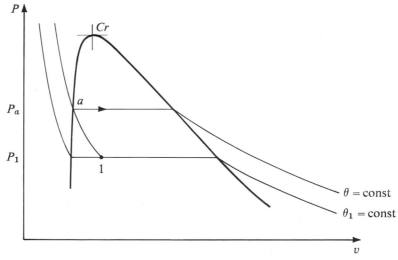

FIGURE 7.31. *Supersaturation.*

stable equilibrium. It is useful to think about systems in metastable states as if they had developed *internal constraints* which are removed by stirring, by the introduction of impurities, nuclei of condensation, and so on. In this manner, the transition from a metastable to a stable state is analogous to the irreversible process, described in Section 4.6, which occurred upon the removal of a tangible, internal constraint of the system. In the present case, the internal constraint is of a more subtle nature. The behavior of systems in metastable states is very important in metallurgy and in the physics of solids. An ingenious use of undercooled vapors is made in C. T. R. Wilson's cloud chamber.

Reverting to the example of the metastable, undercooled vapor in state 1, it is clear that state 2 is not the only stable state which can be reached from it, just as the sphere in Figure 7.30(d) can reach either one of the troughs *m* or *n*. The particular new state of equilibrium reached depends on the *external constraints* imposed on the system. In the mechanical analog, the constraint is provided by the shape of the curved surface which forces the ball to move in a certain way. In the case of the undercooled vapor, the constraints were provided by the adiabatic insulation and the volume of the vessel containing it. Had the undercooled vapor been flowing through an adiabatically insulated pipe, the new state of equilibrium, say state 2′, would be constrained by the requirements of equal pressure and enthalpy

$$P_{2'} = P_1 \quad \text{and} \quad h_{2'} = h_1. \tag{7.41}$$

Hence,

$$h_1 = h_{2'}'' - (1 - x_{2'})(h_{2'}'' - h_{2'}'), \tag{7.41a}$$

where $h_{2'}''$ and $h_{2'}'$ would be taken from the usual tables listing the properties for stable states at pressure $P_{2'} = P_1$. The value of h_1, on the other hand, must be found in the table for metastable states. Thus, equation (7.41a) permits us to determine the dryness fraction $x_{2'}$ directly and without trial and error. The equality of enthalpy, naturally, follows from the application of the First Law for a closed system at constant pressure with $Q = 0$.

The properties of systems in their metastable states must be determined by direct measurements, in the same way as the properties of systems in stable states. Owing to the inherent difficulties of experimentation, the amount of information available is disappointing. In general, it can be said that the state surface of a pure substance (or of a mixture, for that matter) acquires additional branches; these form continuous extensions of the curved portions which correspond to the stable states of single phases. An isometric sketch of two such continuations is shown in Figure 7.32. It is clear that these continuations project themselves in a way which superimposes a network of level lines on a portion already covered by the corresponding network for a set of stable states. Thus, once again, the impression is created that the equation of state is multivalued. However, in line with our remarks in the preceding section, it is realized that the knowledge as to whether a stable or a metastable state exists under a given set of circumstances allows us to identify a unique state-point in each case.

As a rule, the double region covers only a portion of the area of stable two-phase states, and its limits must also be determined through experimentation.

Frequently, and by way of a heuristic approximation, the thermodynamic properties of the metastable states are determined by a direct extrapolation of the adjoining single-

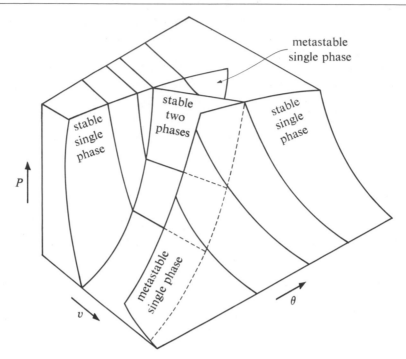

FIGURE 7.32. *Metastable states.*

phase region. The limit of the metastable region for water vapor, the so-called cloud limit, is described in Table XIII. It is noteworthy that for lower pressures this limit coincides with the line $x = 0.98$.

7.4.12   *The properties of helium*

Although helium cannot be classed as an anomalous substance in the same way as water, it, nevertheless, possesses certain unique properties which merit attention. Helium is the only known substance which can exist in the liquid phase right down to absolute zero of temperature, and for this reason, as we shall see, helium cannot develop a triple point in which all three states of aggregation coexist. Helium is encountered in two isotopic variations, the lighter He[3] of atomic mass 3.0169806 kg/kmol, and the heavier He[4] of atomic mass 4.0038742 kg/kmol on the physical scale.[†] Normal helium extracted from the atmosphere or mined[‡] consists predominantly of helium 4 and contains about one part per million of helium 3.

The P, θ phase diagram for helium 4 is shown in Figure 7.33. The diagram, which has been obtained in the course of very extensive experiments, shows that the vapor-pressure curve for the evaporation of helium extends from its critical point at $P_{cr} = 2.26$ atm and $\theta_{cr} = 5.25°$K to absolute zero, with the normal, atmospheric boiling point at 4.125°K, and has the now familiar, near-exponential shape. In contrast with all other

[†]On the carbon-12 scale, the values are 3.0160215 and 4.0026014, respectively.
[‡]In the United States, the Soviet Union, Canada, and the Union of South Africa.

substances, the melting curve starts at 25 atm with a horizontal tangent and increases upwards. The fact that the tangent to the melting curve of helium 4 is horizontal provides an experimental proof of the validity of the Third Law of thermodynamics discussed in Volume II.

The phase diagram shows that at absolute zero of temperature helium 4 exists in its liquid phase between zero pressure and 25 atm. The solid cannot exist at all at pressures lower than 25 atm, which is considerably higher than the critical pressure of 2.26 atm, and cannot sublimate.

A second unusual property of helium is its transition from liquid helium I to liquid helium II along the nearly straight λ line *ab* shown in the figure. Liquid helium I and II constitute two different phases of liquid helium 4 with markedly different properties, but the transition from one to the other does not involve a latent heat in the same way as a first-order transition does. For this reason it is called a second-order transition. The transition from helium I to helium II can be effected either by cooling at constant pressure or by reducing the pressure at constant temperature. The designation λ line and λ transition stem from the fact that the diagram of the variation of the specific heat of liquid helium shown in Figure 7.34 has the shape of the Greek letter lambda, its peak being located at the lambda point.

The two points *a* and *b* represent two triple points in which the two fluids coexist with the solid and vapor, respectively, but a triple point of coexistence for all three states of aggregation is absent from the diagram.

Liquid helium II has very peculiar properties which occupied the attention of physicists for many years, but which we are not in a position to discuss in detail in this book. We shall merely mention that liquid helium II has an abnormally low viscosity which causes it to flow with very little resistance through very narrow annuli thus earning

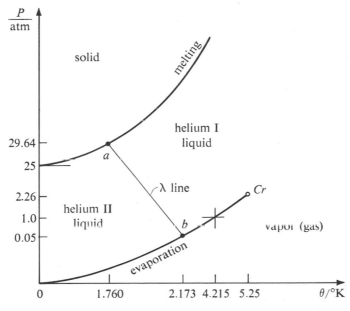

FIGURE 7.33. *Phase diagram for helium 4. (Not to scale.)*

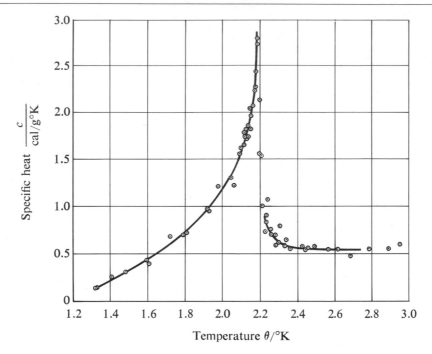

FIGURE 7.34. *Specific heat of liquid helium 4. (From W. H. Keesom,* Helium, Elsevier, 1942, p. 215.)

for it the adjective "superfluid." Liquid helium II can be made to mount a narrow capillary by slight heating, or even to squirt out of it, the phenomenon being known as the "fountain effect." The fountain effect can be produced by the experiment illustrated in Figure 7.35. The inner tube *a*, placed in liquid helium II contained in a Dewar flask *b*, is filled with fine emery particles which are heated by radiation from a flashlight. This heating causes the liquid helium II to squirt out to a considerable height. Finally, liquid

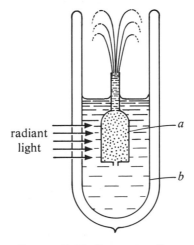

FIGURE 7.35. *Fountain effect.*

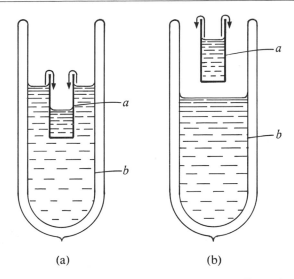

(a)   (b)

FIGURE 7.36. *Creeping film of liquid helium II. (a) Filling. (b) Emptying.*

helium II can form a microscopically thin creeping film and so transfer to a lower level over the brim of a vessel. The inner vessel *a* in Figure 7.36(a) can be filled from the larger container *b*, or emptied into it, as shown in Figure 7.36(b), owing to the formation of such a thin film.

The diagrams in Figure 7.37 show the P, v, θ surface for helium 4 and the corresponding P, v diagram. Line p in the P, v diagram represents the variation of the specific volume of the solid with pressure at zero temperature, whereas line q represents it for liquid helium II; the area for solid-liquid equilibrium lies far above the critical point.

The phase diagram for helium 3 is similar to that for helium 4, except that its critical point is at $P_{cr} = 1.15$ atm and $\theta_{cr} = 3.33°K$; on the other hand, the lowest pressure at which the solid can exist is at $P = 27$ approximately, the exact value being still uncertain. Helium 3 does not undergo the second-order λ transition and does not become superfluid, but mixtures of He^3 and He^4 do.

The very peculiar phase diagram of helium makes it possible to use the vapor-pressure of both helium 3 and helium 4 for the measurement of very low temperatures by the observation of the pressure of boiling helium in a bulb. Two auxiliary temperature scales, one based on He^3 and the other on He^4 have been proposed for international adoption. The He^3 scale, known as T_{62}, extends from $0.2°K$ to $3.324°K$,[†] whereas the He^4 scale, known as T_{58}, extends from $1.0°K$ to $5.2°K$.

7.4.13   *Elementary, reversible processes in pure substances*

A knowledge of the properties of pure substances allows us to study reversible processes in them. In particular, reversible processes at constant pressure, volume, or temperature in closed systems can be easily studied with reference to loci of $P = $ const, $v = $ const, or $\theta = $ const discussed in detail in the various diagrams of this section. It is

[†]This is a more precise value for the critical temperature of He^3 than that quoted previously.

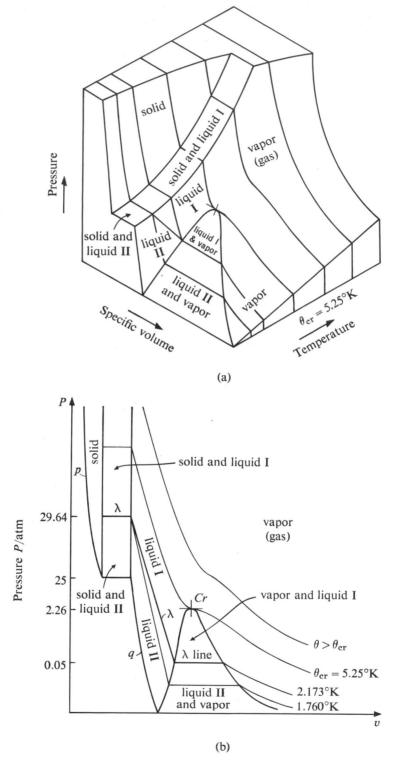

(a)

(b)

FIGURE 7.37. *P, v, θ surface and P, v diagram for helium 4. (Not to scale.)*

seen, however, that the sequence of states can become quite complex when changes in phase may be produced. In this, the number of possible cases is much larger than that which is encountered in the study of similar processes in incompressible fluids or perfect gases. Consequently, it is not possible to provide a general discussion, and it must be realized that each particular problem must be solved on its own. In this connection, it is necessary to bear in mind the general relations between heat and work on the one hand and internal energy and enthalpy on the other, which were derived in Section 5.14. Values of specific internal energy, u, and specific enthalpy, h, are quoted in tables in the form of empirical results. If necessary, lines of constant internal energy or enthalpy can be introduced into the diagrams to facilitate computations. In practice, this is done in special diagrams, and not in the P, v; P, θ; and θ, v diagrams discussed here. We shall devote some time to them in Section 11.2.

When numerical problems are solved with the aid of tables, it is necessary to perform multiple interpolations and the work may become tedious, so much so, that in modern practice digital computers are often resorted to. In order to keep track of possible phase transitions, particularly if two-phase regions or triple points are encountered, it is advisable to follow the calculation on at least a sketch of a diagram, the most suitable diagram depending on the problem in hand. This is necessary, because the extensive specific properties of two-phase systems are not tabulated and must be computed with the aid of the general formula, equation (7.29b).

For example, reference to the P, v diagram (of a normal pure substance) reproduced in Figure 7.38 shows that the details of the isochoric process of cooling a superheated

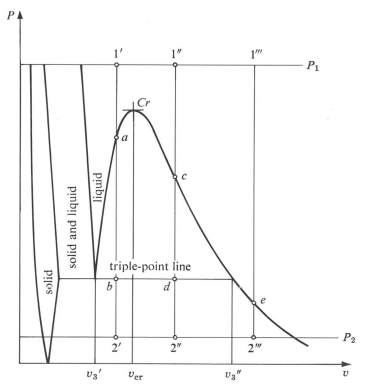

FIGURE 7.38. *Isochoric cooling of superheated vapor.*

vapor from pressure P_1 downwards to a pressure P_2 depend strongly on the numerical value of the specific volume $v = V/m$ which remains constant. When $v_3' < v < v_{cr}$, state 1', the gas will continuously transform into a liquid; it will partly evaporate at a and reach the triple point at b. Subsequent cooling will cause the liquid to disappear, and the final state 2' will consist of a mixture of the solid phase—in the form of ice or snow—and of the vapor. When $v_{cr} < v < v_3''$, state 1'', the vapor will condense at c, and when $v > v_3''$ the vapor will turn into ice or snow at e without going through the liquid phase at all.

As another example, we may consider the P, v diagram of Figure 7.12 together with the two P, θ diagrams, Figure 7.17 for a normal substance and Figure 7.22 for water. From the course of the isotherms we can infer that the details of the process of reversible, isothermal compression of a gas depend on the temperature level at which the process is conducted. If $\theta < \theta_3$, the gas will solidify and the pressure of the solid will increase very rapidly for a very small change in volume if the substance is normal. An anomalous substance will subsequently liquefy, but the final pressure required to achieve it will be very high. If $\theta_3 < \theta < \theta_{cr}$, the gas will liquefy, and the pressure of the liquid will increase rapidly until solidification eventually occurs; however, this will happen only to a normal substance. For $\theta > \theta_{cr}$ the transition from the gas to the liquid is continuous, but a normal substance eventually solidifies. An anomalous substance will not solidify.

The process of reversibly heating a two-phase, liquid-vapor system has been described in Section 7.4.3.

When reversible processes are analyzed in detail, due attention must be paid to the possibility of the emergence of metastable states and of abrupt and irreversible transitions to stable states. However, the details of such processes can become very complex.

Regardless of whether the system remains in a single phase or whether several phases coexist, the *work of a reversible process* is always

$$dW = P\,dV.$$

As in all reversible processes, both P and V in this expression represent properties of the system. However, when metastable states are reached, and abrupt transitions to stable states occur, complications may arise, because the latter are inherently irreversible.

The properties discussed so far do not enable us yet efficiently to study the sequence of states which occur during a reversible, adiabatic process, that is, during an isentropic process, even though the step-by-step procedure outlined in Section 5.14.5 could be followed, albeit laboriously. A more satisfactory method will emerge as a result of the study of the Second Law of thermodynamics, Chapters 9 and 10.

7.4.14   The specific heats of a vapor

It was mentioned in Section 7.3, though not yet proved, that the specific heats of a perfect gas, that is, of a real gas in the extrapolated limit of zero pressure, are functions of temperature alone. Furthermore, the two specific heats were related to each other through equation (7.23). No such simplification exists in the case of a vapor of a pure substance, that is, in the case of a real gas, when both specific heats, c_p and c_v, depend on *two* independent parameters. These are usually chosen as the pressure P and temperature θ.

Figure 7.39 contains the isobars of the specific heat c_p of steam as an illustration. Curve a represents the vapor-pressure line, and the line labeled $P = 0$ bar represents the values c_p^o of c_p extrapolated to $P \to 0$. These are the values which are ascribed to the semiperfect counterpart of a real vapor, Tables XVIa. It is noteworthy that at the critical point $c_p \to \infty$, and that c_v can be calculated from c_p if the thermal equation of state is known, though the relation between c_p and c_v is much more complex than $c_p - c_v = R$ which is valid when $P \to 0$.

All such matters will be gone into more thoroughly in Chapter 12 and Volume II.

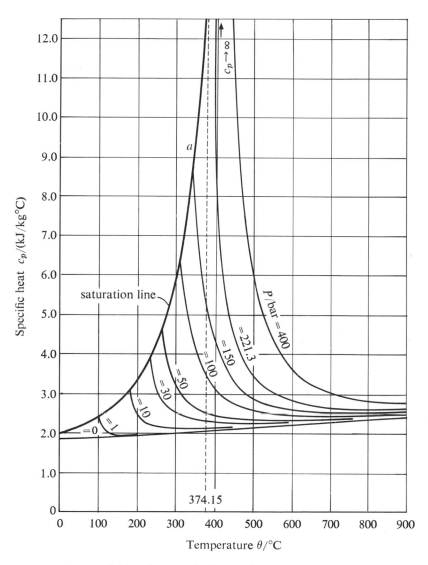

FIGURE 7.39. *The specific heats of water vapor (steam).*

7.5   Mixtures of pure substances; diffusion

When two or more chemically inert substances are allowed to mix, it is found, in general, that in the final equilibrium state, the system separates into several distinct phases, even though the pressure P and the temperature θ are uniform throughout and even though no chemical reaction takes place. For example, if common salt (NaCl) is dissolved in water, and if the mass of the salt exceeds a certain characteristic quantity, the final state will consist of two phases: of a so-called saturated solution of salt in water and of undissolved, solid salt crystals. Two liquids may form three phases: a solution of one liquid in the other and two nearly pure liquid phases. A detailed study of mixtures from this point of view would, obviously, exceed the scope of this course owing to the complexity of the process, even though it properly belongs to the subject of thermodynamics. For this reason, we shall restrict attention to the simplest case when only a single, homogeneous phase exists in the final state.†

Until comparatively recently, it was thought that all gases, regardless of their initial pressure and temperature and regardless of the mass ratio in which they are mixed, always produce a single, mixed phase. Thus, it was thought that even in a complex, heterogeneous system which consists of any number of solid and liquid phases, there can exist at most one gaseous phase. It is now known, however, that this rule is true only in a distinct range of pressures, different for every temperature and composition of the mixture. For example, in the case of binary mixtures of ammonia and nitrogen at 100°C, Figure 7.40, a single phase is formed at pressures which lie below the curve shown in the diagram. The characteristic pressure for a given temperature depends on the composition of the mixture. For each temperature, there exists a characteristic composition, point K, for which the highest pressure when a single, gaseous phase is formed is a minimum. When an attempt is made to adjust the state to a point above the curve, for example, to 5000 atm and 50% NH_3 at 100°C, the system separates into two *gaseous* phases. One gaseous phase has a composition corresponding to point a, and the other has a composition corresponding to point b. The mass ratio of these two phases is such as to secure an average composition which corresponds to the initial proportions of the components. In general, the limiting pressures of the single-phase range of states are quite high. The preceding typical example shows that at any temperature, and for any gaseous mixture, there exists a wide range of pressures over which heterogeneous systems display a single gaseous phase. We shall now confine our attention to these simple cases.

When the mixture of pure substances exists in a single phase, it is desirable to develop methods for the calculation of the thermodynamic properties of the mixture in terms of the thermodynamic properties of the components, each taken at the temperature θ and the pressure P of the mixture. At the present time, no such general methods exist, except for two very simple classes of mixtures: mixtures of gases at low enough pressures, when the gases can be considered to be perfect, and very dilute solutions of solids, liquids, or gases in a liquid or a solid.

† More extensive studies of mixtures can be found in books on chemical thermodynamics. For example, the following references may be consulted: Prigogine, I., in collaboration with Bellemans, A., and Mathot, V., *The Molecular Theory of Solutions* (Amsterdam: North-Holland, 1957); Kirillin, V. A., and Sheindlin, A. E., *Termodinamika rastvorov* (Gosenergeozdat, 1956) (English translation by Pelech, I., to be published by Blaisdell); Prigogine, I., and Defay, R., *Chemical Thermodynamics*, translated by D. H. Everett (London: Longmans, 1954).

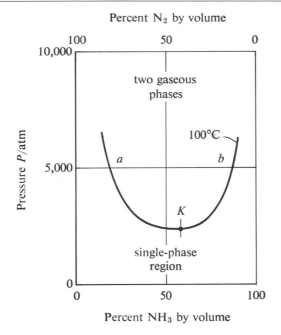

FIGURE 7.40. *Single-phase region for mixtures of* N_2 *and* NH_3 *at 100°C.*

Before we can establish these methods, it is necessary to understand the process of mixing in physical terms, and we must begin the description by first establishing a quantitative measure of composition.

7.5.1   Measures of composition

It is clear that the state of a mixture is not described completely by indicating its pressure P and temperature θ alone, because mixtures can differ with respect to their composition. There exist in use several quantitative measures of composition, and it is useful to understand the relations between them.

Probably the most convenient measure of composition is related to the numbers of mols $n_1, \ldots, n_\alpha$ of the α components in a mixture. Since only mixtures of chemically inert substances are considered, the numbers of mols are preserved, and the relative amount of each component can be defined by indicating the ratio

$$x_i = \frac{n_i}{\sum\limits_{\alpha} n_i} = \frac{n_i}{n} \tag{7.42}$$

of the number of mols n_i of each component to the total number of mols

$$n = \sum_{\alpha} n_i. \tag{7.43}$$

Evidently,

$$\sum_{\alpha} x_i = 1. \tag{7.44}$$

The ratio x_i is known as the *mol fraction*, and a list of values of x_i for a mixture is known as its *molar composition*. The mol fraction constitutes an intensive property of the mixture, and it is noted that only $\alpha - 1$ of the α ratios can be prescribed independently, because their sum is always equal to unity.

An alternative description consists in indicating the ratios

$$\mu_i = \frac{m_i}{\sum\limits_{\alpha} m_i} = \frac{m_i}{m} \qquad (m = \sum\limits_{\alpha} m_i) \tag{7.45}$$

of the mass of each component to the total mass of the mixture. These ratios are known as *mass fractions*. Evidently,

$$\sum\limits_{\alpha} \mu_i = 1. \tag{7.46}$$

There is no difficulty in indicating the relation between the molar and mass fractions. Since

$$m_i = n_i M_i,$$

where M_i is the molecular mass of component i, we can write

$$\mu_i = \frac{n_i M_i}{\sum\limits_{\alpha} n_i M_i} = \frac{(n_i/n) M_i}{\sum\limits_{\alpha} (n_i/n) M_i} = \frac{x_i M_i}{\sum\limits_{\alpha} x_i M_i}. \tag{7.47}$$

Conversely,

$$x_i = \frac{n_i}{\sum\limits_{\alpha} n_i} = \frac{m_i/M_i}{\sum\limits_{\alpha} m_i/M_i} = \frac{(m_i/m)/M_i}{\sum\limits_{\alpha} (m_i/m)/M_i} = \frac{\mu_i/M_i}{\sum\limits_{\alpha} \mu_i/M_i}. \tag{7.48}$$

The average mass of a mixture taken per one mol of mixture is known as the (apparent or average) molecular mass M of the mixture. Thus,

$$M = \frac{m}{n} \quad \text{with} \quad m = \sum\limits_{\alpha} m_i \quad \text{and} \quad n = \sum\limits_{\alpha} n_i.$$

Hence,

$$M = \frac{\sum\limits_{\alpha} n_i M_i}{n} = \sum\limits_{\alpha} x_i M_i. \tag{7.49}$$

Two slightly different measures of composition are used in the study of solutions. The *molar concentration* of a solute in a liquid solvent is defined as the ratio

$$c_i = \frac{n_i}{V} \tag{7.50}$$

of the number of mols n_i of the solute to the total volume of the solution. The *molality* (for which we shall also use the symbol μ) of a solution is defined as the number of mols of a solute dissolved in 1 kilogram† of the solvent. Denoting the solvent (usually water) by subscript 1, we see that its volume $V = n_1 M_1/\rho$, where ρ is the density in kg/liter. Hence,

$$\mu_i = \frac{n_i}{n_1 M_1} = \frac{x_i}{x_1 M_1}. \tag{7.51}$$

†Some authors refer molality to 1 liter of solvent; if water is the solvent, 1 liter has, approximately, the mass of 1 kg, and the two definitions are equivalent numerically.

When discussing solutions of solids in water, it must be remembered that in electrolytes the solid (usually a salt) dissociates into positive and negative ions of characteristic valence, so that the number of mols of solute in the solution need not be the same as before the substance has been dissolved, in the same way as in the presence of a chemical reaction.

7.5.2   Isothermal-isobaric mixing

In the absence of nuclear reactions, the mass of a mixture remains equal to the sum of the masses of its components. In the further absence of chemical reactions, the number of mols of a mixture is equal to the sum of the numbers of mols of its components. However, no such conservation laws apply to volumes, pressures or any other thermodynamic properties.

In order to see this more clearly, we revert to the discussion of the process of adiabatic mixing contained in Section 6.13, except that we shall concentrate on the more important case of mixing at constant pressure and temperature. For the sake of simplicity, we consider two gases 1 and 2 at a specified initial state, both gases being under the same initial pressure P and temperature θ, Figure 7.41, realizing, however, that the ensuing remarks apply to all homogeneous mixtures. In the initial state a, the gases are separated by a diathermal wall and retain their separate identities. We shall use subscripts 1 and 2 (or, generally, $1, 2, \ldots, i, \ldots, \alpha$) to distinguish between the quantities relating to the two gases, the parameters at the initial state being written without superscripts, and without subscripts when they have common values for both gases. At a certain instant, the slide is removed and the gases are allowed to mix, the process whereby one gas spreads over the volume first occupied by the other gas alone being known as *diffusion*. Eventually, at state b, the two gases will form a homogeneous phase in equilibrium, and the process $a \rightarrow b$ is clearly seen to be irreversible, because the reverse process of gas separation cannot occur spontaneously under the circumstances.

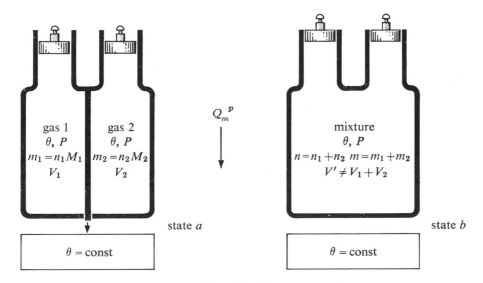

FIGURE 7.41. *Isothermal-isobaric mixing of gases.*

At the final equilibrium state b there exists a homogeneous mixture of gases at pressure P, at temperature θ, and of a predetermined composition given by $x_1 = n_1/n$ and $x_2 = n_2/n$ with $x_1 + x_2 = 1$. During the process of diffusion the system absorbs a quantity of heat $-Q_m^p$ from the infinite reservoir at $\theta = $ const, it being recalled that Q_m^p represents the heat of mixing at constant pressure. Experiments show, as already mentioned, that generally all extensive properties (denoted with a prime at state b) change their values, and that only the mass and number of mols is conserved. In particular, the volume V' ceases to be equal to the initial volume $V = V_1 + V_2$. The resulting change in volume must be determined experimentally as a function of composition for all possible mixtures of gases. The First Law allows us to write the relation between enthalpies in the form

$$(H_1 + H_2) - H' = Q_m^p, \tag{7.52}$$

but in it, too, the heat of mixing must be known from experiment as a function of composition for all possible mixtures of gases.

Similar circumstances prevail when diffusion occurs isothermally but at constant volume, and the reader should experience no difficulty in describing the latter process from a knowledge of the isothermal-isobaric process of mixing on which our attention will continue to be concentrated.

Although the exact relation between the value of an extensive property of a mixture and those of the separated components at the same pressure and temperature must be determined by direct experiment, as already stated, the *mathematical form* of this relation is not quite arbitrary. This is due to the fact that the extensive property of the mixture, for example, its volume, is a function of the numbers of mols n_1 and n_2 of its components

$$V = V(n_1, n_2, P, \theta). \tag{7.53}$$

Now, if the numbers of mols n_1 and n_2 are simultaneously increased by a common factor, say λ, *at constant pressure and temperature*, the total volume must increase in the same ratio. The same is true of any extensive property regardless of the number of pure components. This can be written

$$V(\lambda n_1, \lambda n_2) = \lambda V \qquad \text{at } P = \text{const}, \theta = \text{const}. \tag{7.54}$$

A function of several variables which possesses the property (7.54) *identically* is known in mathematics as a homogeneous function, and its properties are governed by an important theorem due to L. Euler. We must, therefore, pause to derive Euler's theorem on homogeneous functions for the reader's ease of reference.

7.5.3   *Euler's theorem on homogeneous functions*

A function

$$y = f(x_1, \ldots, x_\alpha) \tag{a}$$

of α variables x_i is called homogeneous of degree m if it possesses the property that the value of the function, y, increases by a factor λ^m when each variable x_i is multiplied by an arbitrary factor λ. In other words, a homogeneous function of order m in the α variables x satisfies the *identity*

$$f(\lambda x_1, \lambda x_2, \ldots, \lambda x_\alpha) \equiv \lambda^m y, \tag{b}$$

for any factor λ. Taking the derivative of both sides of equation (b) with respect to the parameter λ, we obtain a second identity:

$$m\lambda^{m-1}y \equiv \frac{\partial f}{\partial(\lambda x_1)}x_1 + \frac{\partial f}{\partial(\lambda x_2)}x_2 + \cdots + \frac{\partial f}{\partial(\lambda x_\alpha)}x_\alpha.$$

The last identity is true for any value of λ, hence, it must also be true for $\lambda = 1$. With this substitution, we obtain

$$my \equiv \frac{\partial f}{\partial x_1}x_1 + \frac{\partial f}{\partial x_2}x_2 + \cdots + \frac{\partial f}{\partial x_n}x_n,$$

or

$$\sum_\alpha \frac{\partial f}{\partial x_i}x_i \equiv my. \tag{c}$$

In thermodynamics we shall be interested in two particular cases. The first case concerns extensive properties, like the volume in equation (7.54) which are of degree $m = 1$. For such functions, equation (c) assumes the special form

$$y \equiv \sum_\alpha x_i \frac{\partial f}{\partial x_i}, \tag{d}$$

which relates the function $y(x_1, \ldots, x_\alpha)$ to its α partial derivatives. The converse of the preceding reasoning is also true,[†] and it is possible to assert that any function which satisfies equation (d) must be homogeneous of first degree.

The second important, particular case concerns intensive properties whose values must not change when the numbers of mols are changed by a common factor λ. Thus, intensive properties must be homogeneous functions of degree zero. For them, the identity (c) takes the form

$$\sum_\alpha x_i \frac{\partial f}{\partial x_i} \equiv 0. \tag{e}$$

Conversely, any function whose derivatives satisfy identity (e) is homogeneous of degree zero in the variables $x_1, \ldots, x_\alpha$, and the function itself possesses the property

$$y = f(x_1, \ldots, x_\alpha) = f(\lambda x_1, \ldots, \lambda x_\alpha) \tag{f}$$

identically.

Naturally, a homogeneous function of several variables x_i may be homogeneous with respect to a reduced number of them only.

7.5.4 *Partial specific quantities of a mixture*

Application of Euler's theorem to the volume of a binary mixture at $P = $ const, $V = $ const shows that it must be of the form

$$V = n_1\left(\frac{\partial V}{\partial n_1}\right)_{n_2,\theta,P} + n_2\left(\frac{\partial V}{\partial n_2}\right)_{n_1,\theta,P} \qquad (\text{at } \theta = \text{const, } P = \text{const}). \tag{7.55}$$

The partial derivatives

$$v_1(n_1, n_2, \theta, P) = \left(\frac{\partial V}{\partial n_1}\right)_{n_2,\theta,P} \quad \text{and} \quad v_2(n_1, n_2, \theta, P) = \left(\frac{\partial V}{\partial n_2}\right)_{n_1,\theta,P} \tag{7.55a}$$

which are, in principle, functions of the same variables as the volume itself, are known as the partial, molar volumes of the components in the mixture at the given pressure

[†] See, for example, Apostol, T. M., *Calculus* (Blaisdell, 1962), II, p. 180; Courant, R., *Differential and Integral Calculus* (London: Blackie, 1936), II, p. 109.

and temperature. They are intensive properties, because their value does not change when the mol numbers n_1 and n_2 are multiplied by a factor λ. Indeed, since V becomes multiplied by the same factor, we must have

$$v_1 = \left(\frac{\partial(\lambda V)}{\partial(\lambda n_1)}\right)_{n_2,\theta,P} = \left(\frac{\partial V}{\partial n_1}\right)_{n_2,\theta,P},$$

and identically for v_2.

With this notation

$$V = n_1 v_1 + n_2 v_2; \tag{7.56}$$

introducing the mean specific volume per mol of mixture $v = V/n$, we can also write

$$v = x_1 v_1 + x_2 v_2. \tag{7.56a}$$

Partial quantities could equally well be defined with respect to the mass of the mixture, for example,

$$v_1 = \left(\frac{\partial V}{\partial m_1}\right)_{m_2,\theta,P},$$

and so on, so that

$$V = m_1 v_1 + m_2 v_2 \quad \text{and} \quad v = \mu_1 v_1 + \mu_2 v_2,$$

remembering that the numerical values of v, v_1, and v_2 have changed on changing units. Since the mol proves to be a more convenient unit in the study of mixtures, and since the translation of equations from mol units to mass units is very simple, we shall discontinue rewriting our equations in the alternative form from now on.

Generally with α components

$$v_i = \left(\frac{\partial V}{\partial n_i}\right)_{n_j,\theta,P}, \tag{7.57}$$

where the subscript n_j serves as a reminder that all mol numbers, except n_i, are kept constant. Similarly,

$$V = \sum_\alpha n_i v_i \quad \text{and} \quad v = \sum_\alpha x_i v_i. \tag{7.58a, b}$$

In fact, the preceding definitions carry over to any extensive property Φ, and the related molar specific property is

$$\phi_i = \left(\frac{\partial \Phi}{\partial n_i}\right)_{n_j,\theta,P}, \tag{7.59}$$

with

$$\Phi = \sum_\alpha n_i \phi_i \quad \text{or} \quad \phi = \sum_\alpha x_i \phi_i. \tag{7.60a, b}$$

The partial quantities (per mol or unit mass) are not independent of each other. In a binary mixture

$$\left(\frac{\partial v_1}{\partial n_2}\right)_{\theta,P} = \left(\frac{\partial^2 V}{\partial n_1 \partial n_2}\right)_{\theta,P}.$$

Making use of the fact that the order of forming the second derivative is immaterial, it is seen that the two partial volumes satisfy the *reciprocal relation*

$$\left(\frac{\partial v_1}{\partial n_2}\right)_{\theta,P} = \left(\frac{\partial v_2}{\partial n_1}\right)_{\theta,P}. \tag{7.61}$$

Upon dividing by $n = n_1 + n_2$, it is seen that, similarly

$$\left(\frac{\partial v_1}{\partial x_2}\right)_{\theta,P} = \left(\frac{\partial v_2}{\partial x_1}\right)_{\theta,P}. \tag{7.61a}$$

Furthermore, from the fact that the specific properties are intensive, that is, homogeneous of degree zero in the mol numbers, it follows that identity (e) in Section 7.4.3 must be satisfied. Hence, for v_1, it is possible to write

$$n_1\left(\frac{\partial v_1}{\partial n_1}\right)_{\theta,P} + n_2\left(\frac{\partial v_1}{\partial n_2}\right)_{\theta,P} = 0, \tag{7.61b}$$

or, in view of equation (7.61),

$$n_1\left(\frac{\partial v_1}{\partial n_1}\right)_{\theta,P} + n_2\left(\frac{\partial v_2}{\partial n_1}\right)_{\theta,P} = 0, \tag{7.61c}$$

that is,

$$x_1\left(\frac{\partial v_1}{\partial x_1}\right)_{\theta,P} + x_2\left(\frac{\partial v_1}{\partial x_2}\right)_{\theta,P} = x_1\left(\frac{\partial v_1}{\partial x_1}\right)_{\theta,P} + x_2\left(\frac{\partial v_2}{\partial x_1}\right)_{\theta,P} = 0. \tag{7.62a, b}$$

In general, for any specific properties ϕ_i and ϕ_j

$$\sum_{\alpha} n_i\left(\frac{\partial \phi_i}{\partial n_j}\right)_{\theta,P} = \sum_{\alpha} n_i\left(\frac{\partial \phi_j}{\partial n_i}\right)_{\theta,P} = 0, \tag{7.63}$$

or

$$\sum_{\alpha} x_i\left(\frac{\partial \phi_i}{\partial x_j}\right)_{\theta,P} = \sum_{\alpha} x_i\left(\frac{\partial \phi_j}{\partial x_i}\right)_{\theta,P} = 0. \tag{7.63a}$$

7.5.5 *Partial specific properties and specific properties of the pure components*

As already mentioned, the variation of the value of an extensive (or specific) property with composition must be determined experimentally. The schematic diagram in Figure 7.42 represents the variation of the molar specific volume v of a binary mixture on the molar fractions x_1 and x_2 of its components at a particular pressure P and temperature θ. Since $x_1 + x_2 = 1$, the scale for x_1 is shown varying from 0 to 1 at the bottom of the diagram, and the scale for x_2 is shown drawn in the opposite direction at the top of the diagram.

At $x_1 = 0$, $v = v_2^0$ and at $x_2 = 0$ we have $v = v_1^0$. Thus, v_1^0 and v_2^0 represent the molar specific volumes of the pure components at pressure P and temperature T and correspond to state a in Figure 7.41. Noting in Figure 7.42 that

$$\frac{\overline{C'C''}}{x_1} = \frac{\overline{BB''}}{1},$$

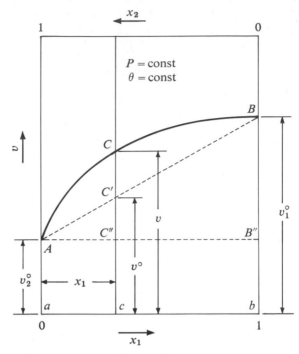

FIGURE 7.42. *Schematic diagram of specific volume v of a binary mixture.*

we can easily compute the abscissa $\overline{C'C}$ which we shall denote by v^0. Since $\overline{C'C''} = v^0 - v_2^0$, we have

$$\frac{v^0 - v_2^0}{x_1} = v_1^0 - v_2^0,$$

or

$$v^0 = x_1 v_1^0 + x_2 v_2^0. \tag{7.64}$$

This expression is identical in form with equation (7.56a), and the comparison confirms that the partial molar specific volumes v_1 and v_2 of the components in the mixture differ from the molar specific volumes of the separated components at the same pressure and temperature. In actual fact, for most mixtures, as shown on the diagram, the specific volume increases upon mixing since $v > v^0$. However, there exist solutions which contract upon mixing; a dilute solution of magnesium sulphate (MgSO₄) in water possesses this property.

If no contraction or expansion occurred during mixing, the diagram of molar specific volume *versus* composition would be represented by the straight line $AC'B$ in Figure 7.42, and the partial volumes v_1 and v_2 would become equal to the volumes v_1^0 and v_2^0 of the pure components, respectively. Under such conditions, the volume of the mixture of two components would be equal to the sum of the volumes of the separated components at the same pressure and temperature. When components mix in accordance with this, exceptional, rule, we say that they satisfy the *Amagat-Leduc law of mixing*.

In general, when the diagram of the variation of a specific property ϕ *versus* composition departs from a straight line, the molar specific properties differ from the specific properties of the separated components at the same pressure and temperature. Reciprocally, the value of the extensive property for the mixture differs from the sum of the values of the extensive properties of the separated components taken in proportion to their mol numbers.

7.5.6 *The Bakhuis-Rooseboom rule*

In a binary mixture, it is possible to represent the partial molar properties at a given composition, characterized by the mol fractions x_1 and x_2 ($x_1 + x_2 = 1$), with the aid of a very simple construction known as the Bakhuis-Rooseboom rule. The construction is shown in Figure 7.43 for specific volume. If a tangent is drawn at an arbitrary point $C(x_1, x_2)$, it will intercept a segment v_1 on the axis $x_1 = 1(x_2 = 0)$ as well as a segment v_2 on the axis $x_2 = 1(x_1 = 0)$. This property of the diagram hinges on the fact that the rates of change of the partial, molar specific properties with composition are not independent of each other as well as on the fact that $v = \overline{Cc}$ in Figure 7.43 satisfies equation (7.56) for the same geometrical reasons as v^0 satisfies equation (7.64) in Figure 7.42.

The required relation in our present case can be obtained by differentiating the specific volume

$$v = x_1 v_1 + x_2 v_2 = x_1 v_1 + (1 - x_1) v_2$$

with respect to x_1. This gives

$$\left(\frac{\partial v}{\partial x_1}\right)_{\theta,P} = x_1 \left(\frac{\partial v_1}{\partial x_1}\right)_{\theta,P} + v_1 + \left(\frac{\partial v_2}{\partial x_1}\right)_{\theta,P} - v_2 - x_1 \left(\frac{\partial v_2}{\partial x_1}\right)_{\theta,P}.$$

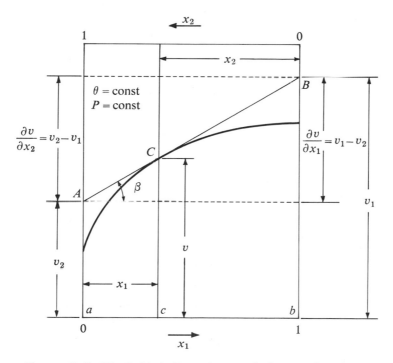

FIGURE 7.43. *The Bakhuis-Rooseboom rule for specific volume.*

Remembering that $x_1 + x_2 = 1$ and taking into account equation (7.62) we obtain simply

$$\left(\frac{\partial v}{\partial x_1}\right)_{\theta,P} = v_1 - v_2. \tag{7.65}$$

Since $x_2 = 1 - x_1$, and by symmetry, we must also have

$$\left(\frac{\partial v}{\partial x_2}\right)_{\theta,P} = v_2 - v_1 = -\left(\frac{\partial v}{\partial x_1}\right)_{\theta,P}. \tag{7.66}$$

This expression allows us to calculate the intercepts $\overline{Aa}$ and $\overline{Bb}$ in Figure 7.43 directly. Owing to symmetry, it is sufficient to calculate $\overline{Aa}$. Since

$$\frac{\overline{Cc} - \overline{Aa}}{x_1} = \tan \beta = \left(\frac{\partial v}{\partial x_1}\right)_{\theta,P},$$

we can conclude that

$$\overline{Aa} = \overline{Cc} - x_1\left(\frac{\partial v}{\partial x_1}\right)_{\theta,P}$$

$$= v - x_1(v_1 - v_2) = x_1 v_1 + x_2 v_2 - x_1 v_1 + x_1 v_2 = (x_1 + x_2)v_2 = v_2.$$

Similarly, we could prove that $\overline{Bb} = v_1$.

7.5.7 The Gibbs-Duhem-Margules relation

Equation (7.63) constitutes a particular case of a more general relation which is valid for all extensive properties and which is known as the Gibbs-Duhem-Margules relation; it is a direct consequence of the fact that every extensive property Φ must be a homogeneous function of order one of the mol numbers n_i at $\theta = $ const and $P = $ const. Taking the total derivative of equation (7.60a), we obtain

$$d\Phi = \sum_\alpha \phi_i dn_i + \sum n_i d\phi_i \qquad (\theta = \text{const}, P = \text{const}). \tag{7.67}$$

On the other hand, the direct total differential of the function $\Phi = \Phi(\theta, P, n_1, \ldots, n_\alpha)$ is

$$d\Phi = \sum_\alpha \left(\frac{\partial \Phi}{\partial n_i}\right)_{n_j,\theta,P} dn_i = \sum_\alpha \phi_i dn_i \qquad (\theta = \text{const}, P = \text{const}). \tag{7.68}$$

Upon comparing equations (7.67) and (7.68), we derive the desired relation in the form

$$\sum_\alpha n_i d\phi_i = 0. \tag{7.69}$$

Equations (7.63) and (7.63a) can be derived from it without difficulty.

7.5.8 Ideal mixtures

The considerations of the preceding sections have demonstrated the complex nature of the relations between the properties of mixtures and their separated components. Nevertheless, as announced in the introductory section, mixtures of low-density gases as well as highly dilute solutions of solid, liquids, or gases in a liquid or solid obey very simple relations.

The heat of mixing of gases is generally extremely low. As the pressure P of mixing is made smaller and smaller, the heat of mixing Q_m^p vanishes in the limit. Furthermore, in the same limit, the Amagat-Leduc law is satisfied more and more closely, and the partial specific volumes become equal to the specific volumes of the separated components; the diagram of specific volume v *versus* composition for a binary mixture becomes a straight line, Figure 7.44. Simultaneously, the thermal equation of the component tends to the very simple limit of a perfect gas, $Pv = \mathbf{R}\theta$. These three circumstances simplify matters to such an extent that a complete theory becomes possible.

Similar circumstances exist in the case of *dilute solutions* when the amount of solvent (n_1) is very large compared with the amount of any solute ($n_2, \ldots, n_\alpha$):

$$n_2 \ll n_1, \ldots, n_\alpha \ll n_1. \tag{7.70}$$

Any extensive property is a homogeneous function of first degree of the form

$$\Phi = \Phi(n_1, n_2, \ldots, n_\alpha, \theta, P),$$

or, dividing by n_1,

$$\Phi = n_1 \Phi\left(\frac{n_2}{n_1}, \frac{n_3}{n_1}, \ldots, \frac{n_\alpha}{n_1}, \theta, P\right).$$

Developing this expression in a power series in the ratios n_2/n_1 and so on, we obtain

$$\Phi = \Phi_1(\theta, P) + \frac{n_2}{n_1} \Phi_2(\theta, P) + \cdots + \frac{n_\alpha}{n_1} \Phi_\alpha(\theta, P),$$

when terms of higher order are neglected.

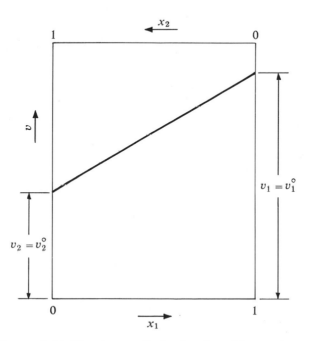

FIGURE 7.44. *The Amagat-Leduc law for a binary mixture.*

The first term, Φ_1, represents the value of the extensive parameter for the solvent, whereas the much smaller terms $(n_i/n_1)\Phi_i(\theta, P)$ represent the proportionate values of the extensive property Φ of the solutes at pressure P and temperature θ before mixing. Thus,

$$\Phi = \Phi_1(\theta, P) + \sum_2^\alpha \frac{n_i}{n_1} \Phi_i(\theta, P).$$ (7.71)

In particular, the volume of the solution of a single component, say, in water, is

$$V = V_1(\theta, P) + \frac{n_2}{n_1} V_2(\theta, P).$$

The ratios n_2/n_1 and so on are closely related to the mol fractions. Since

$$n = n_1 + \sum_2^\alpha n_i,$$

we have

$$x_i = \frac{n_i}{n_1 + \sum_2^\alpha n_i} \approx \frac{n_i}{n_1} \quad \text{if } \sum_2^\alpha n_i \ll n_1.$$ (7.71a)

Thus, the theory of dilute solutions is very close to the theory of mixtures of inert perfect gases. Owing to its importance in engineering applications, we shall now concentrate on the theory of gaseous mixtures.

7.5.9   *Mixtures of inert perfect gases. Dalton's law*

When two low-density gases are mixed at constant pressure and temperature in a manner illustrated in Figure 7.41, the total volume remains unchanged and no heat is exchanged. Conversely, if two gases were allowed to diffuse through each other adiabatically at constant total volume in an arrangement shown schematically in Figure 7.45, the final state *b* would be identical with the final state *b* from Figure 7.41, provided that the initial state were the same.

The Amagat-Leduc (empirical) law leads to the immediate conclusion that an ideal mixture of inert perfect gases must also obey the perfect-gas law. The thermal equations

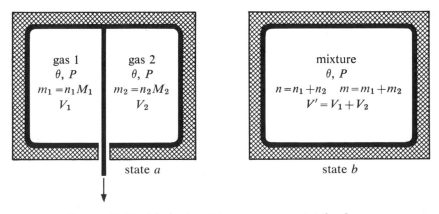

FIGURE 7.45. *Adiabatic mixing at constant total volume.*

of state for the two components will be, respectively,

$$PV_1 = n_1\mathbf{R}\theta,$$
$$PV_2 = n_2\mathbf{R}\theta,$$

and their sum

$$P(V_1 + V_2) = (n_1 + n_2)\mathbf{R}\theta$$

assumes the perfect-gas-law form for the mixture

$$PV = n\mathbf{R}\theta, \tag{7.72}$$

in view of the conservation laws $V_1 + V_2 = V$ and $n_1 + n_2 = n$. It is instructive to write the same equations in terms of mass units:

$$PV_1 = m_1R_1\theta,$$
$$PV_2 = m_2R_2\theta,$$

adding up to

$$PV = (m_1R_1 + m_2R_2)\theta. \tag{7.72a}$$

The factor of θ can be represented as

$$mR = m_1R_1 + m_2R_2,$$

showing that

$$R = \mu_1R_1 + \mu_2R_2 \tag{7.72b}$$

can be taken to represent the gas constant of the mixture in mass units. For α components

$$R = \sum_1^\alpha \mu_iR_i, \tag{7.72c}$$

and the equation of state of the mixture is

$$PV = mR\theta. \tag{7.73}$$

A comparison of equations (7.72) and (7.73) shows that

$$n\mathbf{R} = mR,$$

and since $m = nM$, equation (7.49), we have

$$R = \frac{\mathbf{R}}{M} = \frac{\mathbf{R}}{\Sigma x_iM_i} \tag{7.74}$$

for a mixture as well as for a pure component.

It is now instructive to compare the mixture of gases with a composite system consisting of the components imagined expanded singly into the total volume V and at the common temperature θ. The components will, obviously, assume different pressures, P_1 and P_2, respectively, which are known as the *partial pressures* of the components in the mixture, Figure 7.46. From the equations of state of the components

$$P_1V = n_1\mathbf{R}\theta,$$
$$P_2V = n_2\mathbf{R}\theta,$$

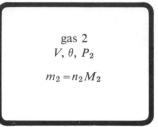

gas 1
V, θ, P_1

$m_1 = n_1 M_1$

gas 2
V, θ, P_2

$m_2 = n_2 M_2$

FIGURE 7.46. *Dalton's law of partial pressures.*

we can deduce by addition that

$$(P_1 + P_2)V = (n_1 + n_2)\mathbf{R}\theta. \tag{7.75}$$

On comparing this equation with equation (7.72), we conclude that the *total pressure P* of the mixture is equal to the sum of the partial pressures of its components. When α components are present

$$P = \sum_1^{\alpha} P_i. \tag{7.75a}$$

The additivity of partial pressures on mixing was first discovered by J. Dalton and is known as *Dalton's law* (of partial pressures).

The preceding derivation has shown that Dalton's law is a consequence of the Amagat-Leduc law when the validity of the perfect-gas law can also be assumed. Reciprocally, assuming the validity of Dalton's law (instead of the Amagat-Leduc law as we have done here), we would be led to the latter, again provided that the perfect-gas law is applicable. Thus, the two empirical statements express an identical physical fact when applied to perfect gases.

When gases are mixed under conditions under which their equations of state depart materially from the perfect-gas law, neither of the two laws are satisfied with good precision. An analysis of available experimental material† reveals that mixtures at high pressures frequently obey one or the other law of mixing. For example, mixtures of methane and nitrogen or of oxygen and argon conform approximately to the law of additive volumes of Amagat-Leduc. On the other hand, mixtures of argon and ethylene more nearly approximate Dalton's law of additive partial pressures. The difficulty in handling mixtures of high density turns on the circumstance that it is not known beforehand which of the two empirical laws will provide a better approximation. This can only be determined by experiment, but when the results are available, there is no need to make use of a law of mixing any more.

In engineering practice, the composition of gaseous mixtures is frequently specified by indicating the ratios

$$\nu_i = \frac{V_i}{V} \qquad (\sum_1^{\alpha} \nu_i = 1) \tag{7.76}$$

of the volumes of the separated components, measured at the temperature θ and the

---

† Newitt, D. M., *The Design of High Pressure Plant and the Properties of Fluids at High Pressures* (Oxford: Clarendon, 1940), p. 226.

total pressure P, which are known as *parts by volume*. The complete specification of the parts by volume is known as the *volumetric composition* of the gas. Since

$$PV_i = n_i \mathbf{R}\theta$$

and

$$PV = n\mathbf{R}\theta,$$

it follows that

$$\nu_i = \frac{V_i}{V} = \frac{n_i}{n} = x_i. \tag{7.77}$$

Thus, the parts by volume are identical with mol fractions, but only for perfect gases, that is, for real gases at very low densities.

Recalling that

$$P_i V = n_i \mathbf{R}\theta,$$

it is easy to show that

$$x_i = \frac{P_i}{P}, \tag{7.78}$$

under the same restrictions.

Since low-density gases mix without a heat of mixing, we conclude that for a mixture

$$\left. \begin{aligned} u &= \sum_{1}^{\alpha} \mu_i u_i \quad \text{or} \quad u = \sum_{1}^{\alpha} x_i u_i, \\ h &= \sum_{1}^{\alpha} \mu_i h_i \quad \text{or} \quad h = \sum_{1}^{\alpha} x_i h_i, \\ c_v &= \sum_{1}^{\alpha} \mu_i c_{v,i} \quad \text{or} \quad c_v = \sum_{1}^{\alpha} x_i c_{v,i}, \\ c_p &= \sum_{1}^{\alpha} \mu_i c_{p,i} \quad \text{or} \quad c_p = \sum_{1}^{\alpha} x_i c_{p,i}, \end{aligned} \right\} \tag{7.79}$$

depending on whether mass or molar units are used. However,

$$\gamma \neq \Sigma \mu_i \gamma_i \quad \text{or} \quad \Sigma x_i \gamma_i.$$

Mixtures of high-density gases deviate from these relations, but, as stated on several occasions, precise experimental data on their behavior are scarce.

List of Symbols for Chapter 7

Latin letters

A Constant
B Constant
C Constant
c Specific heat; molar concentration
c_p Specific heat at constant pressure

c_v	Specific heat at constant volume
E	Energy
E_k	Kinetic energy
E_p	Potential energy
f	Number of independent intensive properties, equation (7.25) (number of degrees of freedom)
F_e	External force
G	Weight
g	Gravitational acceleration
H	Enthalpy
h	Specific enthalpy
l	Latent heat of evaporation
l_m	Latent heat of melting or fusion
l_s	Latent heat of sublimation
m	Mass; order of homogeneous function, equation (a) on p. 326
n	Number of mols; refractive index
P	Pressure
p	Momentum
Q	Heat
Q_m^p	Heat of mixing at constant pressure
R	Universal gas constant
r	Displacement vector
T	Temperature
u	Specific internal energy
V	Volume
v	Specific volume
v°	Partial specific volume, equation (7.64)
$\mathcal{V}$	Velocity vector
W	Work
W_a	Work of the atmosphere
x	Coordinate; dryness fraction; mol fraction; variable, equation (a) on p. 326
y	Coordinate; function, equation (a) on p. 326
z	Coordinate

Greek letters

α	Number of pure components, equation (7.25); number of variables, equation (a) on p. 326
β	Number of phases, equation (7.25); coefficient of (volume) expansion
γ	Ratio of specific heats $(= c_p/c_v)$
θ	Temperature
θ_m	Melting temperature
κ	Isothermal coefficient of compressibility
λ	Factor in equation (7.54)
μ	Mass fraction; molality
ν	Parts by volume
π	Coefficient of tension
ρ	Density

Φ	General extensive property
ϕ	General molar specific property
$\phi^{(e)}$	Vapor-pressure curve, equation (7.25)
$\phi^{(m)}$	Melting curve, equation (7.32)
$\phi^{(s)}$	Sublimation curve, equation (7.35)

Marks over letters

$-$	Average value of respective quantity
$\cdot$	Time rate of change of respective quantity

Superscripts

$'$	Refers to liquid phase
$''$	Refers to vapor phase
$'''$	Refers to solid phase
0	Refers to pure component in mixture

Subscripts

cr	Refers to the critical point
max	Maximum value
3	Refers to the triple point

CHAPTER **8**

Thermodynamic Systems II

8.1 Surface tension†

We have stated in Section 7.4 that the thermodynamic properties of a multiphase system change discontinuously on crossing the phase boundary. Observation confirms that a clearly discernible phase boundary is always present and that it can be thought of as a mathematical surface of discontinuity in the majority of problems. However, on closer examination it is found that the transition from the properties of one phase, say, a liquid, to those of another, say, a vapor, is continuous and takes place over a finite, but extremely small thickness. This circumstance is illustrated in Figure 8.1 which shows that a representative thermodynamic property ϕ has the constant value ϕ' over the bulk of the liquid and changes continuously to the value ϕ'' over a layer of thickness δ. Experiments show that the change from ϕ' to ϕ'' is extremely rapid over a distance δ which is of the order of 10^{-6} or 10^{-7} cm and which is, therefore, of a magnitude comparable with molecular dimensions.

8.1.1 Microscopic origin of surface tension

If we adopt for a moment the microscopic point of view, we shall be able to appreciate that the molecules in layer δ are attracted with different forces by those in the liquid as opposed to those in the vapor phase, even if the pressure is the same in both of them. This difference is particularly important with respect to the closely packed

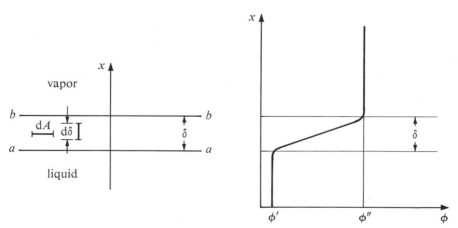

FIGURE 8.1. *Surface film.*

† This section contains only a very elementary study of surface tension. For a fuller treatment see: Reiss, H., *Methods of Thermodynamics* (Blaisdell, 1965).

molecules of liquids and solids which have positioned themselves close to the phase boundaries. As a consequence, the force which acts across a small surface within the layer δ depends on the orientation of the surface in contrast with one drawn in the bulk of any one of the two phases and at a considerable distance away from this layer. If we imagine an elementary rectangular area dA parallel to aa and bb, we shall notice that the force transmitted across it will be PdA, where P is the uniform pressure of the system, on account of symmetry. However, if the element dA is drawn at right angles to aa and bb it will be discovered that the molecules in the layer exert additional, tensile forces upon each other, and that their resultant is proportional to the height δ of element dA. Hence, the total force transmitted will be

$$PdA - \sigma'd\delta \cdot dl,$$

where dl is the dimension of the elementary area in a direction perpendicular to the plane of the drawing.

Owing to the very small magnitude of the thickness δ, the region across which the phase properties change can be thought of as a very thin *surface* or *capillary layer* which transmits an additional *surface tension*

$$\sigma = \int \sigma'd\delta.$$

In the more general case when the two phases are not necessarily identical in chemical composition, the term *interfacial tension* is used.

The existence of surface or interfacial tension in layers between distinct phases affects the mechanical forces transmitted across phase boundaries and hence also the conditions of equilibrium between them; it is responsible for the phenomenon of *capillarity* and exerts an important influence on the formation of metastable states. Soap bubbles or thin films of oil found on solid or liquid surfaces provide examples of capillary layers in which the phases on their two sides are of different chemical compositions.

8.1.2 *Thermal equation of state for surface film*

The surface film can be treated as an autonomous thermodynamic system, and the preceding description convinces us that its state can be described by its total area A, by its surface tension σ, and by its temperature θ. Experience shows that the surface tension σ is independent of its total area A and is a function of temperature alone. Hence, its thermal equation of state has the simple form

$$\sigma = \sigma(\theta). \tag{8.1}$$

In the case of a surface film between a liquid and its vapor, the distinction between the two phases disappears at the critical point, and the surface tension must vanish to zero at the critical temperature. In principle, the exact form of the equation of state can be calculated from a knowledge of the intermolecular forces, but this is possible only in isolated cases, particularly in relation to crystalline solids. In the majority of systems, it is determined experimentally and correlated into an empirical formula. An earlier semitheoretical formula, proposed by R. Eötvos, has the form

$$\sigma = \frac{2.22}{v^{2/3}} (\theta - \theta'_{cr}), \tag{8.2}$$

where v is the molar specific volume of the liquid. A purely empirical equation due to J. D. van der Waals has the form

$$\sigma = \sigma_0 \left(1 - \frac{\theta}{\theta'_{cr}} \right)^{1+a},$$

$$(8.3)$$

where σ_0 and a are constants, with $a = 2/9$, approximately, for microscopically simple substances such as neon, argon, nitrogen, or oxygen. Although σ must vanish for $\theta = \theta_{cr}$, it is found empirically that at temperatures not too close to the critical, it is preferable to replace θ_{cr} itself by $\theta'_{cr} = \theta_{cr} - \theta'$ where θ' ranges from 6°C to 8°C, as was done in the preceding formulae. Values of surface tension for several substances can be found in Table XXVII, and it is noteworthy that it decreases very nearly linearly with temperature.

8.1.3   *Mechanical equilibrium in droplets and bubbles*

The existence of surface films explains the fact that lumps of liquid tend to form into spherical droplets when surrounded by the vapor, or another gaseous phase for that matter. At a uniform temperature, the lump of liquid can be imagined contained inside a film stretched by the surface tension in all directions. The conditions of mechanical equilibrium will then force it to assume a spherical shape, Figure 8.2.

It is clear that the pressure of the liquid inside the droplet cannot be equal to the pressure of the vapor outside it, in the same way as the pressure of the air inside a balloon is higher owing to the tensile stress present in the balloon's material. The difference between a droplet and a balloon consists in the fact that blowing up the latter at constant temperature causes an increase in the tensile stress of its envelope, whereas the surface tension of a growing droplet remains constant at constant temperature. Thus, the area of a droplet grows by virtue of an increase in the mass of liquid contained in the surface film.

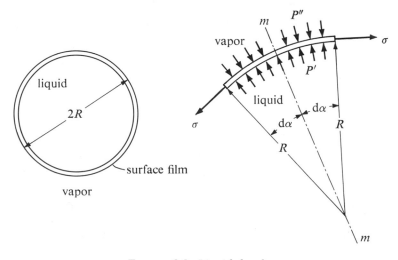

FIGURE 8.2. *Liquid droplet.*

A consideration of the balance of forces on an element of curved surface film shown in Figure 8.2 leads to the conclusion that the pressure P' of the vapor exceeds that of the liquid, P''. Projecting all forces on the center line mm of the element of spherical surface of radius R subtended by a cone of included angle $2d\alpha$, we can establish the condition for mechanical equilibrium. The area of the element is

$$\pi R^2 (\sin d\alpha)^2 \approx \pi R^2 (d\alpha)^2;$$

the resultant of the pressure forces is

$$(P' - P'')\,\pi R^2 (d\alpha)^2,$$

whereas the resultant of the surface tension forces acting on the perimeter $2\pi R d\alpha$ is

$$(2\pi R\sigma\, d\alpha)\sin d\alpha \approx 2\pi R\sigma\,(d\alpha)^2.$$

Hence,

$$(P' - P'')\pi R^2 = 2\pi R\sigma$$

or

$$\Delta P = P' - P'' = \frac{2}{R}\,\sigma. \tag{8.4}$$

In the case of a surface of nonspherical shape, the equation changes to

$$\Delta P = P' - P'' = \sigma\!\left(\frac{1}{R_1} + \frac{1}{R_2}\right), \tag{8.5}$$

where R_1 and R_2 are the principal radii of curvature, as the reader may well know from the theory of membranes.† Equations (8.4) and (8.5) are known as *Lord Kelvin's formulae*; they show that the pressure is always higher on the concave side of the capillary layer. Interchanging the liquid and the vapor merely changes the sign of the curvature and this causes $P' - P''$ to be replaced by $P'' - P'$.

The preceding considerations lead to the conclusion that the relation between the temperature θ, the pressure of the vapor, P'', and that of the liquid, P', at equilibrium depends on the curvature of the surface, the difference between them disappearing in the case of a plane surface since then $R \to \infty$ (or $R_1 \to \infty$ and $R_2 \to \infty$) and $\Delta P = P' - P'' \to 0$. Thus, the vapor-pressure curve discussed in Section 7.4.2 or the equilibrium curves discussed in Section 7.4.4 imply that equilibrium has been established across a surface of negligible curvature. In general, therefore, the equilibrium equations (7.26), (7.32), and (7.35) must contain the radius of curvature R as a parameter. However, the difference $P' - P''$ from equation (8.4) is extremely small unless the radius R is very small itself. For example, in water at 100°C, $\sigma = 50$ dyne/cm. Thus, for a radius $R = 1$ mm $= 0.1$ cm, we would find

$$P' - P'' = \frac{2 \times 50}{0.1}\,\frac{\text{dyne}}{\text{cm}^2} = 1000\,\frac{\text{dyne}}{\text{cm}^2} \times 10^{-6}\,\frac{\text{bar}}{\text{dyne/cm}^2} \times 0.99\,\frac{\text{atm}}{\text{bar}}$$
$$= 0.99 \times 10^{-3}\text{ atm}$$

which can be completely disregarded, except in studies of nucleation and drop formation.

† See, for example, Sommerfeld, A., *Lectures on Theoretical Physics*; Vol. 2, *Mechanics of Deformable Bodies*, transl. by G. Kuerti (Academic, 1950), p. 124.

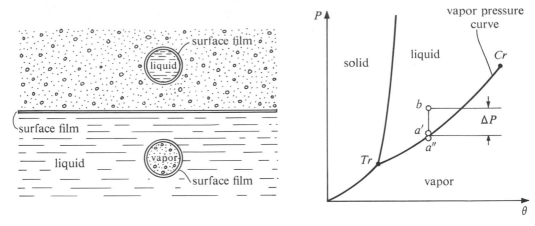

FIGURE 8.3. *Liquid drop and vapor bubble.*

In order to appreciate these relations a little more clearly, we shall examine in Figure 8.3 a liquid drop immersed in a large expanse of vapor and a vapor bubble immersed in a large expanse of liquid, both in equilibrium across a flat capillary film. The bulk of the liquid and vapor are in equilibrium at temperature θ and pressure P, both lying on the vapor-pressure curve, points a' and a'' in the adjacent phase diagram. The pressure in the liquid drop must exceed that in the vapor by an amount $\Delta P = 2\sigma/R$ in conformity with Kelvin's law. Accordingly, the liquid in it is compressed compared with the bulk liquid, and its state is represented by point b (exaggerated in scale in the figure). Similarly, the pressure of the vapor bubble is also increased by an equal amount if its radius is the same and its state is also represented by point b which falls within the liquid area of the diagram. It follows that the vapor in the bubble is supersaturated, that is, that it is in a metastable state.

In practical applications it is important to investigate whether a liquid droplet or a vapor bubble under such conditions is stable, that is, whether it retains its size or whether it grows or disappears due to evaporation or condensation.

8.1.4   The meniscus in a capillary

The existence of surface tension can be exhibited very clearly by observing the position of the meniscus in a capillary, Figure 8.4(a). When the material of the capillary is wetted by the liquid, for example, water on glass, the meniscus rises and shows a free surface which is concave upwards. When the liquid does not wet the capillary, for example, mercury on glass, the meniscus is depressed and its surface is convex upwards. In both cases, the pressure on the concave side is higher by $\Delta P = 2\sigma/R$, where R denotes the radius of curvature of the surface of the meniscus, assumed spherical in shape. This pressure difference is balanced by the hydrostatic pressure of the column of liquid in the wetted capillary or by the depression in the nonwetting case.

More precisely, the mechanical equilibrium can be computed by considering the forces acting near the surface film, as shown in detail for the wetting case in Figure 8.4(b). It must be remembered that the meniscus forms a characteristic angle α with the solid wall and that the magnitude of this angle depends on the combined properties of the liquid and the solid. The vertical component of the surface tension forces which act on the rim of the meniscus is

$$F = 2\pi r\sigma \cos \alpha;$$

it supports a column of liquid of height h, and must be equal to its weight G in the surrounding vapor. Denoting the densities of the liquid and vapor by ρ' and ρ'', respectively, we have

$$G = \pi r^2 h(\rho' - \rho'')g,$$

where g is the acceleration due to gravity. Equating G and F and noting that the radius of curvature

$$R = \frac{r}{\cos \alpha},$$

we find that

$$h = \frac{2\sigma}{R} \cdot \frac{1}{g(\rho' - \rho'')}. \tag{8.6}$$

The same relation could, obviously, be also obtained by noting that the hydrostatic pressure at height h is $hg(\rho' - \rho'')$ and that the pressure difference across the meniscus is given by Kelvin's formula.

The magnitude of the contact angle α depends on the combination of the microscopic properties of the liquid and the solid wall, but it has been verified that the force acting

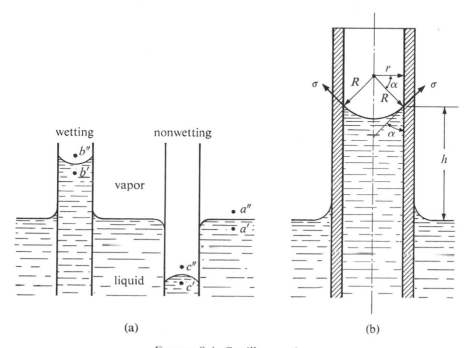

(a)   (b)

FIGURE 8.4. *Capillary action.*

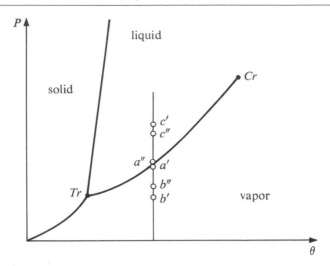

FIGURE 8.5. *Phase diagram.*

around the rim of the meniscus is equal to the surface tension of the capillary layer in the liquid, as assumed intuitively in the preceding derivation.

For wetting liquids, the angle α is very close to zero, and $R = r$ approximately. For completely nonwetting liquids $\alpha \approx \pi$. In the latter case $R = -r$, and h is negative as shown in Figure 8.4(a). The observation of a capillary rise or depression provides the best method of measuring surface tension in relation to equation (8.6).

It is noteworthy that the pressure at points a' and a'' near the flat phase boundary constitutes the saturation pressure for the temperature θ of the system, Figure 8.5. On the other hand, near the meniscus, the pressure in the vapor at b'' has decreased by $\rho'' g h$ and is

$$P_{b''} = P - \frac{2\sigma}{R} \frac{\rho''}{\rho' - \rho''},$$

whereas that at b' has decreased by $\rho' g h$ and becomes

$$P_{b'} = P - \frac{2\sigma}{R} \frac{\rho'}{\rho' - \rho''}.$$

The difference between them is exactly

$$\Delta P = \frac{2\sigma}{R}$$

in accordance with Kelvin's formula. The states b' and b'' are shown in the phase diagram in Figure 8.5. It is seen that the vapor is superheated, but that the liquid at b' is metastable. Similarly, in the nonwetting case

$$P_{c''} = P + \frac{2\sigma}{R} \frac{\rho''}{\rho' - \rho''} \quad \text{and} \quad P_{c'} = P + \frac{2\sigma}{R} \frac{\rho'}{\rho' - \rho''}.$$

Now the vapor is metastable, but the liquid is stable.

The reader will, naturally, appreciate that the distances of points b', b'', c', and c'' in the diagram from the common point $a'a''$ have been grossly exaggerated.

When the exterior of the liquid is filled with a gas other than the vapor of the liquid, the system is no longer a pure substance. The gaseous phase above the liquid contains some vapor of the liquid, and it is possible to think of it as being substantially at the saturation pressure P for temperature θ, even though the combined pressure of the vapor and the gas is much higher.

8.1.5   Reversible work

When a surface film grows or decreases in size in a reversible manner, work must be done on or by the system. The surface film, treated as a thermodynamic system, is not a closed one, since a change in its area involves a change in mass, in contrast with a rubber membrane whose mass remains constant when we subject it to stretching.

Suppose that a surface film grows by the action of the surface tensions σ, Figure 8.6. The work can be calculated by noting that a force σl performs work on the system over a distance dx. Hence, the work is $-\sigma l\,dx$. In addition, the volume of the system increases by $dV = l\delta\,dx$, where δ is the thickness of the film. Hence,

$$dW = P\,dV - \sigma\,dA, \tag{8.7}$$

since $dA = l\,dx$. Owing to the extreme thinness of the film $P\,dV \ll \sigma\,dA$ and it is sufficient to put

$$dW = -\sigma\,dA. \tag{8.8}$$

At constant temperature, σ is constant, and

$$W_{1,2} = -\sigma(A_2 - A_1).$$

The considerations of this section are not restricted to the study of surface films between liquid and gaseous phases and can be extended to include solid phases.

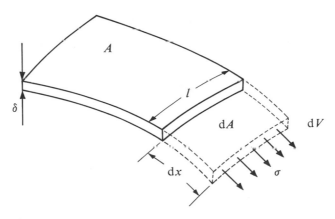

FIGURE 8.6. *Work of surface-tension forces.*

8.2   Galvanic cells

8.2.1   *Electrochemical processes in cells*

In the next example we propose to consider a system in which electrical and chemical phenomena occur simultaneously, namely a galvanic cell. There exist many types of galvanic cells which differ from each other by the selection of materials used in their construction, but we shall confine the description to a particular type of cell, the so-called Daniell cell.† A schematic diagram of such a cell is given in Figure 8.7. A galvanic cell possesses two electrodes, the positive anode, in this case a copper bar 1, and the negative cathode, in this case a zinc bar 4. The electrodes are immersed in a suitable salt solution called the electrolyte. In a Daniell cell the electrolyte consists of a saturated aqueous solution of copper sulphate ($CuSO_4$), 2, for the copper, and of zinc sulphate ($ZnSO_4$), 3, for the zinc, the two being separated by a porous clay partition, p.‡ The regions 1, 2, 3, 4, and 5 within the cell which differ in their physical properties can be regarded as different *phases* within the cell. An arrangement of this type produces a potential difference, the electromotive force (emf), $\mathcal{E}$, between the electrodes, the copper electrode being positive with respect to the zinc, as mentioned. It is convenient to imagine that a copper terminal, 5, has been connected to the zinc electrode in order to ensure that the emf is measured between identical metals thus excluding any contact emf's, that is, the emf's which are produced, for example, at the junctions of thermocouples. The emf, $\mathcal{E}$, depends on the current drawn from the cell, and is largest when the current is zero, that is, when the emf is measured on a potentiometer circuit, as shown in Figure 8.8. This is referred to as the emf of the "open cell."

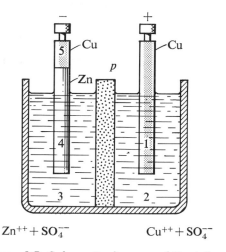

$$Zn^{++} + SO_4^{--} \qquad\qquad Cu^{++} + SO_4^{--}$$

FIGURE 8.7. *Schematic diagram of Daniell cell.*

---

†Invented in 1836.

‡The porous partition impedes the mixing of the two solutions and prevents the deposition of copper ions on the zinc electrode; it only allows the SO_4^{--} ions to pass. This property of the partition is described by the statement that it constitutes a *semipermeable membrane*.

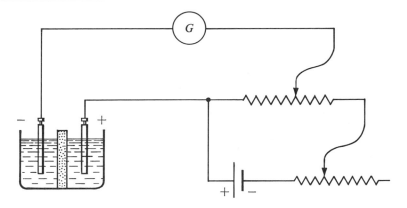

FIGURE 8.8. *Potentiometer circuit.*

The processes of charging or discharging a cell are accompanied by chemical reactions which involve the electrodes and the electrolyte. From the microscopic point of view, the electrolyte contains mobile charged particles, namely, ions. In the present case, as shown in the figure, it contains positive ions of zinc and copper, and negative ions of SO_4, all of them being of valence 2, which means that the Zn^{++} and Cu^{++} ions have lost, and that the SO_4^{--} ions have gained two electrons each. The chemical reaction in a Daniell cell can be written

$$Zn + CuSO_4 \rightleftharpoons Cu + ZnSO_4.$$

During discharge, equilibrium shifts from left to right, and zinc from the anode enters into solution, copper precipitating on the cathode. During charging the opposite reaction takes place. Since the zinc atoms lose electrons (acquire a positive charge), and since the positively charged copper ions acquire electrons from the electrode on deposition (become neutralized), the chemical reaction has the effect of transferring a positive charge internally from the zinc to the copper electrode. This is compensated by an *external* transfer of charge from copper to zinc, that is, by an electric discharge current. The opposite occurs during charging, and these additional reactions can be written

$$Zn \rightleftharpoons Zn^{++} + 2e \tag{8.9}$$

$$Cu^{++} + 2e \rightleftharpoons Cu, \tag{8.9a}$$

with the same convention regarding directions as before. Here, the symbol e denotes one electron.

The overall reaction affecting the electrodes is

$$Zn + Cu^{++} \rightleftharpoons Zn^{++} + Cu \tag{8 9b}$$

and according to Faraday's second law of electrolysis,[†] the transformation of one mol of zinc or copper carries a charge of ζF, where ζ denotes the number of valence electrons. We shall follow the convention that $\zeta = +2$ for Zn and $\zeta = -2$ for Cu when the

[†] See, for example, Planck, M., "Theory of Electricity and Magnetism" in *Introduction to Theoretical Physics*, transl. by H. L. Brose (Macmillan, 1932), p. 159.

reaction proceeds from left to right. The universal physical constant

$$\mathbf{F} = 9652.2 \text{ emu/gmol}\dagger$$
$$= 2.8937 \text{ esu/gmol}\dagger$$
$$= 96,516 \times 10^3 \text{ Coulomb/kmol (physical scale)}$$

is *Faraday's equivalent charge.* Thus, a given transfer of positive electricity on discharge can be interpreted as a loss in charge Δz (product of current and time) to which there corresponds the transformation of a definite quantity, say Δn mols, of copper or zinc. Hence,

$$\Delta z = \zeta \mathbf{F} \Delta n. \tag{8.9c}$$

Since during discharge $\Delta z < 0$, and $\zeta > 0$, $\Delta n < 0$ for zinc, and $\zeta < 0$, $\Delta n > 0$ for copper. Equation (8.9c) demonstrates the existence of a relation between the extent of the chemical reaction and the change in the charge of a cell, first discovered by Michael Faraday in 1791.

When the chemical processes in the galvanic cell do not involve the liberation or absorption of gases, its state is independent of pressure. In addition, if the electrolytic solutions are saturated, for example, when a Daniell cell contains an excess of crystals of copper and zinc sulphate, the chemical concentration will remain unaffected by the processes of charging or discharging. A cell whose emf is balanced by a potentiometer, as shown in Figure 8.8, is said to be in electrical equilibrium; it is then also in chemical equilibrium since the chemical reactions do not occur, and the cell is said to be in thermodynamic equilibrium. The state of a cell can then be described by its emf, $\mathcal{E}$, its charge, z, measured from an arbitrary level, and by its temperature θ, so that an equation of state

$$f(\mathcal{E}, z, \theta) = 0 \tag{8.10}$$

with two independent variables exists. When gases are evolved or when the electrolytes are not saturated, additional independent variables must be added. In many cases, the equation of state (8.10) is independent of charge, and only one independent variable determines its state, so that the emf, $\mathcal{E}$, becomes a unique function of temperature. This can be often represented in the form

$$\mathcal{E} = a + b\theta + c\theta^2,$$

where a, b, and c are constants for a given cell. For example, the emf of a so-called Weston cell is often used for standardizing potentiometer circuits. A Weston cell consists of a mercury and a cadmium-mercury amalgam electrode in contact with a saturated solution of cadmium sulphate ($CdSO_4$) in the presence of cadmium sulphate crystals and mercurous sulphate ($HgSO_4$) paste. Its equation of state is

$$\frac{\mathcal{E}}{\text{volt}} = 1.01827 - 4.06(t - 20) \times 10^{-5} - 9.5(t - 20)^2 \times 10^{-7} + (20 - t)^3 \times 10^{-8}, \tag{8.11}$$

where t is the temperature in degrees Celsius.

The work performed by a galvanic cell during charging or discharging has been discussed at length in Section 4.8.1.

---

† Cohen, E. R., Crowe, K. M., and Dumond, J. W. M., *Fundamental Constants of Physics.* (Interscience, 1957), p. 267; the uncertainty is about 2 parts in 10^5. The value recommended by the National Bureau of Standards is $(96,487.0 \pm 1.6) \times 10^3$ Coulomb/kmol on the physical scale [*Natl. Bur. Std. (U.S.) Tech. News Bull.*, **47**, (1963) 176].

8.2.2   Fuel cells

A galvanic cell cannot be operated continuously, because the chemical reaction which occurs in it during the process of discharging the electric current consumes the reactants and transforms them into the products of the reaction. For example, in a Daniell cell zinc from the anode is consumed, and copper sulphate is replaced by zinc sulphate. Since the reactants are not replenished, and the products are not removed, the chemical reaction must, eventually, come to a standstill, and the cell becomes exhausted.

In an electric accumulator (a "battery" in an automobile), the chemical process is very nearly reversible, and the reactants can be restored periodically from the products by reversing the direction of flow of the electric current, that is, by charging the accumulator. Thus, the accumulator constitutes a device in which electric energy can be stored for future use, but in which the chemical energy of the electrodes and electrolyte reverts cyclically to its original value.

During the last decade or two, great efforts have been made to perfect cells in which a continuous flow of reactants and products is maintained in the presence of indestructible electrodes, making it possible continuously to convert the chemical energy released by the reaction directly into the work of a dc electric current. Devices of this type are known as *fuel cells*. The first fuel cell seems to have been built by Sir Humphry Davy as early as 1802, the first hydrogen-oxygen fuel cell having been built by Sir William Grove in 1839. However, the development of viable fuel cells proved too difficult until quite recently.

It will be shown in Volume II that the conversion of the energy released by a chemical reaction, such as a combustion process, is fundamentally more efficient in a fuel cell than it can be in a power plant in which the chemical energy of the reaction is imparted to a working fluid in the form of a flux of heat. Nevertheless, for practical reasons, no fuel cells have yet been developed which could compete with large thermal power stations, though quite practical, small units are available and are in use, notably as power sources in space vehicles.

The emf of a single, open fuel cell is of the order of 1 volt and only direct current can be produced. Furthermore, the current density in a single cell is limited,† and a practical installation must consist of a large number of individual fuel cells connected in parallel and in series. Table 8.1 gives typical values of the emf developed in a reversible fuel cell under ideal conditions, depending on the nature of the chemical reaction employed in the cell.

TABLE 8.1

Ideal, Reversible, Open Electromotive Force, $\mathcal{E}$, in a Fuel Cell when Operating at 1000°K.

Reaction	$\mathcal{E}/V$
$H_2 + \frac{1}{2}O_2 \rightarrow H_2O$ (vapor)	0.997
$CO + \frac{1}{2}O_2 \rightarrow CO_2$	1.013
$CH_4 + 2O_2 \rightarrow CO_2 + 2H_2O$	1.039
$C_2H_6 + \frac{7}{2}O_2 \rightarrow 2CO_2 + 3H_2O$	1.082

From: *Fuel Cells*, ed. W. Mitchell, Jr. (Academic, 1963), p. 55.

†Values range up to 100–125 A/ft² of electrode.

There exist numerous types of fuel cells, and the determination of their relative merits is still under investigation. It is, therefore, not possible to provide a comprehensive survey in this book. By way of example, we shall discuss briefly the operation of a fuel cell in which so-called diffusion electrodes are used, and in which the fuel is gaseous, the oxygen required for the combustion reaction being introduced directly in pure form or as a component of air. The diagram in Figure 8.9 represents such a fuel cell. The fuel, hydrogen gas in this example, and oxygen are supplied continuously into chambers d and c, respectively. The oxygen chamber is adjacent to the porous anode a, whereas the hydrogen chamber remains in contact with the porous cathode b. The space e between the electrodes is exposed to a stream of electrolyte, potassium hydroxide in the present example.

The gas, oxygen or hydrogen, becomes adsorbed in the microscopic pores in the respective electrodes, as shown schematically in Figure 8.10. The hydrogen gas reacts with the negative ions OH^- present in the electrolyte according to the equation

$$H_2 + 2OH^- \rightarrow 2H_2O + 2e, \tag{a}$$

whereas at the anode, the oxygen reacts in conformity with the equation

$$\tfrac{1}{2}O_2 + H_2O + 2e \rightarrow 2OH^-. \tag{b}$$

Thus, the electrons produced in step (a) are transferred externally to the anode maintaining the flow of a current, whereas internally the current is maintained by a flow

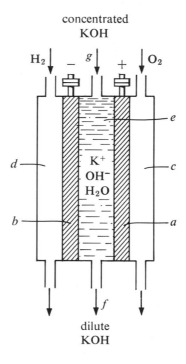

FIGURE 8.9. *Schematic diagram of fuel cell.*

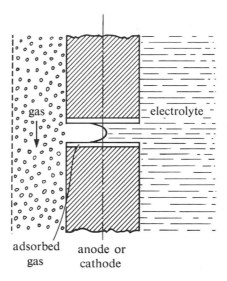

FIGURE 8.10. *Detail of electrode.*

of hydroxyl ions produced in step (b). The net reaction is one of oxydization

$$H_2(gas) + \tfrac{1}{2}O_2(gas) \rightarrow H_2O \text{ (liquid)},$$ (c)

and the liquid water evolved in the process dilutes the solution of potassium hydroxide. Consequently, it is necessary to maintain a flow of electrolyte and to regenerate it, that is, to drive off some of the water between exit at *f* and re-entry at *g*. Evidently, the quantities of hydrogen and oxygen leaving the cell are smaller than those entering, a continuous flow rather than feeding being maintained for practical reasons. When the cell operates at higher temperatures, or with different fuels, the products of combustion may be gaseous.

A fuel cell should operate indefinitely. However, the electrodes are very sensitive to small impurities and often become "poisoned" when the latter are deposited on them; they may also corrode. It is then necessary to regenerate or replace the electrodes.

Fuel cells can operate at various temperatures, ranging from room temperature to one as high as 1000°C. Different arrangements of fuel, electrolyte, and electrodes operate most satisfactorily at different levels of temperature. The efficiency of a fuel cell can be enhanced by the introduction of catalysts.

In principle, any oxidation reaction may form the basis of the design of a fuel cell; in practice, oxidants are generally limited to oxygen, pure or carried in air, and to hydrogen peroxide. Living organisms, in particular the human body, can be looked upon as constituting fuel cells. In a living organism the food intake serves as the fuel and the blood stream plays the part of the electrolyte. The chemical reaction is enhanced by the catalytic action of enzymes, and as a result energy is produced by direct conversion from the chemical energy of the fuel-oxygen intake. A portion of this energy is electrical in nature. However, in contrast with man-made fuel cells, living organisms cannot operate in steady state over their life span, and cannot be regenerated; the irreversible changes which occur in them inevitably drive them to death.

8.3 Shearing of a fluid lamina; viscosity

We have emphasized in Section 7.4 that the state of a mass m of fluid is independent of its shape. When pressure is applied to a fluid, that is, when a fluid is subjected to a system of *normal* stresses, for example, by the action of a piston in a cylinder, the shape as well as the volume of the system are changed, but only the volume V enters the equation of state. The shape of a mass of fluid can be changed without changing its volume by the application of a suitably chosen system of *shearing* stresses. This can be achieved most easily when a mass of fluid is placed between two concentric cylinders as shown in Figure 8.11(a), the outer one rotating at a steady angular velocity ω.

We shall assume that the gap $\delta = r_2 - r_1$ is very small ($\delta \ll r_1$ and $\delta \ll r_2$), that the cylinders are "infinitely" long in the direction normal to the plane of the sketch and that the velocity of rotation ω is small enough so that no turbulence is developed in the fluid. Owing to the no-slip condition (Section 6.4), the fluid will adhere to the solid surfaces, which means that it will be stationary at the surface of the inner cylinder and that it will move with a velocity $V \approx \omega r$ at the outer edge of the gap, where r denotes its average radius. This will cause a velocity field to appear in the fluid. Owing to the fact that the gap δ is small compared with both radii r_1 and r_2, Figure 8.11(b), we can neglect the curvature and approximate the flow field by one which exists between two "infinite" planes. Under such conditions the velocity will change linearly from zero to V over the distance δ, the fluid motion consisting of the gliding of fluid laminae over each other. This will give rise to the appearance of shearing stresses τ at the solid-fluid interfaces. Thus, it will be possible to maintain the motion only if an

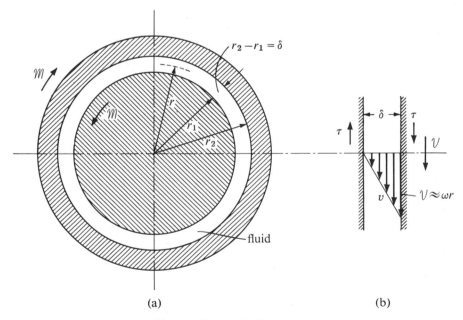

(a)   (b)

Figure 8.11. *Fluid in shear.*

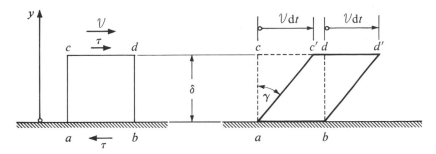

FIGURE 8.12. *Change of shape.*

external torque $\mathcal{M}$ is applied. This will be balanced by an equal and opposite torque acting on the inner cylinder. Owing to symmetry

$$\mathcal{M} = (2\pi r l \tau) \times r \qquad (8.12)$$

per length l of cylinder, and work must be supplied at a rate

$$\dot{W} = \mathcal{M}\,\omega = (2\pi r^2 l)\tau(\mathcal{V}/r) = 2\pi r l \tau \mathcal{V}. \qquad (8.12a)$$

It is clear that every fluid element retains its volume, but that its shape is changed. More precisely, if we consider at time t a rectangular slab of fluid of height l, Figure 8.12, we shall discover that after a lapse of time dt its shape will have changed. The corners a and b will remain stationary, but the upper corners c and d of the slab of fluid will be displaced to c' and d', respectively, each by a distance $\mathcal{V}\,dt$. The angle $\gamma \approx \mathcal{V}\,dt/\delta$ can be taken as a measure of the change in shape undergone by the fluid element, and it can be said that the rate of change in shape is described by the rate of change of strain,

$$\dot{\gamma} = \mathcal{V}/\delta. \qquad (8.13)$$

When a process of this kind occurs at constant temperature θ, we must say that the thermodynamic state of the element has not changed, since the two properties θ and V remain constant. Consequently, the internal energy u of the fluid remains constant (the kinetic energy is also constant) and the First Law leads to the conclusion that

$$\dot{Q} - \dot{W} = 0. \qquad (8.14)$$

This means that an isothermal process can be performed only if the equivalent of the work (8.12a) is continuously removed in the form of heat. Evidently, this is an irreversible process at constant state, and the expression in equation (8.12a) represents the work performed *irreversibly*. Naturally, equation (8.12a) remains valid when the process is not necessarily isothermal, that is, when the irreversible process forces a change in the thermodynamic state.

It is convenient to put equation (8.12a) in the form

$$\frac{dW}{dt} = V\tau\frac{\mathcal{V}}{\delta} = V\tau\frac{d\gamma}{dt},$$

where $V \approx 2\pi r l\delta$ denotes the volume of the fluid element of length l which fills the annulus. This is equivalent to

$$dW = \tau(V\,d\gamma) \tag{8.15}$$

which states that the work is represented by the product of the intensive quantity, τ, into the increment of the extensive quantity $V\,d\gamma$. Since the process is irreversible, the quantities τ and γ which appear in the expression for work *do not represent thermodynamic properties of the system*.

Shearing stresses are measured in units of

$$\frac{lbf}{ft^2}, \quad \frac{lbf}{in^2}, \quad \frac{kp}{m^2}, \quad \frac{kp}{cm^2}, \quad \frac{N}{m^2},$$

according to circumstances. The angle γ is dimensionless.

Experience teaches that the shearing stress τ is proportional to the spatial gradient of velocity

$$\frac{d\mathcal{V}}{dy} = \frac{\mathcal{V}}{\delta},$$

where the coordinate y is measured in a transverse direction as shown in Figure 8.12. Thus,

$$\tau = \mu\,\frac{d\mathcal{V}}{dy}, \tag{8.16}$$

where the coefficient of proportionality, μ, is known as the *viscosity* of the fluid, first mentioned in Section 6.2.2, equation (6.5). The commonly used units of viscosity are

$$1\ \text{Poise}^\dagger = 1\ \frac{g}{cm\ sec}; \quad \frac{kp\ sec}{m^2}; \quad \frac{lbm}{ft\ sec}; \quad \text{or} \quad \frac{lbf\ sec}{ft^2}.$$

The empirical fact expressed in equation (8.16) is known as *Newton's law of fluid friction*. Experience shows that the relation between the shearing stress and rate of strain expressed by Newton's law in equation (8.16) is linear for a limited, though very wide, class of fluids only. Accordingly, such fluids are called *Newtonian*. In other fluids the relation becomes more complex and nonlinear. All gases, water, and many more fluids which are important in practical applications are Newtonian. Certain paints, blood, and many physiological fluids are *non-Newtonian*.

It is clear that work is performed by shearing forces on a fluid only if the rate-of-change of strain is finite. In the limit, when $\mathcal{V} \to 0$, $d\mathcal{V}/dy \to 0$ and $\tau \to 0$. Thus, an infinitely slow deformation, that is, an infinitely slow change in shape (at constant volume) requires no work. At the same time, the temperature remains constant without cooling.

In a more general flow field, that is, in a more complex continuous system, the description of the stresses and rates of change of strain becomes considerably more complex. We shall deal with such cases briefly in Volume II, noting that the study of problems of this kind properly belongs to the subject of fluid mechanics. We shall merely remark here that the preceding simple flow field is known as *Couette flow*, after the French physicist M. Couette who studied it extensively. The viscosity, μ, of a

---

†After the French physicist J. L. M. Poiseuille.

Newtonian fluid depends on the thermodynamic state of the fluid, say its pressure P and temperature θ. The viscosity can be measured by an arrangement consisting of an outer cylinder rotating about an inner stationary cylinder, the gap between them containing the fluid. The arrangement, except for the effect at the ends of the cylinder, is identical with that discussed in conjunction with Figure 8.11(a); it is known as a Couette viscometer, and the viscosity is computed from measured values of the angular velocity ω and the torque $\mathscr{M}$ acting on the inner cylinder.

Frequently, the equations of fluid dynamics contain the ratio

$$\nu = \frac{\mu}{\rho} \qquad (= \mu v) \tag{8.17}$$

of viscosity to density. This ratio, measured in units of

$$\frac{\text{m}^2}{\text{sec}} \quad \text{or} \quad \frac{\text{ft}^2}{\text{sec}}$$

is known as the *kinematic* viscosity of the fluid. The viscosity μ is frequently called the *dynamic* or *absolute* viscosity to avoid confusion.

8.4 Solid rods stressed in one dimension

8.4.1 Stress and strain

The simplest state of strain in a solid body, such as a metal or a piece of rubber, is obtained when a thin, slender rod of length L_0 and uniform cross section A is extended or compressed by the action of two equal and opposite forces F, Figure 8.13. The force per unit area, or *stress*

$$\sigma = \frac{F}{A}, \tag{8.18}$$

can then be assumed uniform across the section. It is customary to adopt the convention that tensile forces and stresses are positive, whereas compressive forces and stresses are negative. Thus, pressures also become negative. The units of stress are, evidently, identical with those of pressure.

The material is said to be *strained* under the action of the external forces, changing its shape and volume. In a rod, the strain is measured by the change in length from L_0 to L under tension or compression, and experiments show that this change in length $\Delta L = L - L_0$ is very small for many materials, metals in particular, even in the presence

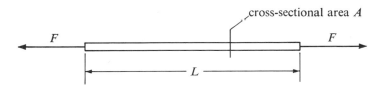

FIGURE 8.13. *Thin solid rod in tension.*

of forces which are close to rupturing it, that is,

$$\Delta L \ll L_0 \tag{8.19}$$

in the majority of problems of practical interest. In certain other materials, such as rubber, condition (8.19) is not satisfied, and the change in length may become several times the original length. In the former case, a theory of infinitely small strain is developed.† In the latter case, a finite strain theory is required.

Within the limits of validity of assumption (8.19), that is, in the theory of infinitely small strain, the strain ϵ is defined as

$$\epsilon = \frac{\Delta L}{L_0}. \tag{8.20}$$

Here, L_0 denotes an arbitrary reference length, usually the length at $\sigma = 0$ and at a specified temperature θ_0. Thus, a small change in strain, $d\epsilon$, is given by

$$d\epsilon = \frac{dL}{L_0}. \tag{8.20a}$$

Strain is described by a ratio of two linear quantities, and is, therefore, dimensionless. In actual fact, when a thin solid rod is stressed even in the simplest manner, its transverse dimensions will also change and become strained. The ratio of the unit lateral contraction to the unit axial elongation is known as *Poisson's ratio*. We shall ignore the existence of such additional variables in the interests of simplicity of description.

If the initial temperature θ_0 of the rod is changed, the stress σ remaining constant, the material will also show a change in length or strain. It appears, therefore, that an equilibrium state of such a system can be described by the variables L, θ, F and that the equation of state will have the form

$$f(L, \theta, F) = 0. \tag{8.21}$$

In the study of strained solids, it is customary to replace the force F and the length L by the stress σ and the strain ϵ which are proportional to them, respectively, and to write the equation of state in the equivalent form

$$f(\epsilon, \theta, \sigma) = 0. \tag{8.21a}$$

The application of a high pressure uniformly around the bar would also change its dimensions, even at constant values of stress and temperature, and the pressure ought to appear as an additional variable. However, the effect of uniform pressure is negligible unless it becomes comparable to the stress itself. Thus, ordinary variations in pressure can be ignored. When a solid is subjected to a uniform pressure P which may vary over a wide range in the absence of stresses caused by external forces, its equation of state $f(P, V, \theta) = 0$ becomes the thermal equation of state of a pure substance known to the reader from Section 7.4.

The equation of state (8.21a) is determined experimentally and it is usual to plot it in the form of isothermal *stress-strain diagrams* which must be obtained with very slow, quasistatic loading and unloading. Three such typical diagrams, undoubtedly familiar to the reader, are shown in Figure 8.14. During the performance of such experiments, two complicating factors are encountered. When the system is tested under tension,

---

† The usual theory studied in elementary courses.

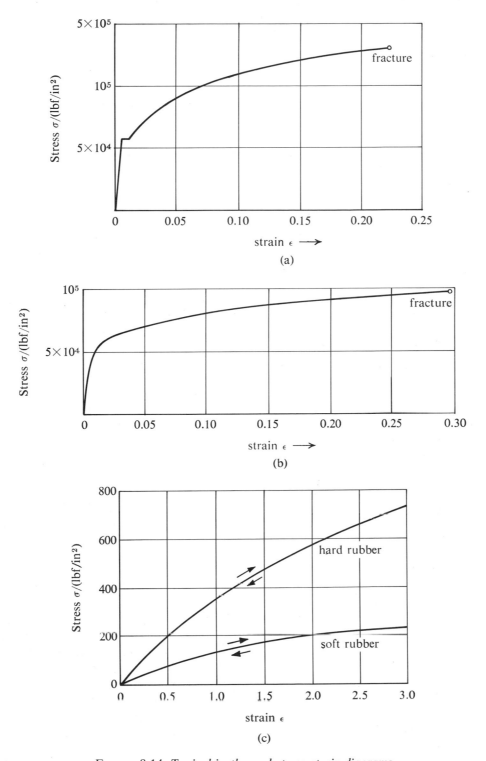

FIGURE 8.14. *Typical isothermal stress-strain diagrams.*
(a) Mild steel. (b) High-grade aluminum alloy. (c) Rubber.
Diagrams give so-called true stress referred to actual cross-sectional area when "necking" occurs.

ductile materials develop local "necks" and undergo a considerable contraction of area locally at some point along their length when the tensile force is large. This complication has been removed in Figure 8.14 in that so-called "true" stress referred to the minimum cross section has been plotted. When a slender rod is tested in compression, even very slight misalignments between its axis and the external force cause buckling. When the rod is buckled, the stress ceases to be even approximately uniform over its cross section and a continuum description must be resorted to. In our present studies, we shall simply ignore this possibility and assume a perfect alignment of forces.

8.4.2   *Elastic range, inelastic behavior, and equation of state*

All materials exhibit a characteristic range in which the stress is proportional to strain according to the linear relation

$$\sigma = E\epsilon \qquad (\text{at } \theta = \text{const}) \tag{8.22}$$

which is known as *Hooke's law*. The coefficient of proportionality, measured in units of stress (that is, pressure), is termed the *isothermal modulus of elasticity* or the isothermal *Young's modulus* of the material. The modulus of elasticity, E, decreases somewhat with increasing temperature for most materials, and is constant only at constant temperature. In rubber, for which the proportionality range is quite small, the modulus of elasticity increases with increasing temperature. Hooke's law is valid only up to a certain point, the *limit of proportionality*. When the stress is increased beyond that point, the relation between stress and strain becomes nonlinear; the modulus of elasticity is then defined as the rate of change of stress with strain at constant temperature

$$\left(\frac{\partial \sigma}{\partial \epsilon}\right)_\theta = \frac{L_0}{A}\left(\frac{\partial F}{\partial L}\right)_\theta = E. \tag{8.23}$$

From the point of view of thermodynamics, the most important characteristic of the behavior of stressed rods is connected with the process of unloading and reloading. We shall now proceed to describe these processes in terms of the hypothetical diagram shown in Figure 8.15, noting that the essential feature, namely the occurrence of permanent strains, is independent of the details of the stress-strain curves such as those shown in Figure 8.14.

The isothermal stress-strain relation which a material exhibits on unloading and subsequent reloading depends on the extent to which it had been stressed prior to unloading, or, as is loosely stated, on the "history" of the specimen. When unloading begins from any point below a certain limit denoted by B in Figure 8.15, the stress-strain relation is identical with that which was observed during the initial loading, and any subsequent reloading will show no deviation from the originally established relation. This behavior is described by the term *elastic*, and the point B is said to constitute the upper limit of the *elastic range* $0B$ at the temperature indicated. Such a process of loading and reloading performed quasistatically is, evidently, reversible. In many materials, notably in metals, the limit A of the validity of Hooke's law and the elastic limit B are so close to each other that the distinction can be ignored.

When unloading proceeds from any point beyond the elastic range, say from point C in Figure 8.15, the stress-strain changes to that denoted by CD in the diagram. The slope of the curve of unloading which is proportional to the isothermal modulus of

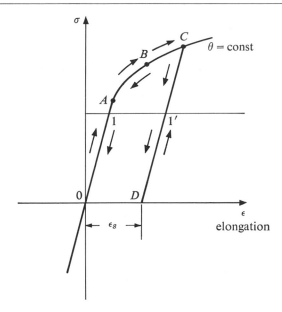

FIGURE 8.15. *Unloading and reloading. A — Limit of proportionality. B — Elastic Limit.*
0B — Elastic Range. BC — Inelastic or Plastic Range.

elasticity, E, remains the same as in the elastic range,† but upon unloading to zero
stress the specimen retains a *permanent strain* or *permanent set*, ϵ_s. On further reloading, from D, or from any point between D and C, the preceding sequence of phenomena repeats itself, the behavior is elastic along DC, and the only difference consists
in the fact that the elastic limit has been increased from B to C through so-called *strain-
hardening*. Strictly speaking, the curves for unloading and reloading are not quite identical but form a very narrow hysteresis loop whose existence will be disregarded. Thus,
although it is possible to traverse the points on the isothermal stress-strain curve which
lie outside the elastic range in the direction of loading, it is impossible to do so in the
opposite direction. The behavior of the material in this range is said to be inelastic, and
the range beyond the elastic limit B is known as the *plastic range*. We conclude, therefore, that the process of isothermal, quasistatic loading beyond the elastic limit is irreversible, whereas the process of quasistatic unloading is reversible.

The preceding description shows that the behavior of the system in the plastic range
causes serious difficulties with the thermal equation of state whose form appears to be
affected by whether or not the system had been previously strained beyond the elastic
limit. As long as the stress and the strain are confined to the elastic limit, the equation of
state (8.21a) is adequate to describe any equilibrium state reached within it. However,
the states represented by unloading along CD do not satisfy this equation because for a
given stress and temperature the strain has a different value, that is, the value corresponding to the preceding elastic range augmented by the permanent set ϵ_s, as shown
by points 1 and 1' in the diagram. Whether the system has reached that different value

† This is not always the case; consequently, the ensuing description is restricted to the class of materials for
which this is true.

or the value corresponding to the preceding elastic range does not seem to depend on any conditions at that instant but on the processes which went on *before*. A new equation of state can be formulated for the range CD if strains are measured with respect to the length of the bar at D but not at 0. In other words, the behavior of the system seems to suggest that the thermal equation of state (8.21a) ceased to be single-valued. This situation is paradoxical, and for a long time it was thought that no equation of state *existed* for systems stressed beyond the elastic limit. We shall resolve this paradox in Section 8.4.6, after we have understood the nature of the equation of state for processes in the elastic range.

Different materials, Figure 8.14, differ in the details of their stress-strain relations. Mild steel shows a short, horizontal *ideal-plastic* range and does not work-harden appreciably. Ductile materials, such as aluminum, possess properties which are very close to those sketched in the ideal diagram of Figure 8.15. Other materials, for example, rubber, exhibit only a very short proportional range, the stress-strain relation in the elastic range being essentially nonlinear. However, these differences have no bearing on the preceding remarks concerning the existence of an equation of state and apply to all materials with equal force.

8.4.3   Equation of state for infinitely small strains in the elastic range

In order to write down the equation of state for a thin rod stressed in the elastic range, it is convenient to choose the strain, ϵ, as the independent variable, so that

$$\epsilon = \epsilon(\sigma, \theta).$$

The perfect differential of ϵ is

$$d\epsilon = \left(\frac{\partial \epsilon}{\partial \sigma}\right)_\theta d\sigma + \left(\frac{\partial \epsilon}{\partial \theta}\right)_\sigma d\theta. \tag{8.24}$$

The first partial derivative represents the reciprocal of the isothermal modulus of elasticity, E, from equation (8.23); we shall consider materials for which it is a function of temperature alone. The second partial derivative

$$\alpha = \left(\frac{\partial \epsilon}{\partial \theta}\right)_\sigma = \frac{1}{L_0}\left(\frac{\partial L}{\partial \theta}\right)_F; \qquad \{\alpha\} = \frac{1}{\deg} \tag{8.25}$$

describes the relative change in the length of the system as its temperature is changed at constant load; it is known as the linear coefficient of thermal expansion, and its definition is seen to be analogous to that of the volumetric coefficient of thermal expansion, β, discussed in Section 3.5, except that here the reference length L_0 rather than the instantaneous length L is used. As long as the assumption (8.19) of the theory of infinitely small strains remains valid, both possible choices lead to practically identical values of the coefficient. In finite elasticity, this difference must be taken into account.

Introducing the coefficients E and α into equation (8.24), we obtain the thermal equation of state in differential form:

$$d\epsilon = \frac{d\sigma}{E} + \alpha \, d\theta. \tag{8.26}$$

The equation shows that the increase in total strain, $d\epsilon$, is the sum of the elastic strain,

$d\sigma/E$, and of the thermal strain, $\alpha d\theta$, as is known from the elementary study of *thermal stresses*.

In the general case, the coefficients E and α constitute properties of the system and are functions of the two selected independent variables σ and θ,

$$E = E(\sigma, \theta) \quad \text{and} \quad \alpha = \alpha(\sigma, \theta).$$

Within the limits of validity of Hooke's law, the isothermal modulus E is independent of stress. In many practical problems of engineering, the range of temperatures encountered is so narrow that a constant value of Young's modulus may be accepted.

The coefficients of $d\sigma$ and $d\theta$ in equation (8.24) must satisfy the integrability criterion (3.26), and hence,

$$\left\{ \frac{\partial(1/E)}{\partial\theta} \right\}_\sigma = \left(\frac{\partial\alpha}{\partial\sigma} \right)_\theta, \tag{8.27}$$

which shows that they are not independent of each other. Within the limits of validity of Hooke's law, the first derivative is a function of temperature alone, and integration with respect to stress at constant temperature shows that

$$\alpha = \eta\sigma + \alpha_0 \quad \text{where} \quad \alpha_0 = \alpha_0(\theta) \quad \text{and} \quad \eta(\theta) = \left\{ \frac{\partial(1/E)}{\partial\theta} \right\}_\sigma. \tag{8.28}$$

Here, $\alpha_0(\theta)$ represents the variation of the linear coefficient of thermal expansion at zero stress. It is now clear that it is possible to make two thermodynamically consistent sets of assumptions regarding the coefficient of linear thermal expansion, α. When E is assumed constant, η vanishes identically, and $\alpha = \alpha_0$ can be at most a function of temperature. The simplest theory of elastic thermal stress assumes that α_0 is also a constant. When the variation of the modulus of elasticity with temperature is taken into account, the coefficient of thermal expansion must be a linear function of stress, with α_0 being a constant or a function of temperature alone.

The expression in equation (8.24) can now be easily integrated with respect to the reference state when $\epsilon = 0$ for $\sigma = 0$ at $\theta = \theta_0$. We shall refer to this state as the *natural state* of the system. Since the result of the integration must be independent of the path, we choose a path at $\sigma = 0$ from θ_0 to θ, Figure 8.16(a), and continue to σ along an isotherm, proceeding from 0 to b through a. Thus,

$$\epsilon = \frac{\sigma}{E(\theta)} + \int_{\theta_0}^{\theta} \alpha_0(\theta)\, d\theta, \tag{8.29}$$

where

$$\epsilon_{\text{el}} = \frac{\sigma}{E(\theta)} \tag{8.29a}$$

is called the elastic strain, and

$$\epsilon_{\text{th}} = \int_{\theta_0}^{\theta} \alpha_0(\theta)\, d\theta \tag{8.29b}$$

represents the thermal strain.

Equations (8.24) and (8.29) allow us to infer that the isotherms of a rod whose material obeys Hooke's law assume the shape of a family of straight lines in a stress-

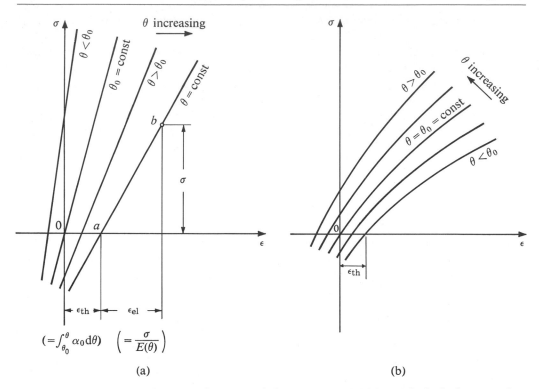

FIGURE 8.16. *Isotherms for a one-dimensional elastic system. (a) Material which obeys Hooke's law with $\alpha_0 > 0$. (b) Rubber, for which $\alpha_0 < 0$. Note: The magnitude of ϵ_{th} has been highly exaggerated, particularly in Figure 8.16(b).*

strain diagram, as shown in Figure 8.16(a). The slopes of these lines are equal to the variable modulus of elasticity taken at the respective temperature. As the temperature is increased, the modulus of elasticity of metals decreases. Some examples of this variation are included in Table 8.2. Since α_0 is always positive for metals, the thermal strain is positive in accordance with the diagram. Thus, for a metal, increasing the temperature at constant strain causes the tensile stress to *decrease*. A compressive stress increases in these circumstances, and cooling would have the opposite effect. This can be demonstrated analytically with the aid of the cyclic relation (3.34) which now assumes the form

$$\left(\frac{\partial \sigma}{\partial \epsilon}\right)_\theta \left(\frac{\partial \epsilon}{\partial \theta}\right)_\sigma \left(\frac{\partial \theta}{\partial \sigma}\right)_\epsilon = -1.$$

Hence, the rate of change of stress with temperature at constant strain is

$$\left(\frac{\partial \sigma}{\partial \theta}\right)_\epsilon = -\alpha E, \qquad (8.30)$$

and is negative for $E > 0$ and $\alpha > 0$. In rubber, the modulus of elasticity increases with increasing temperature at a given stress or strain though it is no longer constant along an isotherm. Since, however, for rubber $\alpha_0 < 0$, heating and cooling at constant strain have an inverted effect on stress compared with a metal. The stress in an extended rubber band increases when its temperature is raised. A sketch of the isotherms of rubber is shown in Figure 8.16(b).

The ruled, spiral-like surface represented by equation (8.29) and by the level lines of Figure 8.16(a) degenerates to the plane

$$\epsilon = \frac{\sigma}{E} + \alpha(\theta - \theta_0) \tag{8.31}$$

when both $E = $ const and $\alpha = $ const may be assumed.

TABLE 8.2
Modulus of Elasticity (Young's Modulus), E, of
Several Steels as a Function of Temperature†

Material	Modulus of elasticity $E/10^6(\text{lbf/in}^2)$ at temperature θ				
	20°C	100°C	200°C	400°C	600°C
Carbon steel	30.4	29.8	28.9	26.3	23.6
Low-alloy steel	30.6	30.1	29.3	27.2	23.8
Ni–Cr steel	28.0	27.1	26.0	22.8	19.0

† A more detailed table can be found in *Metals Reference Book* (Butterworths, 1962), p. 614.

8.4.4   Work

When a rod is strained quasistatically, the applied force F performs work in an amount given by

$$dW = -FdL = -AL_0\sigma \, d\epsilon. \tag{8.32}$$

The negative sign has been inserted because tensile stresses are counted positive but perform (negative) work *on* the system for positive increments in strain. The product AL_0 represents the volume of the rod, V_0, at the natural state, and the product ϵV_0 can be interpreted as a measure of strain in the whole system, that is, a precise measure of the combined change in volume and shape. Owing to the presence of an external, atmospheric pressure, an additional amount of work

$$dW_a = P_a V_0 \, d\epsilon$$

is performed, but this contribution can be neglected unless P_a is of the order of the stress itself.

It is convenient to introduce specific quantities referred to a unit of volume of the system. Thus, the work per unit volume (for which the symbol dW will be retained) is

$$dW = -\sigma \, d\epsilon; \tag{8.32a}$$

it has the familiar form $dW = Y \, dZ$ with

$$Y = -\sigma \quad \text{and} \quad Z = \epsilon \tag{8.32b}$$

of a product of an intensive quantity into the differential of a specific quantity, in the same way as the expression $dW = P \, dv$ for work per unit mass of a pure substance.

It was stated before that the essential difference between stressing in the elastic range as opposed to the plastic range lies in the fact that the former process is reversible, whereas the latter is irreversible. We shall evidence this difference by writing

$$dW° = -\sigma \, d\epsilon \quad \text{for the elastic range, and} \quad (8.32c)$$
$$dW = -\sigma \, d\epsilon \quad \text{in the plastic range,} \quad (8.32d)$$

the superscript ° serving as a reminder of the reversible nature of the process.

In our general discussion of the work of quasistatic processes in Section 4.7 it was pointed out that the parameters in the expression for *reversible* work constitute properties of the system. Hence, both σ and ϵ appear in the thermal equations of state, equations (8.29) and (8.31), of an elastic system. The same is not true about the equation for the irreversible process in the plastic range, and we must conclude that at least one of the parameters σ and ϵ in equation (8.32d) does not represent a property of the system in the plastic range. This remark will help us in resolving the paradox of the apparent nonexistence of an equation of state discussed at the end of Section 8.4.2.

8.4.5   *Strain energy in an elastic system*

The expression for work in an elastic system can be integrated if the relation between stress and strain is known along the path of the process. When the system performs a reversible isothermal process the amount of work is

$$dW° = -E\epsilon \, d\epsilon = -\frac{\sigma}{E} \, d\sigma \quad \text{(for } \theta = \text{const).} \quad (8.33)$$

The negative of the total work performed reversibly and at constant temperature from a state of zero stress, that is, when its strain with respect to the natural state is equal to the thermal strain, is known in the theory of elasticity as the *strain energy* $\mathcal{E}$ of the system. When α and E are functions of temperature alone, the strain energy is obtained by integration from $\epsilon_{th} = \alpha(\theta - \theta_0)$ to ϵ or from $\sigma = 0$ to σ. Hence,

$$\mathcal{E} = -W°_{1,2} = \tfrac{1}{2}E[\epsilon - \alpha(\theta - \theta_0)]^2 = \frac{\sigma^2}{2E} \quad \text{(at } \theta = \text{const).} \quad (8.34)$$

Thus, the isothermal, reversible work per unit volume between states 1 and 2 for which $\theta_1 = \theta_2$ can be represented as a difference in two values of strain energy

$$W°_{1,2} = \mathcal{E}_1 - \mathcal{E}_2 = \tfrac{1}{2}E\{[\epsilon_1 - \alpha(\theta - \theta_0)]^2 - [\epsilon_2 - \alpha(\theta - \theta_0)]^2\} = \frac{\sigma_1^2 - \sigma_2^2}{2E} \quad (\theta = \text{const). (8.34a)}$$

The strain energy is *not* equal to the energy of the system u† per unit volume. Applying the First Law of thermodynamics to this reversible process, we find that

$$du = dQ° + \sigma \, d\epsilon. \quad (8.35)$$

If, as is common in elasticity theory, attention is centered on isothermal processes, we can write

$$d(u - \mathcal{E}) = dQ° \quad (\theta = \text{const only),} \quad (8.35a)$$

† We use the symbol u rather than e to avoid confusion with the modulus of elasticity E when the equations are transcribed for a complete system instead of a unit volume.

which shows that the difference between energy and strain energy is exactly equal to the amount of heat which the system must exchange reversibly with the surroundings at temperature θ. Contrary to what is stated in some elementary books on elasticity, the quantity of heat $Q°$ required to maintain the system at constant temperature is not small compared with the strain energy. In fact it is large, being 20 times the strain energy for aluminum and as much as 40 times for nickel or steel during a process of stressing from the natural state to the yield point, as we shall see in Volume II. The reader may also be interested to know that the quantity of heat $Q°$ required to maintain a constant temperature in a metal in tension is positive, being negative (and quite small) for a rubber band under similar conditions. From this point of view the term "strain energy" is unfortunate. We shall discover later that the strain energy is identical with a thermodynamic potential which we shall call free energy or the Helmholtz function. The process of exchanging heat during reversible, isothermal loading or unloading is sometimes referred to as the *thermoelastic effect*.

8.4.6 *The inelastic range*

In order to acquire an understanding of the process of plastic deformation, it is best to begin with the highly idealized case of an *elastic-ideally plastic* body. Reference to Figure 8.14 shows that some materials possess a short range in which plastic deformation occurs at a constant yield stress σ_y. A hypothetical material for which this is true over the whole plastic range is known as elastic-ideally plastic. The isothermal stress-strain diagram of an elastic-ideally plastic material which obeys Hooke's law is shown sketched in Figure 8.17. After being loaded elastically from the natural state 0 to the yield point Y, the system increases its strain at a constant value of stress. Unloading from any point a on the yield line $\sigma = \sigma_y$ releases a reversible process and allows the system to reach any state along the new elastic range ab. When the elastic process is continued into the compressive range, it is possible (ideally) to eliminate the permanent sct $0b$ and to return the system to its natural state. In this manner the system is made

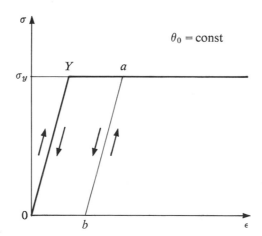

FIGURE 8.17. *Isothermal stress-strain diagram for an ideally plastic body which obeys Hooke's law in the elastic range.*

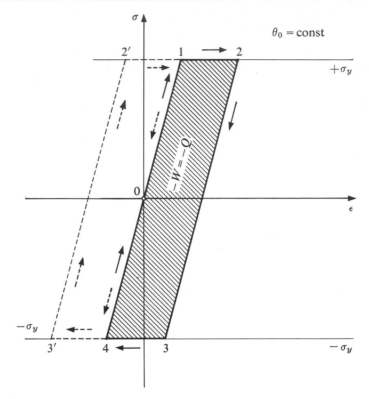

FIGURE 8.18. *Hysteresis loop.*

to perform a *hysteresis loop.* Such an idealized hysteresis loop 012340 is shown sketched in Figure 8.18. Experience shows that as a result of the performance of a hysteresis loop, the system consumes a certain quantity of work W, always negative, and rejects an *equivalent* amount of heat Q, the heat being also always negative. Moreover, at constant temperature the heat rejected, dQ, exactly balances the work absorbed, dW, at every step of the process. This fact is expressed by saying that the work W is *dissipated* into heat by the system, rather like in friction when the temperature is maintained constant. An attempt to reverse the process would not be successful, and the process 043′2′10 would be performed, testifying to the inherent irreversibility of plastic deformation. This second loop would also dissipate work, the conversion of heat into work in the manner of a reversible cycle being impossible. Thus the hysteresis loop constitutes an irreversible cycle. In view of equations (8.32c) and (8.32d), it is clear that the area 012340 encompassed by this cycle is equal to the negative of the total work performed during the cycle as would be the case with a completely reversible cycle; this area is also equal to the negative of the net heat exchanged. The difference between this process and a reversible cycle lies in the circumstance that the former cannot whereas the latter can be reversed completely.

We can apply the First Law of thermodynamics to such an irreversible cycle, and conclude that

$$Q = \oint dQ = \oint dW = W \qquad (Q < 0; W < 0). \qquad (8.36)$$

The work W consists of the sum of the quantities performed along 01, 12, 23, 34, and 40. Hence,

$$-W = \int_{41} \sigma \, d\epsilon + \int_{12} \sigma \, d\epsilon + \int_{23} \sigma \, d\epsilon + \int_{34} \sigma \, d\epsilon. \tag{8.36a}$$

The process of unloading 23 is an exact reverse of the process of loading 41, and

$$\int_{41} \sigma \, d\epsilon + \int_{23} \sigma \, d\epsilon = 0. \tag{8.36b}$$

The same is true about the reversible heat, so that, consequently,

$$Q = \int_{12} dQ + \int_{34} dQ \quad \text{and} \quad -W = \int_{12} \sigma \, d\epsilon + \int_{34} \sigma \, d\epsilon. \tag{8.37}$$

In order to calculate the changes in energy u, we add the quantities of heat to those of negative work, and obtain

$$Q - W = \int_{12} (dQ + \sigma \, d\epsilon) + \int_{34} (dQ + \sigma \, d\epsilon).$$

As we know, experiments show that

$$\int (dQ + \sigma \, d\epsilon) = 0 \qquad (\theta = \text{const}), \tag{8.38}$$

regardless of the magnitude of the plastic deformation. Recalling the form of the First Law, $du = dQ + \sigma \, d\epsilon$, we discover that *the internal energy of the system remains constant during isothermal plastic deformation.*

We now compare the state of the system at any two points along the yield line $\sigma = \pm \sigma_y$ and notice that the stress and the temperature, as well as the energy, remain constant, and that the only variable quantity is the strain. Since the state of the system depends on two properties only, and all along the plastic line as many as three retain fixed values, we must accept the result that *isothermal plastic straining does not change the state of the system,* and that, therefore, the variable strain ϵ does not constitute a parameter of state.[†] Plastic deformation appears to be a process of energy dissipation at constant state, rather like the shearing of a lamina of fluid described in Section 8.3.

In order to identify the proper strain parameter for an arbitrary point a along the yield line, it is expedient to allow the system to unload and to "relax" to point b, Figure 8.19. For this process, the reversible work is

$$dW^\circ = \sigma \, d\epsilon^\circ,$$

where ϵ° is measured from point b. It is now clear that the total strain ϵ from which the permanent set ϵ_s has been subtracted, and not the total strain ϵ itself, constitutes the true parameter of state at an intermediate point c. We, therefore, split the total strain according to the equation

$$\epsilon = \epsilon_s + \epsilon^\circ, \tag{8.39}$$

[†] This conclusion seems to have been first enunciated in this book. See also Bridgman, P. W., "The Thermodynamics of Plastic Deformation," Rev. Mod. Phy., **22** (1950) 56.

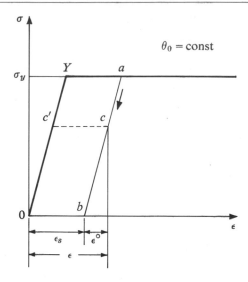

FIGURE 8.19. *Identification of state variables.*

and note that only the *reversible strain* ϵ° can enter the thermal equation of state or the expression for energy, u. We record this by writing

$$\left(\frac{\partial u}{\partial \epsilon_s}\right)_\theta \equiv 0 \quad \text{but} \quad \left(\frac{\partial u}{\partial \epsilon^\circ}\right)_\theta \not\equiv 0. \tag{8.39a}$$

On comparing the elastic strains at points such as c and c' in Figure 8.19, for which the stresses are the same, we infer that they represent identical states. Thus, the thermal equations of state (8.29) or (8.31) remain valid in the plastic range on condition that $\epsilon^\circ = \epsilon - \epsilon_s$ is substituted for ϵ. This induces us to make a clear distinction between an isothermal stress-strain diagram and an isotherm in a stress-strain *state diagram*. The latter is shown sketched in Figure 8.20 and displays two isotherms, $\theta_0 = \text{const}$ and $\theta > \theta_0 \, (= \text{const})$ according to equation (8.31). Naturally, only the reversible stress

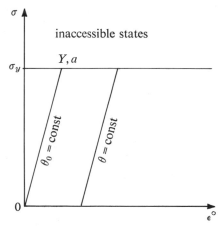

FIGURE 8.20. *State diagram.*

ϵ° may now be used as a coordinate. Since the present idealized system can never sustain a stress which exceeds the yield stress $\pm\sigma_y$, the parts of the diagram for $|\sigma| > \sigma_y$ represent states which are completely inaccessible to the system.

We note for future reference that at any temperature

$$\epsilon^\circ = \frac{\sigma}{E(\theta)} \tag{8.40}$$

for a material which obeys Hooke's law, and that the expressions of work should be written

$$dW^\circ = -\sigma \, d\epsilon^\circ \quad \text{(elastic)} \tag{8.41a}$$
$$dW = -\sigma \, d\epsilon_s \quad \text{(plastic)}. \tag{8.41b}$$

The preceding results can also be understood from an interpretation of the characteristics of plastic deformation revealed by metallurgists. Detailed microscopic[†] observation show that metals are not truly homogeneous but consist of a large number of small but still macroscopic, sensibly homogeneous crystalline grains. During plastic deformation it is observed that macroscopic parts of the system are displaced with respect to each other along discrete crystallographic planes within the grains, the rearrangement requiring the performance of plastic work according to equation (8.41b). At constant temperature, the equivalent of this work is removed in the form of a flux of heat. In the ideal case there is no further elastic deformation and the whole system remains at a constant state. It appears that the rearrangement in the system produces merely a change in shape, the volume remaining constant. Hence, the system begins to slip when the internal energy associated with its deformed shape has reached a maximum value. This aspect is connected with a very famous *yield criterion* in the theory of the strength of materials discovered independently (but not at the same time) by M. T. Huber in Poland, R. von Mises in Germany, and B. P. Haugh in Great Britain. A detailed exposition of this connection would exceed the scope of this course.

8.4.7 Strain-hardening

The principles established in the preceding section for an elastic-ideally plastic material carry over to the case of a strain-hardening material with little modification.[‡] The diagram in Figure 8.21 represents a somewhat idealized hysteresis loop with the reversible portions 41 and 23, and the irreversible, strain-hardening portions 12 and 34. The lowering of the yield limit upon compression from 2 to 3 displayed in the diagram is actually observed and is known as the *Bauschinger effect*, whereas the yield strength at 4 is (at least approximately) equal to that at 1, the yield strength in compression at 3 after the material had been first extended beyond the yield point is lowered. The existence of the Bauschinger effect makes it possible to perform a hysteresis loop with a strain-hardening material. Equation (8.36) remains valid, but equation (8.36a) must now be written

$$-W = \int_{3'1} \cdots + \int_{12} \cdots + \int_{21'} \cdots + \int_{1'3} \cdots + \int_{34} \cdots + \int_{43'} \cdots . \tag{8.42}$$

† Through a microscope, that is, not on an atomic scale!
‡ It must, however, be stressed that the ensuing description is grossly simplified.

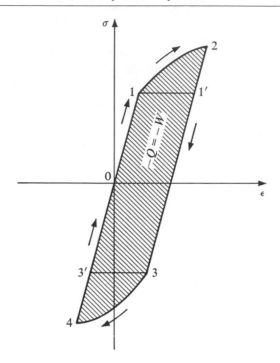

FIGURE 8.21. *Hysteresis in a strain-hardening material.*

In this case, the integrals of reversible heat and work cancel only along $3'1$ and $1'3$, and the counterpart of equation (8.37) must be written

$$Q = \int_{12} dQ + \int_{21'} dQ + \int_{34} dQ + \int_{43'} dQ \quad \text{and} \quad -W = \int_{12} \sigma \, d\epsilon + \int_{21'} \sigma \, d\epsilon + \int_{34} \sigma \, d\epsilon + \int_{43'} \sigma \, d\epsilon. \quad (8.42a)$$

Continuing the argument of the preceding section, it is noticed that strain-hardening causes the integrals along the reversible paths $21'$ and $43'$ to remain in the expressions. It is not difficult to accept now that the change in the energy u along the irreversible path 12 is exactly equal and opposite in sign to that along the reversible path $21'$, and that the same is true for paths 34 and $43'$. Since states 2 and 4 are chosen arbitrarily (on condition that the stress there is smaller than the rupture stress σ_r), it is easy to see that states of equal stress are identical regardless of the differences in strain.

In order to identify the stress parameter which represents a thermodynamic property, we use the device of determining the expression for reversible work in unloading, and conclude that the reversible stress

$$\epsilon^{\circ} = \frac{\sigma}{E(\theta)} \quad (8.43)$$

with

$$\epsilon = \epsilon_s + \epsilon^{\circ} \quad (8.44)$$

continues to play that part. The method of determining ϵ° is suggested by Figure 8.22 which is in essence identical with Figure 8.19, except for the fact that the yield stress

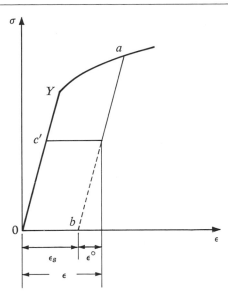

FIGURE 8.22. *The reversible stress $\epsilon°$.*

σ_y is now variable, being given by an empirical relation, instead of being constant. The thermal equation of state with the substitution of $\epsilon°$ for ϵ and equations (8.41a, b) retain their validity, together with the condition (8.39a) for internal energy. The state diagram is identical with that shown previously in Figure 8.20, except that the field of inaccessible states is bounded by the rupture stress σ_r instead of the yield stress σ_y. Such a diagram is shown in Figure 8.23 in which only one isotherm $\theta = \theta_0$ has been drawn, but in which the relation of this isotherm to the yield curve has been indicated.

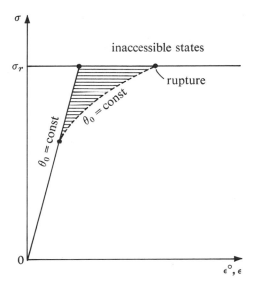

FIGURE 8.23. *The state diagram σ, $\epsilon°$ with stress-strain diagram σ, ϵ superimposed on it.*

The horizontal lines show points on the yield curve and the true isotherm θ_0 whose states are identical.

In the isothermal stress-strain diagram of Figure 8.24, area $0Yaa'$ represents the negative of the total work of straining at constant temperature. Area baa' represents the strain energy at a, that is, the negative of the reversible work of straining to point a. The difference (or the shaded area $0Yab$) represents the heat which must be extracted from the system during the *irreversible* portion of the process Ya. The reversible heat exchanged along the elastic portion $0Y$ is not included. In general, the elementary strip $maa'm'$ represents $dW = -\sigma\, d\epsilon$, the elementary strip $mabn$ represents the plastic work $dW_p = -\sigma\, d\epsilon_s$, whereas the elementary strip $paa'p'$ represents the reversible work $dW^\circ = -\sigma\, d\epsilon^\circ$.

According to many experiments, the strain-hardening portion of an isothermal stress-strain diagram can be expressed by the empirical equation

$$\epsilon - \frac{\sigma_y}{E} = \left(\frac{\sigma - \sigma_y}{B}\right)^n \qquad (\text{at } \theta = \text{const}) \tag{8.45}$$

in which n is known as the *strain-hardening exponent*. The stress σ_y corresponds to the lowest yield point Y in Figure 8.22, and this constant, together with the constants B and n, is different for different materials. The strain-hardening exponent is usually high and of the order of 10 to 20. The constant B is of an order of magnitude which is comparable with Young's modulus E.

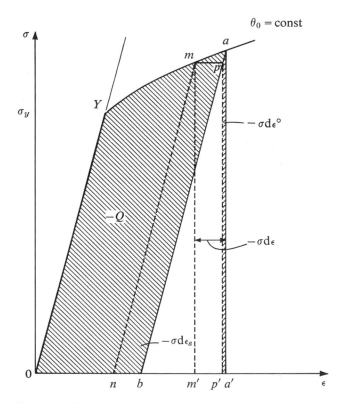

FIGURE 8.24. *Areas in the isothermal stress-strain diagram.*

8.4.8 *A remark on equilibrium*

When a thin plastic-ideally elastic rod is loaded by a force which produces in it a stress σ in excess of the yield stress σ_y, the rod will appear to flow indefinitely, never reaching equilibrium. Thus, it may be thought that the behavior of this type of system contradicts the principle which was enunciated in Section 2.10 and which asserted that every system reaches a state of equilibrium within the bounds of its constraints. The present apparently contradictory conclusion was reached as a result of an excessive simplification introduced into the analysis. First, the force which exceeds the one needed to produce yield will accelerate the elements of the rod in flow and, eventually, it will become necessary to include in our considerations the kinetic energy of the system. In other words, the process will not be truly quasistatic as stipulated. Secondly, all real materials begin to strain-harden and the system will either reach equilibrium at one of the higher yield points or else it will rupture. In the latter case it will also, eventually, reach a state of equilibrium. Finally, the cross-sectional area will not remain constant throughout, and the analysis will have to be continued in terms of a continuous system. In fact, the system will eventually reach a new state of equilibrium as asserted originally.

8.4.9 *Creep and relaxation*

So far, we have assumed that an elastic system subjected to a stress σ will indefinitely retain the strain ϵ which corresponds to it at temperature θ. In other words, we assumed that the equation of state had the form of a relation

$$f(\epsilon, \sigma, \theta) = 0 \tag{8.46}$$

between stress, strain, and temperature, as indicated earlier in equation (8.21a). The complication which occurred in the presence of plastic deformation was connected with the fact that only the elastic portion ϵ° of the strain could be included in the equation.

The fact that the equation of state of a stressed solid is of the form of equation (8.46) conforms with experiments conducted on a relatively short time scale only. Experiments which extend over periods of time measured in thousands of hours reveal the existence of further complications in the properties of metallic and other solid materials.

When a rod is strained by a static load which produces in it a definite stress σ in the elastic range, it will, of course, elongate to a definite strain ϵ in an environment of given temperature θ as recorded in equation (8.46). Continuing observation over long periods of time, particularly at higher, though constant, temperatures, reveals that the strain ϵ does not retain its initial value indefinitely, but increases continuously with time at a very slow rate. This process is known as *creep*. Thus, on a larger time scale of observation, the equation of state cannot possibly be of the form of equation (8.46), because $\sigma = $ const and $\theta = $ const does not imply $\epsilon = $ const, as demanded by it.

Similarly, if a rod is extended elastically to a given strain, ϵ, it is necessary to produce in it a definite stress, σ, at a given temperature, θ. Now, if arrangements are made to maintain a constant strain in the rod at $\theta = $ const, measurement extended over very long periods of time reveal that the stress in the rod decreases with time, the process in question being described by the term *relaxation*.

During the processes of creep and relaxation two of the three properties which appear in equation (8.46) remain constant while the third property undergoes a change. This signifies that an equation of state containing three properties only, that is, one of the form of equation (8.46), can no longer describe the state of the system. We must, therefore, come to the conclusion that the equation of state for a system undergoing creep or relaxation contains at least one more property. At the present state of knowledge, it is not possible to indicate with assurance the physical nature of this additional property or to state that only one additional property is involved. For the sake of the present argument, we shall assume that only one additional property is involved, and we shall denote it by the symbol ξ. Hence, we will write the equation of state in the form

$$F(\epsilon, \sigma, \theta, \xi) = 0. \qquad (8.46a)$$

When observed on a short time scale, the system behaves as if $\xi = \text{const}$. Viewed on a long time scale, with $\theta = \text{const}$ and $\sigma = \text{const}$ in creep or $\epsilon = \text{const}$ during relaxation, it is observed that the property ξ varies, forcing a variation of ϵ in creep and of σ during relaxation. It is noted, evidently, that the very slow variation of strain (creep) or stress (relaxation) with time signifies that ξ varies very slowly with time too. It will be discovered later in Volume II that a similar set of circumstances exists in systems undergoing very slow chemical reactions.

According to this view, a solid body subjected to stress undergoes a very slow process, which, owing to its slowness, remains undetected during observations of relatively short duration. In such cases, the system can be treated as if this slow process were impeded or arrested ($\xi = \text{const}$). During observations extending over a long period of time, this is not admissible. Thus, the system is seen to change its state when two of its parameters are kept constant, and exists, at every instant, in a state of quasiequilibrium only, undergoing an internal change but at a very slow rate. This internal change is described by the parameter ξ which, for this reason, is called an *internal degree of freedom*, or an *internal parameter of state* (property).

It is thought that the internal parameters of state are introduced into the system by slow processes of intercrystalline diffusion and possible chemical reactions.

8.4.10   Viscoelasticity

So far, we have assumed that all processes of loading and unloading occurred at such low rates that differences in them had no effect on the process. In other words, we studied the limit when the strain rate $\dot{\epsilon} \to 0$. Experiments show that at finite and high rates of strain $\dot{\epsilon}$, the stress-strain curves become displaced upwards. A highly simplified diagram for an elastic material which obeys Hooke's law is shown sketched in Figure 8.25. For a given temperature, there exists a separate stress-strain relation for each value of $\dot{\epsilon}$ which now appears as a parameter. The first impulse is to assume that the equation of state has acquired an additional variable, $\dot{\epsilon}$, and to write it as

$$f(\sigma, \epsilon, \dot{\epsilon}, \theta) = 0. \qquad (8.47)$$

However, this would be an erroneous conclusion, because experiments indicate that only the process at $\dot{\epsilon} = 0$ is reversible, the processes at $\dot{\epsilon} > 0$ being irreversible. This observation contradicts equation (8.47), because, if it applied, it would be possible to devise a reversible process, that is, a sequence of equilibrium states, characterized by

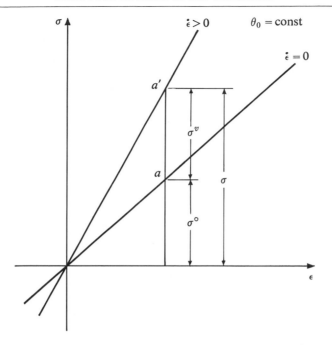

FIGURE 8.25. *Viscoelasticity.*

the constraint that $\dot{\epsilon} = $ const. This is possible for $\dot{\epsilon} = 0$ only, and the appearance of $\dot{\epsilon}$ as a thermodynamic property is thereby excluded.

The rate of performing (irreversible) work at $\dot{\epsilon} > 0$ is

$$\dot{W} = -\sigma\,\dot{\epsilon},$$

which is equivalent to

$$dW = -\sigma\,d\epsilon. \tag{8.48}$$

Similarly, for $\dot{\epsilon} = 0$ the reversible work is

$$dW^\circ = -\sigma^\circ\,d\epsilon, \tag{8.49}$$

but now $\sigma^\circ < \sigma$ as is known from experiment. This identifies σ° as the true parameter of state for a given set of values of ϵ and θ. It follows that now the stress must be subdivided into a reversible portion σ° and a viscous portion σ^v, with

$$\sigma = \sigma^v + \sigma^\circ. \tag{8.50}$$

From the point of view of thermodynamics, states a and a' are identical, and the elastic equation of state (8.29) or (8.31) can continue to be used subject to the substitution of σ° for σ. The expressions for work are

$$\dot{W} = -\sigma\dot{\epsilon} \quad \text{and} \quad \dot{W}^\circ = -\sigma^\circ\dot{\epsilon}, \tag{8.51}$$

and the energy cannot depend on σ^v but exclusively on σ°. Thus,

$$\left(\frac{\partial u}{\partial \sigma^v}\right) \equiv 0 \quad \text{but} \quad \left(\frac{\partial u}{\partial \sigma^\circ}\right) \neq 0. \tag{8.52}$$

The process undergone by a viscoelastic rod is in many ways analogous to the example of Couette flow in Section 8.3. Here, the excess stress σ^v plays the same part as the shearing stress in a viscous fluid causing dissipation of work into heat.

Viscoelastic behavior can also be caused by variations in the internal variable ξ in equation (8.46a). At this stage, we are not in a position to substantiate this statement, and must defer a more detailed discussion to Volume II.†

8.4.11   A remark on rupture

All known materials rupture if the stress imposed upon them is sufficiently large. Just before rupture, the system is strained plastically, and is in a near-equilibrium state, but the corresponding equilibrium state is known. After rupture, the system acquires a new equilibrium state, characterized by the fact that its cohesion has now been lost. In order to return to the original state, it would be necessary to melt the two parts of the system and so to restore their union. It is then possible to repeat the processes which created the original equilibrium state and to recreate it, if necessary, even reversibly in this manner. It appears that all those steps can be analyzed by the methods of classical thermodynamics, even though the complexity of such an analysis is overwhelming. This complexity prevents us from including rupture in the list of processes normally studied in classical thermodynamics.

8.4.12   Electrical resistance of a wire strained elastically

The electric resistivity ρ of a thin rod or wire is also a property, the total resistance being

$$R = \rho AL.$$

It follows that in the elastic range the resistance R must be a function of two independent properties of the system, say, of the strain ϵ and the temperature θ,

$$R = R(\theta, \epsilon). \tag{8.53}$$

Thus, a thin homogeneous wire can be used as a measuring instrument for either one of the independent variables, θ or ϵ. In the first case we obtain the already familiar *resistance thermometer*, and the form of equation (8.53) clearly demonstrates the importance of maintaining the strain ϵ at a constant value in actual applications. It is easiest to maintain it at $\epsilon = 0$ during calibration and measurement, but care must be taken to eliminate thermal stresses on cooling by suitably designing the thermometer mounting. Improper design may lead to serious errors from this source.

In the second case we obtain a *strain gauge*. The wire is mounted on a specimen, usually by bonding, in such a way that its own strain bears a definite relation to the strain of a specimen. As a rule the strains are equal, and this fact is established by calibration, so that a measurement of the electric resistance will enable us to determine the strain ϵ of the strain gauge, and hence that of the specimen. Since the electric resistance R depends on temperature in addition to strain, it is essential to maintain a constant temperature and to correct, or compensate, for temperature differences which inevitably arise during the measurement.

† In this connection see Meixner, J., "Relaxationserscheinungen und ihre thermodynamische Behandlung," Ned. Tijdschr. Natuurk, **26** (1960), 259.

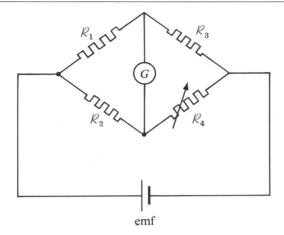

FIGURE 8.26. *Typical arrangement for measuring strains.*

The alloys used for strain gauges (for example, the alloy "Advance") produce a change in resistance of about 0.2% per 0.1% change in length. In order to measure the change in resistance, it is possible to use a Wheatstone bridge, the compensating strain gage and the one used for measurement being shunted into two adjoining arms of the bridge. A typical arrangement for measuring strains is shown in Figure 8.26. Here R_1 and R_2 denote the resistances of the measuring strain gauge and of the compensating strain gauge, respectively. The resistance of the measuring strain gauge differs from its value R_0 at zero strain and at the reference temperature by two quantities, by a resistance R' due to the change in temperature from its reference value θ_0 to its value at the measuring station, θ. The second quantity R'' is due to an increase in strain, so that

$$R_1 = R_0 + R' + R''.$$

On the other hand the compensating strain gauge is arranged to remain unstrained, and to undergo only a change in resistance R' due to an identical change in temperature. This can usually be achieved by proper mounting. Hence,

$$R_2 = R_0 + R'.$$

When the bridge is balanced, we have

$$\frac{R_1}{R_2} = \frac{R_0 + R' + R''}{R_0 + R'} = \frac{R_3}{R_4},$$

where the ratio

$$k = \frac{R_3}{R_4}$$

is known from the measurement. It is then easy to derive that

$$R'' = (k - 1) R_0 + (k - 1)R'.$$

Since k is rather close to unity, and since R' is usually much smaller than R_0, the temperature correction can be neglected in this equation, giving

$$R'' \approx (k-1) \, R_0.$$

In the absence of compensation, we would have

$$R_1 = R_0 + R' + R'',$$

and the resistance R_2 would be set arbitrarily; it is usually adjusted so that $R_2 \approx R_0$. The measurement would then yield

$$\frac{R_0 + R' + R''}{R_0} = \frac{R_3}{R_4} = k,$$

and

$$R'' = (k-1) \, R_0 - R'.$$

Thus, the change in resistance due to a change in temperature, R', is seen to enter the equation to its full value, instead of being multiplied by the small number $k-1$ when the compensation principle is applied.

8.5 Systems interacting through fields

With the exception of gravitation, we have so far considered systems which exchanged work with the surroundings by contiguous action only. In the present section we propose to discuss cases in which forces exerted at a distance play a part in modifying the state of a system and in performing work on it. The most essential physical concept which is employed for the description of action at a distance is that of a *field* which may exist in empty space as well as in matter. This concept replaces the need to discuss action at a distance—which is physically unsatisfactory—by the interaction with a contiguous physical entity—the field.

In this section we shall concern ourselves with gravitational, electrostatic, and magnetostatic fields only. Normally, at any instant of time, the intensities of the field vary with position in a continuous way. Thus, in the presence of a field, the system is essentially a continuous one. When the field varies with time, the system undergoes a process.

The variation of the field intensities can be thought of as produced by the displacement of masses in a gravitational field, or of electric charges in an electrostatic field. In a magnetostatic field, the electric charges are displaced through conductors in the form of currents.

We assume that the reader has studied such fields in his courses in mechanics and electromagnetism.† It should be realized that in such studies the possibility that the

---

† Elementary accounts can be found in Halliday, D., and Resnick, A., *Physics for Students of Science and Engineering* (Wiley, 1962), in particular Chaps. 16 and 26–37. More advanced accounts can be found in the following: Gravitation—Planck, M., "General Mechanics," in *Introduction to Theoretical Physics*, transl. by H. L. Brose (Macmillan, 1933); Landau, L., and Lifshitz, E., *The Classical Theory of Fields*, transl. by M. Hamermesh (Addison-Wesley, 1951). Electricity and Magnetism—Becker, R., and Sauter, F., *Electromagnetic Theory and Relativity*, transl. by A. W. Knudsen, in *Electromagnetic Fields and Interactions*, Vol. 1 (Blaisdell, 1964), particularly Sec. 33, p. 118; Landau, L. D., and Lifshitz, E. M., *Electrodynamics of Continuous Media* (Vol. VIII of *Course in Theoretical Physics*) transl. by J. B. Sykes and J. S. Bell (Addison-Wesley, 1960), particularly Sec. 10, p. 47; Sec. 11, p. 52; Sec. 30, p. 126; Sec. 31, p. 129; and Sec. 32, p. 131. A very terse but incisive exposition can be found in a paper by Meixner, J., "Thermodynamik in Gegenwart elektromagnetischer Felder," Intern. J. Eng. Sci., **1** (1963), 177.

system may exchange heat with the surroundings and that its temperature may change is ignored. Consequently, in a manner reminiscent of elasticity (Section 8.4.5), the expression for work can be integrated and appears as electrostatic and magnetostatic energy of the field. However, in general this is not the case, and we must develop a criterion which will enable us to make this distinction.

When the concept of a field is employed, it is said that the whole field "stores energy," and an *energy density* is associated with every elementary volume dV of the field. It follows that the *whole field* must be included as part of the system, as we shall see in detail in Section 8.5.3.

All three types of fields exert distributed forces on material systems and produce in them strains and stresses. We shall discuss stress and strain fields in Volume II, but will neglect their existence in our present account, except for noting that they give rise to additional work terms. The appearance of stresses in material systems placed in electrostatic and magnetostatic fields is described by the terms *electrostriction* and *magnetostriction*. No special term is used for the corresponding effect in a gravitational field.

The study of fields is best begun by considering a uniform system placed in a uniform field. The expression for work in such a system together with our physical understanding of its characteristics enables us to determine the number of independent thermodynamic properties which are needed to describe its state, and recognize the form of its thermal equation of state. The principle of local state serves to extend our understanding to truly continuous systems.

The principal difficulty is to recognize the manner in which the field intensities must enter into the thermodynamic description of the state. We propose to discuss this problem first in general terms, bearing in mind the particular examples of a gravitational field (Section 7.1) and of an elastic rod (Section 8.4.5).

8.5.1 *Criterion for the additivity of field energy*

Whether or not an integrated work term represents an additive term in the expression for energy depends on the characteristics of the process, and can be judged with reference to the First Law written for a *reversible* process,[†]

$$d\mathcal{U} = dQ^\circ - dW^\circ. \tag{8.54}$$

In this expression the work dW° will, in general, consist of a term

$$dW_1^\circ = -Y\, dZ, \tag{8.55}$$

where the variables Y and Z refer to the field in a uniform system. The expression d$W^\circ = -\mathcal{E}\, dz$ in equation (4.28) for a galvanic cell was of this type; the negative sign is added merely for our future convenience. In addition, work may be performed in some other way, for example, by a deformation of the boundary through electrostriction or magnetostriction. We shall use the symbol dW_2° for this work, and display only one such term. Generalization to several terms of this kind, when required, presents no difficulty.

The form of expression (8.55) allows us to choose the variables Y and Z as independent, because, as we know from Section 4.7, they must represent true parameters of state. If more than two variables are independent, we can add as many (provisionally

---

† Since the symbol E will be required for the absolute value of the electric field intensity **E**, we employ the symbol $\mathcal{U}$ for total energy.

unspecified) variables x_i to make up the required number. Thus, the thermal equation of state will be of the form

$$\theta = \theta(Y, Z, x_i), \tag{8.56}$$

where the symbol x_i stands for several variables. Now one of two cases may arise.

Case A. Energies are additive
  The *adiabatic* work

$$dW^\circ_{\text{ad}} = -Y \, dZ$$

does *not* produce a change in temperature or x_i, and conversely, a change in x_i or temperature does not change Y or Z. For example, this is the case with gravitation or with electrostatic and magnetostatic systems in empty space. There exists then a unique relation

$$F(Y, Z) \tag{8.56a}$$

between the variables Y and Z during a reversible, adiabatic process. In our examples this relation will turn out to be a linear one, and we can write it as

$$Z = CY \qquad (C = \text{const}), \tag{8.57}$$

with C independent of temperature and x_i. Then the adiabatic work associated with a process in which only Y and Z change from zero to some finite value is

$$W^\circ_{\text{ad}} = -\int_0^Z Y \, dZ \qquad \text{along reversible adiabatic path.}$$

In view of relation (8.57), this integral can be worked out explicitly, and its value becomes independent of the path. In our present case

$$W^\circ_{\text{ad}} = -\frac{1}{2} \, CY^2 = -\frac{1}{2} \frac{Z^2}{C}. \tag{8.58}$$

This proves that W°_{ad} constitutes a potential for the Pfaffian (8.55) regardless of whether the temperature θ and the variables x_i are kept constant or not. Moreover, the expression (8.58) represents the change in the energy of the system at $\theta = \text{const}$ and $x_i = \text{const}$ when Y and Z change from zero to their prescribed values.

  The *negative* of the expression in equation (8.58) is called a potential energy (gravitational, electrostatic, magnetostatic) for which we shall use the symbol U_p. Thus,

$$U_p = \frac{1}{2} \, CY^2 = \frac{1}{2} \frac{Z^2}{C}, \quad \text{and} \quad dW^\circ_{\text{ad}} = -dU_p. \tag{8.58a, b}$$

It is seen from equation (8.57) that the two variables Y, Z cease to be independent under the present circumstances. Moreover, a change in either of them produces no change in temperature. Hence, the equation of state (8.56) assumes the simplified form

$$\theta = \theta(x_i), \tag{8.59}$$

which, together with the independent equation (8.57), replaces the original, more complicated form.

  We now imagine a process during which the variables x_i are changed by dx_i at $Y = 0$ and $Z = 0$, causing a change in the temperature θ and energy U. The First Law for this process is

$$d\mathcal{U} = dQ^\circ - dW_x \qquad (= dU) \tag{8.60}$$

and the variation in total energy $\mathcal{U}$ is equal to the variation in what in Section 5.6 was called the *internal* energy U. We now follow up this process with one during which the variables Y and Z are changed. This process involves no further addition of heat. Thus,

$$d\mathcal{U} = dQ^\circ - dW_x - dW_i^\circ, \tag{8.61}$$

where dW_i° is performed adiabatically. Combining equations (8.60) and (8.58b) with equation (8.61), we can write the First Law as

$$d\mathcal{U} = dU + dU_p \quad \text{or} \quad \mathcal{U} = U + U_p. \tag{8.62}$$

Thus, we have demonstrated that under our present assumptions the potential field energy U_p is simply added to the internal energy of the system.

Recapitulating, we recognize that the additivity of the internal and potential energy turns on the fact that the performance of work $dW^\circ = -Y\,dZ$ is adiabatic when $\theta = \text{const}$ and $x_i = \text{const}$. As a corollary, the thermal equation of state (8.56) separates into two independent equations, equation (8.57)† and equation (8.59), and the total energy $\mathcal{U}$ is of the form

$$\mathcal{U}(x_i, Z) = U(x_i) + U_p(Z).\ddagger$$

Case B. Energies are not additive; caloric effect

In the more general case of which the elastic system of Section 8.4.5 provides a preliminary example, the adiabatic work $dW_{ad}^\circ = dW_i^\circ = -Y\,dZ$ produces a change in x_i and so also in temperature. If the relation between Y and Z continues to exist and to be linear at $\theta = \text{const}$, the factor C in equation (8.57) will become dependent on θ and x_i, so that

$$Z = C(\theta, x_i) \cdot Y. \tag{8.63}§$$

In such cases one of the variables Y, Z, say Y, ceases to be independent, and equation (8.56) simplifies to

$$\theta = \theta(Z, x_i), \tag{8.64}$$

which, together with equation (8.63), plays the part of the thermal equation of state.

It is clear that now the total energy

$$\mathcal{U} = \mathcal{U}(Z, x_i) \tag{8.64a}$$

does *not* separate into two additive terms, and that the First Law must be written

$$d\mathcal{U} = dQ^\circ + Y\,dZ - dW_x. \tag{8.65}$$

In the cases which will interest us later, the work dW_x is negligible, unless electrostriction and magnetostriction are important, and so the First Law simplifies to

$$d\mathcal{U} = dQ^\circ + Y\,dZ \tag{8.65a}$$

---

† Or the more general relation (8.56a).
‡ Evidently, $U_p(Y)$ can also be chosen, when $\mathcal{U} = \mathcal{U}(x_i, Y)$.
§ It should be noted that the thermal equation of state for an elastic system, equation (8.29) is of a different mathematical form because it contains the additive term $\int \alpha_0\,d\theta$.

and leads to the conclusion that a quantity of heat $dQ° \neq 0$ must be exchanged during an isothermal process. The appearance of a quantity of reversible heat $dQ°$ during an isothermal process, closely linked to the change in temperature which occurs during the performance of adiabatic work $-Y\,dZ$, is described as the *electrocaloric* or *magnetocaloric* effect, respectively. These effects are analogous to the thermoelastic† effect discussed earlier, and we conclude that a thermogravitational effect does not exist.

During an isothermal process at $x_i = $ const, equation (8.63) can still be integrated explicitly to yield

$$W°_{\text{isoth}} = -\frac{1}{2}\,CY^2 = -\frac{1}{2}\frac{Z^2}{C} \qquad (\theta = \text{const}; \ x_i = \text{const}). \qquad (8.66)$$

If we denote

$$W°_{\text{isoth}} = -U_p \qquad (dW° = -dU_p \text{ at } \theta = \text{const}; \ x_i = \text{const}) \qquad (8.66a)$$

in analogy with equations (8.58a, b), and if $dW°_x \approx 0$, we can write the First Law in the form

$$d(\mathcal{U} - U_p) = dQ° \qquad (\theta = \text{const}; \ x_i = \text{const only}), \qquad (8.66b)$$

as we have done in equation (8.35a) with U_p standing for the strain energy $\mathcal{E}$.

8.5.2   Gravitational field

We now proceed to a review of the field concept which will allow us to introduce the very important field *energy density*. We shall do this on the example of the simplest field, namely the gravitational field.

The structure of a centrally symmetric gravitational field is determined by Newton's law of universal gravitation

$$F = G_n \frac{mM}{r^2}, \qquad (8.67)$$

where r denotes the distance between the centers of mass m and M. The universal gravitational constant G_n has the value given in equation (1.15).‡ We repeat again that the force of gravitation depends only on the masses of the system; it is independent of the value of their other thermodynamic properties and of their chemical composition. In particular, the force is unaffected by changes in temperature, and, in turn, changing the force has no effect on the thermodynamic state of the masses, except that work must be performed. Thus, a change in configuration described by the separation r is achieved by the performance of work, the process being adiabatic, and disregarding the work of deformation. Consequently, the gravitational parameters do not enter the thermal equation of state of the system, and potential energy is additive to internal energy.

Adopting the point of view of field theory, we say that any mass M creates around it a vectorial gravitational field of an intensity **g**. The magnitude and direction of the field intensity **g** is measured with reference to an "infinitely small" test mass dm, and is

---

† The term *thermoelectric* effect is reserved for similar phenomena which occur in a thermocouple loop.
‡ We shall use the symbols G_n and g_n for the universal gravitational constant **G** and the standard gravitational acceleration **g** in order to avoid confusion with the vectorial quantities which appear later.

defined as

$$\mathbf{g} = \frac{d\mathbf{F}}{dm},$$ (8.68)

where the vectorial form of $d\mathbf{F}$ from equation (8.67) is

$$d\mathbf{F} = -\frac{G_n M}{r^3}(dm)\mathbf{r},$$ (8.67a)

so that

$$\mathbf{g}(\mathbf{r}) = -\frac{G_n M}{r^3}\mathbf{r}.$$ (8.68a)

Here the vector $\mathbf{r}$ is directed from the center 0 of mass M to an arbitrary point A at which the test mass dm is located, as shown in Figure 8.27. The intensity $\mathbf{g}$ has the dimension of an acceleration

$$[\mathbf{g}] = LT^{-2},$$

and the vector field $\mathbf{g}$ is a potential one. An impression of this field is conveyed by Figure 8.28; it is the same as that of sink flow familiar from fluid mechanics. Since the field is a potential one, we may write†

$$\mathbf{g}(\mathbf{r}) = -\text{grad } \phi$$ (8.69)

with

$$\phi = -\frac{G_n M}{r}.$$ (8.69a)

The potential surfaces are concentric spheres, as shown in Figure 8.28, the value of the potential vanishing for $r \to \infty$. The latter is set by convention, because, in principle, an arbitrary constant ϕ_0 could be added to the potential ϕ without altering anything essential in the description.

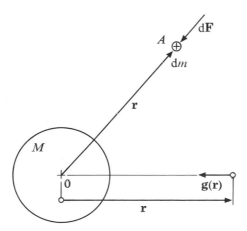

FIGURE 8.27. *Gravitational field intensity.*

† The assumption $\mathbf{g}(\mathbf{r}) = +\text{grad } \phi$ is equally admissible.

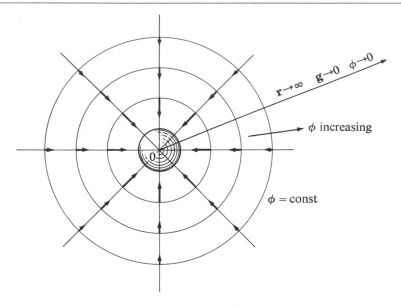

FIGURE 8.28. *The gravitational field around a single mass.*

The work of quasistatically and reversibly displacing the test mass dm in the field is

$$dW = d\mathbf{F} \cdot d\mathbf{r}. \qquad (8.70)$$

In view of equations (8.68) and (8.69), we can also write

$$dW^\circ = (\mathbf{g} \cdot d\mathbf{r})dm = -[(\text{grad } \phi) \cdot d\mathbf{r}]dm.$$

Integrating this expression for a finite path between two equipotential surfaces $\phi_1 = \text{const}$ and $\phi_2 = \text{const}$, we obtain

$$dW^\circ = -(\phi_2 - \phi_1)dm, \qquad (8.71)$$

because

$$\int (\text{grad } \phi) \cdot d\mathbf{r} = \phi_2 - \phi_1.$$

The symbol dW° has been retained, because the work refers to an elementary mass dm. The negative of this quantity constitutes the amount by which the potential energy of the field has been increased. When we disregard the field and adopt the view that gravitational forces are exerted "at a distance," we associate this change in energy with the change in the configuration of the system composed of masses M and dm. In terms of field theory, this change is associated with the field itself.

The potential energy, defined as

$$dW^\circ = -dU_p$$

of a system of n masses, two representative masses m_i and m_j being separated by a distance $r_{i,j}$, is thus

$$U_p = -\sum_{i>j} \frac{G_n m_i m_j}{r_{i,j}}, \qquad (8.72)$$

the sum consisting of $\frac{1}{2} n(n-1)$ terms. Here

$$- \frac{G_n m_i}{r_{i,j}}$$

is the potential of mass m_j in the field of mass m_i, and all potentials due to the other masses are simply added. The expression is so constructed that the potential energy U_p is assumed to be zero when all the masses have been dispersed to points at infinity, when they exert no forces upon each other. The energy U_p from equation (8.72) is called the *configurational energy* from the point of view of action at a distance, and its negative is known as the *binding energy*, because it represents the absolute value of the external work which must be expended to disperse the masses to points at infinity.

When a mass m is placed in the terrestrial gravitational field at height z, the distance from the earth's center is $r = R + z$, where R denotes the radius of the earth conceived as a sphere of mass M. Thus,

$$\phi = - \frac{G_n M}{R+z} = - \frac{G_n M}{R} \left(1 + \frac{z}{R}\right)^{-1}.$$

With $z \ll R$, we expand $(1 + z/R)^{-1}$ into a series and retain two terms, so that

$$\phi \approx - \frac{G_n M}{R} \left(1 - \frac{z}{R}\right).$$

Hence,

$$W^\circ = m(z_1 - z_2) g_n,$$

where

$$g_n = \frac{G_n M}{R^2} = \frac{(6.67 \times 10^{-11} \mathrm{m}^3/\mathrm{sec}^2\mathrm{kg})(5.97 \times 10^{24}\mathrm{kg})}{(6.37 \times 10^6)^2 \mathrm{m}^2} \approx 9.81 \text{ m/sec},$$

because $R = 6.37 \times 10^6$ m and $M = 5.97 \times 10^{24}$ kg. The difference between this value and the standard value $g_n = 9.80665$ m/sec^2 is due to approximations regarding the shape of the earth and so on.

The energy of mass m is

$$U_p(z) = \phi m \approx \left(-G_n \frac{M}{R} + g_n z\right) m.$$

As we have often done in the past, the energy is written

$$U_p(z) = m g_n z \quad \text{with} \quad U_p = 0 \quad \text{at} \quad z = 0$$

because $-G_n M m/R$ is an additive constant.

Incidentally, we note that the escape velocity V_e of a rocket, that is, the velocity which it would acquire if it fell from infinity, is given by

$$\tfrac{1}{2} m V_e^2 = U_p(\infty) - U_p(R) \quad \text{with} \quad U_p(\infty) - U_p(R) = \frac{G_n M m}{R}.$$

Hence,

$$V_e^2 = \sqrt{2 \frac{G_n M}{R^2} R} = \sqrt{2 g_n R} \cong 11.18 \text{ km/sec} \approx 25{,}000 \text{ mile/h}.$$

The escape velocity is seen to be equal to that velocity which the rocket would acquire if it fell from a height of one earth's radius in a *uniform* standard gravitational field of intensity g_n.

According to the point of view adopted in field theory, we imagine that the potential energy is "stored" in the field itself; we ascribe to the field a "real" physical existence, and must, consistently, assume that every volume element dV of the field stores its appropriate share of potential energy. The amount of potential energy stored per unit volume of the field is known as the *potential energy density, u_p*. Naturally, the energy density u_p must vary from point to point, because its integral over the infinite extent of the field must be equal to the finite potential energy of the configuration. For this reason, *the whole field must be included with the system.*

8.5.3   Potential energy density

We assert that the energy density u_p of a field (of the type being discussed here) is represented by the expression

$$u_p = -\frac{1}{8\,\pi G_n}\,\mathbf{g}^2. \tag{8.73}$$

In order to verify the correctness of this equation, we consider two point-masses m_1 and m_2 separated by a distance $\mathbf{r}_{1,2}$. These are shown in Figure 8.29, mass m_1 being placed at the origin of a system of coordinates, with mass m_2 placed along the z axis. The position of an arbitrary point A in space will be indicated by the spherical coordinates r, ϕ, θ, selected with m_1 in the center. Thus, the distance between the arbitrary point A and mass m_2 is

$$\mathbf{r}' = \mathbf{r} - \mathbf{r}_{1,2}.$$

The field intensity at point A is equal to the vectorial sum

$$\mathbf{g} = \mathbf{g}_1 + \mathbf{g}_2$$

of the intensities

$$\mathbf{g}_1 = -G_n \frac{m_1}{r^3}\,\mathbf{r} \quad \text{and} \quad \mathbf{g}_2 = -G_n \frac{m_2}{|\mathbf{r} - \mathbf{r}_{1,2}|^3}\,\mathbf{r}'.$$

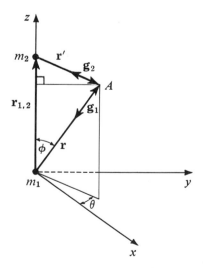

FIGURE 8.29. *Potential energy density in a gravitational field.*

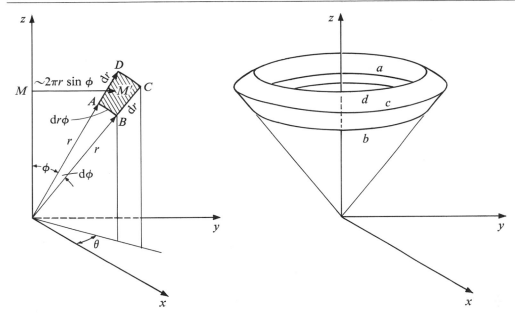

FIGURE 8.30. *Element of space.*

By the cosine theorem for triangle $m_1 m_2 A$, we find that

$$r' = |\mathbf{r} - \mathbf{r}_{1,2}| = (r^2 + r_{1,2}^2 - 2r\,r_{1,2}\cos\phi)^{1/2}.$$

We now proceed to integrate the expression from equation (8.73) over the whole space occupied by the field:

$$\int_{\text{all space}} u_p\,\mathrm{d}V$$

and choose for this purpose the element of volume $\mathrm{d}V$ shown sketched in Figure 8.30. The volume $\mathrm{d}V$ is swept by the elementary quadrangle $ABCD$ arising from a change in radius vector by $\mathrm{d}r$ and in the angle ϕ by $\mathrm{d}\phi$. The area of the quandrangle is $r\,\mathrm{d}\phi\,\mathrm{d}r$, and therefore, the elementary volume† swept by it is

$$\mathrm{d}V = 2\pi r^2 \sin\phi\,\mathrm{d}\phi\,\mathrm{d}r.$$

The integral will consist of three parts, because

$$\mathbf{g}^2 = \mathbf{g}_1^2 + \mathbf{g}_2^2 + 2\mathbf{g}_1 \cdot \mathbf{g}_2.$$

It is easy to see that

$$-\int_{\text{all space}} \frac{1}{8\pi G_n}\,\mathbf{g}_1^2\,\mathrm{d}V = -\int_{\text{all space}} \frac{1}{8\pi G_n}\,\mathbf{g}_2^2\,\mathrm{d}V = -\infty. \qquad (8.74)$$

† We apply *Guldin's theorem* which states that the volume swept by a plane figure of area A rotating about an axis in its plane is equal to $2\pi r_0 A$, where r_0 is the distance from the center of mass of the area to the axis.

Taken separately, each of these two terms is independent of the other mass and represents the negative of the binding energy of each one of the masses, that is, the energy required to assemble a point-mass from elementary masses at infinity. An infinite value is obtained because of the idealized assumption that point-masses are stipulated. A finite, but complicated expression would be obtained, if the correct shape of the mass were taken into account, but we prefer to avoid this possibility in order to keep our argument simple.† In any case, the integrals (8.74) refer to the energy of each one of the masses separately, and their values can be disregarded, because they only affect the arbitrary constant of the potential energy.

We now proceed to evaluate the integral of $\mathbf{g}_1 \cdot \mathbf{g}_2$ which represents the potential energy of the configuration of two masses, and hence of the field. We note that the product $\mathbf{g}_1 \cdot \mathbf{g}_2$ contains the scalar product

$$\frac{\mathbf{r}}{r^3} \cdot \frac{\mathbf{r} - \mathbf{r}_{1,2}}{(r^2 + r_{1,2}^2 - 2r\, r_{1,2} \cos \phi)^{3/2}}.$$

that is, the product $\mathbf{r} \cdot (\mathbf{r} - \mathbf{r}_{1,2})$. This is best computed by noting in Figure 8.29 that the projection of $\mathbf{r}$ on $\mathbf{r}_{1,2}$ is $r \cos \phi$. Hence,

$$\mathbf{r} \cdot (\mathbf{r} - \mathbf{r}_{1,2}) = r^2 - r\, r_{1,2} \cos \phi,$$

and

$$U_p = \int\limits_{\text{all space}} u_p \mathrm{d}V = -\frac{2G_n}{8\pi}\, m_1 m_2 \int\limits_{\text{all space}} \frac{r(r - r_{1,2} \cos \phi)}{r^3(r^2 + r_{1,2}^2 - 2r\, r_{1,2} \cos \phi)^{3/2}}\, 2\pi r^2 \sin \phi\, \mathrm{d}\phi\, \mathrm{d}r,$$

or explicitly

$$U_p = -\tfrac{1}{2}\, G_n m_1 m_2 \int_0^\infty \mathrm{d}r \int_0^\pi \frac{r - r_{1,2} \cos \phi}{(r^2 + r_{1,2}^2 - 2r\, r_{1,2} \cos \phi)^{3/2}} \sin \phi\, \mathrm{d}\phi.$$

The integration with respect to r can be performed at once if it is noted that

$$\int \frac{r - r_{1,2} \cos \phi}{(r^2 + r_{1,2}^2 - 2r\, r_{1,2} \cos \phi)^{3/2}}\, \mathrm{d}r = -\frac{1}{(r^2 + r_{1,2}^2 - 2r\, r_{1,2} \cos \phi)^{1/2}},$$

and that

$$\left| -\frac{1}{(r^2 + r_{1,2}^2 - 2r\, r_{1,2} \cos \phi)^{1/2}} \right|_0^\infty = \frac{1}{r_{1,2}}.$$

Consequently, the final integration leads to

$$U_p = -\tfrac{1}{2}\, G_n m_1 m_2 \int_0^\pi \frac{\sin \phi\, \mathrm{d}\phi}{r_{1,2}} = -\frac{G_n m_1 m_2}{r_{1,2}}. \tag{8.75}$$

Making use of the vectorial additivity of field intensities, and noting that for n masses

$$\mathbf{g}^2 = \mathbf{g}_1^2 + \mathbf{g}_2^2 + \cdots + \mathbf{g}_n^2 + 2(\mathbf{g}_1 \cdot \mathbf{g}_2 + \cdots + \mathbf{g}_1 \cdot \mathbf{g}_n + \mathbf{g}_2 \cdot \mathbf{g}_n + \cdots),$$

†For a distributed mass this would be

$$-\tfrac{1}{2} \int_V \rho \phi\, \mathrm{d}V,$$

the integral being taken over the volume of the mass.

we may extend equation (8.74) to an arbitrary number of masses and write

$$U_p = -\sum_{i \neq j} \frac{G_n m_i m_j}{r_{i,j}}.$$

This expression is identical with equation (8.72). Thus, we have shown that according to the field point of view, the energy is distributed continuously throughout the whole extent of the gravitational field with a density $u_p = -\mathbf{g}^2/8\pi G_n$ per unit volume of space.

8.5.4   *Electrostatic field in a vacuum*

The forces in an electrostatic field in a vacuum are governed by Coulomb's law

$$F = \frac{z_1 z_2}{4\pi\epsilon_0 r^2}. \tag{8.76}$$

Here z_1 and z_2 are two point charges separated by a distance r, and ϵ_0 denotes the *electric permittivity of empty space*. Coulomb's law has been written in the rationalized MKSA system which we shall favor in this book in preference to the older, Gaussian system of units. Consequently, care must be exercised when comparisons are made with formulae which have been written in the latter. Table 8.3 contains a list of electromagnetic units and constants together with their dimensions in the MKSA system for the convenience of the reader.

Coulomb's law is formally analogous to Newton's law of universal gravitation, equation (8.67), except for the constant of proportionality which has been chosen differently to secure a convenient set of electromagnetic units. For this reason, the electrostatic field created by electric charges *in a vacuum* is analogous to the gravitational field discussed previously. The only difference so far turns on the circumstance that all gravitational forces are attractive, whereas electric charges produce attractive or repulsive forces depending on whether they are of unlike or like kind.

Noting the formal similarity between equations (8.76) and (8.67) when the substitutions of z for m and $1/4\pi\epsilon_0$ for $-G_n$ are made, we can write the following formulae: the *electric field intensity* is

$$\mathbf{E(r)} = \frac{z}{4\pi\epsilon_0 r^3}\,\mathbf{r} = -grad\ \phi, \tag{8.77}$$

and the electric potential is

$$\phi = \frac{z}{4\pi\epsilon_0 r}. \tag{8.77a}$$

The work of displacing a small charge is

$$dW = -dz(\phi_2 - \phi_1), \tag{8.77b}$$

where the potential difference

$$\mathcal{E} = \phi_2 - \phi_1 \tag{8.77c}$$

is normally defined as the "voltage" or emf of the system. Thus, we obtain the relation

$$dW = -\mathcal{E}\,dz \tag{8.77d}$$

which is familiar to us from equation (4.28). In contrast with our previous discussion, particularly that in Section 4.4, our present derivation allows us to appreciate the direct connection between the performance of electric work and the displacement of a force which substantiates Planck's definition of work in thermodynamics with respect to electric work. Similar considerations apply to electromagnetic fields in general.

TABLE 8.3
Electromagnetic Units in the Rationalized MKSA System.

Quantity	Symbol	Dimension	Derived unit
Capacitance	C	$M^{-1}L^{-2}T^2Q^2$	Farad
Charge	z	Q	Coulomb
Current	I	$T^{-1}Q$	Ampere
Dielectric constant	κ	dimensionless	No name
Electric displacement	D	$M^{-2}Q$	Coulomb/m^2
Electric field strength	E	$MLT^{-2}Q^{-1}$	Volt/m
Electric polarization	P	$M^{-2}Q$	Coulomb/m^2
Electric potential	ϕ	$ML^2T^{-2}Q^{-1}$	Volt (=J/Coulomb=Nm/Coulomb)
Electromotive force	$\mathcal{E}$	$ML^2T^{-2}Q^{-1}$	Volt (=J/Coulomb=Nm/Coulomb)
Inductance	L	ML^2Q^{-2}	Henry
Magnetic field strength or intensity	H	$MT^{-1}Q$	A m
Magnetic flux	Φ_B	$ML^2T^{-1}Q^{-1}$	Weber (= Volt sec)
Magnetic induction	B	$MT^{-1}Q^{-1}$	Weber/m^2
Magnetization	M	$L^{-1}T^{-1}Q$	A/m

Permittivity of empty space

$$\epsilon_0 = \frac{10^7}{4\pi c^2} \approx 8.85 \times 10^{-12} \; \frac{\text{Coulomb}^2}{\text{Nm}^2}$$

$$\frac{1}{4\pi\epsilon_0} = 9 \times 10^9 \; \frac{\text{Nm}^2}{\text{Coulomb}^2}$$

Speed of light *in vacuo*

$$c = (2.997925 \pm 0.000003) \times 10^8 \; \frac{\text{m}}{\text{sec}}$$

Magnetic permeability constant

$$\mu_0 = 4\pi \times 10^{-7} \; \frac{\text{Weber}}{\text{A m}}$$

Practical unit of magnetic induction

$$1 \text{ Gauss} = 10^{-4} \text{ Weber/m}^2$$

Note: The symbol Q is used here for the dimension of an electric charge to conform to the usage which is common in electromagnetic theory.

The expression in equation (8.77d) represents the work, positive or negative, performed on or by the field (that is, the system) when a charge dz (positive or negative) is displaced in it from a region of potential ϕ_1 to one of potential ϕ_2. In a vacuum, the processes of displacing electric charges are necessarily adiabatic, and the work, which is proportional to the potential, can itself be derived from a potential for all processes. Thus, the potential electric energy of a field *in vacuo* is additive to the internal energy.

The energy density of the electrostatic field can be transcribed from equation (8.73), and is

$$u_{el} = \tfrac{1}{2}\, \epsilon_0 \mathbf{E}^2. \tag{8.78}$$

The integral, taken over *the whole field* provides us with the electrical binding energy

$$U_{el} = \int\limits_{\text{all space}} \tfrac{1}{2}\, \epsilon_0 \mathbf{E}^2 \, dV = \sum_{i \neq j} \frac{z_i z_j}{4\pi\epsilon_0 r_{i,j}} \tag{8.78a}$$

for a system of point charges, if the infinite binding energy of each point charge taken separately is disregarded.

The most important difference between an electrostatic and a gravitational field comes to the fore when a material body is placed in the former. Material bodies can be thought of in terms of two extremes of behavior. The surface charges on an *electric conductor* are such that the electric field intensity, **E**, inside it is completely neutralized, regardless of its temperature. Thus, every metallic body constitutes an equipotential region where

$$\mathbf{E} = 0 \quad \text{and} \quad \phi = \text{const.} \tag{8.79}$$

In a *dielectric*, the electric field is not neutralized; it becomes modified by *polarization*. From the microscopic point of view, nonpolar material bodies develop *electric dipoles* under the influence of an external, electrostatic field. *Polar* substances possess such dipoles even in the absence of the field. Whether the dipoles existed before, or were created by induction in the external field produced by the *applied charges z*, they become partially aligned in it, and modify its structure. Complete alignment is prevented by thermal motion. The net macroscopic effect is to cause the appearance of equal and opposite *induced surface charges z′*.†

The adiabatic polarization of a dielectric does not occur isothermally, and this signifies that the characteristics of the field must enter into its thermal equation of state directly. Similarly, the electrical energy of the field in a dielectric does not contribute an additive term to the internal energy of the system.

8.5.5 *Capacitors*

The simplest system with an electrostatic field is represented by a capacitor. Geometrically, the simplest electrostatic field occurs in a parallel-plate capacitor in which "fringing" at the edges has been neglected. Similar conditions exist between "infinite" concentric cylinders or concentric spheres when the gap *d* between them is very small compared with the mean radius.

From a purely operational point of view, we notice that the reversible work of charging a capacitor is

$$dW° = -\mathcal{E}\, dz, \tag{8.80}$$

because the metallic plates constitute regions of constant potential. Here *z* denotes the

---

† Certain waxes retain a permanent polarization if they have been polarized in the molten state and then solidified. Such *ferroelectric* materials develop hysteresis loops, and this complicates their description in terms of the equations of thermodynamics. We shall refrain from discussing them here.

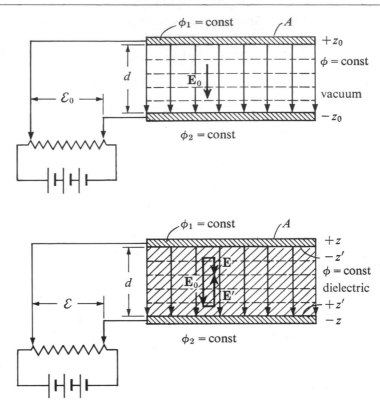

FIGURE 8.31. *Parallel-plate capacitor.*

applied charge which is imagined supplied by an external source of variable emf, as shown in Figure 8.31 for the case of a parallel-plate capacitor.

The form of equation (8.80) suggests that the potential difference $\mathcal{E}$ and the applied charge z constitute a pair of thermodynamic parameters of a capacitor. Regardless of whether a dielectric is involved or not, the applied charge z is directly proportional to the emf, and we may write

$$z = C\mathcal{E}, \tag{8.81}$$

where C is the *capacitance* of the capacitor. Clearly, the charge z is an extensive, and the potential difference $\mathcal{E}$ is an intensive property. In general, the capacitance of a capacitor filled with a *homogeneous* and *isotropic* dielectric is

$$C = \kappa\epsilon_0 L, \tag{8.81a}$$

where L is a geometrical constant of the arrangement. For a parallel-plate capacitor

$$L = \frac{A}{d}, \tag{8.81b}$$

corresponding expressions for other arrangements being available in books on electromagnetic theory. The dimensionless *dielectric constant κ* constitutes the single parameter which characterizes the polarizability of an isotropic dielectric. In crystals, the relations are more complex, because their polarizability depends on direction, but we shall refrain from discussing them in this course.

The thermal equation of state of a capacitor depends on the characteristics of the dielectric. In a vaccum

$$\kappa = 1,$$

and we recognize that the thermal equation of state of the metallic plates is divorced from the electric equation (8.81). In this case, the state of the capacitor is described by one of the two parameters z, $\mathcal{E}$ and the temperature θ, of the (incompressible) metallic plates, the process of charging being completely independent of the process of heating. The energy

$$U_{el} = \frac{1}{2} \frac{z^2}{\epsilon_0 L} = \frac{1}{2} \epsilon_0 L \mathcal{E}^2 \tag{8.82}$$

forms an additive term in the expression for total energy $\mathcal{U}$.

Similar conditions prevail in the case when

$$\kappa = \text{const}$$

may be assumed, except that

$$U_{el} = \frac{1}{2} \frac{z^2}{\kappa \epsilon_0 L} = \frac{1}{2} \kappa \epsilon_0 L \mathcal{E}^2. \tag{8.82a}$$

In liquid and solid dielectrics, the dielectric constant κ may be assumed to be a function of temperature alone,

$$\kappa = \kappa(\theta). \tag{8.83}$$

Thus, the thermal equation of state is

$$z = \kappa(\theta) \epsilon_0 L \mathcal{E}, \tag{8.83a}$$

and the state of the system is determined by two of the three parameters θ, $\mathcal{E}$, z, the third one being given by the equation. The electrical energy can no longer be added to the internal energy. It is clear that this system will exhibit the electrocaloric effect, electrostriction being negligible if the liquid and solid are regarded as incompressible.

In gases, the dielectric constant is governed by the semitheoretical *Clausius-Mossotti equation*

$$\frac{\kappa - 1}{\kappa + 2} \cdot \frac{1}{\rho} = \mathcal{A}, \tag{8.84}†$$

where $\mathcal{A}$ denotes a constant, different for each gas and independent of temperature. Values of this constant together with some values of the dielectric constant for solid and liquid substances can be found in Table XXVIII. In this case, the relation

$$z = \kappa(\rho) \epsilon_0 L \mathcal{E} \tag{8.85}$$

together with the usual equation of state

$$F(P, \rho, \theta) = 0 \tag{8.85a}$$

† For very high densities, the right-hand side of the Clausius-Mossotti equation can be expressed as a virial series $\mathcal{A} + \mathcal{B}\rho + \mathcal{C}\rho^2$, and so on.

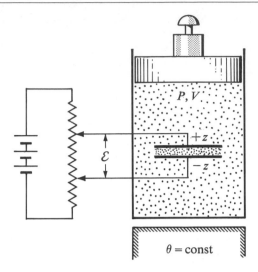

FIGURE 8.32. *Effect of electrostriction on a gaseous dielectric.*

jointly constitute the thermal equation of state of the system. Given any three of the five variables z, $\mathcal{E}$, P, ρ, θ, we can compute the remaining two from the equations. Thus, the state of the system is determined by *three* independent variables. A system of this type exhibits the electrocaloric effect and electrostriction. For example, in the arrangement shown in Figure 8.32, the electrostrictive pressure causes the gas to be drawn into the space between the plates when the density increases at the expense of the gas outside, even at constant pressure and temperature. The First Law of thermodynamics must now be written

$$d\mathcal{U} = dQ^\circ - P\,dV + \mathcal{E}\,dz. \tag{8.86}$$

8.5.6   Electrostatic field in a dielectric

In order to extend the preceding equations to a continuous system, it is necessary to replace the parameters which appear in them by the local parameters of the electrostatic field. For this purpose we shall employ a heuristic method based on the consideration of the two parallel-plate capacitors from Figure 8.31. The resulting equation for the work of a field will have general validity though this will not be certain from the derivation. A satisfactory derivation of the same equation can be obtained from Maxwell's field equations by students who are conversant with them.

Compared with a vacuum, a dielectric develops the induced charges z' which create a field $\mathbf{E}'$ in opposition to the original field $\mathbf{E}_0$. Restricting attention to isotropic dielectrics, it is seen that an electrostatic field in them can be described by three parallel, related vectors $\mathbf{E}_0$, $\mathbf{E}'$, and $\mathbf{E}$. In practice, it proves convenient to employ vectors $\mathbf{D}$ and $\mathbf{P}$, known as the *electric displacement* and *electric polarization* respectively, which are equal to the products $\epsilon_0\mathbf{E}_0$ and $-\epsilon_0\mathbf{E}'$, so that

$$\mathbf{D} = \epsilon_0\mathbf{E} + \mathbf{P}. \tag{8.87}$$

In a vacuum

$$\mathbf{D}_0 = \epsilon_0\mathbf{E}_0 \quad \text{and} \quad \mathbf{P} = 0. \tag{8.87a}$$

The vector **P** represents the *dipole moment* per unit volume of the microscopic, elementary dipoles.

By Gauss' theorem

$$\frac{z}{A} = D, \quad \frac{z'}{A} = P, \quad \frac{z_0 - z'}{A} = \epsilon_0 E, \quad \text{and} \quad \frac{z_0}{A} = E_0, \tag{8.87b}$$

so that for $z = z_0$, we have

$$\mathbf{D} = \mathbf{D}_0. \tag{8.87c}$$

The electric equation of state

$$z = \kappa \epsilon_0 \frac{A}{d} \mathcal{E}$$

assumes the form

$$AD = \kappa \epsilon_0 \frac{A}{d} Ed,$$

because $\mathcal{E} = Ed$. Hence,

$$\mathbf{D} = \kappa \epsilon_0 \mathbf{E}. \tag{8.88}$$

This is the so-called *constitutive equation* for an isotropic dielectric; together with the equation of state $F(P, \rho, \theta) = 0$, it describes the *local* relations between the three field vectors. We have passed to vectorial symbols in accordance with our prefatory remarks and simply inform the reader that equation (8.88) remains valid for any electrostatic field in an isotropic dielectric. The polarization vector is now

$$\mathbf{P} = (\kappa - 1)\epsilon_0 \mathbf{E}, \tag{8.88a}$$

and

$$\mathbf{E}_0 = \kappa \mathbf{E}. \tag{8.88b}$$

The expression for work in equation (8.80) can now be transformed to

$$dW° = -(Ed)d(AD) = -(Ad)E \, dD.$$

Thus, the work per unit volume $V = Ad$, for which we use the symbol $dw°$, is

$$dw° = -\mathbf{E} \cdot d\mathbf{D}. \tag{8.89}$$

We have again passed to vectorial symbols and state that equation (8.89) remains valid for any electrostatic field (not necessarily in an isotropic dielectric). It follows that for the whole field

$$dW° = -\int_{\text{all space}} (\mathbf{E} \cdot d\mathbf{D}) \, dV, \tag{8.89a}$$

where the integration must be performed over the whole space occupied by the field. In our present example this field does not extend outside the plates owing to shielding. However, in general, the integration must be extended over the dielectric as well as over the space outside it. For this reason, the expression in equation (8.89a) is not very convenient, and it is useful to obtain a different form for it by the introduction of the hypothetical electric field intensity $\mathbf{E}_0$ which would be created in a vacuum by the *applied charges* z; this field would exist in an identical capacitor *in vacuo*, charged to a *different* voltage $\mathcal{E}_0$, but carrying *the same* free charge $z_0 = z$. Restricting ourselves to the relations for isotropic dielectrics, we see that

$$\mathbf{E} = \mathbf{E}_0 - \mathbf{P}/\epsilon_0 \quad \text{and} \quad \mathbf{D} = \mathbf{D}_0 = \epsilon_0 \mathbf{E}_0.$$

Thus,

$$dw^\circ = -\{\epsilon_0 \mathbf{E}_0 \cdot d\mathbf{E}_0 - \mathbf{P}\, d\mathbf{E}_0\}.$$

Here

$$-\epsilon_0 \mathbf{E}_0 \cdot d\mathbf{E}_0 = -d(\tfrac{1}{2}\,\epsilon_0 \mathbf{E}_0^2) = du_{\text{el}} \tag{8.90}$$

represents the negative of the electrical energy of empty space which is normally combined with the total specific energy $\mathcal{U}$. Thus, the reversible work

$$dW^\circ = \int_V (\mathbf{P} \cdot d\mathbf{E}_0)\, dV. \tag{8.90a}\,†$$

Now the integral extends only over the volume V of the dielectric, because the electric polarization $\mathbf{P}$ vanishes in a vacuum.

An alternative form of this equation is obtained in the case when the applied field $\mathbf{E}_0$ is uniform, because then $d\mathbf{E}_0$ constitutes a constant parameter in the integration over the volume. We denote

$$P = \int_V \mathbf{P}\, dV,$$

and find that

$$dW^\circ = P \cdot d\mathbf{E}_0. \tag{8.90b}$$

It is worth remembering that

$$\mathcal{U} = U + \int (\tfrac{1}{2}\,\epsilon_0 \mathbf{E}_0^2)\, dV, \tag{8.91a}$$
$$\text{all space}$$

and that a uniform applied field $\mathbf{E}_0$ creates a uniform field $\mathbf{E}$ in an ellipsoid;‡ the field $\mathbf{E}$ is not necessarily parallel to $\mathbf{E}_0$.

Bearing in mind the different expressions for reversible work, we may write the First Law of thermodynamics for a reversible process in a dielectric in the following equivalent forms:

$$d\mathcal{U} = dQ^\circ + \int (\mathbf{E} \cdot d\mathbf{D})\, dV \tag{8.92a}$$
$$\text{all space}$$

$$d(\mathcal{U} - U_{\text{el}}) = dU = dQ^\circ - \int_V (\mathbf{P} \cdot d\mathbf{E}_0)\, dV \tag{8.92b}$$

---

† A more formal and rigorous derivation of this equation is given in: Heine, V., "The Thermodynamics of Bodies in Static Electromagnetic Field," Proc. Cambridge Phil. Soc. **52** (1956) 546.
‡ See, for example, Becker and Sauter, *loc. cit.* (on p. 380 in this book), p. 102. The field is uniform but $\mathbf{E}_0$ is no longer $\mathbf{D}/\mathbf{E}_0$.

$$dU = dQ^\circ - \mathcal{P} \cdot d\mathbf{E}_0. \tag{8.92c}$$

In each of these equations, the work of electrostriction has been neglected.

Later in the course we shall learn to determine the reversible heat dQ°; this will enable us to show that the process of polarizing a dielectric at constant temperature and density requires cooling ($dQ^\circ < 0$).

8.5.7   *Magnetostatic field in a vacuum*

The structure of a magnetostatic field is analogous to that of a gravitational field or an electrostatic field even though the direct analog of Newton's law of universal gravitation or Coulomb's law of electric forces does not exist. The latter is a consequence of the fact that isolated magnetic charges do not occur in nature, the smallest entity producing a magnetostatic field being a *dipole*. Magnetic dipoles are approximated by small permanent magnets or by elementary loops carrying a dc current. In this book we are not in a position to provide a complete justification of this and the subsequent statements regarding magnetostatic fields and must direct the reader to the reference books quoted in the footnote on p. 380 for details.

The magnetostatic field created by a current in a vacuum is described by the vector of *magnetic induction*, $\mathbf{B}$, which plays the same part as a field intensity in spite of the fact that a different vector, $\mathbf{H}$, is called the *magnetic field strength* or *intensity*. In a vacuum the difference is of no importance, the two vectors being proportional to each other:

$$\mathbf{B} = \mu_0 \mathbf{H}; \tag{8.93}$$

here μ_0 is the magnetic *permeability constant*; μ_0 is a universal physical constant, but we refrain from using a boldface symbol for it in this section to avoid confusion with vectors.

A uniform magnetic field $\mathbf{B}$ is created with a good degree of approximation in a toroidal body shown in Figure 8.33(a) when the linear dimensions of its cross section A are small compared with the mean radius of the torus. The field can be created by passing a dc current I through the spirally wound conductor. Such an arrangement is known as a *Rowland ring*. Another possibility is to produce a closely wound, "infinite" solenoid.

We now wish to examine the work of *reversibly* changing the uniform magnetic field $\mathbf{B}$ by $d\mathbf{B}$. However, the winding which passes the current possesses a finite resistance which makes this impossible. Consequently, we shall disregard this resistance and ignore the emf required to overcome it. In this manner we extrapolate to the case when the wire cross section, A', of the winding tends to infinity. A good, practical approximation to such conditions can be achieved at very low temperatures when many metals become *superconducting*, their resistivity decreasing to virtually zero.

The work of changing this field in a vacuum is governed by *Faraday's law of magnetic induction* which leads to the conclusion that the inductance of the coil creates in it a "back-emf" whose value depends on the number of flux linkages Φ. In a vacuum, the number of flux linkages Φ_0 in a length l of solenoid or torus is measured by the product of the flux $\Phi_B = \mathbf{B}_0 A$ of vector $\mathbf{B}_0$ through the cross-sectional area A of the torus

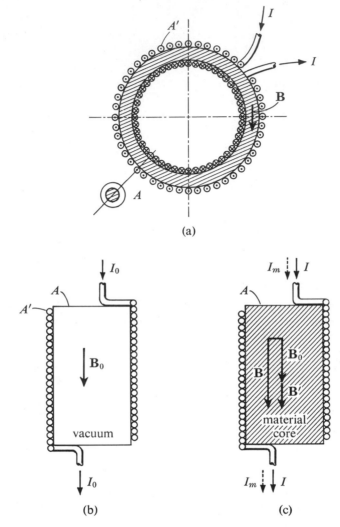

FIGURE 8.33. *Infinite solenoid or Rowland ring. (a) Rowland ring. (b) Solenoid in empty space. (c) Solenoid with material core.*

or solenoid into the number N of windings in that length. Hence,

$$\Phi_0 = N\Phi_B = NB_0 A. \tag{8.93a}$$

According to Ampère's law,

$$B_0 = \mu_0 I_0 n, \tag{8.93b}$$

where n is the number of turns per unit length of solenoid.

The back-emf is given by the equation

$$\mathcal{E}_0 = -\frac{d\Phi_0}{dt}, \tag{8.94}$$

and depends only on the rate of change of the number of flux linkages with time. This emf acts in a direction which forces the current I_0 to perform work *on* the system when Φ_0 increases, it being noted that no work is performed ($\mathcal{E}_0 = 0$) to maintain steady-state. The external source must provide an opposite emf, and

$$\frac{dW^\circ}{dt} = -\left(-\mathcal{E}_0 \frac{dz}{dt}\right) = -I_0 \frac{d\Phi_0}{dt}.$$

This equation is equivalent to

$$dW^\circ = -I_0 \, d\Phi_0. \tag{8.94}$$

The form of equation (8.94) suggests that we may choose the current I_0 and the number of magnetic flux linkages Φ_0 as two thermodynamic parameters of state. The situation is analogous to that which is familiar from the discussion of a capacitor in a vacuum, because the relation between these two parameters is independent of the thermodynamic parameters of the rest of the system — the wire. To complete the analogy, the relation is linear, the inductance

$$L = \frac{d\Phi_0}{dI_0} \tag{8.94a}$$

being a constant. For a solenoid

$$L = \mu_0 n^2 l A. \tag{8.94b}$$

Thus, the energy of a magnetic field *in vacuo* is

$$U_m = \tfrac{1}{2} L I_0^2 \tag{8.95}$$

and the energy density can be computed to be

$$u_m = \frac{U_m}{Al} = \frac{1}{2} \frac{B_0^2}{\mu_0}, \tag{8.95a}$$

per unit volume. It is now possible to say that a more general derivation would lead to the more general expressions

$$u_m = \frac{1}{2} \frac{\mathbf{B}_0^2}{\mu_0} = \frac{1}{2} \mu_0 \mathbf{H}_0^2. \tag{8.95b}$$

The process in a vacuum does not lead to a magnetocaloric effect, and the energy u_m can be combined with the total energy $\mathcal{U}$ by the definition

$$\mathcal{U} = U + \int_{\text{all space}} \left(\frac{1}{2} \frac{\mathbf{B}_0^2}{\mu}\right) dV = U + \int_{\text{all space}} \left(\frac{1}{2} \mu_0 \mathbf{H}_0^2\right) dV. \tag{8.95c}$$

The reversible work of magnetizing the empty space is, therefore, equal to $-dU_m$, that is, to

$$dW^\circ = -\int_{\text{all space}} (\mathbf{H}_0 \cdot d\mathbf{B}_0) \, dV, \tag{8.95d}$$

or, per unit volume

$$dw^\circ = -\mathbf{H}_0 \cdot d\mathbf{B}_0. \tag{8.95e}$$

8.5.8   *Magnetostatic field in a material body*

The presence of a material core in a solenoid causes the vector of magnetic induction to change depending on the magnetic properties of the substance.

A. *Diamagnetism*

From a microscopic point of view every electron orbiting around the nucleus can be regarded as an elementary current loop which produces a magnetic dipole. In the absence of an external magnetic field all such dipoles cancel owing to the randomness of their distribution. The application of an external magnetic field affects the frequency of orbiting without changing the radius, and by Lenz's rule it can be shown that the resulting change in the dipole moment always *weakens* the applied field. Thus, all material substances are diamagnetic. However, this diamagnetic weakening is so small† that it represents no further interest to us in this course. The diamagnetism of certain substances is overshadowed by their paramagnetism or ferromagnetism.

B. *Paramagnetism*

In certain materials the magnetic effects of orbiting electrons together with the effects of electron spin do not cancel and cause their atoms to behave like elementary magnetic dipoles which tend to align with an applied, external field and to reinforce it. Thus, the resultant vector of magnetic induction, $\mathbf{B}$ in Figure 8.33(c), becomes larger by a vector $\mathbf{B}'$ compared with the applied magnetic induction $\mathbf{B}_0$. The effect of this alignment can be imagined to have been produced *in vacuo* by a hypothetical, *magnetizing current* I_m which reinforces the applied current $I = I_0$.

In isotropic bodies the three vectors $\mathbf{B}$, $\mathbf{B}'$, and $\mathbf{B}_0$ are parallel, and the additional vector $\mathbf{B}'$ provides a measure of the magnetic moment of the aligned, elementary dipoles. Instead of using the additional vector $\mathbf{B}'$ and the applied vector $\mathbf{B}_0$ for the description of the resulting magnetic field, it is customary to employ two different vectors, the magnetic field intensity $\mathbf{H}$ and the magnetization $\mathbf{M}$ per unit volume which differ by a multiplicative constant and which are linked by the equation

$$\mathbf{B} = \mu_0\mathbf{H} + \mu_0\mathbf{M}. \qquad (8.96)$$

In empty space $\mathbf{M} = 0$, and $\mathbf{B}_0 = \mu_0\mathbf{H}_0$ as we know from the preceding section. The magnetic field intensity $\mathbf{H}$ is used to replace the applied field $\mathbf{B}_0$. In our case

$$\mathbf{H} = \mathbf{H}_0 = \frac{\mathbf{B}_0}{\mu_0}. \qquad (8.96a)$$

In isotropic paramagnetic substances the resultant vector $\mathbf{B}$ is proportional to the applied vector $\mathbf{B}_0$, provided that the applied field is not very large. The coefficient of proportionality κ_m, known as the *permeability* of the substance, completely characterizes its magnetic properties. All metals are paramagnetic above a certain characteristic temperature known as the *Curie* (or *Néel*) *temperature*. Certain salts of the transition and rare-earth elements, for example, gadolinium sulphate $[Gd_2(SO_4)_3 \cdot 8H_2O]$, chro-

---

† It is of some significance in alkali halides (such as LiBr, NaCl), in some aromatic crystals and in certain metals, notably bismuth and γ-brass.

mium potassium alum [$CrK(SO_4)_2 \cdot 12H_2O$] and many others belong to this group. The rare gases [argon (Ar), neon (Ne), and so on] are also paramagnetic.

Hence, for homogeneous and isotropic paramagnetic substances we may write

$$\mathbf{B} = \kappa_m \mu_0 \mathbf{H} \qquad (= \kappa_m \mathbf{B}_0). \tag{8.96b}$$

The permeability κ_m of a paramagnetic substance is greater than unity, being very slightly lower than unity for diamagnetic substances for which equation (8.96b) also holds.†

Equation (8.96) shows that

$$\mathbf{M} = \chi_m \mathbf{H}, \qquad \text{where } \chi_m = \kappa_m - 1, \tag{8.97a, b}$$

is known as the *magnetic susceptibility* of the material.

By Ampère's law, in a vacuum

$$I_0 = \oint \frac{\mathbf{B}_0}{\mu_0} \cdot \mathbf{dl} = \oint H_0 \cdot \mathbf{dl},$$

where l is a vector measured from an origin 0 along any closed loop taken around the current-carrying wire. Similarly, in the presence of a paramagnetic body,

$$I = \oint \mathbf{H} \cdot \mathbf{dl}, \quad I + I_m = \oint \frac{\mathbf{B}}{\mu_0} \cdot \mathbf{dl}, \quad I_m = \oint \mathbf{M} \cdot \mathbf{dl}. \tag{8.98}$$

Faraday's law of magnetic induction remains valid, and hence, for a solenoid, we can transform equation (8.94) to

$$dW^\circ = -(lA) \, H dB \tag{8.99}$$

if we substitute

$$H = I_0 n \quad \text{and} \quad \Phi_0 = nlBA$$

from equations (8.98) and (8.93a), remembering that $N = ln$.

We can assert once more that equation (8.99) enjoys universal validity in the form

$$dw^\circ = -\mathbf{H} \cdot \mathbf{dB}, \tag{8.99a}$$

leading to

$$dW^\circ = -\int_{\text{all space}} (\mathbf{H} \cdot \mathbf{dB}) \, dV. \tag{8.99b}$$

The *constitutive equation* (8.96b) contains the permeability κ_m which depends on the remaining thermodynamic parameters of the paramagnetic substance. Most paramagnetic substances of interest can be treated as incompressible, and the permeability κ_m is a function of temperature alone. Thus, equation (8.96b) plays the part of the thermal equation of state of the general form

$$B = \kappa_m(\theta) \cdot \mu_0 H, \ddagger \tag{8.100}$$

† This means that the inductance of a solenoid with a diamagnetic or paramagnetic core is κ_m times larger than that of the same solenoid *in vacuo*.
‡ Vectorial symbols are here superfluous because the vectors are parallel in isotropic substances.

in which *two* variables are independent. In a paramagnetic gas, the permeability depends on two variables, and equation (8.96b) together with the P, v, θ relation provide a thermal equation of state with *three* independent variables. As we already know, the dependence of permeability on the other parameters of state implies the existence of a magnetocaloric effect. This effect plays an important part in the production of extremely low temperatures by the process of adiabatic demagnetization of paramagnetic salts to be discussed in Volume II.

In practice, instead of equation (8.100), use is made of the equivalent relation in equation (8.97). Here the magnetic susceptibility χ_m of a paramagnetic substance can be represented as a function of temperature by *Curie's law* which has the form

$$\chi_m = \frac{C}{\theta}.$$

Here C denotes the *Curie constant* which is characteristic of a particular substance. This equation is equivalent to

$$M = C\frac{H}{\theta}. \tag{8.101}$$

At low temperatures, the equation of state is better approximated by the *Curie-Weiss equation*

$$M = C\frac{H}{\theta - \theta_0}, \tag{8.101a}$$

where θ_0 is another constant. For $\theta \gg \theta_0$, equation (8.101a) can be replaced by the simpler equation (8.101). Values of the constants C and θ_0 have been listed for several substances in Table XXIX. The table also lists the Curie (or Néel) temperatures of the substances, it being remembered that they are paramagnetic *above* the Curie temperature. When the temperature is reduced, the substances acquire more complicated magnetic properties and become ferromagnetic, antiferromagnetic or ferrimagnetic.

In view of the preferred form of the paramagnetic thermal equation of state, it is useful to transform the expressions for reversible work to display the proper parameters explicitly. This is done in a manner similar to that employed in Section 8.5.6 for dielectrics. From equation (8.96), with $H = H_0$, we obtain

$$d\mathbf{B} = \mu_0\, d\mathbf{H}_0 + \mu_0\, d\mathbf{M}.$$

Hence,

$$dw^\circ = -\mu_0\mathbf{H}_0 \cdot d\mathbf{H}_0 - \mu_0\mathbf{H}_0 \cdot d\mathbf{M}.$$

The change in the magnetic energy of empty space

$$d(\tfrac{1}{2}\mu_0\mathbf{H}_0^2)$$

can be combined with the total energy $\mathcal{U}$, and the expression for reversible work is

$$dW^\circ = -\int_V (\mu_0\mathbf{H}_0 \cdot d\mathbf{M})\, dV. \tag{8.102}$$

The integral extends here over the volume V of the paramagnetic material only, because outside it $M = 0$. For a uniform external field

$$dW° = - \mu_0 \mathbf{H}_0 \cdot d\mathcal{M},$$ (8.102a)

where the symbol $\mathcal{M}$ has been introduced for the integral

$$\mathcal{M} = \int_V \mathbf{M} dV.$$ (8.102b)

It must be realized that the preceding derivations are not quite rigorous, just as was the case with electrostatic fields in Section 8.5.6; a more complete derivation can be found in the references quoted in the footnote of p. 380.

With these equations, we can now write the First Law of thermodynamics for a reversible process of magnetization in the following alternative forms:

$$d\mathcal{U} = dQ° + \int_{\text{all space}} (\mathbf{H} \cdot d\mathbf{B}) dV$$ (8.103a)

$$d(\mathcal{U} - U_m) = dU = dQ° + \int_V \mu_0 \mathbf{H}_0 \cdot d\mathbf{M}$$ (8.103b)

$$dU = dQ° + \mu_0 \mathbf{H}_0 \cdot d\mathcal{M}.$$ (8.103c)

In each of these the work of magnetostriction has been neglected. As was the case with an electrostatic field, the isothermal magnetization of a paramagnetic substance requires cooling ($dQ° < 0$), the temperature increasing upon adiabatic magnetization.

It is seen from equation (8.96a) that Curie's law and the Curie-Weiss law continue to apply when H is replaced by H_0 and M is replaced by $\mathcal{M}$.

C. Ferromagnetism

Certain metals, iron (Fe) being the best known of them [the others are: cobalt (Co), nickel (Ni), gadolinium (Ga), and dysprosium (Dy)], show very strong effects resulting from the alignment of dipoles. In such ferromagnetic materials groups of atoms form so-called Weiss domains inside which the elementary dipoles are magnetically aligned, the direction of the resultant magnetic moment varying from domain to domain. Thus, an external field causes the alignment of magnetic moments of rather large magnitude with the result that the magnetic susceptibility is very large and depends on the strength of the applied field. The process of magnetization in ferromagnetic substances is not reversible, the reverse process forming a hysteresis loop with the forward process. This circumstance greatly complicates the thermodynamic analysis of such systems and we shall refrain from pursuing the matter any further, except for reiterating that all ferromagnetic substances become paramagnetic above their Curie temperature. The same applies to ferrimagnetic materials (such as ferrites). Antiferromagnetic materials (for example, magnesium oxide MnO) are essentially nonisotropic below the Curie temperature, and we shall also refrain from discussing them here,† except for noting that ferrimagnetic powders are essentially isotropic and are characterized by a magnetic susceptibility which *increases* with temperature, unlike that of a paramagnetic substance which decreases with temperature.

† A more complete treatment can be found in: van Vleck, J. H., *The Theory of Electric and Magnetic Susceptibilities* (Oxford Univ. Press, 1932).

List of Symbols for Chapter 8

Latin letters

A	Area
a	Constant
$\mathcal{A}$	Constant in Clausius-Mossotti equation, equation (8.84)
b	Constant
$\mathbf{B}$	Magnetic induction
$\mathcal{B}$	Constant in Clausius-Mossotti equation, equation (8.84)
C	Capacitance; Curie constant; constant
c	Constant
$\mathbf{c}$	Speed of light *in vacuo*
$\mathcal{C}$	Constant in Clausius-Mossotti equation, equation (8.84)
$\mathbf{D}$	Electric displacement
E	Isothermal modulus of elasticity or isothermal Young's modulus
$\mathbf{E}'$	Induced electric field strength
$\mathbf{E}$	Electric field strength
$\mathcal{E}$	Electromotive force (emf); strain energy
$\mathcal{E}_0$	Back-emf
F	Vertical component of surface tension forces; force
$\mathbf{F}$	Faraday's equivalent charge; force vector
G	Weight
G_n	Universal gravitational constant
g	Gravitational acceleration
g_n	Standard gravitational acceleration
$\mathbf{g}$	Intensity of vectorial gravitational field
h	Height
$\mathbf{H}$	Magnetic field strength or intensity
I	Current
k	Resistance ratio
L	Inductance; length
l	Length
$\mathbf{l}$	Length vector
L	Dimension of length
M	Mass
m	Mass
$\mathbf{M}$	Magnetization
M	Dimension of mass
$\mathcal{M}$	Torque; magnetization
n	Number of mols; strain-hardening exponent; number of turns per unit length of a solenoid
P	Pressure
P_a	Atmospheric pressure
$\mathbf{P}$	Electric polarization; dipole moment per unit volume
$\mathcal{P}$	Electric polarization when applied electric field is uniform
Q	Heat

Q	Dimension of electric charge
R	Radius of curvature
$\left.\begin{array}{l}R_1\\R_2\end{array}\right\}$	Principal radii of curvature
r	Radius; distance
r	Radius vector
$\mathcal{R}$	Resistance
t	Temperature; time
T	Dimension of time
U	Internal energy
U_{el}	Energy of electric field *in vacuo*
U_m	Energy of magnetic field *in vacuo*
U_p	Configurational energy, see equation (8.72); potential energy
u	Internal energy
u_{el}	Energy density of electrostatic field *in vacuo*
u_m	Energy density of magnetic field *in vacuo*
u_p	Potential energy density
$\mathcal{U}$	Total energy
V	Volume
v	Molar specific volume; specific volume
$\mathcal{V}$	Velocity
$\mathcal{V}_e$	Escape velocity
W	Work
W_a	Work due to atmospheric pressure
w	Work per unit volume
x	Coordinate; independent variable
Y	Intensive thermodynamic property
y	Coordinate
Z	Extensive thermodynamic property
z	Electric charge; coordinate
z'	Induced electric charge

Greek letters

α	Angle; linear coefficient of thermal expansion
β	Volumetric coefficient of thermal expansion
γ	Angular strain
δ	Thickness
ϵ	Strain
ϵ_s	Permanent strain or permanent set
ϵ_0	Electric permittivity of empty space
ζ	Number of valence electrons
η	Quantity defined in equation (8.28)
θ	Temperature
θ_0	Constant in Curie-Weiss equation, equation (8.101a)
κ	Dielectric constant
κ_m	Permeability of paramagnetic substance
μ	Dynamic or absolute viscosity

μ_0	Magnetic permeability
ν	Kinematic viscosity
ξ	Internal variable (degree of freedom)
ρ	Density; electrical resistivity
σ	Surface tension; stress
σ_0	Constant
τ	Shearing stress
Φ	Number of flux linkages
Φ_B	Magnetic flux
ϕ	Potential; electric potential; general thermodynamic property
χ_m	Magnetic susceptibility
ω	Angular velocity

Superscripts

$'$	Liquid phase
$''$	Vapor phase
$\cdot$	Time rate of change
$\circ$	Reversible process
v	Viscous

Subscripts

ad	Adiabatic quantity
cr	Critical point
el	Elastic
isoth	Isothermal process
0	Reference value; value for empty space
th	Thermal
r	Rupture point
y	Yield point

CHAPTER 9

The Second Law of Thermodynamics.
Elementary Formulation

9.1 Introductory remarks

In the preceding chapters of this book we have analyzed a number of reversible and irreversible processes, recognizing that all natural processes are irreversible, and that reversible processes merely constitute convenient idealizations. The Second Law of thermodynamics recognizes these facts and reduces the preceding observations to a clear verbal formulation which can subsequently be given a precise, mathematical form.

Traditionally, the reasoning which leads to a mathematical formulation of the Second Law is based on R. Clausius' original presentation in his *Mechanische Wärmetheorie*. We shall first follow this tradition, introducing some of the improvements due to M. Planck and contained in the latter's *Vorlesungen über Thermodynamik*.† It will be recognized later that though correct in its conclusions, the elementary development is unnecessarily restrictive in scope. Full generality and economy in the derivation was achieved by C. Carathéodory in cooperation with M. Born. However, an understanding of this formulation and, particularly, of the resulting theory, is based on mathematical theorems which, though quite elementary, are not normally studied in courses on mathematical analysis.

C. Carathéodory succeeded in extracting the most fundamental physical contents of the Second Law from the observation that natural phenomena are essentially irreversible, which implies that under certain well-defined conditions it is impossible to attain certain states of a system. He was then able to demonstrate the connection between this observation and the properties of Pfaffian forms and equations. Thus, he succeeded in reducing the argument to an elegant and general mathematical form, arriving at conclusions which are otherwise identical with those due to Clausius and Planck. We shall attempt to familiarize the reader with the necessary background and with the resulting theory in the succeeding chapter.

The gist of the Second Law was first perceived by a French military engineer, Sadi Carnot, in his celebrated memoir entitled *Réflexions sur la puissance motrice du feu et sur les machines propres à developper cette puissance*,‡ published in 1824. It appeared

---

† *Treatise on Thermodynamics*, translated by A. Ogg (London: Longmans, 1927). See also Planck, M., *Einführung in die Theorie der Wärme* (S. Hirzel, Leipzig, 1930), translated by H. L. Brose as *Theory of Heat* (Macmillan, 1932).
‡ *Reflections on the Motive Power of Heat and on Machines Fitted to Develop This Power*, translated by R. H. Thurston, first published in 1890, reprinted by the American Society of Mechanical Engineers in 1943.

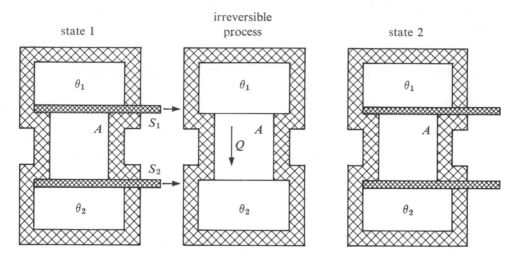

FIGURE 9.1. *Clausius' statement of the Second Law of thermodynamics.*

there in a vague and imprecise form. Nevertheless, Carnot succeeded in deriving a number of important, and correct, principles in an intuitive way.

9.2 Traditional formulation of the Second Law of thermodynamics

There exist several alternative, and equivalent, traditional formulations of the Second Law which have the common characteristic in that they single out a particular irreversible process and assert that its reverse cannot occur in nature, carefully specifying the process in all its details.

The first precise statement of the Second Law was given by R. Clausius in 1850; it can be paraphrased as follows:

A. Heat cannot pass spontaneously from a body of lower temperature to a body of higher temperature.

In order to appreciate the full meaning of this statement, it is necessary to visualize two heat reservoirs, Figure 9.1, at temperatures θ_1 and θ_2, respectively, θ_2 being lower than θ_1. The reservoirs are connected by any system of bodies, A, whatsoever. In the simplest case a metal rod may be imagined. The whole system is pictured enclosed in a rigid adiabatic container, and two adiabatic slides, S_1 and S_2, are provided. The system is now in equilibrium in state 1. When the constraints, the slides S_1 and S_2, are removed the system will undergo an irreversible process involving the flow of heat Q. It is asserted that the *net* flow of heat can occur in *one direction only*, namely, from θ_1 to θ_2, but *never* in the reverse direction. In other words, when the slides are returned, and a state of equilibrium, state 2, has been allowed to set in, it is maintained that the energy of reservoir 1 has decreased, and that of reservoir 2 has increased, the opposite being impossible. It is realized, of course, that in actual fact the temperatures θ_1 and θ_2 will change, but there is no difficulty in idealizing the process to the one outlined by attributing ideal properties to the reservoirs as was done in Section 5.13, and by assuming that the energy of subsystem A has remained constant.

The second alternative formulation concentrates on the process of transformation of heat into work. The First Law of thermodynamics stated the equivalence of heat and work and placed no restrictions on the transformation of one into the other. Experience teaches, however, that whereas the transformation of work into heat, for example, through friction, is not circumscribed by any restrictions, the reverse process, the transformation of heat into work, is subject to definite limitations. It is, for instance, impossible to transform into work the internal energy of the water in the sea by extracting a flow of heat from it, if no other changes occur in the surroundings simultaneously. Thus, it is impossible to utilize the inexhaustible store of energy in the high seas in order to propel ships.

A machine which could create work from nothing was called a perpetual-motion engine of the first kind, Section 5.10. The First Law asserted the impossibility of the construction of such an engine.

Wilhelm Ostwald introduced the concept of a *perpetual-motion engine of the second kind*, that is, of an engine which could perform work solely by cooling a body. A perpetual motion engine of the second kind would not contradict the First Law, because it would perform work at the expense of the internal energy of a source, but from the practical point of view it would afford the same advantages as a perpetual-motion engine of the first kind, since it could make use of the enormous potential of extracting heat from our surroundings on the earth. All attempts at constructing a perpetual-motion engine of the second kind have failed, and this experience underlies the following principle, enunciated by W. Thomson (Lord Kelvin) in 1851:

B. It is impossible to build an engine which would extract heat from a given source and transform it into mechanical energy without bringing about some additional changes in the systems taking part.

M. Planck formulated the principle in a similar way, except that he asserted the impossibility of constructing a machine which would work *periodically* and *continuously* and perform work at the expense of heat extracted from only one source. By inserting the qualifying words "periodically and continuously," it is emphasized that the machine operates on a cyclic process, and reverts periodically to a given state.

The preceding two, evidently equivalent, statements refer to a system shown sketched in Figure 9.2. The system, confined within an adiabatic enclosure, consists of a single heat source θ which supplies heat at a rate $\dot{Q}$ to a machine M, however com-

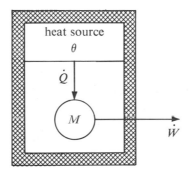

FIGURE 9.2. *The Planck-Kelvin statement of the Second Law of thermodynamics.*

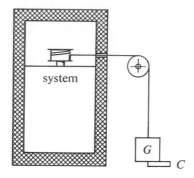

FIGURE 9.3. *Alternative statement of Second Law.*

plex. The machine supplies *positive* work at a rate $\dot{W}$ to an outside consumer. It is asserted that an arrangement of this kind cannot be realized.

Another possibility consists in concentrating on Joule's paddle-wheel experiment, Section 5.2. In that experiment a system was confined in a rigid adiabatic enclosure, Figure 9.3, and was connected to a weight G. Whereas it is possible to increase the internal energy U of the system by allowing the weight G to reach a lower level after the removal of the mechanical constraint C, it is impossible to achieve the reverse, that is, to raise a weight and simultaneously to decrease the energy of a system which exists in equilibrium inside a rigid adiabatic enclosure. Hence, the Second Law can be restated in the following way:

C. It is impossible to produce work by reducing the energy of a system existing in thermal equilibrium and confined within a rigid, adiabatic enclosure.

The reversible isoenergetic process discussed in Section 5.14.3 might at first appear to contradict statement B of the Second Law, for as we know work is performed at the expense of heat supplied by an external source. However, at the same time the state of the system is changed even if its energy is kept constant. Thus, the process can be performed only as long as there is a supply of the substance at the initial state, and must come to an end when this is exhausted. Alternatively, the initial state must be restored, but then a cycle will be created, and statement B will be found to apply.

Many skeptics find it impossible to reconcile themselves to the hard physical facts contained in the above statements. They persist in thinking that the assertions can be refuted by wit and subterfuge which usually manifest themselves in an inordinate complexity of the systems invented for the purpose. In defiance of the fact that in every single case attempted so far, the inventor has failed in his object, the Patent Offices of every country are being presented with applications which purport to have designed a perpetual-motion engine of the second kind. To a certain extent one must sympathize with the attitude of the unlucky inventors because, in principle, the fact that an event has *not* been observed to occur in the past does not preclude it from happening in the future. Thus, the Planck-Kelvin statement must be recognized as a bold generalization and extrapolation from known facts. Its ultimate scientific truth, just as that of the First Law, rests on the circumstance that *all* known *consequences* of this statement have been verified by experiment and none has been refuted. Just as was the case with the First law, at present, in any particular case when a discrepancy has apparently been discovered, it is believed that a fault in reasoning or in the evaluation of the experiment *must* be involved.

More precisely, the fact that no successful perpetual-motion engine of the second kind has been invented makes it *unlikely* that it ever will be. Similarly, the fact that bodies enclosed in rigid adiabatic envelopes have always tended towards equilibrium makes it *unlikely* that they will undergo a process which will make them move away from it. Thus, all statements of the Second Law contain an element of *probability*. This aspect of the Second Law, that is, its *statistical interpretation*, is very important when the microscopic point of view is adopted and will be touched upon in Volume II.

9.3 Logical relation between alternative statements of the Second Law

The possibility of providing alternative formulations of the Second Law raises the question as to the logical relations which may exist between them. In particular, it is necessary to assure oneself that the most general statement is selected for further derivation in order to be certain that of all the possible consequences, none has been overlooked. In fact, it turns out that such a choice is unnecessary, because it can be proved that all preceding statements are *entirely equivalent*, meaning that all consequences of one are inherent in the others, and that no consequence can be derived from one, if it is not also implied in the others. In doing this, it is necessary to have recourse to the principles of *mathematical logic*. These assert that two statements, A and B, are completely equivalent,

$$A \equiv B, \qquad (9.1)$$

if, and only if, the negation of one, $-A$, implies the negation of the other, $-B$, and *vice versa*.† The symbol for "implies" is written $\supset$, and so, equation (9.1) is true if, and only if

$$-A \supset -B \qquad (9.2)$$

and

$$-B \supset -A. \qquad (9.3)$$

It is easy to verify that the statements of the Second Law satisfy this restriction.

We now proceed to demonstrate that the Clausius (A) and Planck-Kelvin (B) statements are equivalent, leaving it to the reader to do the same for the third statement, or for any additional statements that he may wish to formulate on the established pattern.

Suppose, then, that a machine contradicting the Planck-Kelvin statement were possible, and that work W could be produced at the expense of the internal energy of a reservoir θ_2, that is, by extracting heat Q from it. This work could be used to operate a friction brake b which would transform the work into heat Q. That quantity of heat could be then transferred to a source of higher temperature θ_1, in contradiction to the Clausius statement, Figure 9.4.

Conversely, Figure 9.5, suppose that heat Q can be made to flow spontaneously from a reservoir at temperature θ_2 to one at temperature $\theta_1 > \theta_2$, in contradiction to

†This can easily be proved by the methods explained, for example, in Chapter 3 of I. M. Copi's *Symbolic Logic* (Macmillan, 1954). If $-A \equiv p$ and $-B = q$, then $p \supset q$ and $q \supset p$; hence $(p \supset q) \cdot (q \supset p) \equiv (p \equiv q)$; but $(p \supset q) = (-q \supset -p)$ or $B \supset A$, and so on.

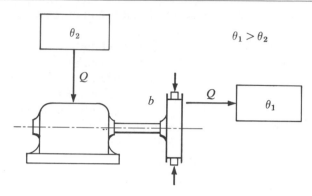

FIGURE 9.4. *Equivalence of two formulations of the Second Law.*

Clausius' statement. It is clear that an engine can be designed to produce work if two sources of heat are available. It could not, as we know, if only one heat reservoir were given. Such an engine would extract heat Q_1 from the reservoir at temperature θ_1 and reject another quantity of heat, Q_2, to the reservoir θ_2. Thus, by the First Law, and considering that the engine operates in a cycle, the work performed would be

$$W = Q_1 - |Q_2|.\dagger$$

If Q were made equal to $|Q_2|$, the reservoir θ_2 would neither gain nor lose heat. The reservoir θ_1 would lose heat

$$Q_1 - |Q| = Q_1 - |Q_2| = W,$$

and the net result of the operation would be to extract that heat from a *single* reservoir, θ_1, and to produce an equivalent amount of work in contradiction to the Kelvin-Planck statement of the Second Law.

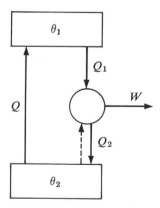

FIGURE 9.5. *Equivalence of two formulations of the Second Law.*

† The reader is reminded that the symbol $|Q_2|$ stands for "absolute (that is, positive) value of Q_2." Hence, the negative sign. The two strokes will be used whenever it is desirable to stress that a quantity is negative and that its absolute value must be *subtracted* from another quantity.

In the preceding argument it has been assumed that heat Q_2 must be *rejected* by the engine. Nothing would be changed in the argument if it were supposed that Q_2 is extracted from reservoir θ_2 as shown by the broken-line arrow in Figure 9.5. The engine would produce work

$$W = Q_1 + |Q_2|,$$

and it would be sufficient to make $|Q| = Q_1$ to obtain an engine contradicting the Planck-Kelvin statement. The engine would extract heat

$$|Q| + |Q_2| = Q_1 + |Q_2| = W$$

from the single reservoir θ_2, producing an equivalent amount of work. It is, however, necessary to appreciate that such an engine cannot exist. If it did, the resulting work W could be returned to reservoir θ_1 by the use of a brake, as in Figure 9.4, and as a result heat would flow spontaneously from θ_1 to θ_2. It is also evident that no work can be produced with both quantities of heat Q_1 and Q_2 being rejected by the engine, as this would be inconsistent with the First Law of thermodynamics.

Thus, the two statements are seen to be exactly equivalent.

9.4 The Carnot cycle

Having recognized in Section 5.10 that the continuous production of power from heat must be based on the performance of a cycle, we are now in a position to design the *simplest possible* cycle, paying due regard to the Second Law of thermodynamics. An understanding of the properties of this cycle is essential for the development of the Second Law, and we must introduce it before we proceed any further. Since it is impossible to produce power continuously with the aid of a flow of heat derived from a single source, it is concluded that *at least two sources* are required. Thus, the simplest possible cycle must exchange heat with two reservoirs, one at temperature θ, the other at temperature θ_0, it being assumed for the sake of being definite that $\theta > \theta_0$. Consequently, the system performing the cycle must be made to undergo two isothermal processes, one at temperature θ, the other at temperature θ_0, the processes being reversible or irreversible. During reversible processes the system itself will be continuously at the respective temperature θ or θ_0. Work can be performed by expanding or compressing a *working fluid*, or in any other suitable way. For example, a galvanic cell might be used and work can be performed by an electric current.

In order to complete the cycle with only two sources of heat available, it is necessary to join the two isotherms with the aid of two adiabatics which, too, can be reversible or irreversible, bearing in mind that two different isotherms cannot have any points in common (Section 2.4). The resulting cycle is known as a *Carnot cycle*, since it was invented by Sadi Carnot whose name has already been mentioned.

When all the processes in the cycle are reversible, the cycle itself will be called reversible. Otherwise, it will be called irreversible. Very often when a Carnot cycle is discussed, a *reversible* Carnot cycle is meant; whenever an *irreversible* Carnot cycle is intended the fact is stated explicitly. The cycle can, evidently, be operated in a forward or in a reverse direction. The direction is called *forward* when the system produces work ($W > 0$) and *reverse* when it consumes it ($W < 0$). With reference to the argument given at the end of the preceding section, it is clear that in forward operation the cycle must extract heat Q from the source θ, and reject heat Q_0 to the *sink* θ_0. Any other mode of operation would be inconsistent with the Second Law of thermodynamics. This results in the production of work

$$W = Q - |Q_0|, \tag{9.4}$$

which is another form of writing

$$\oint dW = \oint dQ$$

for a reversible cycle, equation (5.23a). The ratio of work W done by the system to the heat Q extracted from the source during a cycle

$$\eta = \frac{W}{Q} = 1 - \frac{|Q_0|}{Q} \tag{9.5}$$

is called its *theoretical* or *thermal efficiency*. Since $Q = W + |Q_0|$ as seen from equation (9.4), the Second Law of thermodynamics imposes the condition that

$$\eta < 1. \tag{9.6}$$

The efficiency of any other cycle is defined in the same way, except that in the case of cycles other than the Carnot cycle the quantity of heat Q may be extracted from more than one heat reservoir, that is, over a range of temperatures rather than at a single temperature. The definition of efficiency ignores the fact that some heat reappears at a lower temperature in the sink. In normal arrangements, the sink is at, or near, atmospheric temperature and the heat cannot be utilized in any other way. It is, as it is said, *dissipated*. On the other hand the heat Q must be provided by some costly means, for example, by the burning of conventional or nuclear fuel. Thus, the scientific concept of efficiency is related to the economic assessment of the utility of the cycle, and indicates the fraction of the "expensive" heat Q which has been converted into "useful" work W.

The study of the efficiencies of different cycles constitutes an important problem in engineering thermodynamics, it being evident that it has far-reaching practical and even economic consequences. At this stage it might appear that other cycles could be devised for which the restriction $\eta < 1$ would not apply. It will be seen later that this is not the case, and that a reversible Carnot cycle which is made to operate between the highest and lowest temperatures available has the *highest efficiency of all possible cycles*.

When the working medium is a fluid, say a perfect gas, as discussed in Section 7.3, a reversible Carnot cycle can be imagined performed in a cylinder, Figure 9.6. During the isothermal expansion along 1–2 the working fluid is brought into thermal contact through a diathermal wall with the source of heat whose temperature is θ. During the isothermal compression along 3–4 it is brought into thermal contact with the source of heat whose temperature is θ_0. During the two reversible adiabatic, that is, isentropic, processes sketched as 2–3 and 4–1, respectively, the cylinder is imagined insulated adiabatically.

An alternative arrangement for a cycle with four separate cylinders is shown in Figure 9.7. Instead of operating intermittently, as before, the present arrangement can be operated continuously. Each of the cylinders is made to perform one particular

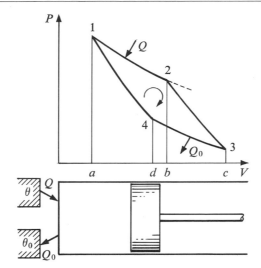

FIGURE 9.6. *The Carnot cycle with a perfect gas as its working medium.*

process, the flow of the working fluid being suitably regulated between them. Cylinders *c* and *d* are made to work as compressors, and cylinders *a* and *b* as expansion machines. The expansion in *a* is isothermal, heat being supplied by the source of heat at temperature *θ*. The compression in *c* is isothermal, heat being rejected by the medium into the sink of heat at temperature *θ₀*. The cylinders *b* and *d* are insulated adiabatically and the processes in them are isentropic, the gas expanding in *b* and being compressed in *d*. The working fluid is passed through the ducts indicated in Figure 9.7 and traverses the cylinders in the directions of the arrows. The numerals 1 to 4 in this figure correspond to the states of the medium in the *P, V* diagram of Figure 9.6. The capacity of the ducts is imagined very large, so that the state of the medium does not change in them with time in spite the fact that it is fed into the ducts and extracted from them periodically.

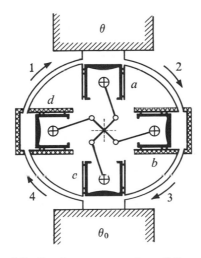

FIGURE 9.7. *Continuous operation of Carnot cycle.*

The reciprocating cylinders in the drawing could be replaced by turbines for the expansion and by turbocompressors for the compression processes, respectively, without affecting the principle of operation of the cycle. The P, V diagram in Figure 9.6 would then correspond to the processes undergone by a fixed mass of fluid as it is made to circulate around the four cylinders.

When any one of the processes, or any part of any one of the processes is irreversible, the whole cycle will be called irreversible. The fact that a particular arrangement of cylinders and heat reservoirs performs an irreversible cycle does not signify that the cycle cannot possibly be reversed. For example, in the arrangement shown in Figure 9.7, the pistons could operate with a certain amount of friction, but by reversing the flow of the working fluid and by suitably governing it, the arrangement could be made to operate in reverse. For such a reverse operation, the total amounts of work and heat exchanged during one cycle would be equal to each other, $Q = W$. There is, however, one important difference between a reversible and an irreversible Carnot cycle. When a reversible Carnot cycle, or, any reversible cycle for that matter, is reversed, all fluxes of heat reverse their direction but do not change in magnitude. This follows immediately from the fact that during a reversible process the system traverses a continuous sequence of states of equilibrium. If work is done by volume expansion, the reversible work

$$dW = P\,dV$$

changes sign, when the sign of dV is changed. The same can be said about the general expression for reversible work

$$dW = \sum_n Y_i\,dZ_i$$

given in Section 4.8, in which, on reversing the process, the signs of the generalized displacements dZ_i will be reversed. Since for a reversible cycle at every step

$$dQ = dE + \sum_n Y_i\,dZ_i,$$

and since dE also reverses its sign, the elements of heat dQ will reverse their signs. The same is clearly true about the reversible cycle as a whole.

In the case of a reversed irreversible cycle, the preceding simple relations cease to apply, and the fluxes of heat and work, having changed their signs, *do not retain the same absolute values*. As we know from Section 4.7, the expressions for work are not even Pfaffians, and some of the variables which appear in them cease to be properties of the system.

In order to complete the description of a reversible Carnot cycle, it is useful to sketch several state diagrams depicting the closed curve which constitutes the path of the cycle. In the case of systems with two independent properties, the path will be represented by a curve on a plane. For example, for a perfect gas the isotherms on a P, V diagram, Figure 9.8(a), will be hyperbolae $PV = R\theta = $ const, and the reversible adiabatics can be constructed step-by-step as outlined in Section 5.14.5. Thus, the cycle consists of a portion of a hyperbola 1–2, an isentropic 2–3, a portion of another hyperbola 3–4, and a portion of a second isentropic 4–1. The work W of the cycle is proportional to the area enclosed by the curve 1234.

In the case of a two-phase mixture, the diagram, Figure 9.8(b), assumes a somewhat simpler form, because isotherms are also isobarics. The diagram for an electric battery,

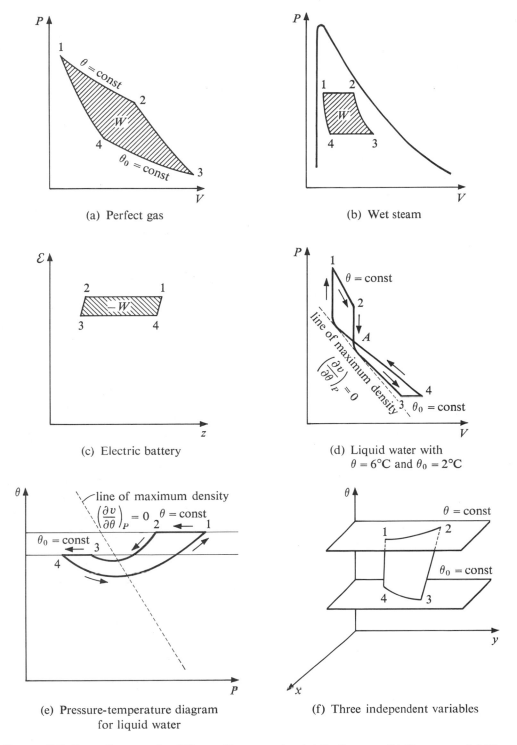

FIGURE 9.8. *State diagrams for different Carnot cycles. (a) Perfect gas. (b) Wet steam. (c) Electric battery. (d) Liquid water with* $\theta = 6°C$ *and* $\theta_0 = 2°C$. *(e) Pressure-temperature diagram for liquid water. (f) Three independent variables.*

Figure 9.8(c), could be drawn, as shown, if the equation of state $F(\mathcal{E}, z, \theta) = 0$ and the relation $E(\mathcal{E}, z)$ for energy were known. In all these cases, the path is a closed curve in a plane, the area enclosed by it being equal to the work W of the cycle.

Carnot cycles performed with liquid water when the two temperatures θ and θ_0 are above and below the temperature of maximum density ($+4°C$ at atmospheric pressure) present a somewhat baffling appearance.† Even though cycles of this type are of no practical significance, it is worth examining one such cycle; the cycle sketched in Figure 9.8(d) corresponds qualitatively to $\theta = 6°C$ and $\theta_0 = 2°C$ with $P_1 = 1$ atm. The isentropic lines 2–3 and 4–1 have been drawn on the basis of empirically established thermodynamic properties of liquid water; for example, the method outlined at the end of Section 5.14.5 could have been used, though, in fact, a more effective procedure was utilized.

In the diagram, the two isentropics 2–3 and 4–1 appear to intersect at A leading to a positive area of work $12A1$ and a negative area $A34A$. If the Carnot cycle were drawn on the state surface for water (Figure 7.20), it would become clear that the two states A lie on separate portions of the P, v, θ surface and merely project as a single point in the P, v diagram. This can be inferred from the θ, P diagram of Figure 9.8(e), where the position of the locus of maximum density (minimum specific volume) should be noted. The reader can imagine a v axis drawn perpendicular to the plane of the sketch and can gauge the elevation of points 1, 2, 3, 4 from Figure 9.8(d). This will enable him to visualize the projection in the θ-direction and on the P, v plane.

In this connection, the remarks about the apparent absence of single-valuedness in the $P, v \theta$ relation for water made in Section 7.4.10 should be recalled. For our present purposes, it is enough to realize that diagrams of Carnot cycles can assume a wide variety of forms.

The diagram for systems whose state is described by more than two variables becomes even more complex. Choosing the temperature θ and two more properties, x and y, as the independent variables, it will be found, Figure 9.8(f), that constant temperature processes are described by lines confined within the planes $\theta = $ const and $\theta_0 = $ const, so that it is not sufficient to allow the system to exchange heat with two reservoirs. In addition, it is necessary to constrain it and to prescribe the paths 1–2 and 3–4 for it. The problem of determining the two isentropics 2–3 and 4–1 would become correspondingly more difficult.

A simple system whose state is described by three independent variables can be obtained when two cylinders, each filled with a different gas, Figure 9.9, are enclosed with the aid of two pistons, and are made to exchange heat through a diathermal wall a. The state of such a system is described by the common temperature θ and, say, by the two volumes V_1 and V_2. Such a system can perform a multitude of isothermal processes, depending on the relation between V_1 and V_2 during the process. When a particular relation between V_1 and V_2 is prescribed, and imposed on the system by suitable cams and weights, the system is said to be *constrained*. Such a constraint is needed for every isothermal process when the number of independent properties exceeds two.

---

† For further details see Thomsen, J. S., and Hartka, T. J., "Strange Carnot Cycles; Thermodynamics of Systems with a Density Extremum," Am. J. Phys. **30** (1962), 26. See also Sommerfeld, A., *Thermodynamics and Statistical Mechanics*, translated by J. Kestin (Academic, 1956), pp. 347, 359 (Problem I.6) and Trevor, J. E., *The General Theory of Thermodynamics* (Ginn, 1927).

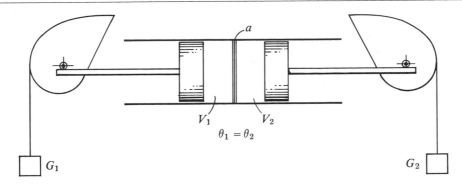

FIGURE 9.9. *System with three independent variables.*

For the two cylinders, and for reversible processes, we could write the equation of the First Law $dQ = dU + PdV$ as

$$dQ_1 = \left(\frac{\partial U_1}{\partial \theta}\right)_{V_1} d\theta + \left[\left(\frac{\partial U_1}{\partial V_1}\right)_{\theta} + P_1\right] dV_1$$

$$dQ_2 = \left(\frac{\partial U_2}{\partial \theta}\right)_{V_2} d\theta + \left[\left(\frac{\partial U_2}{\partial V_2}\right)_{\theta} + P_2\right] dV_2$$

$$(9.7)$$

and for the composite system, since $dQ = dQ_1 + dQ_2$, we have

$$dQ = \left[\left(\frac{\partial U_1}{\partial \theta}\right)_{V_1} + \left(\frac{\partial U_2}{\partial \theta}\right)_{V_2}\right] d\theta + \left[\left(\frac{\partial U_1}{\partial V_1}\right)_{\theta} + P_1\right] dV_1 + \left[\left(\frac{\partial U_2}{\partial V_2}\right)_{\theta} + P_2\right] dV_2. \quad (9.8)$$

The isentropic curves are solutions of the differential equation $dQ = 0$. In order to appreciate the form of this equation, it is noted that the first bracket contains a function of θ, V_1 and V_2, say f, the second a function g(θ, V_1), and the third a function h(θ, V_2). Thus the differential equation is of the form

$$f(\theta, V_1, V_2)\, d\theta + g(\theta, V_1)\, dV_1 + h(\theta, V_2)\, dV_2 = 0, \quad (9.9)$$

with the three independent variables θ, V_1, and V_2; it determines a curve in space as will be seen in detail in Section 10.2.4. For the time being we only note that if a parameter t and the functions

$$\theta(t), \quad V_1(t), \quad V_2(t) \quad (9.10)$$

could be found so that on substitution into equation (9.9) the latter would become an identity, the curve whose parametric representation is given by (9.10) would be the desired isentropic.

It might now appear that the adiabatic performance of an exothermic chemical reaction, such as the one described in Section 6.13.1, would also contradict statement *B* of the Second Law. In a process of this kind, the reactants at temperature θ_0, equal to that of the surroundings, can be made to undergo a chemical reaction at the end of which products at a temperature θ higher than that of the surroundings result. Thus, a source is obtained from which heat can be extracted, for example, by means of a Carnot cycle, which would, in turn, produce work. However, at the same time a quantity of reactants is being consumed and an equal mass of products appears. Hence, the process can be performed only as long as there is a supply of reactants, and must come to an end when the latter becomes exhausted, it being impossible to arrange for the process to operate "periodically." Alternatively, the chemical reaction could be "undone" and the original reactants regenerated by reversing it. This, however, would necessitate the arrangement of a cycle whose operation would be subject to the same limitations. Many engines make use of the possibility of creating heat sources by combustion, and our present-day power economy is based on the large consumption of fossil *fuels*, that is, reactants capable of producing high-temperature sources when they combine with oxygen from the air. A thermodynamically equivalent process is utilized in certain modern nuclear reactors. Their operation in no way contradicts the preceding assertions, in the same way as the existence of isoenergetic processes does not contradict them.

9.5   The reversed Carnot cycle

If the direction of a reversible Carnot cycle is reversed, all quantities of heat and work change their sign, as shown before, so that the cycle consumes a quantity of work W, extracts a quantity of heat Q_0 from a source at lower temperature θ_0, and rejects the sum

$$|Q| = Q_0 + |W| \qquad (9.11)$$

to a sink of higher temperature θ. The operation of a reversed Carnot cycle does not contradict the Second Law of thermodynamics as stated by Clausius, because the transfer of heat from a reservoir of lower to one of higher temperature is no longer "spontaneous," a supply of work W being now required from the surroundings.

A reversed cycle can be utilized for two different purposes, depending on the relation of the two temperatures, θ and θ_0, to that of the surrounding atmosphere, θ_a.

If the temperature θ_0 is made equal to that of the surrounding atmosphere, the reversed cycle can be used to perform what is called *reversible heating*, Figure 9.10. A

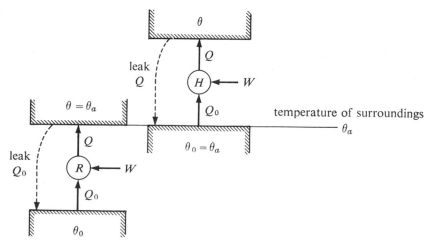

FIGURE 9.10. *Heat pump and refrigerator. H – heat pump. R – refrigerator.*

quantity of heat Q_0 is extracted from the surroundings at no cost, a quantity of work W (at some cost) is performed, and the sum $|Q| = Q_0 + |W|$ is transferred to a system at a higher temperature θ which is then heated. The resulting arrangement is known as a *heat pump*. The effectiveness of a heat pump is assessed by the ratio

$$\epsilon_f = \frac{|Q|}{|W|} = 1 + \frac{Q_0}{|W|} > 1 \qquad (9.12)$$

of heat gained to the work performed for which we shall propose the term *efficacy*. It is seen that the heat supplied, $|Q|$, exceeds the work required, W. If the quantity of work W which is consumed by the heat pump were directly transformed into heat, for example by friction or in an electric heater, only its equivalent would become available for heating, and we would then have $|Q|/|W| = 1$, in accordance with the First Law. The provision of a heat pump supplies a means of obtaining a multiple of this quantity, since $Q_0/|W|$ in equation (9.12) is larger than unity.† In a normal arrangement the compartment whose temperature is maintained at $\theta > \theta_a$ cannot be insulated perfectly, and the heat Q supplied by the heat pump is made to balance the unavoidable heat leak Q. Thus, the temperature of the compartment can be maintained at a higher temperature θ indefinitely.

Another, and more frequently encountered application of the reversed Carnot cycle is found in a *refrigerator* when θ is made equal to θ_a, Figure 9.10. A refrigerator extracts heat Q_0 from a body whose temperature θ_0 is lower than that of the surroundings thus maintaining it at that lower temperature in spite of the inevitable heat leak Q_0. The refrigerator transfers the quantity of heat $|Q| = Q_0 + |W|$ to the surroundings, directly or by means of a stream of cooling water or air. The ratio.

$$\epsilon = \frac{Q_0}{|W|} = \frac{Q_0}{|Q| - Q_0} \qquad (9.13)$$

is called the *coefficient of performance* of the refrigerator; it is employed to assess the usefulness of a refrigerator because it gives the ratio of the *refrigerating effect Q_0*, whose provision is the object of its existence, to the work $|W|$ required; this must be paid for by some means. It is seen that ϵ can become much larger than unity.

9.6 The efficiency of reversible Carnot engines

Given two reservoirs of heat it is possible to operate between them a great variety of Carnot engines. The engines can be of different sizes; they can operate with different working fluids, each obeying a different equation of state; even the mechanisms themselves may be different, it being possible to use fluid systems enclosed in cylinders with pistons, to operate with the aid of a fluid in continuous flow, to use elastic rods, galvanic and fuel cells, and so on. It is remarkable that the efficiency of all such engines must be the same on condition only that the cycles are reversible. The existence of any differences in efficiency between this multitude of possible reversible cycles would provide the means to create effects which would be incompatible with the Second Law of thermodynamics. This fact was clearly recognized by S. Carnot, and we now propose to prove it.

---

†If this is surprising to the novice, it is nevertheless true. Heat pumps are now used commercially; their adoption was first advocated by Lord Kelvin in the middle of the nineteenth century.

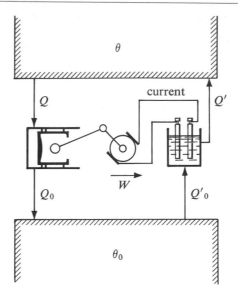

FIGURE 9.11. *Different Carnot cycles.*

Let us imagine two reversible Carnot cycles, Figure 9.11, of two different designs: for example, one may be using a gas and may be providing work by periodic expansion and compression, the other may be using a battery driving an ideal electric motor-generator. Both cycles operate between the same sources of heat θ and θ_0 $(\theta > \theta_0)$ and have equal outputs W per cycle. We then have for the first cycle

$$|W| = |Q| - |Q_0| \tag{9.14}$$

and for the second cycle

$$|W| = |Q'| - |Q_0'|, \tag{9.14a}$$

the prime denoting quantities related to the second cycle. Suppose, for the sake of argument, that

$$|Q'| > |Q|, \quad \text{whence } |Q_0'| > |Q_0|. \tag{9.15}$$

Since both cycles are reversible it is possible to reverse the second engine and use it as a heat pump, the required output of work being supplied by the first engine. Any differences of power output and power requirement resulting from the fact that a reciprocating engine is used can be imagined smoothed out by means of a sufficiently heavy flywheel or some similar ideal device.

Now, the first cycle extracts a quantity of heat $|Q|$ from the heat reservoir θ and the second cycle rejects a quantity of heat $|Q'|$ to it. Similarly, the first cycle rejects $|Q_0|$ units of heat into reservoir θ_0 from which the second cycle extracts $|Q_0'|$. The net result of the adiabatic working of the system comprising the two engines and the two heat reservoirs is to extract $|Q_0'| - |Q_0|$ units of heat from the colder heat source and to transfer an equivalent amount to the hotter source, as with the above assumption $|Q_0'| - |Q_0|$ is a positive quantity. This, by virtue of the Second Law, is clearly impossible, which indicates that the assumption $|Q'| > |Q|$ implying $|Q_0'| > |Q_0|$ is incompatible with the Second Law of thermodynamics. This excluded, we can only have

$$|Q'| \leq |Q| \quad \text{implying} \quad |Q_0'| \leq |Q_0|. \tag{9.16}$$

Assume again, for the sake of argument, that

$$|Q'| < |Q| \quad \text{implying} \quad |Q_0'| < |Q_0|. \tag{9.16a}$$

The preceding line of reasoning can now be retraced, with the only difference that the first cycle is made to work as a heat pump, the second cycle supplying the work to run it. Carrying the argument one step further, we can demonstrate that the net result of the adiabatic operation of the complete system is the transfer of $|Q| - |Q'| = |Q_0| - |Q_0'|$ units of heat from a colder to a hotter source. Thus, this assumption being also incompatible with the Second Law, only one possibility remains, namely,

$$|Q'| = |Q| \quad \text{implying} \quad |Q_0'| = |Q_0|. \tag{9.17}$$

This is the only assumption which does not contradict the Second Law. It is easily seen that during adiabatic operation in either combination, nothing happens. In particular, there is no net flow of heat and no net flow of work.

Since the two outputs of work of the two cycles were assumed equal, it is concluded that

The efficiency of a reversible Carnot cycle is the same for all working fluids, for all modes of operation, and for all sizes, and depends only on the temperatures θ and θ_0 of the two sources.

This can be written

$$\eta = \eta(\theta, \theta_0). \tag{9.18}$$

Making use of equation (9.5), it is noted that the ratio of heat absorbed Q to heat rejected $|Q_0|$ is also a function of the two temperatures, θ and θ_0, only. In fact

$$\frac{Q}{|Q_0|} = \frac{1}{1 - \eta} = q(\theta, \theta_0), \tag{9.19}$$

where $q(\theta, \theta_0)$ denotes a, so far undetermined, function of the two variables indicated. This ratio, too, is independent of the size of the Carnot engine, of its detailed mode of operation, or of the properties of the system undergoing the cycle. It is apparent that the size of engine, characterized by the amount of work W performed per cycle, has no bearing on the argument since the efficiency contains only the ratio of work W to heat Q.

In connection with the discussion on the different systems which could be used to realize a reversible Carnot cycle, it is useful to digress here and to examine whether a thermocouple could be used for the purpose. It might appear that the two junctions of a thermocouple circuit could be made to exchange heat with the two sources, as shown in Figure 9.12, and to drive an ideal motor-generator. The fact that the emf of a thermocouple is small is of secondary importance because a large number of such circuits could be connected in series to provide a sufficiently large total emf. However, it is necessary to recognize that such an arrangement cannot inherently be made reversible.

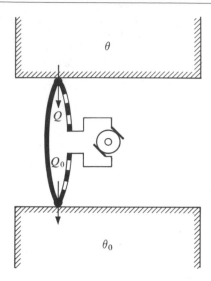

FIGURE 9.12. *Thermocouple circuit.*

In order to avoid the irreversible transformation of work into Joule heat in the circuit it would be necessary to make the cross sections of the wires very large and so to reduce their electrical resistance. All metals which are good electric conductors are also good conductors of heat and such an arrangement would allow a large quantity of heat to be conducted irreversibly from the source θ to the sink θ_0 along the wires. In order to reduce this effect, it would be necessary to use wires of very small cross section, thus increasing the amount of Joule heat evolved in the process. The fact that good electric conductors are also good conductors of heat is not accidental; it is explained by the microscopic theory of metals and is due to the circumstance that the transport of heat as well as of electricity is brought about by the migration of so-called free electrons. Consequently, our inability to combine in one metal high thermal resistance with low electrical resistance renders the processes in a thermocouple inherently irreversible and, consequently, the phenomena in thermocouples must be understood in terms of the thermodynamics of irreversible processes, Volume II. By contrast, a combination of a reversible fuel cell and a reversible galvanic cell can be employed to construct a Carnot engine.

The type of argument which has been developed in this section and which was also used in the preceding section is one often used in the exposition of thermodynamics by the method of R. Clausius. One of the principal laws of thermodynamics is taken as a basis for the argument and certain assumptions are made as to the phenomenon under consideration. The consequences of such assumptions are drawn and tested against the law. If the consequences are inconsistent with the law, the assumptions are considered false, whereas if the two agree, the assumption is accepted as a correct physical fact. The application of the method requires skill and imagination as it is not at all apparent what assumptions should be made. The reasoning cannot be reduced to one of a mathematical nature.

There is no difficulty in recasting the argument into a form in which it is tested against the Kelvin-Planck statement of the Second Law. For this purpose it is sufficient to postulate that in Figure 9.11 the engines had been so chosen as to make $Q_0 = Q_0'$. Thus, the work outputs W and W' would not necessarily be equal, and the gist of the argument would be to show that $W - W'$ must be equal to zero, for otherwise work would be produced by drawing heat $|Q| - |Q'|$ or $|Q'| - |Q|$ from a single source, namely, that at temperature θ. The feasibility of this kind of argument clearly follows from the considerations of Section 9.3.

9.7 The efficiency of irreversible Carnot engines

The analysis of the preceding section can now be extended to the case of irreversible Carnot cycles which differ from reversible Carnot cycles by the fact that on being reversed, they do not simply change the signs of all fluxes of heat and work. Considering such a cycle, Figure 9.13, we can assume without loss of generality that it produces work W per cycle in its forward operation and that it consumes work $-|W|$ in its reverse operation. However, the quantities of heat Q and Q_0 for forward operation change to Q_1 and $Q_{0,1}$ for reverse operation. At present it is impossible to determine whether the former or the latter are larger, but the application of the First Law in either case yields

$$W = Q - |Q_0| = |Q_1| - |Q_{0,1}|$$

or

$$Q - |Q_1| = |Q_0| - |Q_{0,1}|.$$

Comparing the forward and the reverse operation of the irreversible Carnot cycle with a reversible cycle of output W, so that

$$|W| = |Q'| - |Q_0'| \tag{9.20}$$

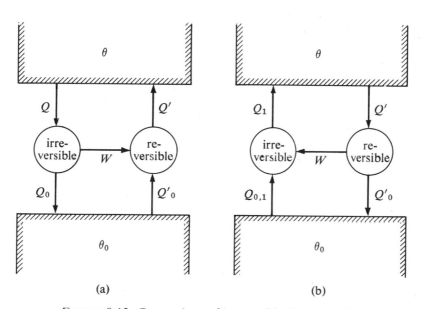

(a)   (b)

FIGURE 9.13. *Comparison of irreversible Carnot cycles.*

in the same way as in the preceding section, and repeating the argument based on the premiss that no combination of engines can exist which would lead to effects incompatible with the Second Law, it is easy to prove, Figure 9.13(a), that

$$|Q'| < Q \quad \text{so that} \quad |Q'_0| < Q_0 \tag{9.21}$$

and hence that the efficiency of the irreversible cycle,

$$\eta_{\text{irr}} = \left(\frac{W}{Q}\right)_{\text{irr}} < \left(\frac{|W|}{Q'}\right)_{\text{rev}} = \eta_{\text{rev}}, \tag{9.22}$$

is smaller than that of the reversible cycle. With reference to Figure 9.13(b), it is now possible to show that

$$|Q_1| < |Q'| \quad \text{so that} \quad |Q_{0,1}| < |Q'_0|. \tag{9.23}$$

Consequently, the coefficient of performance of the irreversible cycle,

$$\epsilon_{\text{irr}} = \left(\frac{|Q_{0,1}|}{|W|}\right)_{\text{irr}} < \left(\frac{Q'_0}{|W|}\right)_{\text{rev}} = \epsilon_{\text{rev}}, \tag{9.24}$$

is smaller than that of the reversible cycle. Similarly, for operation as a heat pump

$$\epsilon_{f,\text{irr}} = \left(\frac{|Q_1|}{|W|}\right)_{\text{irr}} < \left(\frac{|Q'|}{|W|}\right)_{\text{rev}} = \epsilon_{f,\text{rev}}. \tag{9.25}$$

Thus, it is seen that the ratio of the heats $|Q|$ and $|Q_0|$ exchanged at temperature θ and θ_0 by an irreversible Carnot cycle does not satisfy an *equation*, equation (9.18), as was the case with a reversible Carnot cycle. This must now be replaced by the *inequality*

$$\left(\frac{Q}{|Q_0|}\right)_{\text{irr}} < \frac{1}{1 - \eta_{\text{rev}}} \quad \text{or} \quad \left(\frac{Q}{|Q_0|}\right)_{\text{irr}} < q(\theta, \theta_0) \tag{9.26}$$

which is a direct consequence of the inequality (9.22) and the definition (9.18). For reverse operation on the other hand, we have

$$\left(\frac{|Q_1|}{|Q_{0,1}|}\right)_{\text{irr}} > q(\theta, \theta_0). \tag{9.27}$$

In both arguments, the inequalities follow immediately from the fact that the net flow of heat from θ to θ_0, $Q - |Q'| = Q_0 - |Q'_0|$ in Figure 9.13(a), and $|Q'| - |Q_1| = |Q'_0| - |Q_{0,1}|$ in Figure 9.13(b) must be positive or zero for the system, as required by the Second Law.

Strictly speaking, the fact that a zero net flow of heat is also compatible with the Second Law would introduce the possibility that the signs of inequality in (9.21) and (9.23), and so also in (9.22), (9.24), and (9.27), could be replaced by signs of equality, transforming the preceding inequalities into equations. This, however, must be excluded, for if it held, it would be possible to obtain from *equations* (9.21) and (9.23) that

$$Q_1 = Q$$

as for a *reversible* cycle, contrary to the original assumption.

Taking into account the inequalities (9.21) and (9.23), it is seen that

$$|Q_1| < |Q'| < |Q| \quad \text{implying} \quad |Q_{0,1}| < |Q'_0| < |Q_0|. \tag{9.28}$$

Thus, for equal work per cycle, W, the irreversible cycle operating forward exchanges *more* heat with the source of higher temperature than a reversible cycle and than the same cycle when operating in reverse. Accordingly, it exchanges also more heat with the sink θ_0, since in all cases the difference is equal to the work.

The ordering of the quantities of heat in (9.28) should be noted for future reference, due regard being paid to the significance of the symbols and to the fact that they apply to cycles of equal work W. Conversely, for the same quantity of heat extracted from the hotter source θ, the reversible cycle will produce more work, and for the same quantity of heat extracted from the colder sink θ_0, in reverse operation, the reversible cycle will consume less work rejecting less heat to the hotter source θ. Similarly, for the same quantity of heat rejected to the hotter source θ, the reversible cycle will consume less work, extracting more heat from the sink θ_0. Thus, the reversible cycle is more advantageous both in forward and in reverse operation.

Finally, it should be noted that if the irreversible cycle were to reject the same quantity of heat in reverse operation to the hotter source θ as it consumes in forward operation from it, it would require more work for reverse operation than it could produce in forward operation. It would then exchange more heat with the sink θ_0 in *forward* operation.

9.8   The thermodynamic temperature scale

In the preceding sections the temperatures θ and θ_0 of the source and sink used in conjunction with the various Carnot cycles were, naturally, measured on some empirical temperature scale. The relations between the quantities of heat and the common efficiency of all reversible Carnot cycles, equation (9.19), offers an opportunity to reduce temperature measurements to measurements of quantities of heat, that is, to the measurement of a flux of energy which is entirely independent of the measurement of temperature on any empirical temperature scale.

In order to demonstrate the feasibility of such a measurement, we shall consider three heat reservoirs at temperatures $\theta_1 > \theta_2 > \theta_3$, Figure 9.14, and three reversible Carnot cycles, each operating between two of the three heat reservoirs. The first cycle consumes heat Q_1 from θ_1 and rejects heat Q_2 to θ_2. The second cycle absorbs that heat Q_2 at θ_2 and rejects heat Q_3 to θ_3. The cycles produce work W_1 and W_2, respectively. Hence, for the two cycles, according to equation (9.19), we have

$$\frac{|Q_1|}{|Q_2|} = q(\theta_1, \theta_2); \qquad \frac{|Q_2|}{|Q_3|} = q(\theta_2, \theta_3),$$

and upon multiplication, we obtain

$$\frac{|Q_1|}{|Q_3|} = q(\theta_1, \theta_2) \times q(\theta_2, \theta_3). \tag{9.29}$$

The third reversible Carnot cycle, operating directly between the source θ_1 and sink θ_3 will be so arranged that it extracts a quantity of heat Q_1 equal to that of cycle 1 from the source θ_1 and rejects a quantity of heat Q_3 equal to that rejected by cycle 3 to the sink θ_3. In consequence, the work of the third cycle will become equal to the sum of the other two, as seen from the application of the First Law, namely,

$$W_3 = Q_1 - Q_3 = (Q_1 - Q_2) + (Q_2 - Q_3) = W_1 + W_2.$$

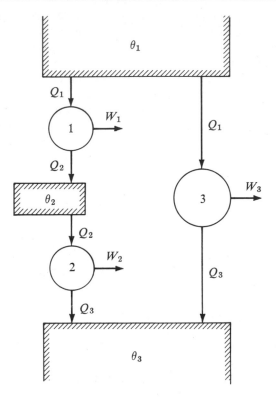

FIGURE 9.14. *Thermodynamic temperature scale.*

Thus, for the third cycle

$$\frac{|Q_1|}{|Q_3|} = q(\theta_1, \theta_3). \tag{9.30}$$

The *function* q which appears in equations (9.29) and (9.30) is, of course, the same in all, as it represents the *universal* relation between the ratios of heat quantities and temperatures of the heat reservoirs for reversible Carnot cycles. The arguments of this function are different in each case and correspond to the arrangement in Figure 9.14. Upon comparing equation (9.29) with equation (9.30), the *functional equation*

$$q(\theta_1, \theta_3) = q(\theta_1, \theta_2) \times q(\theta_2, \theta_3) \tag{9.31}$$

is obtained. Since on the right-hand side of it there appears a value θ_2 of the argument which is absent on the left-hand side, the form of the universal function q must be such as to lead to an elimination of θ_2 on the right-hand side. It is easy to see that a *sufficient condition* for this to be the case is for the function q to be of the form

$$q(\theta, \theta_0) = \frac{\Theta(\theta)}{\Theta(\theta_0)}, \tag{9.32}$$

where $\Theta(\theta)$ is some function of the argument θ, the same for θ as for θ_0. In other words, equation (9.32) indicates a possible form of the function q. We shall now proceed to show that this is the *only* possible form, that is, that the condition is also *necessary*. In order to do this we suppose that $\theta_1 = \theta$ is made to vary, while the temperatures θ_2 and θ_3 are kept constant. It is clear that the relation (9.31) must be satisfied by all possible values of all three temperatures; it must also be satisfied when one is assumed to vary, while the other two remain constant. Hence,

$$\frac{q(\theta, \theta_3)}{q(\theta, \theta_2)} = q(\theta_2, \theta_3) = \text{const} \tag{9.33}$$

under the present assumption. Thus, $q(\theta, \theta_3)$ and $q(\theta, \theta_2)$ can differ only by a constant factor. They can do so only if the function q has the form of a product, say,

$$q(\theta, \theta_0) = u(\theta) \cdot v(\theta_0), \tag{9.33a}$$

because only then will the dependence on θ vanish from the fraction in equation (9.33). It is still possible that the functions of the two variables, $u(\theta)$ and $v(\theta)$ are of different forms. Introducing (9.33a) into equation (9.33), we find

$$\frac{u(\theta)\, v(\theta_3)}{u(\theta)\, v(\theta_2)} = u(\theta_2)\, v(\theta_3) \quad \text{or} \quad \frac{1}{v(\theta_2)} = u(\theta_2),$$

which gives

$$q(\theta, \theta_0) = \frac{u(\theta)}{u(\theta_0)},$$

or a form identical with that in equation (9.32), as the only possibility.

The preceding argument shows that the ratio of heats exchanged in *any* reversible Carnot cycle operating between temperatures θ and θ_0 is

$$\frac{Q}{|Q_0|} = \frac{\Theta(\theta)}{\Theta(\theta_0)}. \tag{9.34}$$

The function Θ must be determined experimentally for any empirical temperature scale θ. If this were done, it would be possible to calculate numerically the efficiency of a reversible Carnot cycle operating between temperatures θ and θ_0, namely

$$\eta = \frac{W}{Q} = \frac{Q - Q_0}{Q} = 1 - \frac{\Theta(\theta_0)}{\Theta(\theta)}. \tag{9.35}$$

For example, if it were possible to construct a series of reversible Carnot engines, it would be possible to operate them between a fixed temperature θ_0, say the triple point of water, and all possible temperatures θ. The function $\Theta(\theta)$ could be determined by measuring the ratios $Q/|Q_0|$ for each temperature θ, and, as already stated, a measurement of this type would be independent of the measurement of temperature on the arbitrary empirical temperature scale θ. If another empirical scale θ' were chosen, the function Θ would then become

$$\Theta = \Theta[f(\theta')] \tag{9.35a}$$

because, as is clear from Chapter 2, there exists a unique relationship $\theta = f(\theta')$ between the isotherms on any two empirical temperature scales. Since the function Θ is determined solely by the measurement of the ratios of heat fluxes $Q/|Q_0|$ exchanged by the reversible Carnot engines, and since this is an independent measurement, the result would be entirely independent of the numerical values assigned to corresponding isotherms by virtue of the conventions inherent in the definition of any empirical temperature scale. For this reason, the values of Θ associated with the corresponding isotherms of all systems would become independent of their individual, and therefore fortuitous, properties.

It is natural to utilize the above circumstance for the definition of a new scale, thus inverting the preceding argument, and to adopt the values Θ *themselves* as the numbers on a new scale. In this manner the function Θ would be made a measure of temperature. This new scale Θ is called the *thermodynamic temperature scale*.† Since the defining equation (9.34) contains only *ratios* of temperatures, it is not yet uniquely defined, for any function

$$T = C\Theta \tag{9.35b}$$

proportional to it will also constitute a thermodynamic temperature scale. This remaining indeterminedness can be removed by a suitable, and otherwise arbitrary, *convention*. In order to retain, as far as possible, the conventions adopted previously in the section on temperature scales, Section 2.6, we shall once more assume for the triple point of water the value

$$T_3 = 273.16°\text{K} = 491.688°\text{R}. \tag{9.36}$$

Thus, the ice-point and steam-point temperatures would become

$$\left.\begin{array}{l} T_i = 273.15°\text{K} = 491.69°\text{R} \\ T_s = 373.15°\text{K} = 671.69°\text{R}, \end{array}\right\} \tag{9.36a}$$

and the interval between them would be

$$T_s - T_i = 100°\text{C} = 180°\text{F}, \tag{9.36b}$$

subject to the experimental errors discussed in Section 2.7.

Setting the thermodynamic temperature proportional to the function Θ together with the convention in equation (9.36) is equivalent to assuming the *thermometric equation*

$$T = \frac{Q}{|Q_3|} T_3 \tag{9.37}$$

in which the heat exchanged by a Carnot cycle plays the part of the thermometric property. All quantities on the right-hand side of equation (9.37) are positive; consequently, with the preceding conventions, *only positive temperatures* can be measured on the thermodynamic temperature scale. If the factor C in equation (9.35b) were chosen negative, negative absolute temperatures could be created by convention.

A thermometer which measures temperatures on this thermodynamic temperature scale would consist of a reversible Carnot engine, Figure 9.15, operating between a reservoir maintained at the reference temperature T_3 of the triple point of water, and the reservoir T whose temperature is to be measured. The determination of temperature T would then consist in the determination of the ratio $Q/|Q_3|$ by measurement.

It should be emphasized that the thermodynamic temperature scale has been defined without reference to any particular properties of systems. Its feasibility is a direct

---

† Some authors call it also *the* absolute temperature scale. However, we shall avoid this designation, reserving the term *absolute temperature* for temperatures measured on the Kelvin or Rankine scales, that is, for temperatures which correspond to a definite choice of the thermometric equation and the associated fixed point, as outlined in Section 2.6.

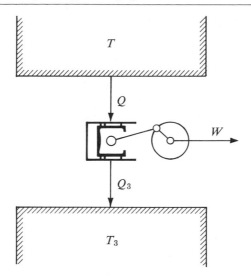

FIGURE 9.15. *Thermometer measuring temperatures on the thermodynamic temperature scale.*

consequence of the Second Law of thermodynamics. However, so far, only its feasibility *in principle* has been established, because the scheme outlined in Figure 9.15 cannot be realized, even if it were practical, owing to the impossibility of constructing *reversible* engines. Thus, it is necessary to investigate further the question of how to perform actual measurements on this, evidently superior scale. We shall consider this matter further in Sections 10.3.2 and 12.3. The inquiry will lead us to the gratifying, and intuitively expected, result that the thermodynamic temperature scale is identical with the perfect-gas temperature scale in the range where the latter can be defined. The inquiry will lead to the additional result that the thermodynamic temperature scale possesses a natural *absolute zero*. Thus, the question of the attainability of this absolute zero will pose itself. This question will be answered in the chapter on the Third Law of thermodynamics in Volume II.

9.9 Evaluation of the efficiency of a reversible Carnot cycle

Having adopted the new, thermodynamic temperature scale, T, it is now possible to write the expression (9.35) for the efficiency of a reversible Carnot cycle in terms of it. We then obtain

$$\eta = \frac{W}{Q} = 1 - \frac{|Q_0|}{Q} = 1 - \frac{T_0}{T}. \tag{9.38}$$

The ratio of the heats $|Q_0|/Q$ is given by equation (9.34) and is

$$q(T, T_0) = \frac{Q}{|Q_0|} = \frac{T}{T_0}. \tag{9.39}$$

It follows at once that the efficacy of a Carnot heat pump, equation (9.19b), is

$$\epsilon_f = \frac{|Q|}{|W|} = \frac{|Q|}{|Q| - |Q_0|} = \frac{T}{T - T_0} \tag{9.40}$$

and that the coefficient of performance of a Carnot refrigerator, equation (9.19c), is

$$\epsilon = \frac{|Q_0|}{|W|} = \frac{T_0}{T - T_0}.$$

(9.41)

In normal circumstances, the temperature T_0 of a power cycle will be equal to the temperature T_a of the surroundings, that is, of the atmospheric air or of the cooling water available for industrial purposes, say from a pond or river. Thus, the efficiency of a reversible cycle will essentially depend on the temperature of the available source T, increasing with it as shown in Figure 9.16, and tending asymptotically to $\eta = 1$ as $T \to \infty$. At lower temperatures, the increase in η is rapid, proving that even a small increase in the temperature T has a large effect on the gain in efficiency when the difference $T - T_0$ is not very large. Conversely, when the difference $T - T_0$ is large, that is, when the efficiency η is high, any additional gain in efficiency, even for comparatively large increases in temperature, is small. In any case, if a high efficiency is to be achieved, the temperature T of the source of heat must be *as high as possible*. The limit of high temperature which is feasible in practical applications is determined by the high-temperature properties of available materials. In practice, there is no difficulty in creating sources of high temperature by combustion or in nuclear reactors. The difficulty lies in providing materials which could confine such high-temperature sources without becoming destroyed, and which could safely be exposed to the working fluid at that high temperature and yet maintain the strength required for operation.

The possibility of increasing the efficiency of a reversible Carnot cycle by reducing T_0 below the available temperature is of no practical importance, since that reduced temperature would have to be maintained artificially, say with the aid of a reversed

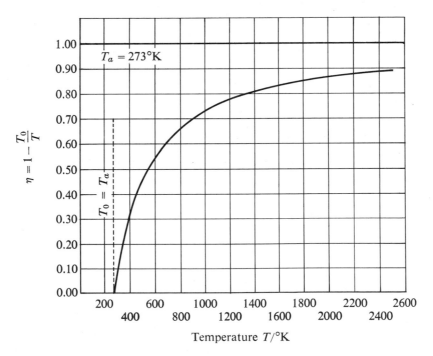

FIGURE 9.16. *Efficiency of Carnot cycle in terms of the temperature T of the source.*

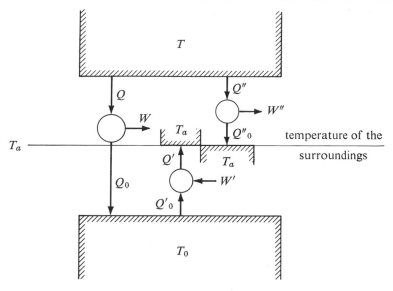

FIGURE 9.17. *Efficiency of a Carnot cycle for $T_0 < T_a$.*

Carnot cycle operating as a refrigerator, Figure 9.17. In order to sustain the operation and to maintain the sink T_0 at a constant temperature $T_0 < T_a$ it is necessary to arrange the refrigerator to provide the refrigerating effect

$$|Q_0'| = |Q_0|.$$

Comparing the operation of the combined Carnot power cycle and Carnot refrigerator with a Carnot power cycle operating directly between the temperatures T and T_a, as shown in the sketch, it is seen that

$$\frac{|Q'|}{T_a} = \frac{|Q_0|}{T_0} = \frac{Q}{T},$$

which follows from equation (9.39). Thus, the work

$$W' = Q' - |Q_0'|$$

required to drive the refrigerator would become

$$W' = |Q'| - |Q_0'| = (T_a - T_0)\frac{Q}{T}$$

and the net work produced is

$$W - W' = \frac{Q}{T}(T - T_0) - (T_a - T_0)\frac{Q}{T} = \frac{Q}{T}(T - T_a);$$

it is equal to the work W''' of the cycle operating between T and T_a directly, and could be obtained at the expense of heat Q without the need to employ a refrigerator at all.

The statement, sometimes encountered, that the efficiency could be made equal to unity if T_0 were made equal to zero, thus rendering $Q_0 = 0$, has no practical importance, because, at best, the maintenance of a sink at *absolute zero temperature* would require so much work as to wipe out the advantage. It is, further, sometimes stated that a

Carnot cycle operating between a temperature T and $T_0 = 0$ would be inconsistent with the Second Law, since in effect, with $Q_0 = 0$, it would extract heat from one source only and produce work. Thus, it is concluded that it is impossible to attain absolute zero temperature. Whereas the conclusion itself is correct, and we shall derive it rigorously in the chapter on the Third Law of thermodynamics in Volume II, it does not follow from the preceding argument. Clearly, two sources are *required*: one source at T without the other at $T_0 = 0$ would *not* produce work, and what is needed is the investigation of a mathematical process of going over to the limit $T_0 \to 0$, when simultaneously $|Q_0| \to 0$. The process involves the existence of a singular point because the isothermal rejection of heat at $T_0 = 0$ would also be adiabatic and, consequently, the two adiabatic processes, together with the isothermal-adiabatic process $T_0 = 0$, would tend to merge into one. The question has no easy and obvious answer and we must abandon it for the time being.†

Equations (9.40) and (9.41), represented graphically in Figure 9.18, show that the efficacy of a reversible heat pump and the coefficient of performance of a reversible refrigerator increase as the temperature difference $T - T_0$ is *reduced* leading to a requirement which is opposite to that for forward operation when the largest possible difference $T - T_0$ assured high efficiency. The fact that $\epsilon_f \to \infty$ as well as $\epsilon \to \infty$ for $T - T_0 \to 0$ is of no importance and constitutes merely a singularity in the expressions without physical significance, since for $T = T_0$ neither a refrigerator nor a heat pump would be needed. In the design of refrigerators and heat pumps, the temperature $T > T_a$ for a heat pump, and the temperature $T_0 < T_a$ for a refrigerator do not, as a rule, constitute adjustable design parameters, because they are usually given in the specification.

The simplicity of the expressions for the efficiency of a reversible Carnot cycle, or for the efficacy and coefficient of performance of a reversed, reversible Carnot cycle,

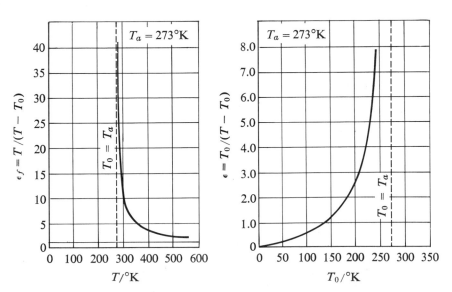

FIGURE 9.18. *Efficacy of Carnot heat pump and coefficient of performance of Carnot refrigerator.*

† See, for example, Pippard, A. B., *Classical Thermodynamics* (Cambridge Univ. Press, 1957), p. 48.

in terms of thermodynamic temperature T, and due to the simplicity of the expression for the ratio of the two heats, equation (9.39), might at first appear somewhat puzzling. However, as is easily recognized, this simplicity is entirely consequent upon the fact that the thermodynamic temperature scale, equation (9.37), has been *defined* in terms of these heat quantities. Had any of the empirical scales θ been adopted, the expressions would become quite complex because the inverse function $T(\theta)$ can be quite complex. In this, we have proceeded somewhat on the same lines as when the perfect-gas temperature scale was defined in Section 2.6. Then, the fact that the perfect-gas temperature scale was based on the common, extrapolated properties of all gases (for $P \rightarrow 0$) resulted in a very simple equation of state of a perfect gas. Here, the fact that the thermodynamic temperature scale has been based on the common properties of all reversible engines led to the present simplicity of equation (9.37). If it were not for the fact, which has already been emphasized before, that both scales will be shown to be identical, it would be necessary to make a final decision and to abandon one or the other simplification. As things are, both can be retained, and it is concluded that expressing the equations of thermodynamics, as we shall from now on do, in terms of thermodynamic temperature on the absolute scale, is likely to result in a good deal of simplification in general. Nevertheless, it must not be forgotten that all practical measurements are always performed with reference to the empirical scale of the particular thermometer used (for example, the International Practical Temperature Scale) and that, therefore, this simplicity in the equations can be retained only if careful calibration and correction to the thermodynamic temperature scale is undertaken.

9.10   Clausius integral. Entropy

In spite of the fact that for the time being no operational basis has been provided for the concept of thermodynamic temperature, no practical method of measuring temperature in terms of the thermodynamic scale having been indicated, the concept is of great theoretical importance, and we now propose to analyze its consequences. Reverting to equation (9.39), it is seen that for a reversible forward Carnot cycle

$$\frac{Q}{T} - \frac{|Q_0|}{T_0} = 0. \qquad (9.42)$$

For a reversible reversed Carnot cycle the corresponding relation would be written

$$\frac{|Q|}{T} - \frac{Q_0}{T_0} = 0. \qquad (9.42a)$$

By dropping the strokes which denote the absolute values of the quantities of heat and reverting to the usual algebraic notation in which the symbol includes the sign, it is seen that the two preceding equations contract to

$$\frac{Q}{T} + \frac{Q_0}{T_0} = 0,$$

which can also be written

$$\Sigma \frac{Q}{T} = 0. \qquad (9.43)$$

Since in a reversible Carnot cycle heat is exchanged only at the two temperatures, T and T_0, the quantity under the summation sign represents the sum of all quantities dQ/T evaluated around this particular cycle. In other words, it represents the *line integral* of the integrand dQ/T around a particular closed path, namely, that representing a Carnot cycle. Moreover, equation (9.43) shows that irrespective of the direction in which the cycle is traversed, the line integral vanishes, that is, that

$$\oint_C \frac{dQ}{T} = 0, \tag{9.44}$$

where the symbol C under the integral serves as a reminder that it applies to a Carnot cycle. In thermodynamics, it has become customary to call the line integral

$$\int_1^2 \frac{dQ}{T} \tag{9.45}$$

of the integrand dQ/T a *Clausius integral*. Equation (9.44) represents a Clausius integral taken around the closed curve which corresponds to a reversible Carnot cycle.

The property of the integrand dQ/T expressed in equation (9.44) leads to a very important conclusion. It will be recalled from the discussion in Sections 4.2 and 4.3 that the vanishing of a line integral around a closed curve signifies that the integrand can be expressed as the perfect differential of a potential. Denoting this potential by the symbol S, we can write

$$dS = \frac{dQ^\circ}{T}, \tag{9.46}$$

where the superscript $^\circ$ has been added to emphasize the fact that equation (9.44) is valid only for reversible processes.

Before proceeding with the physical interpretation of equation (9.46), it is necessary to make several explanatory remarks. In general, for any reversible process undergone by a system with n independent variables x_i, the expression for heat has the form

$$dQ^\circ = dE + \sum_n Y_i \, dZ_i, \tag{9.47}$$

where the energy E, the generalized forces Y_i, and the generalized displacements Z_i are all known functions of the independent properties x_i. For example, in the case of a simple system whose independent variables are chosen as the pressure P and the volume V, the energy $E = U(P, V)$, and equation (9.47) would be simplified to

$$\begin{aligned} dQ^\circ &= dU + P \, dV \\ &= \left(\frac{\partial U}{\partial P}\right)_V dP + \left\{\left(\frac{\partial U}{\partial V}\right)_P + P\right\} dV. \end{aligned} \tag{9.47a}$$

This is a Pfaffian of the form

$$dQ^\circ = M(P, V) \, dP + N(P, V) \, dV. \tag{9.47b}$$

Similarly, it is easy to see that the Pfaffian in equation (9.47) will be of the general form

$$dQ^\circ = \sum_n M_i(x_1, \ldots, x_n) \, dx_i, \tag{9.47c}$$

where the functions M_i can be evaluated from the known relations $E(x_1, \ldots, x_n)$,

$Y_i(x_1, \ldots, x_n)$, and $Z_i(x_1, \ldots, x_n)$. Now, a line integral taken around a closed path, regardless of whether the path is in the form of a Carnot cycle or in any other form, will not vanish, for example,

$$\oint dQ^\circ = \oint \sum_n M_i(x_1, \ldots, x_n) \, dx_i \neq 0. \qquad (9.48)$$

Indeed, for a forward Carnot cycle, as we know

$$\oint dQ^\circ = Q - |Q_0| = W > 0.$$

This is due to the circumstance, discussed fully in Section 4.1, that the Pfaffian dQ° is not a perfect differential, that is, that the associated vector field $\mathbf{F}(M_1, \ldots, M_n)$ is rotational. It is, therefore, *not* equal to the gradient of any scalar function.

When the Pfaffian dQ° is divided by the thermodynamic temperature T, another Pfaffian is obtained. The thermodynamic temperature, being a property, also depends on the independent variables of the system. It can be regarded as the function $T(x_i, \ldots, x_n)$. Thus, the Pfaffian dQ°/T has the general form

$$\frac{dQ^\circ}{T} = \sum_n \zeta_i(x_1, \ldots, x_n) \, dx_i, \qquad (9.49)$$

where

$$\zeta_i(x_1, \ldots, x_n) = \frac{M_i(x_1, \ldots, x_n)}{T(x_1, \ldots, x_n)}.$$

Now, this modified Pfaffian is associated with a vector field $\mathbf{G}(\zeta_1, \ldots, \zeta_n)$ which is irrotational, as evidenced by equation (9.44). The fact that equation (9.44) has been proved for a Carnot cycle is immaterial because the connection between the nature of a vector field and a circular line integral is independent of the particular shape of the path. If the circular line integral vanishes for one closed path, it will vanish for all closed paths on condition that each of them can be contracted to a point. Hence, in testing for this property, it is always possible to choose the simplest or most convenient path. In the present case, the most convenient path turns out to be a reversible Carnot cycle. The same fact can be derived rigorously with the aid of Stokes' theorem given in equation (4.14). An arbitrary point a in the space determined by the independent properties of the system can be enclosed by a Carnot cycle C, as shown for $n = 3$ in Figure 9.19(a). According to equations (4.14) and (9.44)

$$\oint_C \frac{dQ^\circ}{T} = \oint_C \mathbf{G} \cdot d\mathbf{s} = \iint_A (\text{curl } \mathbf{G})_n \, dA = 0.$$

Here dA denotes an element of a surface which includes the curve C as well as the point a. On going over to the limit, that is, on choosing Carnot cycles closer and closer to point a, but still confined to surface A, we find that at any point

$$(\text{curl } \mathbf{G})_n = 0,$$

which proves that the vector $\mathbf{G}$ associated with the Pfaffian dQ°/T possesses a vanishing normal component G_n. Thus, the vector $\mathbf{G}$ must be tangent to the arbitrary surface A, as shown in Figure 9.19(b). Bearing in mind the remarks made at the end of Sec-

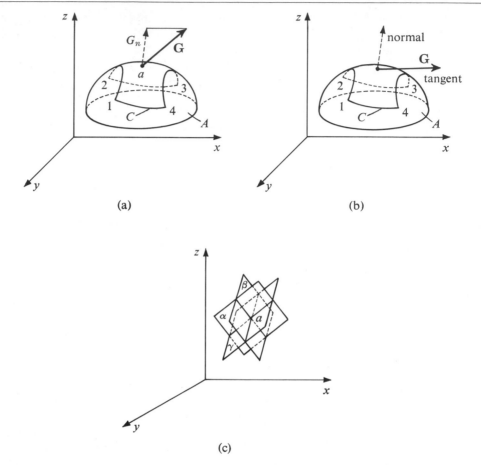

FIGURE 9.19. *Proof that* $dQ°/T$ *is a perfect differential.*

tion 9.4 about the freedom inherent in the design of Carnot cycles for systems with more than two independent variables, it is easy to imagine three mutually orthogonal surfaces passing through point a. Three such orthogonal surfaces, drawn in the shape of the planes α, β, γ for simplicity, have been sketched in Figure 9.19(c). The preceding reasoning can be applied to a series of Carnot cycles, each confined to a single surface, and each contracting to point a. It will then transpire that the normal component of the vector $\mathbf{G}$ to each of the three orthogonal surfaces α, β, and γ must vanish in turn. Since a vector whose three mutually orthogonal components vanish must itself vanish, we conclude that at any point a,

$$\text{curl } \mathbf{G} = 0.$$

Hence, it follows that *the vector field* $\mathbf{G}(x, y, z)$, associated with the Pfaffian $dQ°/T$ is irrotational. The extension of the preceding argument to the case when there are n *independent properties* $x_i, \ldots, x_n$ follows at once from the extended form of Stokes' theorem given in equation (f) on p. 119.

A function, like T in equation (9.49), which transforms an imperfect differential, like $dQ°$, into a perfect differential $dQ°/T$ is called the *integrating denominator of the Pfaffian* $dQ°$. Thus, the thermodynamic temperature constitutes the integrating denominator for reversible heat. It must not be assumed that all Pfaffian expressions possess an integrating denominator. On the contrary, the existence of one is an exception and not the rule.† It is seen, therefore, that the existence of an integrating denominator in the case of reversible heat is a consequence of the Second Law of thermodynamics. By the same token, the fact that the thermodynamic temperature constitutes the integrating denominator is also a consequence of the Second Law of thermodynamics. In particular, it is clear that an empirical temperature θ would not constitute an integrating denominator. If it were decided to retain a particular empirical temperature θ in the equations of thermodynamics, then the function $\Theta(\theta)$ from equation (9.32) or (9.34), different for each different empirical temperature scale, would constitute the integrating denominator, and equation (9.46) would be written

$$dS = \frac{dQ^\circ}{\Theta(\theta)}. \qquad (9.46a)$$

This is one more simplification in the equations of thermodynamics which results from the adoption of the thermodynamic temperature scale.

The potential S suggested by these considerations constitutes a new, important property of the system, and is called its *entropy*. As is usual for potentials, only *differences in entropy between different states of a single closed system* can be measured. The difference in entropy between any two states 1, 2 is measured by evaluating the integral

$$S_2 - S_1 = \int_1^2 \frac{dQ^\circ}{T} \qquad (reversible\ path), \qquad (9.50)$$

that is, by measuring at every step the quantity of heat dQ° exchanged, as well as the thermodynamic temperature T, *along a reversible path*. Since the entropy is a potential, it is associated with a *state* and not with a process. Given two states, 1 and 2, it is possible to determine the entropy difference $S_2 - S_1$ regardless of the actual process which the system may have performed, and regardless of whether the process was reversible or irreversible, as long as states 1 and 2 are equilibrium states. Hence, in order to *calculate* this difference it is possible to choose *any reversible* path joining them without reference to the process being analyzed. In practice, a reversible path leading to the simplest form of the integral will be chosen, and the results will be tabulated.

Entropy is an extensive property, since the elements of heat dQ° are proportional to the mass of a homogeneous system. Entropy is measured in one of the following units:

$$\frac{kcal}{{}^\circ K}, \quad \frac{Btu}{{}^\circ R}, \quad or \quad \frac{J}{{}^\circ K},$$

and the specific entropy

$$s = \frac{S}{m} \qquad (9.50a)$$

of a homogeneous system is measured in

$$\frac{kcal}{kg\,{}^\circ K}, \quad \frac{Btu}{lbm\,{}^\circ R}, \quad or \quad \frac{J}{kg\,{}^\circ K},$$

† A more complete argument will be given in Chapter 10.

that is, in the same units as specific heat, regardless of the fact that the physical natures of specific heat and entropy are different. For the reasons explained in Section 5.11, the first two of the latter three units are equal. The molar specific entropy is measured in

$$\frac{\text{kcal}}{\text{kmol}°\text{K}}, \quad \frac{\text{Btu}}{\text{lbmol}°\text{R}}, \quad \text{or} \quad \frac{\text{J}}{\text{kmol}°\text{K}}.$$

Since along an isentrope $dQ° = 0$ at every step of the process, we must also have $dS = 0$. Hence, *during a reversible adiabatic process the entropy of the system remains constant*. This statement provides a justification for the designation "isentropic" for such processes. In any reversible but not necessarily adiabatic process, the element of heat $dQ°$, as seen from (9.46), can be written

$$dQ° = T\,dS \tag{9.46a}$$

as the product of an intensive quantity T and the perfect differential of an extensive property S. This, naturally, does not cause $dQ°$ to be a perfect differential itself, but simplifies it considerably; instead of the n terms in equation (9.49) it now contains only *one* term, $T\,dS$.

The consequences which flow from the Second Law of thermodynamics, and which have been derived so far, constitute the *first part* of the mathematical formulation of the Second Law. They are also known as *Carnot's theorem* which can be summarized in the statement:

> *For any closed system there exists a potential S, called its entropy. For all systems there exists a common temperature scale T, called the thermodynamic temperature scale. For any reversible process taking place in a closed system the expression for heat dQ° can be represented as the product TdS of thermodynamic temperature and the perfect differential of entropy. Thus, the thermodynamic temperature constitutes the integrating denominator for dQ°, and such an integrating denominator exists for all systems.*

Inserting the general expression for $dQ°$ from the First Law, we can also write

$$dS = \frac{dE + \sum_n Y_i\,dZ_i}{T}. \tag{9.51}$$

In particular, for simple systems undergoing compressions or expansions only, we can write

$$dS = \frac{dU + P\,dV}{T}, \tag{9.51a}$$

or

$$dS = \frac{dH - V\,dP}{T}, \tag{9.51b}$$

since $dQ = dU + P\,dV = dH - V\,dP$ as shown in Section 5.14.6. With the aid of the equation (9.51a), integration for entropy can first proceed along a path $V = \text{const}$, Figure 9.20(a), from state 1 to state 1', the resulting increase in entropy being

$$S_{1'} - S_1 = \int_1^{1'} \frac{dU}{T}.$$

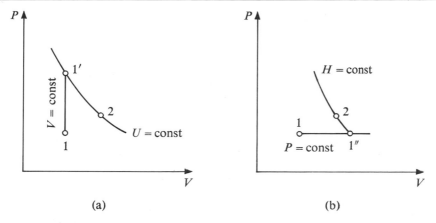

FIGURE 9.20. *Integration of equations (9.51a) and (9.51b).*

The second step from 1′ to 2 produces the additional entropy increase

$$S_2 - S_{1'} = \int_{1'}^{2} \frac{P}{T}\, dV.$$

It is possible to proceed similarly in the case of equation (9.51b) when

$$S_2 - S_1 = \int_{1}^{1''} \frac{dH}{T} - \int_{1''}^{2} \frac{V}{T}\, dP.$$

The path of integration of equation (9.51) could consist of n segments, each at $x_i = $ const, as is apparent from equation (9.47).

From the fact that entropy is a potential, it follows that the net change in entropy around an irreversible cycle is zero, if the initial and the identical final point of the cycle is a state of equilibrium. We can write it as

$$\oint dS = 0, \tag{9.52}$$

ignoring the fact that no integrand dS can be indicated for the irreversible steps in the cycle. The same cannot be said about the quantities dQ/T. We can write this in the form of the statement that

$$\oint \frac{dQ}{T} \neq 0 \tag{9.52a}$$

for an irreversible cycle. Clearly, the exact physical meaning of the process of summing up the quantities dQ/T around the cycle must be investigated further, and we shall do this in Section 9.11.

Next, let us consider any reversible cycle and inquire into the entropy change of the isolated system composed of the subsystem performing the cycle and all the sources supplying and receiving heat during one cycle. The latter, obviously, will not perform a cycle but only processes from one state of equilibrium to another. It is clear that the changes in the entropy of the sources are exactly equal to the changes in entropy of the subsystem, the two having opposite signs, provided that the exchange of heat is reversible. Hence, the change in entropy

$$\Delta S = 0 \qquad (9.53)$$

and the Clausius integral

$$\Sigma \int_a^b \frac{dQ^\circ}{T} = 0. \qquad (9.53a)$$

The Clausius integral is evaluated here from some state a to some state b for every source, and the sum over all sources is taken. In other words: *During any reversible process, the entropy of an isolated system remains constant.*

The above statement is valid for any reversible process and for any system, however complex, because no restrictive assumptions were made in the argument. In particular, it is also valid for reversible chemical processes taking place within the system. A method whereby chemical processes can be made to occur reversibly will be discussed in Volume II.

In the preceding argument it has been assumed that all sources exchanging heat are ideal reservoirs, as they were defined in Section 5.13. Such ideal reservoirs are assumed not to change their temperature as they acquire or deliver a quantity of heat, finite in the case of the isothermal process in a Carnot cycle, or infinitely small, as the case may be. Since the properties of such heat reservoirs are highly idealized, it must be realized that their energy cannot be assumed to have remained unchanged. By the First Law

$$dQ^\circ = dE,$$

since $dW = 0$. Hence, the change in entropy of a heat reservoir is given by

$$dS = \frac{dQ^\circ}{T} = \frac{dE}{T}, \qquad (9.54)$$

so that $dS > 0$ when the *reservoir* acquires heat (heat extracted from the system) and $dS < 0$ when the reservoir gives up heat (heat added to the system). This change in entropy is independent of whether the heat reservoir and the system are of equal temperature, that is, of whether the process as a whole is reversible or not. In order to see this, it is necessary to choose *for the heat reservoir* a reversible path, and then to calculate its entropy change. It is easy to perceive that with the idealizations adopted, the reservoir will exchange the same amount of heat at the same temperature as those inserted in equation (9.54). If heat quantities are reckoned with respect to the system, the signs in equation (9.54) must be reversed. Thus, if a system of temperature $T' < T$ receives heat Q from a heat reservoir at temperature T, the latter will lose entropy

$$\Delta S = -\frac{Q}{T}. \qquad (9.54a)$$

Similarly, if a system at temperature $T_0' > T_0$ rejects heat $|Q_0|$ to a reservoir at temperature T_0, the latter gains the entropy

$$\Delta S = \frac{|Q_0|}{T_0}.$$

Thus, equations (9.42) and (9.42a), rewritten as

$$-\frac{Q}{T} + \frac{|Q_0|}{T_0} = 0$$

or

$$\frac{|Q|}{T} - \frac{Q_0}{T_0} = 0$$

express the fact that in the operation of a Carnot cycle, whether forward or reverse, one heat reservoir gains exactly the same amount of entropy (but not of heat) as the other loses.

In order to complete the discussion of the characteristics of the new potential, entropy, it is necessary to re-emphasize that changes in entropy can be calculated only between two equilibrium states and along *reversible paths* joining them. It is, therefore, implied that a reversible path *exists* and *can be specified*. From many previous remarks it should by now be clear that this is not always the case. For example, when metal bars or pieces of rubber are strained to rupture, it is either impossible or very difficult to indicate a reversible path between the initial, unstrained state, and the final state. Hence, the associated change in entropy can be neither measured nor calculated. Although it is intuitively believed that the principles of thermodynamics apply to such processes, their application in practice encounters difficulties which have not, so far, been completely overcome.

As a final remark, we wish to draw the reader's attention to the fact that the expression for work in a quasistatic *irreversible* process often has the *superficial appearance* of a Pfaffian. For example, in Section 4.7 we found that $dW = P_{ext}\, dV$; similarly in Section 8.4.4 we found that the work per unit volume $dW = -\sigma\, d\epsilon$ for a rod stretched beyond the elastic limit, that is, irreversibly. Even though $dQ = dE + dW$ by the First Law, it should not be forgotten that here $dQ \neq dQ°$. We must, therefore, resist the impulse to write

$$dS = \frac{dE + P_{ext}\, dV}{T} \quad \text{or} \quad dS = \frac{dE - \sigma\, d\epsilon}{T}$$

for the above two processes, because such equations are *false*.

9.11 The second part of the mathematical formulation of the Second Law. The Principle of Entropy Increase

The first part of the mathematical formulation of the Second Law, in the form of Carnot's theorem stated in Section 9.10, was derived from an analysis of the properties of reversible Carnot cycles given in Section 9.6. The consequences which follow from the limitations imposed on irreversible cycles, Section 9.7, have so far been left unexplored and will now be examined.

Reverting to the inequality (9.26), and replacing the function $q(\theta, \theta_0)$ by $q(T, T_0)$ from equation (9.39), we obtain

$$\frac{Q}{|Q_0|} < \frac{T}{T_0} \quad \text{or} \quad \frac{Q}{T} < \frac{|Q_0|}{T_0}. \tag{9.55}$$

Transferring, and dropping the strokes in Q_0, it is easily seen that equation (9.55) is replaced by the inequality

$$\sum \frac{Q}{T} < 0. \tag{9.56}$$

The inequality (9.56) has been obtained by considering an irreversible Carnot cycle operating in a forward direction. The inequalities (9.24) and (9.25) applicable to reverse operation would lead to the same result. Taking into account that

$$\frac{|Q|}{Q_0} > \frac{T}{T_0} \quad \text{or} \quad \frac{|Q|}{T} > \frac{Q_0}{T_0},$$

Q being negative, whereas Q_0 is positive, it is easy to see that the expression (9.56) applies to forward as well as to reverse cycles. It follows that the succeeding derivation, which will be based on the inequality (9.56), will apply to irreversible processes regardless of the direction of the flow of heat.

The counterpart of equation (9.44) cannot now be written, because an irreversible path is not a succession of states of equilibrium, a fact stressed many times in this book, and the mathematical process of going over to the limit, which would be implied by the inequality

$$\oint \frac{dQ}{T} < 0$$

cannot be performed, except for a quasistatic cycle.

Let us now consider any irreversible process $1 \rightarrow 2$, Figure 9.21. In general, during the process the system will exchange heat with several sources of different temperatures. Suppose that there are n such sources, each exchanging a quantity of heat $Q_1, \ldots, Q_i, \ldots, Q_n$ and that their temperatures are $T_1, \ldots, T_i, \ldots, T_n$, respectively. Suppose further that A_i, B_i are the states of equilibrium which the system assumes before and after an exchange of heat Q_i with source i at temperature T_i. Such states can always be identified, because any irreversible process can always be *imagined* performed in small steps, as outlined in Section 4.7. It is clear that it is not now possible to calculate the entropy difference $S_2 - S_1$ by summing up the quantities Q_i/T_i, since the process is irreversible. In order to compare the entropy difference $S_2 - S_1$ with the sum $\Sigma\ Q_i/T_i$, it is necessary to devise a reversible path which restores state 1 from state 2. That this can be done is always implied, as stated in Section 9.10. A detailed description of how this can be done for the particular example of throttling

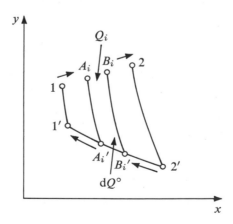

FIGURE 9.21. *Irreversible process.*

was given in Section 6.17.3. It is convenient to devise a return path composed of the isentropics B_iB_i' and $A_i'A_i$ for each heat source involved, together with an arbitrary isothermal $2'1'$. Thus, for each heat source, the summation along the reversible path will yield

$$\int_{B_i}^{A_i} \frac{dQ^\circ}{T} = S_{A_i} - S_{B_i} = S_{A_i'} - S_{B_i'},$$

the reversible heat dQ° being exchanged only along the isothermal portion $B_i'A_i'$. Substituting this value into inequality (9.56), we obtain

$$\frac{Q_i}{T_i} + S_{A_i} - S_{B_i} < 0$$

for one source. The evaluation for all sources, that is, for the whole irreversible process $1 \rightarrow 2$, will yield the sum $\sum_{n} Q_i/T_i$ for the first term. The sum of all the entropy terms is simply $S_1 - S_2$, and we obtain

$$\sum_{n} \frac{Q_i}{T_i} + S_1 - S_2 < 0$$

or

$$S_2 - S_1 > \sum_{n} \frac{Q_i}{T_i}. \tag{9.57}$$

This expression is sometimes called the Clausius inequality, particularly when symbolically the sum is written in the form of an integral, not really admissible for irreversible processes other than quasistatic ones. It expresses the fact that the change in entropy in an irreversible process *exceeds* the sum of the terms Q_i/T_i, each evaluated for a source of temperature T_i. This constitutes an essential difference with reversible processes for which the change in entropy is *equal to* that sum.

The application of the inequality (9.57) is particularly important when applied to isolated systems, that is, to the case when $Q_i = 0$ for every source. Hence, in an *isolated system*

$$S_2 - S_1 > 0. \tag{9.58}$$

The entropy in an isolated system must increase when an irreversible process takes place in it between an initial and a final equilibrium state, such as would take place when a constraint on the initial state were removed.

The preceding statement constitutes the celebrated *principle of entropy increase* which constitutes the second part of the mathematical formulation of the Second Law. It was seen in Section 9.10 that the entropy of an isolated system remained constant when reversible processes took place in it. Thus, the change in the value of the entropy of such a system (and *only of such a system*) turns out to be a criterion, as well as a measure, which determines whether the processes taking place in it are reversible or irreversible. It is clear from the derivation that a *decrease in entropy* cannot occur and corresponds to an *impossible process*, that is, to a process whose occurrence would be inconsistent with the Second Law, in other words, a reversed irreversible adiabatic process.

Since any process can be discussed in terms of an isolated system by simply including in it all sources with which heat is being exchanged during the process, the principle of entropy increase provides a powerful analytic means for the study of irreversible processes. In summary, it is possible to make the following classification, denoting the change in entropy during any process in an isolated system by ΔS:

$$\left.\begin{array}{l} \Delta S < 0 \text{ signifies an impossible process} \\ \Delta S = 0 \text{ signifies a reversible process} \\ \Delta S > 0 \text{ signifies a natural, or irreversible process} \end{array}\right\} \qquad (9.59)$$

taking place in an *isolated system*.

When an isolated system is in thermal equilibrium and a constraint is removed, it will reach another state of equilibrium characterized by a higher value of entropy. Conversely, when the entropy of a system is known, and when the system is subjected to a set of constraints which admit the existence of a series of states, it can be asserted that the system will assume that state whose entropy is a maximum under the given conditions as we shall see in more detail in Volume II. Similarly, if after the removal of a series of constraints, any further removal of constraints would cause the entropy to decrease, the system will persist in that equilibrium state whose entropy is highest. For example, if two dissimilar substances are placed in one adiabatic enclosure, it is possible to determine whether the substances will mix or remain separated by calculating the entropy of the mixture and of the separated substances. That state will prevail whose entropy is higher. The same facts can be expressed by asserting that a state of higher entropy is *more probable* than a state of lower entropy under a given set of conditions. This idea is developed in detail in statistical mechanics, where the preceding, qualitative statement will be given a precise, mathematical form. It follows that the principle of entropy increase should prove valuable in the study of equilibria of all kinds, including chemical and phase equilibria, as will be shown in Volume II. Furthermore, it should prove of value in the study of the stability of systems, that is, in the study of changes which might occur in systems when they have been slightly disturbed from a given state of equilibrium.

Since the principle of entropy increase has been enunciated in terms of an isolated system, the already familiar impulse to equate the "universe" with an isolated system presents itself in this context too, and the statement is made that the "entropy of the universe" increases. This together with the parallel statement that the "energy of the universe" remains constant leads to the speculation about the gloomy consequence which would follow when the entropy of the universe will have reached a maximum so that it could increase no more. All processes would be arrested and "the universe would die an entropy death." For reasons outlined in Sections 1.4 on p. 23 and 5.9 on p. 169, we do not believe that any physical meaning can be ascribed to statements of this kind.

The principle of entropy increase, as stated in the present section, can only be applied to isolated systems. For this reason it is not flexible enough for an efficient inquiry because it forces us to draw into consideration not only the system on which attention may center at any particular moment, but also all the sources of heat which participate in the process. It will be possible to restate the principle in terms of the characteristics of the system itself, Sections 13.7 and 13.8, and later to extend its validity to include continuous systems, Volume II. However, we propose to delay all these developments for the time being. We shall first deal with some minor points and then shall rederive the two parts of the mathematical formulation of the Second Law by the method of Carathéodory (Chapter 10), as announced at the beginning of this chapter. This will enable us to develop the consequences of the Second Law of thermo-dynamics on a sounder mathematical basis.

In concluding the present section, we wish to draw the reader's attention to the fact that it is easy to imagine a quasistatic but irreversible process which consists of a sequence of near-equilibrium states of constant entropy. As already announced in Section 5.14.5, we shall not describe such processes by the term *isentropic*, but re-serve the designation *quasi-isentropic* for them. It is clear that a quasi-isentropic process cannot be adiabatic. Since the process is irreversible, its entropy dS would increase at every step as evidenced by equation (9.59). In order to maintain a constant value of entropy it would be necessary to provide a suitable amount of cooling.

In order to see this more clearly, we can imagine a quantity of gas enclosed in a cylinder and first performing an isentropic process, Figure 9.22(a). In this manner it will be possible to determine the relation between pressure and volume which corre-sponds to a constant entropy, and so determine the increments dV and dP on perform-ing an elementary step $1 \rightarrow 2$ in the process, Figure 9.22(b).†

The diagram in Figure 9.23(a) represents a system which performs a quasistatic but irreversible process. If the system is now allowed to perform a small step *adiabatically*, say until temperature $T_2 = T + dT$ is attained, its entropy will have increased by an amount dS, as shown in Figure 9.23(b). This change in entropy cannot be negative owing to the operation of the principle of entropy increase in adiabatic processes. The

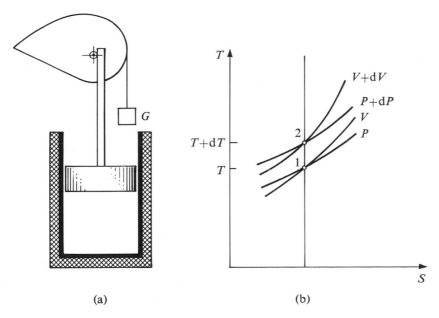

(a)   (b)

FIGURE 9.22. *Isentropic process.*

† The use of diagrams in which entropy is employed as a coordinate is explained in more detail in the suc-ceeding section and in Chapter 11.

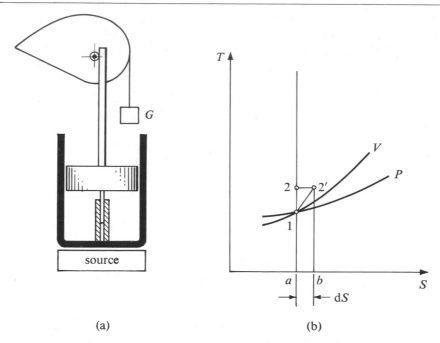

(a)   (b)

FIGURE 9.23. *Quasi-isentropic process.*

entropy can be made to decrease by the amount dS if the system is allowed to exchange a quantity of heat

$$dQ = T\,dS$$

reversibly with a source of temperature T. The quantity of heat dQ is proportional to the area $a22'b$ in the diagram, and can be calculated if the amount dS is known. Thus, state 2 for which $S_2 = S_1$ can be attained.

By suitably managing the compression (or expansion) in a continuous way, the entropy can be maintained constant. It must, however, not be forgotten that the system, the gas in this case, cannot possibly traverse a sequence of *equilibrium* states; if it did, the process would be reversible, and if it continued to exchange heat, its entropy d$S = dQ°/T$ could not remain unchanged.

9.12   Isentropics of various systems. Entropy diagrams

The reversible adiabatics that is *isentropics* (or isentropes) of a system can be determined experimentally, at least in principle, by measuring the quantities of heat, d$Q°$, and the temperatures along suitable reversible paths. They can also be calculated if the properties of the system are known. In other words, if the internal energy and the work of a reversible process, d$W°$, is known, use can be made of the fact that d$Q° = dE + dW°$. Isentropic processes are represented by *curves* in state diagrams regardless of the number of independent properties possessed by the system, since all reversible processes are represented by curves.

In the case of systems with two independent variables, the isentropics form a discrete family of curves. This is a direct consequence of the fact that isentropics are potential lines. The same conclusion can be reached from the existence and uniqueness theorem quoted at the end of Section 5.14.5 where an isentropic process of a simple substance has been discussed. A set of isentropics and isothermals is shown sketched in Figure 9.24 for the case of a system with two independent variables x, y. The isothermals also form a nonintersecting family, since with any state x, y there can be associated only one value of temperature (or entropy).

It is clear that the thermodynamic temperature T and the entropy S can be chosen as the two independent variables. Thus, instead of the variables x, y (for example P, V), it is possible to choose the variables T, S as independent. The lines $x = \text{const}$ and $y = \text{const}$ can now be transferred point-by-point into the new diagram as shown in the sketch, Figure 9.24(b). Given any reversible process $1 \rightarrow 2$, Figure 9.22(c), it is seen that an element of area in the T, S diagram under the curve is equal to $T\mathrm{d}S$, and hence to $\mathrm{d}Q°$, as seen from equation (9.46b). Thus, the area under the curve of the process represents the heat

$$Q°_{1,2} = \int_1^2 T\,\mathrm{d}S \tag{9.60}$$

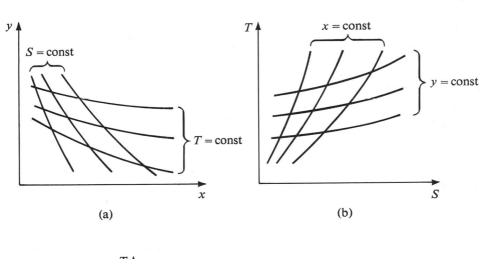

(a)   (b)

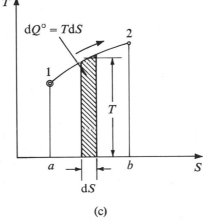

(c)

FIGURE 9.24. *Isentropics, isothermals, and entropy diagram.*

on condition that the process is reversible, and that the diagram has been drawn from $T = 0$ upwards. For this reason T, S diagrams are also sometimes called *heat diagrams*. The heat can also be calculated as a line integral of the vector $(T, 0)$ in the same way as was done with work in Sections 4.5.1 and 4.8. When Y and Z denote the generalized force and generalized displacement $(P, V; -\sigma, \epsilon;$ and so on), the area under the corresponding curve $1 \rightarrow 2$ in the x, y diagram represents work. In the particular case when a cycle is considered, equation (9.51) shows that

$$W° = \oint Y \, dZ = \oint T \, dS = Q°,$$

the superscripts ° serving as reminders that the respective quantities refer to reversible processes. Thus, the area enclosed by the corresponding closed curves in the two diagrams become equal, Figure 9.25. Recalling the properties of Jacobians discussed in Section 3.7.3, we can say that the Jacobian of the transformation $(Y, Z) \rightarrow (T, S)$ is constant, and equal to unity, or

$$\frac{\partial(Y, Z)}{\partial(T, S)} = 1. \tag{9.61}$$

In particular,

$$\frac{\partial(P, V)}{\partial(T, S)} = 1. \tag{9.61a}$$

This is due to the fact that the Jacobian of a transformation is equal to the ratio of the elementary areas in the two corresponding diagrams, as stated previously.

The Carnot cycle assumes a particularly simple shape in the T, S diagram, being represented by a rectangle, Figure 9.26. The area $12ba$ represents the heat added, Q, and the area $43ba$ represents the heat Q_0 rejected during the cycle. The work of the cycle $W = Q - |Q_0|$ is represented by the area of the rectangle 1234. The formula for efficiency

$$\eta = \frac{W}{Q} = \frac{T - T_0}{T}$$

and the relationship $Q/|Q_0| = T/T_0$ can be verified directly from the figure, since both rectangles have equal widths and their areas are proportional to their heights. The

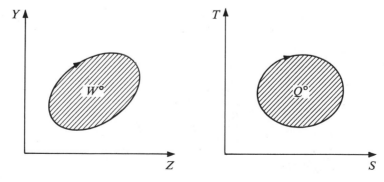

FIGURE 9.25. *Cycles.*

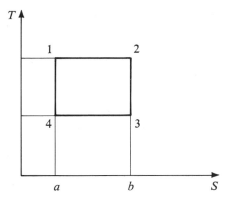

FIGURE 9.26. *Carnot cycle.*

coefficient of performance of a reversed Carnot cycle, or the efficacy of a heat pump

$$\epsilon = \frac{Q_0}{W} = \frac{T_0}{T - T_0}; \qquad \epsilon_f = \frac{|Q|}{W} = \frac{T}{T - T_0}$$

can be verified in an equally simple way. In order easily to recall the formulas, it is advisable to visualize the drawing in Figure 9.26.

In the case of systems with n independent properties $x_1, \ldots, x_n$, there exist two non-intersecting $(n - 1)$-dimensional families of hypersurfaces. Any line in an isothermal surface, and any line in an isentropic surface, represents an isothermal or an isentropic process, respectively. The case when $n = 3$ is shown illustrated in Figure 9.27. The potential surfaces $S = \text{const}$ do not intersect, and each one of them contains an infinity of isentropics. Thus, through any state point, such as point 3 in the sketch, there pass an infinite number of isentropics, for example, 31 and 32, in contrast with systems for which $n = 2$. Now, it is no longer possible to select T and S as the independent variables,

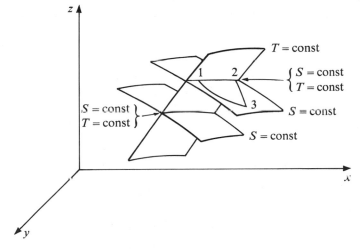

FIGURE 9.27. *Surfaces of constant entropy and temperature for a system with three independent properties.*

because three (or more) are required, but the variables T, S can be included among the n independent variables selected.

Each isentropic surface intersects each isothermal surface along a line, for example, line 12 in Figure 9.27. In general, this trace will be an entity of $n-2$ dimensions. In the case of three variables, the line of intersection represents a reversible isothermal process. The cycle 123 consists of one reversible isothermal and two reversible isentropic processes. In the case of $n = 2$ such cycles are impossible, because the isentropics do not intersect. The existence of such a cycle for $n = 2$ would also contradict the Second Law since it would produce work drawing heat from a single source of heat. In the case of three variables, the existence of such a cycle does not conflict with the Second Law. Around the cycle 123 in Figure 9.27 we must have

$$\oint \mathrm{d}Q = \oint \mathrm{d}W$$

as for any cycle. However,

$$\oint \mathrm{d}Q = 0,$$

since no heat is exchanged along the isentropics 23 and 31, or along the isothermal-isentropic 12. Consequently,

$$\oint \mathrm{d}W = 0,$$

and the cycle is incapable of producing work. In this connection it must be remembered that now the area enclosed by the curve 123 is no longer proportional to reversible work. This is true only in the case of systems with two independent variables for which $\mathrm{d}W = Y\mathrm{d}Z$ and only in diagrams in Y, Z coordinates, consisting of a generalized force Y and a generalized displacement Z.

An isothermal-isentropic process can be performed with the aid of the system shown in Figure 9.28.[†] The system consists of two diathermally coupled cylinders a and b, each closed with an ideal, adiabatic piston. We can imagine that cylinder a is filled with

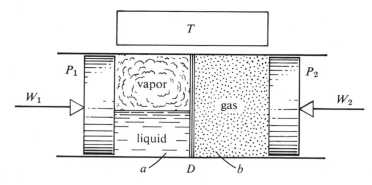

FIGURE 9.28. *Isothermal-isentropic process.*

[†] See Kestin, J., "On Intersecting Isentropics," Am. J. Phys., **29** (1961), 329.

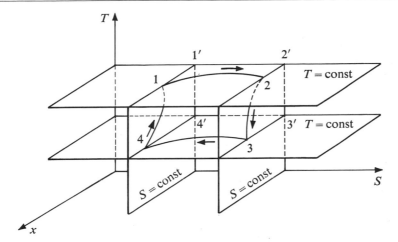

FIGURE 9.29. *Carnot cycle for n = 3.*

a two-phase mixture of a pure substance of pressure P_{1a} and at the corresponding temperature T_1, say steam with a dryness fraction x_1. The cylinder b can be filled with a gas, that is, with a highly superheated vapor. When the gas in b is slowly compressed, the whole system being in contact with a heat reservoir at temperature T_1 equal to that of the wet steam and the gas, the resulting process will be both isothermal and adiabatic. The work of compression will serve to increase the dryness fraction in cylinder a if the pressure in it is maintained constant, so that the temperature also remains constant. Thus, no heat will be exchanged with the reservoir T_1 and the same process would occur if both cylinders had been perfectly insulated. This process corresponds to 12 in Figure 9.27. During the second and third process, 23 and 31, it is possible reversibly and adiabatically to compress and expand the steam and the gas in a variety of ways, until state 1 has been recreated. It can be asserted that the net work done around the cycle 123 is zero.

In the case of systems with more than two independent variables, the use of heat diagrams is impossible. When the thermodynamic temperature T and the entropy S are chosen as two of the n independent variables, a Carnot cycle no longer retains its simple form. For example, with $n = 3$, Figure 9.29, the variables chosen are T, S and an unspecified variable x. The three-dimensional sequence of curves 1234 represents a possible Carnot cycle. It projects as the rectangle 1'2'3'4' in the plane T, S, and regains its appearance from Figure 9.26. One such T *vs.* S diagram corresponds to an infinite number of Carnot cycles for the system, depending on the variation of x with T in the planes $S = $ const and on the variation of x with S in the planes $T = $ const. Thus, in the diagram in Figure 9.26, the Carnot cycles will differ by the manner in which the third independent variable, x, varies on traversing the cycle from 1 to 1 through 2, 3, and 4. In that projection heat quantities can once again be computed from the respective areas.

It is easy to see that a cycle like 123 in Figure 9.27 which is confined to one surface $S = $ const would project in the form of a line segment enclosing zero area in the T, S diagram.

List of Symbols for Chapter 9

Latin letters

C Coefficient of proportionality in equation (9.35b)
E Energy
$\mathcal{E}$ Electromotive force
G Weight
$\mathbf{G}$ Vector associated with the Pfaffian $dQ°/T$ in Figure 9.19(a), (b)
H Enthalpy
m Mass
P Pressure
Q Heat
$Q°$ Heat exchanged during a reversible process
R Gas constant
S Entropy
s Specific entropy
$\mathbf{s}$ Radius vector of curve
T Thermodynamic temperature
t Parameter, equation (9.10)
U Internal energy
u Specific internal energy
V Volume
v Specific volume
W Work
X_i Generalized displacement
x General property; coordinate
Y_i Generalized force
y General property; coordinate
Z_i Generalized displacement
z Coordinate; electric charge

Greek letters

ϵ Coefficient of performance of refrigerator, defined in equation (9.13)
ϵ_f Efficacy of heat pump, defined in equation (9.12)
η Theoretical or thermal efficiency of cycle, defined in equation (9.5)
ζ Function defined in equation (9.49)
Θ Function defined in equation (9.32)
θ Temperature on empirical scale

Subscripts

a   Refers to ambient conditions
irr   Refers to irreversible process or cycle
rev   Refers to reversible process or cycle

Superscripts and marks above symbol

·   Derivative with respect to time or time-rate of respective quantity
°   Refers to reversible process or cycle

CHAPTER 10

The Second Law of Thermodynamics.
The Born-Carathéodory Formulation

10.1 Verbal statement of the Second Law

In the preceding chapter the mathematical formulation of the Second Law was derived from the Clausius and from the Kelvin-Planck statement, it having been previously demonstrated that the two were exactly equivalent. Each of these statements, as already mentioned, asserted that a particular adiabatic irreversible process could not be reversed. C. Carathéodory, on a suggestion first advanced by M. Born, succeeded in providing an alternative formulation which is based on a common characteristic of all irreversible processes. In this manner he was able to achieve greater elegance and generality of exposition. The only obstacle in appreciating this economical formulation is presented by the general lack of familiarity with the mathematical propositions required for the purpose. We shall give an account of this mathematical theory in Section 10.2. It is clear from the argument given in Chapter 9 that it will consist in an exposition of further properties of Pfaffian forms, in continuation of the description contained in Section 4.2.

In arriving at a primary formulation of the Second Law of thermodynamics, attention is centered, just as was the case with the formulation of the First Law, on *adiabatic processes* taking place in *closed systems*. This does not restrict the scope of the law, because whether or not a given process is adiabatic depends only on the choice of the system. It merely means that all sources and sinks with which the original system exchanges heat must be included in the analysis.

From the examples given in Sections 5.4 and 5.14 as well as elsewhere in this book, it is clear that irreversible processes can be performed in small steps or quasistatically ensuring that the final state is not far removed from the initial state. Again, without loss in generality, we shall restrict attention to such *neighboring states*. For example, the Joule experiment in which a gas undergoes an unresisted expansion, Section 5.4, can be performed so that the change in volume, ΔV, is small compared with the initial volume V. Equally, the Joule Thomson porous plug experiment, Section 6.17.3, can be so performed that the pressure drop ΔP is small compared with the initial pressure P.

In both examples, a final state 2 is reached from an initial, neighboring state 1. Moreover, whereas state 2 *can* be reached from state 1 *adiabatically*, the converse is not true. State 1 *cannot* be reached from state 2 *adiabatically*. This, as emphasized previously, does not imply that state 1 cannot be reached from state 2 *at all*. The manner of

457

reaching state 1 from state 2 in the Joule-Thomson experiment was described in Section 6.17.3 when a compressor and a cooler were used for the purpose. The new process was no longer adiabatic.† In the Joule experiment, the gas could be imagined recompressed at constant internal energy. It was shown in Section 5.14.3 that this would require the removal of the work of compression in the form of heat, and the process of restoring state 1 could not be performed adiabatically. More generally, state 1 can be restored from state 2 by a process $2 \rightarrow 1$ which together with the irreversible, adiabatic process $1 \rightarrow 2$ forms a cycle. It is a matter of experience, as illustrated with the aid of the preceding examples, that the process $2 \rightarrow 1$ *cannot be adiabatic*. In general, both an exchange of heat and work will be required. In stating the Second Law, we shall use the graphic description in which it will be said that state 1 is *inaccessible* from state 2, whereas state 2 is *accessible* from state 1, implying accessibility along an adiabatic path, reversible or irreversible.

An additional illustration of the concept of accessibility can be obtained by examining the process of expanding a gas in a cylinder as shown in Figure 10.1. For the sake of simplicity we shall assume that the cylinder is adiabatic, and in order to take into account the work performed, we shall imagine that a suitable weight G balancing the pressure with the aid of the familiar cam mechanism is included in the system. The gas

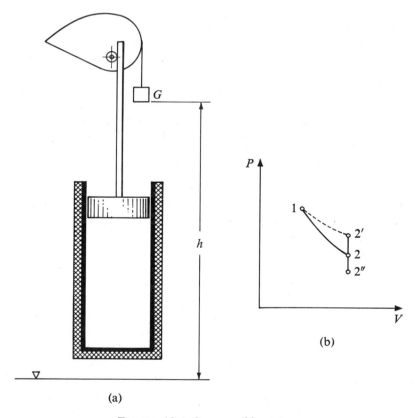

(a)   (b)

FIGURE 10.1. *Inaccessible states.*

† It could only be made adiabatic by including the source of heat with the system, that is, by selecting a different boundary, and by performing *work*.

in the adiabatic cylinder together with the weight G now form an isolated system, that is, one whose boundary is crossed neither by heat nor by work. Denoting the internal energy of the gas by U and the potential energy of the weight by Gh, we notice that their sum must be conserved according to the First Law. Thus,

$$U + Gh = \text{const.} \tag{10.1}$$

First let us imagine that the system performs a reversible process $1 \to 2$ during which the gas expands. For this process

$$(U_2 - U_1) + G(h_2 - h_1) = 0. \tag{10.2}$$

The process undergone by the gas itself is seen sketched in Figure 10.1(b). It is clear that state 2 is accessible from state 1, and that conversely state 1 is accessible from state 2 by a reversible, adiabatic process, since the system can be made to retrace the sequence of states in the reverse direction. There is no difficulty in indicating states which are inaccessible from 2, and hence also from 1, both adiabatically and reversibly. Let us consider the two states 2′ and 2″ for which $V_{2'} = V_{2''} = V_2$. It is clear that the internal energies of the gas associated with these states, $U_{2'}$, $U_{2''}$, and U_2 are different, since the state of the gas is determined by *two* properties, say U and V. Hence, since the states are different, and the volumes are the same, the energies must be different. However, equation (10.1) for the whole system must still be satisfied, and consequently, the corresponding elevations of the weight G, denoted $h_{2'}$ and $h_{2''}$, respectively, must satisfy the relations

$$(U_{2'} - U_1) + G(h_{2'} - h_1) = 0, \tag{10.2a}$$

$$(U_{2''} - U_1) + G(h_{2''} - h_1) = 0. \tag{10.2b}$$

Suppose that $U_{2'} > U_2$, then $h_{2'} < h_2$, and, similarly for $U_{2''} < U_2$ we must have $h_{2''} > h_2$. Now, a change in the internal energy of the gas at constant volume can be brought about either by an exchange of heat or by the performance of work, as discussed in Section 5.14.3. A decrease in the energy can be obtained only by cooling the cylinder, that is, by a nonadiabatic process. Thus, state 2″ could only be attained by the cooling of the gas, compensated by a rise in the position of the weight, since then $h_{2''} > h_2$. Experience teaches that this cannot be done at all in the system under consideration. In order to reach state 2′ it would be necessary to increase the energy of the gas which can be achieved either by heating, that is, by a nonadiabatic process, or by the performance of work, but such a process would be irreversible. Since then $h_{2'} > h_2$ this work could be provided by lowering the weight from $h_{2'}$ to h_2 and by driving with it a paddle wheel, as was done in Joule's experiment (Section 5.2). Alternatively, an intermediate body could be heated by friction and then made to transfer heat to the gas, thus increasing its internal energy. It is apparent that neither state 2′ nor state 2″ could be reached from states 1 or 2 reversibly and adiabatically. Furthermore, state 2″ could not be reached from states 2 or 1 adiabatically even if irreversible processes were admitted. Thus, state 2″ is adiabatically inaccessible from 1 or 2. It should also be apparent that an irreversible adiabatic process could bring the system from state 1 to state 2′ directly, but never to state 2″ for which $U_{2''} < U_2$ and $h_{2''} > h_2$.

We can now repeat the remarks already made in Section 9.11 by stating that all states which can be reached in a reversible way in an adiabatic system are evidently equivalent in a sense, because any state of this class can be reached from any other. When considering irreversible processes, it will be realized that the final state is in some way different from the initial state. Expression is given to this bias in nature by saying that the final state is one of greater *probability*. The term "probability" is used here in its ordinary sense and must not be taken to mean mathematical probability. Statistical mechanics provides a rigorous link between these two concepts, as will be shown in Volume II, when it will transpire that entropy provides a measure of this probability.

The detailed examples discussed in the preceding paragraphs have been, of course, analyzed on the basis of experience. Our familiarity with the phenomena under consideration allowed us to determine which states were, and which states were not accessible from a given state. The preceding observations will now be generalized, and it will be asserted that they apply to all systems whatsoever. Thus, we shall proceed in the same general manner as was done in connection with the First Law, namely, we shall conceive the Second Law as a bold generalization from a limited number of observed facts. We shall formulate the generalization in two parts:

Assertion 1.

In the neighborhood of any given state of any closed system there exist states which are inaccessible from it along reversible, adiabatic paths.

Assertion 2.

In the neighborhood of any given state of any closed system there exist states which are inaccessible from it along any adiabatic path, reversible or irreversible.

This is the statement of the Second Law of thermodynamics first given by C. Carathéodory. Assertion 2 includes in it Assertion 1, but it is convenient to state them separately in order to see clearly the implications of the more restricted statement.

To a student of mathematics possessed of the necessary background, Assertion 1 proves immediately that the integrand of the line integral of heat

$$\mathrm{d}Q^\circ = \mathrm{d}E + \sum_n Y_i \, \mathrm{d}Z_i$$

involving n independent variables x_i is *integrable*, that is, that it can be represented as the product of a property $\mu(x_1, \ldots, x_n)$ and the perfect differential $\mathrm{d}\phi$ of a potential $\phi(x_1, \ldots, x_n)$. Thus,

$$\mathrm{d}Q^\circ = \mu \, \mathrm{d}\phi.$$

In Chapter 9, the factor μ was described as the integrating denominator for $\mathrm{d}Q^\circ$.

We shall now address ourselves to the task of proving that this statement does in fact follow from Assertion 1. We shall further prove that the function μ can be chosen to depend only on the empirical temperature θ of the system, and so pave the way to the introduction of the thermodynamic temperature scale. This will complete the proof of Carnot's theorem. Finally, by invoking Assertion 2, we shall derive the principle of entropy increase.

10.2   Properties of Pfaffians associated with rotational vector fields

We now revert to the consideration of Section 4.2, where it was found desirable to subdivide all vector fields into two classes: the irrotational fields which were derivable from scalar fields, and the rotational fields with which no such scalar, potential function could be associated. It is now necessary further to subdivide the class of rotational fields into two subclasses, those that do, and those that do not possess integrating denominators. We shall call the former *integrable*.† In order clearly to understand this distinction as well as its implications, we must learn more about vector fields.

10.2.1   *Two independent variables. Inaccessible points*

In order to achieve our main purpose, it is necessary to examine the properties of rotational fields separately for the case of $n = 2$ and for $n \geq 3$ independent variables. The former, being more restricted, all belong to one subclass, namely, that for which an integrating denominator always exists. The distinction between integrable and non-integrable Pfaffians becomes significant only from $n = 3$ upwards.

It will be recalled from Sections 4.2 and 4.3 that there exists an intimate connection between the value of a line integral and the properties of the vector field associated with the integrand. If the line integral is independent of the path, the vector field is irrotational, and the integrand is a perfect differential. Given a rotational field, provisionally in $n = 2$ dimensions only, we now propose to analyze a problem which, in a sense, is the inverse of the preceding one. We shall, namely, ask if there exist curves C for which the line integral vanishes identically. Thus, we wish to determine the shape of the curve C for which

$$\int_{1 \atop C}^{2} M(x, y)\, \mathrm{d}x + N(x, y)\, \mathrm{d}y = 0, \tag{10.3}$$

regardless of the initial and final points 1, 2. If the line integral represents work, the curve C will be one along which no work is performed. If the line integral represents heat, the curve C will describe a reversible adiabatic path; the latter problem was discussed in a preliminary way in Section 5.14.5. Any line C for which equation (10.3) is satisfied will be called an *ergomedic*‡ curve. In order for the work, or heat, to be zero regardless of the initial and final point, the integrand itself must vanish

$$\mathrm{d}w = M\, \mathrm{d}x + N\, \mathrm{d}y = 0. \tag{10.4}$$

The condition (10.4) expresses the fact that the vector $\mathbf{F}(M, N)$ is normal to the vector $\mathrm{d}s(\mathrm{d}x, \mathrm{d}y)$, since their scalar product vanishes. Thus, the elements $\mathrm{d}x$, $\mathrm{d}y$ must lie on an ergomedic curve, and equation (10.4), known as a *Pfaffian differential equation*, constitutes the differential equation for the ergomedic curve. This is rather obvious on physical grounds, if the vector field $\mathbf{F}$ is interpreted as a field of force.

Equation (10.4) can also be written

$$\frac{\mathrm{d}y}{\mathrm{d}x} = -\frac{M(x, y)}{N(x, y)}; \tag{10.5}$$

in this form it was first encountered in Section 5.14.5. It was then stated that there

---

† In some treatises on mathematics, the term *integrable* is used in a different meaning, and the readers are cautioned to bear the distinction clearly in mind. These treatises describe a Pfaffian as integrable if its coefficients are *equal* to the partial derivatives of a potential function. We call the latter *perfect differentials* and note that they satisfy the integrability conditions (3.27a). It should also be clear that every Pfaffian can be integrated along a given curve C; this does not render it integrable in the above sense.

‡ From the Greek *ergon*, work, and *meden*, zero, that is, the "zero-work line." Some authors call it a Pfaffian line.

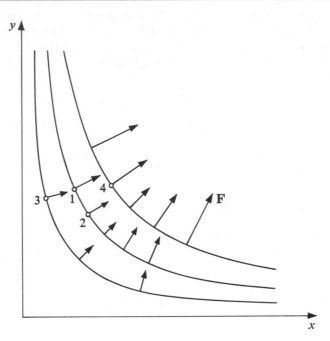

FIGURE 10.2. *Ergomedic curves.*

exists a one-parameter nonintersecting family of curves

$$\phi(x, y) = k \qquad (10.6)$$

whose members satisfy equation (10.5), and so equation (10.4), identically. An exception was made for so-called singular points which, however, play no part in our considerations. This should be clear from the general form given in equation (9.47) and the particular example in equation (9.47a). Hence, equation (10.6) can always be written as a consequence of the existence and uniqueness theorems quoted in Section 5.14.5. Since only one such curve passes through a given point in the plane, the curves do not intersect.

A family of ergomedic curves is seen sketched in Figure 10.2. It is seen that the local vectors are all normal to the curves, and that the curves differ by the value of the parameter k from equation (10.6) assigned to them. At this stage it is convenient to introduce the concept of *mathematical inaccessibility*. Two points, such as 1 and 2 are called *accessible* if an ergomedic path can be found to join them. Otherwise, the points are called *inaccessible*. For example, points 1, 3, and 4 in Figure 10.2 are inaccessible.

In a field of forces it is useful to consider the so-called *lines of forces*, or *field lines* in the general case. These are lines which are everywhere tangent to the vector **F** at the point. In fluid mechanics, in a velocity field, field lines are called *streamlines*. Thus, we wish to determine curves whose elements $\mathrm{d}s'(\mathrm{d}x', \mathrm{d}y')$ are everywhere collinear with, that is, parallel to **F**. This condition is written

$$\frac{\mathrm{d}x'}{M} = \frac{\mathrm{d}y'}{N} \qquad (10.7)$$

and the resulting differential equation

$$\frac{dy'}{dx'} = \frac{N}{M} \tag{10.7a}$$

is identical *in form* with that in (10.5). It follows that such field lines always exist, and that they also form a one-parameter, nonintersecting family of curves

$$\psi(x', y') = k'$$

which are orthogonal to those given by equation (10.6). It is easy to verify that the two slopes, dy/dx and dy'/dx' satisfy the orthogonality condition

$$\left(\frac{dy}{dx}\right)\left(\frac{dy'}{dx'}\right) = -1.$$

A set of ergomedic curves together with the corresponding field lines has been sketched in Figure 10.3.

Given a family of curves, such as the ergomedic curves in equation (10.6), it is possible to determine the differential equation which they satisfy by differentiation. We then obtain†

$$\frac{\partial \phi}{\partial x}\, dx + \frac{\partial \phi}{\partial y}\, dy = 0, \tag{10.8}$$

since the parameter k varies from curve to curve, but is constant along each curve.

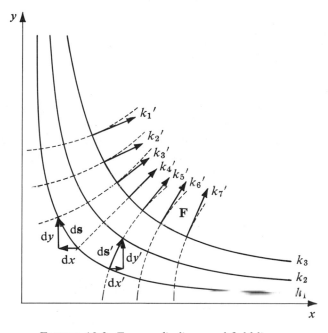

FIGURE 10.3. *Ergomedic lines and field lines.*

† It is convenient here to use the mathematical, rather than the thermodynamic notation for partial derivatives.

This then is also a differential equation for the elements $ds(dx, dy)$ of the ergomedic curves, and as such must be identical with the Pfaffian equation (10.4) or with equation (10.5). Consequently, the slopes dy/dx determined by them must be identical, so that

$$\frac{dy}{dx} = -\frac{M(x, y)}{N(x, y)} = -\frac{\partial\phi/\partial x}{\partial\phi/\partial y}.$$

This signifies that the factors of dx and dy in the two equations, (10.4) and (10.8), must be proportional to each other, or that

$$\frac{\partial\phi/\partial x}{M(x, y)} = \frac{\partial\phi/\partial y}{N(x, y)}. \qquad (10.9)$$

On dividing one function of the independent variables x, y, either $\partial\phi/\partial x$ or $\partial\phi/\partial y$, by another function of x, y, that is, $M(x, y)$ and $N(x, y)$, respectively, yet another function of x, y is obtained. This function is identical in both divisions, and we shall denote it by $\mu(x, y)$. Hence, equation (10.9) leads to

$$\frac{\partial\phi}{\partial x} = \mu(x, y)\, M(x, y) \quad \text{and} \quad \frac{\partial\phi}{\partial y} = \mu(x, y)\, N(x, y). \qquad (10.10)$$

When the expressions for M and N from equation (10.10) are substituted into the Pfaffian form (10.4), we obtain

$$\begin{aligned} dw &= \frac{1}{\mu}\left(\frac{\partial\phi}{\partial x}\, dx + \frac{\partial\phi}{\partial y}\, dy\right) \\ &= \frac{1}{\mu}\, d\phi. \end{aligned} \qquad (10.11)$$

It is clear that the function $\phi(x, y) = k$ from equation (10.6) can be interpreted as a potential. Thus, equation (10.11) expresses the fact that the integrand

$$\mu\, dw = d\phi$$

is the (perfect) differential of a potential. This is equivalent to stating that the *reciprocal* of μ constitutes an integrating denominator for dw, and that it always *exists* for a Pfaffian in two variables. The integrating *factor* μ, rather than the integrating denominator $1/\mu$, has been introduced here merely for the sake of convenience, and its use is entirely equivalent to the use of an integrating denominator.

The preceding result can be restated by asserting that *all Pfaffians in two variables are integrable*. This designation may be misleading if taken too literally. The line integral

$$\int_{1}^{2}{}_{C}\, dw = \int_{1}^{2}{}_{C} \frac{M}{\mu}\, dx + \frac{N}{\mu}\, dy = \int_{1}^{2}{}_{C} \frac{d\phi}{\mu} \qquad (10.12)$$

along an arbitrary curve C cannot be evaluated with reference to the potential ϕ in the same manner as the line integral of a perfect differential could be. The substitutions indicated in equation (4.6) are still required, but a simplification is achieved if μ can be expressed as a function of ϕ along a particular line C, because then the evaluation suggested by equation (10.12) would involve a somewhat simpler quadrature than that in equation (4.6). However, the solution of the inverse problem becomes radically simpler if ϕ is known. With reference to equation (10.11) it is seen that $dw = 0$ implies

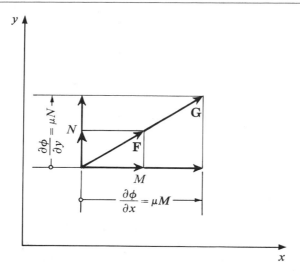

FIGURE 10.4. *Stretching of vector field.*

also $d\phi = 0$. Hence, ergomedic curves are identical with the equipotential lines $\phi = $ const, first encountered in equation (10.6). The potential ϕ does not possess the same physical significance as the potential in an irrotational field, because now ϕ is not a potential for dw, but for the related quantity $\mu\, dw$. The latter, naturally, will be of a different physical nature.

In spite of the fact that the equipotential lines $\phi = $ const are identical with the er-gomedic lines, it must not be concluded that the two associated vector fields $\mathbf{F}(M, N)$ and grad $\phi = \mathbf{G}(\partial\phi/\partial x, \partial\phi/\partial y)$ are identical. Equation (10.10) shows that the components M, N and $\partial\phi/\partial x$, $\partial\phi/\partial y$ are merely proportional to each other, the factor of proportionality $\mu(x, y)$ varying from point to point in the plane, Figure 10.4. Since, however, both components M and N of $\mathbf{F}$ are multiplied by the same factor, the vector $\mathbf{G}$ remains collinear with the vector $\mathbf{F}$ and differs from it in magnitude only. Thus, vector $\mathbf{G}$ can be regarded as a stretched vector $\mathbf{F}$, the amount of stretching being different from point to point. This explains why the two fields possess a common family of curves which are orthogonal to the vectors. They also possess a common family of field lines.

It should be noted for future reference that the scalar product

$$\mathbf{F} \cdot \text{curl } \mathbf{F} = 0, \tag{10.13}$$

since for a two-dimensional field $\mathbf{F}$, curl $\mathbf{F}$ represents a field whose vectors are parallel to each other, all of them being perpendicular to the plane x, y. The same relation holds for the irrotational field $\mathbf{G}$,

$$\mathbf{G} \cdot \text{curl } \mathbf{G} = 0,$$

because in this case curl $\mathbf{G} = $ curl grad $\phi = 0$, as already noted in Section 3.7.1.

It is easy to show that the integrating factor μ is not unique. If $\Phi(\phi)$ denotes *any* single-valued function of the potential ϕ, then

$$\mu' = \mu\frac{d\Phi}{d\phi} \tag{10.14}$$

is also an integrating factor. In order to verify this, we multiply M and N in equation (10.4) by μ' from (10.14), and inquire whether a perfect differential is obtained as a result. Indeed

$$\mu' \, \mathrm{d}w = \frac{\mathrm{d}\Phi}{\mathrm{d}\phi} \, (\mu M \, \mathrm{d}x + \mu N \, \mathrm{d}y).$$

With reference to equation (10.10), it is seen that the last bracket is the perfect differential of the potential ϕ. Hence, the product

$$\mu' \, \mathrm{d}w = \frac{\mathrm{d}\Phi}{\mathrm{d}\phi} \, \mathrm{d}\phi = \mathrm{d}\Phi \qquad (10.14a)$$

is a perfect differential, and the new potential Φ is now associated with the integrating factor μ'. It is clear that for $\mathrm{d}w = 0$, we have simultaneously $\mathrm{d}\phi = 0$ and $\mathrm{d}\Phi = 0$. Thus, the equipotential lines $\Phi = \text{const}$ are ergomedic lines and they are identical with the preceding ones. Since, however, Φ is a unique function of ϕ, there is a difference in that the value of the constant assigned to each line is now different; it is $\phi = k$ in the former case, and $k' = \Phi(k)$ in the latter.

In all preceding considerations the question as to how to compute an integrating factor together with the associated potential was studiously avoided.[†] This should not disturb the student, because the problem of computing these quantities explicitly will not arise. For our purposes it is sufficient to know that they *exist*.

10.2.2   *Pfaffians in more than two independent variables*

The properties of Pfaffian expressions associated with fields described by two independent variables are rather special. When the number of independent variables increases to three, or more, the circumstances are changed, and the precise nature of this difference must now be investigated. It is quite feasible to conduct the argument in an abstract way in terms of n independent variables. However, spaces with more than three independent variables cannot be visualized, nor is it possible to provide pictorial illustrations for them. Since, in addition, the expressions tend to be clumsy, it is preferable to cast the argument in terms of three-dimensional vector fields, as will be done in this section, and as was already done on occasion in the past. The extension to n variables introduces nothing new in essence and can be done by the reader as an exercise in abstraction.

Given a three-dimensional field, and the associated Pfaffian linear differential form, we once again inquire into the nature of ergomedic and field lines, bearing in mind that a surface in space is described analytically by a single relation between the independent variables, say, $\psi(x, y, z) = 0$, and that a curve in space is described by *two* such relations, say, $f_1(x, y, z) = 0$ and $f_2(x, y, z) = 0$; in this manner a line is regarded as the locus of all points common to two surfaces. Retracing the steps described in the preceding section, we can write the differential condition which must be satisfied by an element $\mathrm{d}s(\mathrm{d}x, \mathrm{d}y, \mathrm{d}z)$ of an ergomedic line as

$$\mathrm{d}w = P(x, y, z) \, \mathrm{d}x + Q(x, y, z) \, \mathrm{d}y + R(x, y, z) \, \mathrm{d}z = 0; \qquad (10.15)$$

[†] This problem is discussed, for example, in Sneddon, I. N., *Elements of Partial Differential Equations* (McGraw-Hill, 1957), p. 26.

this is an orthogonality condition $\mathbf{F} \cdot \mathrm{d}s = 0$. Similarly, the element $\mathrm{d}s' (\mathrm{d}x', \mathrm{d}y', \mathrm{d}z')$ of a field line must satisfy the collinearity conditions

$$\frac{\mathrm{d}x'}{P(x', y', z')} = \frac{\mathrm{d}y'}{Q(x', y', z')} = \frac{\mathrm{d}z'}{R(x', y', z')}. \tag{10.16}$$

Speaking loosely, it is seen that the single condition (10.15) imposed on the ergomedic curves is less stringent than the two conditions (10.16) which are satisfied by the field lines. It must, therefore, be expected that an equivalent existence and uniqueness theorem cannot apply to both, as was the case with $n = 2$. Indeed, the difference between the case when $n = 2$ and the present case when $n \geq 3$ consists in the fact that an existence and uniqueness theorem is now valid only for the field lines $\mathrm{d}s' (\mathrm{d}x', \mathrm{d}y', \mathrm{d}z')$. The two conditions (10.16) are equivalent to two nonlinear ordinary differential equations which can be written

$$\left. \begin{array}{l} \dfrac{\mathrm{d}y'}{\mathrm{d}x'} = \dfrac{Q(x', y', z')}{P(x', y', z')} = g_1(x', y', z'), \\[2mm] \dfrac{\mathrm{d}z'}{\mathrm{d}x'} = \dfrac{R(x', y', z')}{P(x', y', z')} = g_2(x', y', z'). \end{array} \right\} \tag{10.16a}$$

If the functions g_1, g_2 are continuous it is possible to prove,† again excepting singular points for which

$$P = Q = R = 0$$

simultaneously, that there does exist a pair of functions $y'(x')$, $z'(x')$ which are unique, continuous, and which satisfy the conditions (10.16a) identically. Moreover, one pair of values $y'(x')$, $z'(x')$ can be indicated for every point in space. In other words, through any point in space there passes one and only one field line (line of force, streamline, and so on). The whole family of field lines thus contains two arbitrary parameters, one each being contained in $y'(x')$ and $z'(x')$, and the curves of the family do not intersect. As mentioned before, no such theorem can be proved in relation to the ergomedic curves.

It will be recalled that the existence of an integrating factor for a two-dimensional Pfaffian was a direct consequence of the existence and uniqueness theorem which cannot be proved for $n > 2$. It must, therefore, be expected that such an integrating factor does not always exist, and it is natural to attempt to establish the conditions under which it does. We assume then that a function $\mu(x, y, z)$ can be indicated which turns $\mathrm{d}w$ from equation (10.15) into a perfect differential. Thus,

$$\mu \, \mathrm{d}w = \mu P \, \mathrm{d}x + \mu Q \, \mathrm{d}y + \mu R \, \mathrm{d}z = \mathrm{d}\phi.$$

It follows that the three products, μP, μQ, μR must be the partial derivatives of a function $\phi(x, y, z)$. In other words, the vector $\mathbf{G}(\mu P, \mu Q, \mu R)$ must be the gradient of ϕ, or

$$\mathbf{G} = \operatorname{grad} \phi.$$

---

† One of the following references may be consulted: Sneddon, I., *Elements of Partial Differential Equations* (McGraw-Hill, 1957), p. 9; Kaplan, W., *Ordinary Differential Equations* (Addison-Wesley, 1958), pp. 23, 473, and 486; Goursat, E., *A Course in Mathematical Analysis*, translated by E. R. Hedrick and O. Dunkel (Ginn, 1917) Vol. II, part II, p. 45; also available in paperback: Dover 1959; Haaser, N. B., LaSalle, J. P., and Sullivan, J. A., *Intermediate Analysis (A Course in Mathematical Analysis*, Vol. II [Blaisdell, 1964]), p. 608.

Thus, the vector field $\mathbf{G}$ must be irrotational, and

$$\text{curl } \mathbf{G} = \text{curl grad } \phi = 0. \tag{10.17}$$

According to the scheme in (4.13), analytically condition (10.17) is written

$$\begin{vmatrix} \mathbf{i} & \mathbf{j} & \mathbf{k} \\ \dfrac{\partial}{\partial x} & \dfrac{\partial}{\partial y} & \dfrac{\partial}{\partial z} \\ \mu P & \mu Q & \mu R \end{vmatrix} = 0,$$

or *in extenso*

$$\left. \begin{aligned} \frac{\partial(\mu R)}{\partial y} - \frac{\partial(\mu Q)}{\partial z} &= 0, \\[2mm] \frac{\partial(\mu P)}{\partial z} - \frac{\partial(\mu R)}{\partial x} &= 0, \\[2mm] \frac{\partial(\mu Q)}{\partial x} - \frac{\partial(\mu P)}{\partial y} &= 0. \end{aligned} \right\} \tag{10.17a}$$

The function μ, if it exists, must satisfy all of the above conditions simultaneously. Evaluating the derivatives of the products, we obtain

$$\left. \begin{aligned} P{:} \quad R\frac{\partial \mu}{\partial y} - Q\frac{\partial \mu}{\partial z} + \mu\left(\frac{\partial R}{\partial y} - \frac{\partial Q}{\partial z}\right) &= 0, \\[2mm] Q{:} \quad P\frac{\partial \mu}{\partial z} - R\frac{\partial \mu}{\partial x} + \mu\left(\frac{\partial P}{\partial z} - \frac{\partial R}{\partial x}\right) &= 0, \\[2mm] R{:} \quad Q\frac{\partial \mu}{\partial x} - P\frac{\partial \mu}{\partial y} + \mu\left(\frac{\partial Q}{\partial x} - \frac{\partial P}{\partial y}\right) &= 0. \end{aligned} \right\} \tag{10.17b}$$

It is noted that the terms in the brackets are simply the components of curl $\mathbf{F}$, where $\mathbf{F}(P, Q, R)$, as might have been expected. It should, further, be noticed that on multiplying the three equations (10.17b) by P, Q, R as indicated, and on adding the three equations, every term outside the parentheses will appear twice, each time with the opposite sign. For example, the first term $PR \, \partial\mu/\partial y$ in the first equation is balanced by $-PR \, \partial\mu/\partial y$ which is the last term outside the parentheses in the third equation. It follows that all these terms will cancel when the three equations are added together. The only remaining terms will involve the common factor μ, which will cancel, and the products of P, Q, R into the components of curl $\mathbf{F}$. Thus,

$$P\left(\frac{\partial R}{\partial y} - \frac{\partial Q}{\partial z}\right) + Q\left(\frac{\partial P}{\partial z} - \frac{\partial R}{\partial x}\right) + R\left(\frac{\partial Q}{\partial x} - \frac{\partial P}{\partial y}\right) = 0. \tag{10.18}$$

This is the scalar product of $\mathbf{F}$ into its own curl, and we can write

$$\mathbf{F} \cdot \text{curl } \mathbf{F} = 0. \tag{10.18a}$$

This is a *necessary* condition for the existence of an integrating factor μ. It is necessary, because having assumed that it exists, it was found that equation (10.18a) must be satisfied irrespective of the form of the integrating factor.

The preceding, necessary condition is the same as that encountered in equation (10.13) of the preceding section, but there is a difference. In the case of two independent variables, this condition was satisfied for *any* two-dimensional vector field *whatever*. Now, in the case of $n \geq 3$ there is no reason for it to be satisfied other than in exceptional cases. It is, therefore, natural to ask whether this condition is also *sufficient* for the existence of an integrating factor, that is, given a field which is normal to its own curl can we assert that the associated Pfaffian is integrable? We now proceed to prove that this is, indeed, the case.

In the case of *n*-vectors with *n* components $X_1, \ldots, X_n$ and *n* independent variables $x_1, \ldots, x_n$, the necessary condition for the existence of an integrating factor $\mu(x_1, \ldots, x_n)$ can be obtained by retracing the preceding argument step by step. The equation (10.15) for an ergomedic line will contain *n* terms

$$dw = \sum_1^n X_i(x_i)\, dx_i,$$

where $X_i(x_i)$ is a contraction for $X_i(x_1, \ldots, x_n)$. There will exist $n - 1$ collinearity conditions (10.16) leading to $n - 1$ ordinary differential equations (10.16a) for which a uniqueness and existence theorem can also be proved.[†] The vector **G** will have *n* components μX_i and the conditions of integrability (10.17a) will have to be satisfied. There will be $n(n - 1)$ such conditions, but only $\frac{1}{2}n(n - 1)$ are independent because

$$\frac{\partial(\mu X_i)}{\partial x_j} - \frac{\partial(\mu X_j)}{\partial x_i} = 0$$

is the same as

$$\frac{\partial(\mu X_j)}{\partial x_i} - \frac{\partial(\mu X_i)}{\partial x_j} = 0.$$

Evaluating the derivatives of the product by the chain rule, we shall be in a position to write *n* equations (10.17b). The terms in the brackets will involve $n(n - 1)$ components ω_{ij} of the antisymmetric, second-order tensor familiar from Section 4.4. On multiplying each equation by one component X_k, namely, that component which does not appear in the corresponding equation (10.17a) that is, when $k \neq i$ and $k \neq j$, we shall be able to add them three by three and to establish the counterparts of the necessary condition of integrability (10.18). In other words, one such condition must be satisfied when the *n*-space is projected into a three-dimensional subspace x_i, x_j, x_k. Since there are $\frac{1}{2}n(n - 1)$ independent conditions of integrability owing to the antisymmetry $\omega_{ij} = -\omega_{ji}$, it is possible to combine each of the $\frac{1}{2}n(n - 1)$ pairs of indices *ij* with the remaining $n - 2$ vectors *k* giving a total of $\frac{1}{2}n(n - 1)(n - 2)$ conditions of the form (10.18). This number will contain all those conditions which arise from a mere permutation of *i, j, k*, and the real number is only $\frac{1}{6}n(n - 1)(n - 2)$. However, only $\frac{1}{2}(n - 1)(n - 2)$ of these conditions are completely independent.

In order to see this more clearly, the reader may replace P, Q, R by X_i, X_j, X_k, replacing x, y, z by x_i, x_j, x_k simultaneously and remembering that the subscripts i, j, k range over $1, \ldots, n$, but are all different. The various conditions can then be counted in a simple manner.

The case of two dimensions is exceptional in that $\frac{1}{2}(n - 1)(n - 2)$ is equal to zero, and there exist *no* special conditions for the Pfaffian to possess an integrating factor. For $n = 3$, we have $\frac{1}{6}n(n - 1)(n - 2) = 1$ as well as $\frac{1}{2}(n - 1)(n - 2) = 1$.

10.2.3   *Sufficient conditions of integrability*

In order to prove that condition (10.18a) is sufficient for the existence of an integrating factor, it is first necessary to prove an auxiliary proposition. This states that stretching a vector field **F** by an arbitrary function $\mu(x, y, z)$ has no effect on condition

---

† Haaser, N. B., LaSalle, J. P., and Sullivan, J. A., *loc. cit.*

(10.18a). In other words, if $\mathbf{F} \cdot \text{curl } \mathbf{F} = 0$, then it follows also that

$$(\mu\mathbf{F}) \cdot \text{curl } (\mu\mathbf{F}) = 0. \tag{10.18b}$$

This property is proved by performing the operations indicated in the contracted vector formula (10.18b). The scalar product involves three terms of the type

$$\mu P\left[\frac{\partial(\mu R)}{\partial y} - \frac{\partial(\mu Q)}{\partial z}\right].$$

The remaining two terms follow by the cyclic permutation $P \to Q \to R \to P$, $x \to y \to z \to x$. On performing the differentiation it is seen that the preceding term will expand to

$$\mu^2 P\left(\frac{\partial R}{\partial y} - \frac{\partial Q}{\partial z}\right) - \mu\left(PQ\frac{\partial\mu}{\partial z} - PR\frac{\partial\mu}{\partial y}\right).$$

The terms multiplying μ will cancel each other, as is easy to see when the permutation is performed. The terms multiplying μ^2 together form the scalar product $\mathbf{F} \cdot \text{curl } \mathbf{F}$. In fact, except for the factor μ, the present calculation is very similar to the one which led to equation (10.17b). Thus,

$$(\mu\mathbf{F}) \cdot \text{curl } (\mu\mathbf{F}) = (\mathbf{F} \cdot \text{curl } \mathbf{F}) \cdot \mu^2$$

and if one side vanishes, the other will vanish simultaneously. The converse of the present theorem is also true. Indeed, substituting $\lambda = \dfrac{1}{\mu}$, we have

$$(\lambda\mu \, \mathbf{F}) \, \text{curl } (\lambda\mu \, \mathbf{F}) = \mathbf{F} \cdot \text{curl } \mathbf{F}$$

and $\mathbf{F} \cdot \text{curl } \mathbf{F}$ must vanish, if $(\mu\mathbf{F}) \cdot \text{curl } (\mu\mathbf{F})$ vanishes.

In order to prove that condition (10.18a) is sufficient for the existence of an integrating factor, we must prove that P, Q, R are proportional to the derivatives of a function

$$\phi(x, y, z) = k$$

as a consequence of condition (10.18a). In order to do this we suppose, provisionally, that in the Pfaffian equation

$$P \, dx + Q \, dy + R \, dz = 0, \tag{10.19}$$

z plays the part of a constant parameter. Hence, it becomes

$$P(x, y, z) \, dx + Q(x, y, z) \, dy = 0. \tag{10.19a}$$

By the theorem on the integrability of Pfaffians of two variables, it is known that there exists a function of two variables, say $U(x, y)$ whose derivatives are *proportional* to P and Q. It is clear that U, as well as P and Q, will contain z as a parameter, and we can write

$$U(x, y, z) = c$$

as the potential, and

$$\frac{\partial U}{\partial x} = \mu P, \qquad \frac{\partial U}{\partial y} = \mu Q.$$

On substituting into equation (10.19), we obtain

$$\frac{1}{\mu}\frac{\partial U}{\partial x}\,dx + \frac{1}{\mu}\frac{\partial U}{\partial y}\,dy + R\,dz = 0. \tag{10.19b}$$

By adding and subtracting $(1/\mu)(\partial U/\partial x)\,dz$, and multiplying by μ, equation (10.19b) can be transformed to

$$\frac{\partial U}{\partial x}\,dx + \frac{\partial U}{\partial y}\,dy + \frac{\partial U}{\partial z}\,dz + \left(\mu R - \frac{\partial U}{\partial z}\right)dz = 0,$$

that is,

$$dU + K(x, y, z)dz = 0, \qquad \text{where } K(x, y, z) = \mu R - \frac{\partial U}{\partial z}. \tag{10.20}$$

Now, it is known that $\mathbf{F} \cdot \text{curl } \mathbf{F} = 0$, therefore, $(\mu\mathbf{F}) \cdot \text{curl }(\mu\mathbf{F}) = 0$ for any function μ. The components of $\mu\mathbf{F}$ are μP, μQ, μR, that is,

$$\mu P = \frac{\partial U}{\partial x}, \quad \mu Q = \frac{\partial U}{\partial y}, \quad \text{and} \quad \mu R = K + \frac{\partial U}{\partial z}.$$

Hence, we can regard the vector $\mathbf{F}$ as the sum of vectors

$$\text{grad } U \text{ with components } \frac{\partial U}{\partial x}, \frac{\partial U}{\partial y}, \frac{\partial U}{\partial z}$$

and

$$\mathbf{K} \text{ with components } 0, 0, K.$$

It follows therefore that

$$\text{curl }(\mu\mathbf{F}) = \text{curl }(\text{grad } U + \mathbf{K}) = \text{curl } \mathbf{K}$$

since curl grad $U = 0$. The components of the curl of $\mathbf{K}$ are $\partial K/\partial y$, $-\partial K/\partial x$, and 0, as is easy to verify. Hence,

$$(\mu\mathbf{F}) \cdot \text{curl }(\mu\mathbf{F}) = \frac{\partial U}{\partial x}\frac{\partial K}{\partial y} - \frac{\partial U}{\partial y}\frac{\partial K}{\partial x} = \frac{\partial(U, K)}{\partial(x, y)}$$

if use is made of the Jacobian, first introduced in Section 3.7.3. It is clear now that

$$\frac{\partial(U, K)}{\partial(x, y)} = 0,$$

so that, by the property of Jacobians quoted in Section 3.7.3, we must conclude that there exists a relation between U and K which does not involve either x or y. Thus, K will be a function of U only, but it will contain the parameter z, and we can write

$$K = K(U, z).$$

Substitution into equation (10.20) shows that it is of the form

$$dU + K(U, z)\,dz = 0,$$

which is again a Pfaffian equation in the two variables U and z. Applying the known property of Pfaffians of two variables we assert the existence of the potential

$$\Phi(U, z) = \text{const.}$$

On replacing U in terms of x, y, z, we obtain a relation

$$\phi(x, y, z) = k$$

which is a potential for the original Pfaffian $dw = Pdx + Qdy + Rdz$, and hence the latter must possess an integrating factor.

By repeating the argument given at the end of Section 10.2.1, it is easy to show that any integrable Pfaffian possesses an infinity of integrating factors. Given one, say μ, and the associated potential ϕ, the function $\mu' = \mu d\Phi/d\phi$, equation (10.14), will also prove to be an integrating factor with $\Phi(\phi)$ playing the part of the associated potential.

The preceding argument shows clearly that it is useful to subdivide all irrotational vector fields into two subsets.

Subset 1. The condition $\mathbf{F} \cdot \text{curl } \mathbf{F} = 0$ is satisfied. The associated Pfaffian possesses an integrating factor.

Subset 2. The condition $\mathbf{F} \cdot \text{curl } \mathbf{F} \neq 0$ is satisfied. The associated Pfaffian does not possess an integrating factor. Pfaffians in two independent variables always belong to subset 1.

10.2.4   *Ergomedic lines and potential surfaces*

We now turn our attention to the potential $\phi(x, y, z)$ which is associated with an integrating factor when and if the latter exists. The family

$$\phi(x, y, z) = k$$

consists of nonintersecting surfaces, each of which has the property that an element of line in it satisfies the orthogonality condition (10.15). This can be seen from the fact that under the present assumptions $dw = \mu d\phi$, and a curve whose element $ds(dx, dy, dz)$ satisfies the equation $dw = 0$, must also satisfy the equation $d\phi = 0$. Thus, the equipotential surfaces are everywhere normal to the vectors $\mathbf{F}(P, Q, R)$ at the point. This property is analogous to that of the equipotential lines for Pfaffians of two variables, except that instead of a line, a surface is obtained. Two such surfaces are seen sketched in Figure 10.5. The field lines are also seen sketched in the diagram. It is remembered that the field lines always exist (under some mathematical restrictions which are of no consequence to our argument), and that they are lines for $n = 2$ as well as for $n \geq 3$.

It should be clear by now that any curve in any surface $\phi = \text{const}$ is an ergomedic curve, and that all possible ergomedic curves trace a one-parameter family of surfaces. Thus, it is impossible to find an ergomedic curve which intersects two equipotential surfaces, irrespective of how close to each other the latter may be. Extending the concept of mathematical accessibility introduced in Section 10.2.1, it is seen that in a vector field associated with an integrable Pfaffian, all pairs of accessible points lie in the same equipotential surfaces. For example points 1, 2 and 3, 4 are pairs of such points whereas points 6, 7 are inaccessible from point 5. This proves *Carathéodory's mathematical theorem* which asserts that,

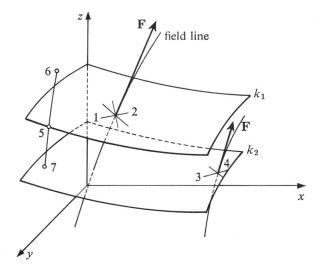

FIGURE 10.5. *Equipotential surfaces and field lines for a vector field associated with an integrable Pfaffian form.*

A.   *In the neighborhood, however small, of any point A in a vector field associated with an integrable Pfaffian there exist points which are inaccessible from A along an ergomedic path.*

The preceding theorem shows clearly the connection which exists between the concepts of integrability and accessibility in the mathematical sense. However, before a firm connection with Carathéodory's formulation of the Second Law can be established, it is useful to clarify the geometric relation for vector fields whose Pfaffians are not integrable.

10.2.5   *Vector fields associated with nonintegrable Pfaffians*

In order to visualize the properties of ergomedic lines in vector fields associated with nonintegrable Pfaffians, and to appreciate the difference in comparison with integrable Pfaffians, it is best to attempt to generalize the method of isoclines used in Section 5.14.5 in connection with two-dimensional Pfaffians. The tracing of an ergomedic line is illustrated in the sketch in Figure 10.6. Suppose that the line is started at point 1, at which the vector $\mathbf{F}(P, Q, R)$ is given. The first element of the curve must be confined to the element of plane σ_1 which is normal to $\mathbf{F}$. In the plane, Figure 10.7, the first element of the ergomedic curve must be confined to an element of *line* normal to the vector. Thus, in the plane the element of the first ergomedic line is fixed, and only one such line can pass through point 1. In a three-dimensional space there is an infinite choice of direction, and through point 1 there will pass as many ergomedic lines as we please. Having selected one direction in the element σ_1, Figure 10.6(b), we establish the neighboring element, σ_2, in which again an infinity of directions can be selected. In the plane, the second element, corresponding to point 2, would be fixed once more. Thus, for $n \geq 3$, and owing to the number of choices available at each step, it is possible to

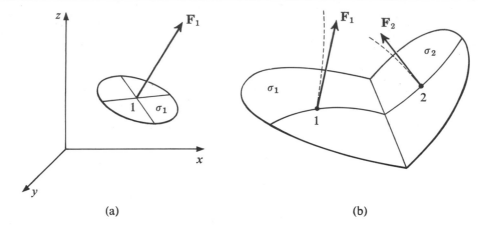

(a)   (b)

FIGURE 10.6. *Tracing an ergomedic line in space.*

reach any desired point in the neighborhood of the initial point 1. In the plane this was impossible. There exists, of course, an exception in space too. It is clear that when the condition $\mathbf{F} \cdot \mathrm{curl}\, \mathbf{F} = 0$ is satisfied, that is, when the associated Pfaffian is integrable, all succeeding elements $\sigma_1, \sigma_2, \ldots$ will be confined to one equipotential surface. It will then be impossible to leave the equipotential surface, and inaccessible points will exist. They do not exist in the case when $\mathbf{F} \cdot \mathrm{curl}\, \mathbf{F} \neq 0$.

   In order to visualize this distinction more clearly, it is possible to proceed in the following way, Figure 10.8. We shall pass an arbitrary surface

$$\psi(x, y, z) = 0 \qquad (10.21)$$

in the space, and attempt to determine the family of ergomedic lines in that surface. By deforming the surface continuously it will then be easy to visualize the presence or absence of inaccessible points. Differentiating equation (10.21), we obtain

$$\frac{\partial \psi}{\partial x}\, dx + \frac{\partial \psi}{\partial y}\, dy + \frac{\partial \psi}{\partial z}\, dz = 0. \qquad (10.21a)$$

The two relations (10.21) and (10.21a) determine z and dz in terms of x, y, dx, dy.

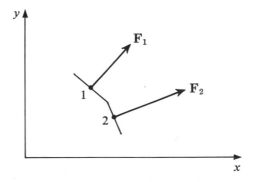

FIGURE 10.7. *Tracing an ergomedic line in the plane.*

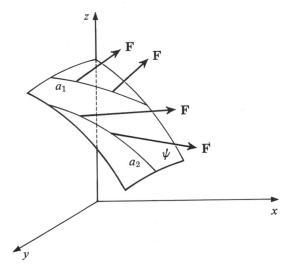

FIGURE 10.8. *Ergomedic curves in arbitrary surface $\psi(x, y, z) = 0$.*

When z from equation (10.21) and dz from equation (10.21a) are substituted into the Pfaffian equation

$$P\,dx + Q\,dy + R\,dz = 0, \tag{10.22}$$

the latter will reduce to the form

$$M(x, y)\,dx + N(x, y)\,dy = 0, \tag{10.22a}$$

because both z and dz can be eliminated from (10.22) with the aid of equations (10.21) and (10.21a). The functions M and N naturally depend on the arbitrary choice of the surface, that is, on the function ψ. The Pfaffian (10.22a), being one in two dimensions, can always be integrated, giving an integral, say

$$\phi(x, y) = k, \tag{10.23}$$

whose form depends on the initial choice of ψ. The pair or relations (10.23) and (10.21) define a family of curves arising from the intersection of the surface ψ with the family of cylinders (10.23). These intersections are all ergomedic curves, because they are orthogonal to the vector $\mathbf{F}(P, Q, R)$, having arisen from equation (10.22). The ergomedic lines a_1, a_2, . . . are seen sketched in Figure 10.8, together with the vectors $\mathbf{F}$. Whereas the lines are normal to the vectors, the arbitrary surface ψ is not. This is a consequence of the fact that a vector is normal to the element of a surface only if it is normal to at least *two* intersecting elements of curve in it. It is also clear that the ergomedic lines in the surface ψ do not intersect, because the cylinders (10.23) which arose from the two-dimensional Pfaffian (10.22a), did not intersect.

In order to see the connection between this process and the existence of an integrating factor, we shall perform the elimination of dz from equations (10.21a) and (10.22) explicitly. In this manner we obtain

$$\left(R \frac{\partial \psi}{\partial x} - P \frac{\partial \psi}{\partial z}\right) dx + \left(R \frac{\partial \psi}{\partial y} - Q \frac{\partial \psi}{\partial z}\right) dy = 0. \tag{10.24}$$

This is not yet the form in equation (10.22a) because it still contains z. The variable z must be eliminated with the aid of equation (10.21). If $\mathbf{F} \cdot \text{curl } \mathbf{F} = 0$, P, Q, R will be proportional to the partial derivatives of a potential, say $\Phi(x, y, z) = \text{const}$. We then have

$$\frac{1}{P}\frac{\partial\Phi}{\partial x} = \frac{1}{Q}\frac{\partial\Phi}{\partial y} = \frac{1}{R}\frac{\partial\Phi}{\partial z} \tag{10.25}$$

so that

$$R\frac{\partial\Phi}{\partial x} - P\frac{\partial\Phi}{\partial z} = 0 \quad \text{and} \quad R\frac{\partial\Phi}{\partial y} - Q\frac{\partial\Phi}{\partial z} = 0.$$

It is clear that the elimination depends on the relation between ψ and Φ. If the arbitrary surface is chosen so that it is *not* a potential surface, the elimination can proceed, but if we were to choose $\psi \equiv \Phi$, the Pfaffian equation (10.22a) would reduce to the identity

$$0 \cdot dx + 0 \cdot dy = 0.$$

Thus, if we happened to have made this choice, there would be no function $\phi(x, y) = c$ solving equation (10.22a). This means that *any* curve in ψ would have the required property of being always at right angles to the vector $\mathbf{F}$. Now the whole surface is everywhere normal to the vector.

Conversely, if $\mathbf{F} \cdot \text{curl } \mathbf{F} \neq 0$ there is no function $\Phi(x, y, z)$ for which condition (10.25) is satisfied, equation (10.22a) is not an identity but leads to an integral whose form is affected by the choice of ψ. Irrespective of the choice made, the surface will always contain a nonintersecting family of ergomedic curves. Given a point in space, say, 1, in Figure 10.9(a), we can draw through it an arbitrary surface; in that surface it is always possible to find an ergomedic curve passing through 1. When all possible surfaces are drawn through point 1, or, which amounts to the same, if the surface is imagined deformed continuously in all possible ways, the ergomedic curves passing through 1 will no longer trace a surface, but will fill an element of space. It is true, as shown in Figure 10.9(b), that "the first element" of any ergomedic curve must be confined to a plane element, denoted by σ in the sketch, which is normal to the local vector $\mathbf{F}$. If we now imagine a small cylinder π based on σ, we shall find that the cylinder contains a family of ergomedic curves, two of which have been drawn in the diagram. One of them can be made to reach any other point in the neighborhood of point 1. When $\mathbf{F} \cdot \text{curl } \mathbf{F} = 0$, this is impossible, because the ergomedic curves will be formed by the intersection of the cylinder π with a family of surfaces, and the ergomedic curves in π will not join those in σ, as suggested by Figure 10.9(c).

10.2.6   *Carathéodory's converse theorem*

The preceding considerations which led to the formulation of Carathéodory's mathematical theorem in Section 10.2.4 demonstrate that the existence of inaccessible points in the neighborhood of a given point in a vector field is a sufficient condition for the associated Pfaffian to possess one, and therefore an infinity, of integrating factors. When an integrating factor exists, then there exist inaccessible points. It is now clear that if the converse of Carathéodory's mathematical theorem were to turn out to be

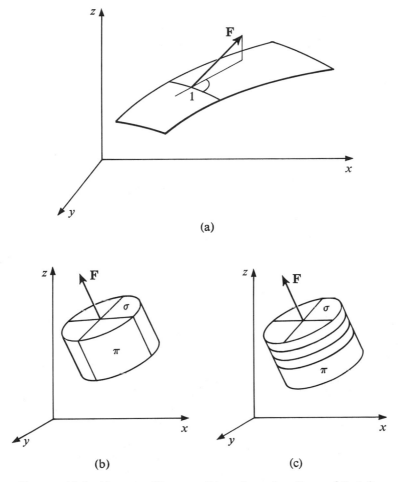

(a)

(b)   (c)

FIGURE 10.9. *Absence of inaccessible points when* **F** • *curl* **F** $\neq$ *0*.

true, there would be established a direct connection between Carathéodory's formulation of the Second Law, and the existence of integrating factors for the Pfaffian of reversible heat $dQ°$.

Accordingly, we now proceed to prove the following proposition:

> B.   *If a vector field has the property that in every arbitrarily close neighborhood of any given point there exist inaccessible points, then the associated Pfaffian is integrable.*

The two theorems, Carathéodory's mathematical theorem and its converse, can be contracted to one statement:

> C.   *The existence of inaccessible points in every arbitrarily close neighborhood of any given point in a vector field is a necessary and sufficient condition for the existence of an integrating factor of the associated Pfaffian differential form.*

There exist three proofs of Carathéodory's converse theorem. The first proof was given by C. Carathéodory himself[†] and is geometrical in nature. A somewhat modified geometrical proof was given by M. Born.[‡] Both proofs are to a certain extent intuitive and cannot be regarded as entirely rigorous. A more abstract, analytic proof was given by H. A. Buchdahl.[§] We shall be satisfied here with a slightly modified geometrical proof modelled on that due to Carathéodory.

It has been shown in Section 10.2.5 that in any arbitrary surface $\psi(x, y, z) = 0$ there can be traced a one-parameter, nonintersecting family of ergomedic curves which are the solution of

$$dw = \mathbf{F} \cdot d\mathbf{s} = P\,dx + Q\,dy + R\,dz = 0, \qquad (10.26)$$

that is, curves whose equations satisfy the above identically, on condition that $\psi = \text{const}$ is not a potential surface when $\mathbf{F} \cdot \text{curl}\,\mathbf{F} = 0$. Referring to Figure 10.10(a) we now suppose that in the neighborhood of an arbitrary point M there exist infinitely many inaccessible points, N being one of them. We draw an arbitrary straight line m through M making sure that m is not an ergomedic element; this can always be done. Through m and N we draw a plane π; we could just as well have drawn a cylinder or surface. In plane π, as in any surface, there will exist an ergomedic curve, curve c in the drawing, which is a solution of equation (10.26). This curve cannot pass through M because then N would be accessible from M contrary to our stipulation. Let curve c intersect line m at point P. By choosing N in a suitable way it is possible to make P lie as close to M as we please. This proves that in the neighborhood of M and on line m there exist points inaccessible from M, because they are all inaccessible from points N which are in turn inaccessible from M. Moreover, these points will lie on both sides of M as closely as we please.

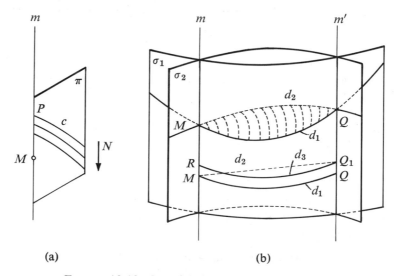

(a)   (b)

FIGURE 10.10. *Carathéodory's converse theorem.*

[†] Math. Ann., **67** (1909) 335.
[‡] *Natural Philosophy of Cause and Chance* (Oxford: Clarendon Press, 1949), p. 144.
[§] Am. J. Phys., **17** (1949) 45. See also Sneddon, I. N., *Elements of Partial Differential Equations* (McGraw-Hill, 1957), p. 35.

We now select another straight line, say m' in Figure 10.10(b), parallel to m, making sure that it too is not a solution of equation (10.26), and pass a surface, say a cylinder σ_1 through m and m'. In this cylinder we can again trace an ergomedic curve, curve d_1 in the sketch. This curve will intersect m' say at Q. Then we span a second cylinder, σ_2, and trace another ergomedic curve d_2. We assert that curve d_2 must intersect line m' at the same point Q as sketched in the upper part of the figure. If this were not so, and if, as drawn in the lower part of Figure 10.10(b), the curve d_2 intersected line m' at a different point, say Q_1, it would be possible to return from Q_1 along an ergomedic curve d_3 in σ_1, and line m would be reached at a point other than M, say R. Then R would be accessible from M along d_2 through Q_1 and d_3. This is contrary to what has been shown before, Figure 10.10(a), namely that the neighboring points to M on m must be inaccessible.

We can now visualize a continuous sequence of cylinders σ passing through m and m'. In each of them there would exist an ergomedic curve passing through M and Q, and it is evident that the locus of these curves will be a surface passing through d_1, d_2, Q, and M, as drawn in the upper part of Figure 10.10(b). Varying M we would obtain a nonintersecting family of surfaces, for otherwise the points on m in the neighborhood of M would cease to be inaccessible. This, as we know, is sufficient to prove the converse of Carathéodory's mathematical theorem.

It is clear that in the case when no inaccessible points exist, the sequence $Qd_1Md_2Q_1d_3R$ drawn in the lower part of Figure 10.10(b) would be permissible, and the ergomedic curves d_1, d_2, d_3 would fill an element of space, and would not coalesce into a surface.

10.3   Carnot's theorem

A comparison between Carathéodory's formulation of the first part of the Second Law of thermodynamics, quoted as Assertion 1 on p. 460, with Carathéodory's mathematical theorem, statement C on p. 477, leads to the immediate conclusion that the Pfaffian (9.47c) for reversible heat, $dQ°$, possesses an integrating factor (or denominator). This is true for any system however complex, and irrespective of the number of independent variables x_i which are needed to describe its state. We can, therefore, write

$$dQ° = \mu(x_i)\, d\phi(x_i). \qquad (10.27)$$

Here, $\mu(x_i)$ is the integrating *denominator* of $dQ°$, since $dQ°/\mu$ is the perfect differential $d\phi$. It follows that any isentropic curve must be completely confined to a potential surface

$$\phi(x_i) = k, \qquad (10.28)$$

since $dQ° = 0$ implies $d\phi = 0$. In the preceding equations, the inclusion of the symbol x_i in the parentheses denotes that the respective function depends on all n independent variables $x_1, \ldots, x_n$, and k is a variable parameter. It has been shown on p. 465 that integrating factors and, therefore, integrating denominators, are never unique. Consequently, it becomes necessary to select from all possible functions $\mu(x_i)$, and all associated potentials $\phi(x_i)$, that pair which will secure the greatest simplicity in the equations of thermodynamics. This must be achieved by a suitable *convention*. It turns out that it is possible to find an integrating denominator which is a unique function of the empirical temperature θ. It is convenient to retain this particular integrating denominator for future use, together with the associated potential. However, before making the choice, it is necessary to demonstrate that such an integrating denominator exists.

10.3.1   *Thermally coupled systems*

In order to introduce the empirical temperature θ into our considerations it is clearly necessary to consider (at least) two diathermally coupled systems, thus making sure that their temperatures are equal. We suppose that the temperature scale selected so far is entirely arbitrary. Let the state of system 1 be described by $m + 1$ independent variables $x_1, \ldots, x_i, \ldots, x_m, \theta$, and that of system 2 by $n + 1$ independent variables $y_1, \ldots, y_k, \ldots, y_n, \theta$, the common temperature θ being included as an independent variable in both equations of state. Thus, the state of the combined system, for which we shall use symbols without subscripts to distinguish them from those of system 1, subscript 1, and system 2, subscript 2, is described by $m + n + 1$ independent variables $x_1, \ldots, x_m, y_1, \ldots, y_n, \theta$. When convenient, dependence on the m variables $x_1, \ldots, x_m$ will be denoted by the single symbol x_i, and that on the n variables $y_1, \ldots, y_n$ by the symbol y_k.

During any *reversible* process, the heat dQ added to the whole system will be equal to the sum of the heats added to the subsystems 1 and 2. Thus,

$$dQ = dQ_1 + dQ_2 \qquad \text{(reversible)}. \qquad (10.29)$$

The superscript $^\circ$ has now been dropped in order to simplify the appearance of the equations, but the restriction to reversible processes must not be lost sight of. First, equation (10.27) is applicable to reversible processes only. Secondly, it must be realized that equation (10.29) is also restricted to reversible processes. This can be appreciated with reference to Figure 10.11 in which two systems are shown in close proximity. During a process, the systems receive the quantities of heat Q_1 and Q_2, and work W_1 and W_2 is done on them in such a way that rubbing occurs along the contact surface ab. An observer in system 1 will record two supplies of heat, Q_1, at the outer boundary, and Q_1' at the common boundary where rubbing takes place. Similarly, an observer in system 2 will notice the two fluxes Q_2 and Q_2'. On the other hand, an external observer will only record the heat flow $Q_1 + Q_2$. Evidently

$$Q_1 + Q_2 \neq Q_1 + Q_2 + Q_1' + Q_2'.$$

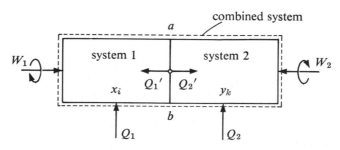

FIGURE 10.11. *The sum* $dQ_1 + dQ_2$ *in an irreversible process.*

It is clear, as explained in detail in Section 5.12, that

$$Q_1' + Q_2' = W_1' + W_2',$$

but from our point of view the distinction between heat and work is essential, and the counterpart of equation (10.29) could not be written for an irreversible process.

Returning to the analysis of reversible processes, and realizing that equation (10.27) applies to the subsystems 1 and 2 as well as to the whole system, it is possible to write

$$\left.\begin{aligned}
dQ &= \mu(x_1, \ldots, x_m, y_1, \ldots, y_n, \theta) \, d\phi(x_1, \ldots, x_m, y_1, \ldots, y_n, \theta) \\
dQ_1 &= \mu_1(x_1, \ldots, x_m, \theta) \, d\phi_1(x_1, \ldots, x_m, \theta) \\
dQ_2 &= \mu_2(y_1, \ldots, y_n, \theta) \, d\phi_2(y_1, \ldots, y_n, \theta)
\end{aligned}\right\} \quad (10.30)$$

in which the variables on which the functions μ, μ_1, μ_2, ϕ, ϕ_1, ϕ_2 depend should be carefully noted. Substitution of these expressions into equation (10.29) leads to

$$\mu \, d\phi = \mu_1 \, d\phi_1 + \mu_2 \, d\phi_2. \qquad (10.31)$$

Since ϕ is a potential which depends on $m + n + 1$ independent variables, equation (10.30), its total differential, will, in general, contain that number of terms. It can be written

$$d\phi = \sum_m \frac{\partial \phi}{\partial x_i} \, dx_i + \sum_n \frac{\partial \phi}{\partial y_k} \, dy_k + \frac{\partial \phi}{\partial \theta} \, d\theta. \qquad (10.32)$$

In this equation the mathematical convention for writing partial derivatives is employed once again, as no ambiguity can arise since the variables have been clearly enumerated in equation (10.30). A comparison between equation (10.32) and the expression in equation (10.31) which can also be written

$$d\phi = \frac{\mu_1}{\mu} \, d\phi_1 + \frac{\mu_2}{\mu} \, d\phi_2, \qquad (10.31a)$$

reveals that the total differential $d\phi$ contains fewer than $m + n + 1$ terms, namely, only two, if ϕ_1 and ϕ_2 are chosen as independent variables. This simplification must be expected to imply important physical consequences which we shall now attempt to make explicit.

The appearance of equation (10.31a) suggests that a change in variables will be advantageous. Since ϕ, ϕ_1, ϕ_2 are potentials, they can be used to replace one variable from among those listed in equation (10.30). Accordingly the state of subsystem 1 will be described by the variables ϕ_1, θ and $m - 1$ variables x_i, that of subsystem 2 by the variables ϕ_2, θ and $n - 1$ variables y_k, and, finally, that of the total system by the variables ϕ_1, ϕ_2, θ and $m + n - 2$ additional variables. For the sake of simplifying the ensuing description, we shall assume that the variables other than ϕ_1, ϕ_2, and θ are kept constant. The reader should satisfy himself later that this restriction has no bearing on the argument at all.

With these observations, and remembering that thermally coupled subsystems 1 and 2 are considered, we can rewrite equation (10.31a) as follows:

$$d\phi(\phi_1, \phi_2, \theta) = \frac{\mu_1(\phi_1, \theta)}{\mu(\phi_1, \phi_2, \theta)} \, d\phi_1 + \frac{\mu_2(\phi_2, \theta)}{\mu(\phi_1, \phi_2, \theta)} \, d\phi_2 \qquad (10.31b)$$

in which the independent variables of each function have again been carefully brought into evidence. Similarly, equation (10.32) which expresses the more general form of the perfect differential would become

$$d\phi = \left(\frac{\partial\phi}{\partial\phi_1}\right)_{\phi_2,\theta} d\phi_1 + \left(\frac{\partial\phi}{\partial\phi_2}\right)_{\phi_1,\theta} d\phi_2 + \left(\frac{\partial\phi}{\partial\theta}\right)_{\phi_1,\phi_2} d\theta. \qquad (10.32a)$$

The two equations, equation (10.31b) and (10.32a) represent *the same perfect differential*; accordingly, they must be identical, and a confrontation shows that

$$\left(\frac{\partial\phi}{\partial\theta}\right)_{\phi_1,\phi_2} = 0, \qquad (10.33)$$

since no term multiplying $d\theta$ appears in equation (10.31b). Thus, ϕ is independent of θ, and a function of ϕ_1 and ϕ_2 only (not counting the $m + n - 2$ remaining variables). Comparing the other terms, it is seen that

$$\left.\begin{aligned}\left(\frac{\partial\phi}{\partial\phi_1}\right)_{\phi_2} &= \frac{\mu_1(\phi_1,\theta)}{\mu(\phi_1,\phi_2,\theta)}, \\[1em] \left(\frac{\partial\phi}{\partial\phi_2}\right)_{\phi_1} &= \frac{\mu_2(\phi_2,\theta)}{\mu(\phi_1,\phi_2,\theta)},\end{aligned}\right\} \qquad (10.34)$$

where the subscript θ in the partial derivatives of ϕ need no longer be retained. Since $d\phi$ is a perfect differential, the second derivative

$$\left(\frac{\partial^2\phi}{\partial\phi_1\partial\theta}\right)_{\phi_2} = \left(\frac{\partial^2\phi}{\partial\phi_2\partial\theta}\right)_{\phi_1} = 0,$$

so that

$$\frac{\partial}{\partial\theta}\left(\frac{\mu_1}{\mu}\right) = \frac{\partial}{\partial\theta}\left(\frac{\mu_2}{\mu}\right) = 0. \qquad (10.35)$$

The fact that the derivatives with respect to temperature of the ratios

$$\frac{\mu_1(\phi_1,\theta)}{\mu(\phi_1,\phi_2,\theta)} \quad \text{and} \quad \frac{\mu_2(\phi_2,\theta)}{\mu(\phi_1,\phi_2,\theta)}$$

vanish signifies that these ratios must be independent of temperature, even though the quantities μ, μ_1, μ_2 are not, as is also clear from equations (10.34). A similar mathematical situation has already been encountered in Section 9.8 where it was shown that this property implies that the functions μ, μ_1, and μ_2 must contain a universal function $g(\theta)$ as a factor. Thus,

$$\left.\begin{aligned}\mu_1 &= h_1(\phi_1)\ g(\theta), \\ \mu_2 &= h_2(\phi_2)\ g(\theta), \\ \mu &= h(\phi_1,\phi_2)\ g(\theta),\end{aligned}\right\} \qquad (10.36)$$

where h_1, h_2, and h are some functions of the arguments as indicated. This can be seen even more clearly when the differentiations indicated in equations (10.35) are performed explicitly. We then obtain

$$\frac{\mu\dfrac{\partial\mu_1}{\partial\theta} - \mu_1\dfrac{\partial\mu}{\partial\theta}}{\mu^2} = \frac{\mu\dfrac{\partial\mu_2}{\partial\theta} - \mu_2\dfrac{\partial\mu}{\partial\theta}}{\mu^2} = 0,$$

or

$$\frac{1}{\mu_1} \frac{\partial \mu_1}{\partial \theta} = \frac{1}{\mu_2} \frac{\partial \mu_2}{\partial \theta} = \frac{1}{\mu} \frac{\partial \mu}{\partial \theta},$$

that is,

$$\frac{\partial(\ln \mu_1)}{\partial \theta} = \frac{\partial(\ln \mu_2)}{\partial \theta} = \frac{\partial(\ln \mu)}{\partial \theta} = g'(\theta), \tag{10.37}$$

where $g'(\theta)$ denotes some function of θ common to all derivatives. The fact that all these derivatives contain the single variable θ is a consequence of their being equal. In principle, μ_1 depends on ϕ_1 and θ, but μ_2 depends on ϕ_2 and θ. Thus, $\partial(\ln \mu_1)/\partial\theta$ cannot contain ϕ_2, and $\partial(\ln \mu_2)/\partial\theta$ cannot contain ϕ_1. By a similar argument it is seen that $\partial(\ln \mu)/\partial\theta$ cannot contain either ϕ_1 or ϕ_2.

Equations (10.37) can now be integrated, and the integration in each case will involve a function of the respective independent variables, excepting θ. We shall denote them by h with a suitable subscript. Hence,

$$\left.\begin{array}{l} \mu_1 = h_1(\phi_1)\, g(\theta), \\ \mu_2 = h_2(\phi_2)\, g(\theta), \\ \mu = h(\phi_1,\, \phi_2)\, g(\theta), \end{array}\right\} \tag{10.36a}$$

where

$$g(\theta) = \exp \int g'(\theta)\, d\theta. \tag{10.36b}$$

These forms are identical with equation (10.36), except for the further detail that $g(\theta)$ turns out to be an exponential function which is essentially positive, so that

$$g(\theta) \geq 0, \tag{10.36c}$$

the sign of equality being retained because $\int g'(\theta)\, d\theta$ can range from $-\infty$ to $+\infty$, at least in principle. All integrating denominators are thus products of a characteristic function h of the system, and an essentially positive, *universal function* of whatever empirical temperature is used in determining thermal equilibrium. Taking this result into account we can write the Pfaffians for reversible heat as

$$\left.\begin{array}{l} dQ = g(\theta)h(\phi_1,\, \phi_2)\, d\phi(\phi_1,\, \phi_2) \\ dQ_1 = g(\theta)h_1(\phi_1)\, d\phi_1 \\ dQ_2 = g(\theta)h_2(\phi_2)\, d\phi_2, \end{array}\right\} \tag{10.38}$$

from which it is clear that a function proportional to $g(\theta)$ can be chosen as a new integrating denominator in all cases. We shall denote it by T, and *define*

$$T = Cg(\theta) = C \cdot \exp \int g'(\theta)\, d\theta. \tag{10.39}$$

The associated potentials are, evidently,

$$\left.\begin{array}{ll} S_1 = \dfrac{1}{C} \int h_1(\phi_1)\, d\phi_1 + C_1 & \text{since} \quad dS_1 = \dfrac{1}{C} h_1(\phi_1)\, d\phi_1, \\[2mm] S_2 = \dfrac{1}{C} \int h_2(\phi_2)\, d\phi_2 + C_2 & \text{since} \quad dS_2 = \dfrac{1}{C} h_2(\phi_2)\, d\phi_2. \end{array}\right\} \tag{10.40}$$

The form of the potential for the whole system requires further elucidation. It is seen from the first equation (10.38) that the term

$$h(\phi_1, \phi_2) \, d\phi(\phi_1, \phi_2) \tag{10.41}$$

occurs in it, in addition to $g(\theta)$, and the question arises as to whether this product constitutes a perfect differential. That this is the case can be shown simply by writing the perfect differential $d\phi$ *in extenso*. Thus, the preceding product is equivalent to

$$h \frac{\partial \phi}{\partial \phi_1} \, d\phi_1 + h \frac{\partial \phi}{\partial \phi_2} \, d\phi_2.$$

The partial derivatives $\partial \phi / \partial \phi_1$ and $\partial \phi / \partial \phi_2$ have been given in equation (10.34). Substituting in them the expressions from equation (10.36), we obtain

$$h \frac{\partial \phi}{\partial \phi_1} = h \frac{\mu_1}{\mu} = h_1(\phi_1)$$

and

$$h \frac{\partial \phi}{\partial \phi_2} = h \frac{\mu_2}{\mu} = h_2(\phi_2).$$

Consequently, applying the test for integrability, we calculate

$$\frac{\partial}{\partial \phi_2} [h_1(\phi_1)] = \frac{\partial}{\partial \phi_1} [h_2(\phi_2)] = 0,$$

and conclude that the product (10.41) is a perfect differential. This proves that $h(\phi_1, \phi_2)$ can be a function of ϕ only, that is, that its dependence on ϕ_1 and ϕ_2 is such that it first depends on ϕ which then in turn depends on ϕ_1 and ϕ_2, or

$$h = h[\phi(\phi_1, \phi_2)].$$

The preceding argument has demonstrated that the potential for the combined system is identical in form with those for the subsystems, and can be written

$$S = \frac{1}{C} \int h(\phi) \, d\phi + C' \quad \text{since } dS = \frac{1}{C} h \, [\phi(\phi_1, \phi_2)] \, d\phi. \tag{10.40a}$$

Thus, for any system we have

$$dQ^\circ = T \, dS, \tag{10.42}$$

which is Carnot's theorem; it states that the Pfaffian expression for reversible heat can be represented as the product of a universal function (10.39) of the empirical scale in use, and the perfect differential of a potential S.

10.3.2 Thermodynamic temperature scale

The universal function T can now be adopted as a new temperature scale. It is called, as we already know, the *thermodynamic temperature scale*. The thermodynamic temperature scale, as seen from equation (10.39), is proportional to an essentially positive function of empirical temperature θ. The coefficient of proportionality C must be fixed by a further convention. In agreement with the conventions already adopted in Section 9.8, we first stipulate that C shall be positive. This has the effect of rendering all temperatures measured on the thermodynamic scale positive, the lowest possible temperature being $T = 0$. Thus, the thermodynamic temperature scale is seen to possess a natural zero, unlike the perfect-gas temperature scale. In addition to postulating $C > 0$, it is necessary to adopt a numerical value for it. This is done, as stated repeatedly, indirectly, by agreeing that the thermodynamic temperature of the triple point of water shall have the value

$$T_3 = 273.16°\text{K}.$$

Hence, C is calculated from

$$Cg(\theta_3) = 273.16,$$

where $g(\theta_3)$ is the value of the universal function g at the triple point of water. The function $g(\theta)$ itself must be determined empirically, but it must be realized that the argument so far has only demonstrated the *existence* of a thermodynamic temperature scale. The argument has not yet produced an operational definition of the thermodynamic temperature scale, that is, one which could be translated into definite instructions for the performance of measurements in terms of it. In this the position is the same as in Section 9.8 when it was stated that the solution of this essential problem must await further study, that is, it must await the demonstration that the thermodynamic temperature scale is identical with the perfect-gas temperature scale in the range where the latter exists.

10.3.3   Entropy

The new potential S is called *entropy*. From the expressions in equations (10.40) and (10.40a) it is clear that the entropy S of a system depends on all the independent properties of that system. In the case of subsystem 1 it depends on ϕ_1 and the $m - 1$ properties left out of account, as announced at the beginning of this section. However, ϕ_1 itself depends on all the independent properties of the system, including temperature, as evidenced in equation (10.30). Hence, the entropy of a system depends on all its independent properties, like all potentials. The same can be said about subsystem 2 and about the combined system, and so about any system whatsoever. Regarding entropy we can now repeat all the remarks made at the end of Section 9.10, namely, that it is possible to measure only *differences in the entropy* between *two different equilibrium states of a single closed system*. Since entropy is a potential, its measurement, or calculation, can proceed without regard to any actual processes taking place between these equilibrium states; these may be reversible or irreversible in any particular case under consideration, but the measurement, or calculation, must proceed along a reversible path and must involve the measurement, or calculation, of the Clausius integral

$$S_2 - S_1 = \int_1^2 \frac{\mathrm{d}Q°}{T} \qquad \text{(reversible path)}.$$

Consequently, such a reversible path must be realizable, or at least known to exist.

Since entropy is calculated with reference to a reversible process, and since in reversible processes quantities of heat are additive, entropy differences are also additive. In other words, if during a given process, reversible or irreversible, several subsystems of a single system have each changed their entropies by $\Delta S_1, \Delta S_2, \ldots$, the whole system will have changed its entropy by

$$\Delta S = \sum_n \Delta S_i, \tag{10.43}$$

where the summation extends over the n subsystems of a system. Equation (10.43) remains true, even though heat quantities are not necessarily additive in irreversible processes.

Instead of always employing entropy differences, in practice, it is convenient to adopt for entropy the same conventions as those discussed in connection with energy in Section 5.5, namely, to fix by convention the value of the entropy of a system at a given state. If this is done, all other states can have "absolute" values of entropy assigned to them. Such values, however, are not truly absolute. A closer approach to the establishment of absolute values of entropy is provided by the Third Law of thermodynamics, Volume II. The reader is, therefore, cautioned not to translate equation (10.43) into one for absolute entropies, namely, into

$$S = \sum_n S_i$$

without studying the problem of normalizing the arbitrary constant in a manner identical with that discussed in Section 6.13.2. In particular, it is seen that the computation of the entropy of mixing (Section 13.5) and of chemical reactions (Volume II) poses problems of great practical importance.

10.3.4   Concluding remarks

The existence of an integrating denominator in the form of a universal function of empirical temperature was inferred from a study of the properties of thermally coupled systems. By retracing the steps of the preceding argument it appears that a similar function should be obtainable for systems coupled in some other way. For example, two systems could be coupled across a floating adiabatic piston, ensuring that their pressures are equal at all times. In this manner an integrating denominator depending on pressure only could be obtained. This new integrating denominator would be associated with a different potential. Any mode of coupling would lead to an integrating denominator depending exclusively on the common property of the two coupled subsystems. It should, however, be recognized that such "bizarre" functions would be of limited utility, and this explains why they are not normally studied.

The fact that alternative integrating denominators do exist has been utilized extensively in this section, but in order to relate them to entropy, it is useful to rewrite equation (10.14) for an alternative integrating factor. Noting that for the Pfaffian of heat $\mu = 1/T$ and $\phi = S$, we put

$$\mu' = \frac{1}{T}\frac{\mathrm{d}\Phi}{\mathrm{d}S} \qquad \text{where } \Phi = \Phi(S).$$

Hence the new integrating denominator $\nu = 1/\mu'$ becomes

$$\nu = T\frac{\mathrm{d}S}{\mathrm{d}\Phi} = \frac{T}{\mathrm{f}(S)}.$$

The arbitrary function $\mathrm{f}(S) = \mathrm{d}\Phi/\mathrm{d}S$ can be chosen so as to impose an alternative condition on the new integrating denominator ν.

10.4   The second part of the Second Law. Principle of entropy increase

The gist of the argument which was designated as the first part of the Second Law of thermodynamics can be summarized by stating that all isentropics of any system are confined to a discrete, nonintersecting family of hypersurfaces of $n - 1$ dimensions, where n denotes the number of independent variables of the system. They are lines for $n = 2$, and surfaces in space for $n = 3$. In other words, all states within one isentropic hypersurface are accessible from each other, and are equally probable.

Since isentropic processes constitute convenient abstractions only, it is now necessary to examine the consequences which follow from Carathéodory's Assertion 2, given at the end of Section 10.1. Assertion 2 relates to real processes and expresses the fact that they are irreversible. We shall now consider a small step in an irreversible adiabatic process undergone by a system with $n = 3$ independent variables. The generalization to $n > 3$ or the specialization to $n = 2$ present no difficulties, as was already realized in the preceding section. It is clear that a small irreversible adiabatic step must involve a change in the entropy of the system since it must lead to a state 2 from which state 1 is inaccessible, and it was seen that all states of the same entropy are accessible from each other. Thus, concentrating on a single system, it can be stated that its entropy either increases during a small step in an adiabatic process, $\Delta S > 0$, or that it decreases, $\Delta S < 0$. We now assert that for all processes of one system, *either* $\Delta S > 0$ *or* $\Delta S < 0$, and that Carathéodory's Assertion 2 excludes the possibility that $\Delta S > 0$ for some processes, and $\Delta S < 0$ for some other processes.

In order to see this clearly, we shall represent the state of the system with the aid of $n - 1$ independent properties (in our case two, say x and y), and choose the entropy S as the additional, nth property. Such a diagram is shown in Figure 10.12(a). The initial state 1 under consideration is confined to some surface $S = $ const, that is, to the plane $S = $ const shown in the sketch. Suppose now that processes for which $\Delta S > 0$, such as $1 \rightarrow 1'$ as well as processes for which $\Delta S < 0$, say $1 \rightarrow 1''$, are equally possible. It is clear that all states in the plane $S + \Delta S$ are accessible from state $1'$ and the latter is accessible from 1; therefore, all states in plane $S + \Delta S$ would be accessible from state 1.

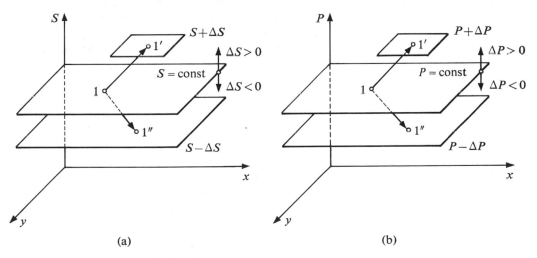

(a)   (b)

FIGURE 10.12. *Sign of change in entropy for a single system.*

Similarly, all states in the plane $S - \Delta S$, accessible from state 1″, would also be accessible from state 1. By taking smaller and smaller steps $1 \to 1'$ and $1 \to 1''$ it would be possible to bring the surfaces $S + \Delta S$ and $S - \Delta S$ closer and closer to surface S. It follows that in the neighborhood of the given state 1, there would be no states inaccessible from it by an adiabatic process, contrary to the accepted statement, Assertion 2. A state of affairs consistent with Assertion 2 demands, therefore, that all irreversible adiabatic processes of a given system must be of one kind; that is, they must be characterized by either an increase or by a decrease in entropy, both being incapable of existing side by side, as asserted earlier.

It might appear at first sight that the same argument could be advanced with respect to any property of a system, say its pressure P, and not necessarily its entropy. In order to see clearly that this is not the case, we shall attempt to reproduce the preceding argument in relation to Figure 10.12(b). The two irreversible processes in question are again denoted by $1 \to 1'$ and $1 \to 1''$, the difference between them consisting in the fact that $\Delta P > 0$ for the first process, and $\Delta P < 0$ for the second. When the surfaces $P + \Delta P = $ const and $P - \Delta P = $ const are drawn, it is realized that all states confined in them are not necessarily mutually accessible. The alternative argument breaks down at this point, and it is seen that it can be completed only in relation to entropy, because only states of equal entropy are accessible from each other adiabatically.

The fact that the entropy of a particular adiabatic system must either increase or decrease when the system performs an irreversible process does not rule out the possibility that there may exist two classes of systems, those for which $\Delta S > 0$ and those for which $\Delta S < 0$. However, a moment's reflection shows that this possibility is also excluded. In order to see this, it is sufficient to realize that two adiabatic systems can always be treated as one by a suitable choice of boundary. Moreover, the mere fact of combining two systems into one for the purpose of analysis changes nothing in their behavior. Suppose now that for subsystem 1, $\Delta S_1 > 0$ and for subsystem 2, $\Delta S_2 < 0$. However, it was shown in Section 10.3, equation (10.43), that entropy differences for systems are additive. Hence,

$$\Delta S = \Delta S_1 + \Delta S_2, \tag{10.43a}$$

and it would now be possible to make ΔS both positive *and* negative depending on the relative magnitudes of ΔS_1 and ΔS_2, but this is exluded by the argument advanced at the beginning.

The preceding reasoning leads to the conclusion that *all irreversible, adiabatic processes in nature* must be characterized by the same direction insofar as the change in entropy in *combinable systems* is concerned. The entropy must *either* decrease *or* increase as a result of such a process. In order to determine which of the directions really prevails in nature, it is sufficient to compute it for *a single* irreversible process. Probably the simplest process to choose for the purpose is that in which a quantity of heat, Q, passes from a reservoir at temperature T to one of lower temperature, T_0. If the quantity of heat Q is imagined transferred very slowly, for example, through a thin thermal conductor of negligible mass, the reservoir T will change its internal energy by $\Delta U = -Q$, whereas the reservoir T_0 will increase its internal energy by $\Delta U_0 = +Q$. Hence, applying the First Law, and recalling the remarks in Section 5.13 concerning infinite heat reservoirs, we see that for reservoir T, $dQ^\circ = dU$, whereas for the second $dQ^\circ = dU_0$. Consequently, for the adiabatic system which includes both reservoirs, the change in entropy is

$$\Delta S = \int_1^2 \frac{\mathrm{d}U}{T} + \int_1^2 \frac{\mathrm{d}U_0}{T_0} = -\frac{|Q|}{T} + \frac{|Q|}{T_0} = |Q| \frac{T - T_0}{TT_0} > 0, \qquad (10.44)$$

which is a *positive quantity* for $T > T_0$. Thus, for *all* irreversible processes in *adiabatic* systems, however complex, *the entropy must increase*. This is the principle of entropy increase in isolated systems which was earlier derived by a different line of reasoning in Section 9.11.

This principle allows us to divide all processes in isolated systems into three classes, according to the sign in the change in entropy, ΔS:

1. Entropy increases, $\Delta S > 0$, the process taking place is a *natural* one, that is, irreversible.

2. Entropy does not change, $\Delta S = 0$, the process taking place is *reversible*, that is, an idealized natural process.

3. Entropy decreases, $\Delta S < 0$, the process is *impossible*, that is, its occurrence is inconsistent with the Second Law of thermodynamics. The appearance of such a process in any calculation, or exploratory investigation, must be taken as a sign of conflict with the Second Law, or as a sign of erroneous reasoning or computation.

The proof of the principle of entropy increase turns on the possibility that systems to which it applies can be coupled with systems exchanging heat in the usual manner. It is possible to speculate that a world might exist in which the opposite direction of entropy change prevails. Its existence would be self-consistent, even if heat had a tendency to flow spontaneously from a colder to a hotter body, and even if work could be produced by decreasing the energy of a single reservoir, the opposite process of increasing its energy by the performance of work being impossible. However, such a world could not be coupled with our ordinary world, since only then would it be impossible to write equation (10.43). In such a world, it would be necessary to change the phrasing of the "conventional" formulations of the Second Law as they were given in Section 9.2, it being noted that the proofs of equivalence also turned on the possibility of coupling the various systems under consideration. By contrast, Carathéodory's formulation of the Second Law would remain unaltered.

It is remarkable that such a world can be said to exist on earth as evidenced by experiments on the demagnetization of the nuclei of certain paramagnetic salts, notably those of pure lithium fluoride, LiF. These could be interpreted alternatively by assuming that irreversible processes in systems thought of as consisting of the nuclear spins in pure lithium fluoride taken by themselves, occur in the direction of *decreasing* entropy or of assigning *negative* values of *absolute temperature* to them. The essential feature of such rare systems is that they are effectively decoupled from the lattice of the crystal during the process of reaching equilibrium.[†] Such decoupling exists for very short periods of time known as relaxation times, and are of the order of 10^{-5} sec. A clear and thorough examination of the thermodynamic properties of such special systems would exceed the scope of this book, and will not be pursued, beyond remarking that the reader must clearly distinguish between the intrinsic part of the Second Law of thermodynamics and those statements which result from convenient conventions.

[†] See Ramsey, N. F., "Thermodynamics and Statistical Mechanics at Negative Absolute Temperatures," *Phys. Rev.*, **103** (1956), 20 and Bazarou, L. P., *Thermodynamics* transl. by F. Immirzi and ed. by A. E. J. Hayes, Pergamon, 1964, Chapter X.

It is realized, of course, that the increasing property of entropy in the more normal systems is conditioned entirely by the choice of the sign of the constant C in equation (10.39). The opposite convention would render T negative and would change the sign of dS in equation (10.40a). Thus, the above statements are consequences of the convention regarding the sign of the constant C. However, a change in sign would alter nothing in the nature of processes, and would only force us to use different phrases to describe them. For example, in the study of nuclear spin systems, consistency imposes upon us the requirement to regard negative temperatures as "hotter" than positive temperatures; in other words such a system can be said to be capable of undergoing heating from absolute zero to $+\infty°$K, which is identical with $-\infty°$K, and to continue to be "heated" from $-\infty°$K to $-0°$K.

10.5   Concluding remarks on the Carathéodory-Born formulation of the Second Law

The derivation of the principle of entropy increase for isolated systems concludes the mathematical formulation of the Second Law of thermodynamics, this time on the basis of the two Assertions due to Carathéodory, and of *one* result derived from a direct (even if somewhat imaginary) experiment. Thus, by using an entirely different line of argument we derived exactly the same equations as those obtained in Chapter 9. It is suggested that the present derivation, admittedly more abstract and mathematical in its nature, is nevertheless more general, perhaps more elegant, and certainly more precise. The reader must decide for himself which of the two he wishes to adopt as his own.

In the more recent past several attempts have been made to reduce the formulation of the Second Law, and even of the whole of thermodynamics, to a closed set of clearly stated axioms, and to build a structure reminiscent of that which Euclid devised for geometry.† Some authors‡ prefer to avoid the physical arguments which lead to the formulation of Carnot's theorem, and adopt the latter as a *postulate* whose truth or falsity is subsequently verified by confronting its consequences with experiment. This leads to the so-called *postulational approach* in thermodynamics. To a person who wishes to use thermodynamics for further applications the choice between the approach adopted in this book (and many others) and the postulational approach is, ultimately, a matter of taste, since for him, the starting point, namely, Carnot's theorem and the principle of entropy increase, are the same. It is thought, however, that a beginner will have much greater difficulty in persuading himself that Carnot's theorem is an expression of verifiable, experimental facts. He will have no such qualms, and will develop less inner resistance, with respect to the other, verbal formulations of the Second Law, including Carathéodory's.

10.6   Review of previous verbal statements of the Second Law. Carnot and other reversible cycles

Since Carnot's theorem, equation (10.42), was derived in this chapter without any reference to the three statements of the Second Law of thermodynamics or to proper-

---

† Landsberg, P. T., *Thermodynamics* (Interscience, 1961). Also Falk, G., and Jung, H., "Axiomatik der Thermodynamik," article in Vol. III/2 of *Handbuch der Physik*, ed., S. Flügge (Berlin: Springer, 1959), p. 119 and Giles, R., *Mathematical Foundations of Thermodynamics* (Pergamon, 1964).
‡ Callen, H. B., *Thermodynamics* (Wiley, 1960). (Approach conceived by L. Tisza.)

ties of Carnot cycles, it is useful to conclude the present chapter by demonstrating explicitly that the latter are direct consequences of the former. In this manner, the development of the subject contained in Chapters 9 and 10 will be brought to the same point, and the considerations of Chapter 11 will follow directly upon those in Chapter 9 as well as upon the arguments in the present chapter.

10.6.1   Clausius' statement of the Second Law of thermodynamics. Available work

We have, in effect, made use of Clausius' statement of the Second Law in Section 10.4. However, in that section any other irreversible process could have been utilized for our purposes, and a short demonstration that Clausius' statement follows from Carnot's theorem, equation (10.42), may not be entirely redundant.

Referring to Figure 10.13, we consider the isolated system consisting of the source of heat at temperature T and the sink T_0. The two are connected by an arbitrary system, say the rod a, whose state does not change with time. As a result, a quantity of heat Q is exchanged, as shown in the drawing. The change in the entropy of this system consists of the loss of entropy $-Q/T$ suffered by the source, and the gain in entropy $+Q/T_0$ of the sink, the change in the entropy of the connecting system a being zero. If the connecting system performs a cycle, without a net flow of work, a number of complete cycles can be considered, so that the change in the entropy of system a is once again equal to zero. According to the principle of entropy increase, the total change in entropy within the isolated system must be positive, or

$$\Delta S = Q\left(\frac{1}{T_0} - \frac{1}{T}\right) = \frac{Q}{T_0}\frac{T - T_0}{T} > 0. \tag{10.45}$$

This shows that for the adopted direction of flow of heat $(Q > 0)$, we must have

$$T > T_0$$

which means that heat can flow spontaneously only from a source of higher temperature to one of lower temperature, in accordance with Clausius' statement.

It is noteworthy that the efficiency of a Carnot cycle, $(T - T_0)/T$, has appeared in the preceding equation. The product of this efficiency into the quantity of heat Q extracted from the source represents the work

$$W = Q\frac{T - T_0}{T}$$

which could be obtained at the expense of heat Q if a Carnot cycle had been available. As it is, this work was not obtained in the process and can be considered "lost." The fact that work W is "lost" does not mean that the energy balance imposed on the sys-

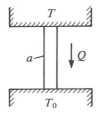

FIGURE 10.13. *Clausius' statement of the Second Law.*

tem has been upset. If work W had been extracted, only the difference $Q_0 = Q - W$ would have been rejected to the sink, instead of the full quantity of heat, Q. Nevertheless, the quantity of work W can be regarded as a loss from the economic point of view. Denoting this work as W_{loss} to bring this point of view into evidence, the relations in (10.45) can be rewritten

$$\Delta S = \frac{W_{\text{loss}}}{T_0} > 0. \tag{10.46}$$

This relation states that the increase in entropy of the isolated system is equal to the quotient of the work lost and of the absolute, thermodynamic temperature T_0 of the available heat sink. Moreover, since $T_0 > 0$, that loss is positive, and can never become a gain.

Sometimes, the quantity of work which could be obtained from a given quantity of heat Q extracted from a source whose temperature T exceeds that of a sink, T_0, is referred to as *available work*. The work lost is the unrecovered available work, and

$$W_{\text{loss}} = T_0 \Delta S > 0. \tag{10.47}$$

The relation in (10.47) reflects a more general conclusion from the Second Law which will be drawn in Section 13.7.

10.6.2   *The Planck-Kelvin statement of the Second Law*

The Planck-Kelvin statement of the Second Law is also a direct consequence of the principle of entropy increase. If heat Q is extracted from a single source at temperature T, or, for that matter, if several quantities of heat Q_i, Figure 10.14, were to be extracted from n sources of temperatures $T_1, \ldots, T_i, \ldots, T_n$, it is clear that each source would lose entropy $-Q_i/T_i$. Hence, if an engine were to operate cyclically by withdrawing heat from these sources, the total change in entropy would be

$$-\sum_n \left(\frac{Q_i}{T_i}\right) < 0,$$

which is a negative quantity. It follows that such a process is impossible, because it is inconsistent with the second part of the Second Law of thermodynamics.

If an engine operates cyclically by exchanging heat with a single source of temperature T, absorbing positive heat Q during part of the cycle, and rejecting negative heat

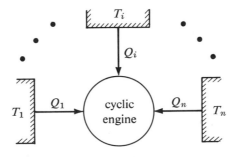

FIGURE 10.14. *The Kelvin-Planck statement of the Second Law.*

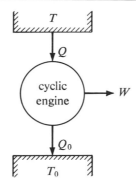

FIGURE 10.15. *The forward Carnot cycle.*

Q_0 during the remainder of the cycle, it would produce a quantity of work

$$W = Q - |Q_0|$$

in the process, as demanded by the First Law. According to the Second Law, the resulting change in entropy would be

$$\frac{|Q_0| - Q}{T} \geq 0.$$

This shows that $W = Q - |Q_0|$ can only be equal to zero, or be negative. Thus, an isothermal cycle of this type cannot *produce* work, but it can consume it, since $Q - |Q_0| < 0$ corresponds to $W < 0$.

The first half of the preceding statement, namely, that which asserts that the work *produced* in a reversible, isothermal cycle is zero is sometimes known as Moutier's theorem.

10.6.3   The Carnot cycle

The considerations of the preceding subsection demonstrate that at least two sources are required for the continuous *production* of work by means of a cycle, and that at least one of the sources must gain entropy, that is, at least one of them must have heat rejected to it. This leads to the two possibilities already known to us from Chapter 9. If the heat reservoir of lower temperature, T_0, is the one which gains entropy, a forward Carnot cycle producing work is obtained, Figure 10.15. The application of the First Law shows that

$$W = Q - |Q_0|$$

and the application of the principle of entropy increase leads to

$$\Delta S = -\frac{Q}{T} + \frac{|Q_0|}{T_0} \geq 0. \tag{10.48}$$

The equality sign in equation (10.48) refers to reversible operation, whereas the sign of inequality refers to irreversible operation. There is now no difficulty in showing that for reversible operation

$$\eta^\circ = \frac{W^\circ}{Q} = \frac{T - T_0}{T}.\tag{10.49}$$

Similarly, for irreversible operation,

$$\eta_{\text{irr}} = \frac{W}{Q} < \frac{T - T_0}{T},\tag{10.49a}$$

where the superscript $^\circ$ serves to recall the reversible nature of the process. It follows that for equal quantities of heat Q and for equal temperatures

$$W < W^\circ\tag{10.50}$$

and, similarly

$$|Q_0| > |Q_0^\circ|,\tag{10.50a}$$

since

$$W = Q - |Q_0| \quad \text{and} \quad W^\circ = Q - |Q_0^\circ|.\tag{10.50b}$$

Translating these equations into practical terms, we can state that any irreversibility in the operation of a power cycle leads to a loss in efficiency, that is, a loss of work compared with reversible operation under similar conditions, and an increase in the quantity of heat rejected to the surroundings.

In the assessment of the operation of a real, that is, irreversible, engine, it is useful to compare its efficiency with the efficiency of a reversible cycle operating in conjunction with the same sources of heat. Thus, the ratio

$$\eta_r' = \frac{\eta_{\text{irr}}}{\eta^\circ} = \frac{W_{\text{irr}}}{W^\circ}\tag{10.51}$$

is a measure of the inferior performance of the real, as compared with the ideal engine.†
The difference

$$W_{\text{loss}} = W^\circ - W$$

is the loss in available energy which remains unrecovered in the actual process. Since by equation (10.50b) this loss appears in the form of additional rejected heat

$$W_{\text{loss}} = |Q_0| - |Q_0^\circ|,$$

the entropy increase from equation (10.48) can now be written

$$\Delta S = \frac{W_{\text{loss}}}{T_0} > 0;$$

it was equal to zero when the engine operated reversibly. Just as was the case in Section 10.6.1,

$$W_{\text{loss}} = T_0 \Delta S$$

and the Second Law is seen to admit a loss ($W_{\text{loss}} > 0$), but not a gain ($W_{\text{loss}} < 0$) in

† In actual practice the ratio η_r' is usually represented as the product of a slightly different efficiency ratio and a quantity known as the mechanical efficiency. At this stage the distinction is irrelevant. See Section 13.2.

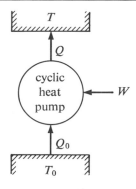

FIGURE 10.16. *The reverse Carnot cycle.*

work. It is not difficult to prove that

$$\Delta S = \frac{W}{T_0}\left(1 - \frac{1}{\eta_{\text{irr}}}\right)$$

in terms of the quantities W and η_{irr} which describe the operation of the real engine.

When the hotter reservoir is the one which gains entropy, a refrigerator or heat pump operating on the reversed Carnot cycle is obtained, Figure 10.16. The principle of entropy increase now leads to the inequality

$$\frac{|Q|}{T} - \frac{|Q_0|}{T_0} \geq 0 \qquad (10.52)$$

from which it follows that the reversible coefficient of performance

$$\epsilon^{\circ} = \frac{T_0}{T - T_0} \qquad (10.52\text{a})$$

and that the real (irreversible) coefficient of performance

$$\epsilon_{\text{irr}} < \frac{T_0}{T - T_0}. \qquad (10.52\text{b})$$

Similarly, for the efficacy of a heat pump

$$\epsilon_f^{\circ} = \frac{T}{T - T_0} \qquad (10.52\text{c})$$

and

$$\epsilon_{f,\text{irr}} < \frac{T}{T - T_0}. \qquad (10.52\text{d})$$

During irreversible operation as a refrigerator, for the same refrigerating effect, Q_0, the irreversible machine requires an increased amount of heat to be rejected in order to render the difference in equation (10.52) positive, since

$$|Q| > |Q^{\circ}|$$

$$|W| = |Q| - |Q_0|$$

and

$$|W°| = |Q°| - |Q_0|,$$

it follows that

$$|W| > |W°|.$$

Thus, the amount of work done on the system is higher for a real, as compared with an ideal refrigerator.† The "loss" now manifests itself as a need to expend more work than would otherwise be the case, and the increase in entropy is

$$\Delta S = \frac{W_{\text{loss}}}{T} = \frac{|W| - |W°|}{T} > 0, \tag{10.53}$$

where T is now the temperature of the surroundings.

Similar conclusions apply in the case of a heat pump. For equal amounts of heat Q supplied, the amount of heat $|Q_0|$ extracted from the heat sink at T_0 becomes smaller in the case of irreversible operation, and the work required for operation increases accordingly. The loss and entropy increase are given by the same equations as for the refrigerator, except that in equation (10.53) T now denotes the temperature of the room being heated.

10.6.4 *Arbitrary reversible cycle*

With very few and insignificant exceptions, the operation of a real engine, refrigerator, or heat pump cannot be based on a Carnot cycle. The reasons for this being so are of a practical nature. Consequently, the operation of a real engine will approximate some other more complex cycle in which heat will be absorbed, or rejected during a process which is not necessarily isothermal. Thus, more than two sources of heat may be involved, and it becomes necessary to investigate the effect that this has on the efficiency of a power cycle, on the coefficient of performance of a refrigerator, or on the efficacy of a heat pump.

Accordingly, we consider first an arbitrary *reversible* power cycle C, shown schematically in Figure 10.17. It has been shown in Section 10.6.2 that during a power cycle some quantities of heat must be rejected in order to provide for an increase in the entropy of the respective heat reservoirs. It will thus be convenient to distinguish between the positive heat elements dQ^+ absorbed by the engine and the negative quantities dQ^- rejected by it. The principle of entropy increase now leads to the statement that for reversible operation

$$-\oint_C \frac{dQ^+}{T} + \oint_C \frac{|dQ^-|}{T} = 0. \tag{10.54}$$

The signs in the above equation have been adjusted to take into account that the source supplying heat dQ^+ loses entropy, whereas the source receiving heat dQ^- gains en-

---

† Since W and $W°$ are both negative quantities, we have

$$W < W°$$

if the symbols include the sign.

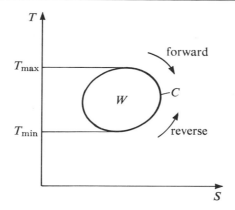

FIGURE 10.17. *Arbitrary reversible cycle.*

tropy. The line integrals are, evidently, taken around the cycle C. It is now convenient to replace the variable temperatures which occur in equation (10.54) by the maximum cycle temperature, T_{max}, for the positive quantities of heat, noting that

$$\oint_C \frac{dQ^+}{T} > \frac{\oint_C dQ^+}{T_{max}}.$$

Similarly, in the case of the negative heat quantities dQ^-, it is convenient to replace the variable temperature T by the minimum temperature of the cycle, T_{min}. Thus,

$$\oint \frac{|dQ^-|}{T} < \frac{\oint |dQ^-|}{T_{min}},$$

and equation (10.54) transforms into the inequality

$$\frac{|Q_0|}{T_{min}} - \frac{Q}{T_{max}} > 0,$$

where $Q = \oint dQ^+$ and $|Q_0| = |\oint dQ^-|$. It follows that the efficiency of this arbitrary reversible cycle

$$\eta = \frac{Q - |Q_0|}{Q}$$

satisfies the inequality

$$\eta < \frac{T_{max} - T_{min}}{T_{max}} = \eta_{Carnot}. \tag{10.55}$$

Hence, it is seen that the efficiency of any reversible power cycle is smaller than the efficiency of a Carnot cycle operating between the source of highest and the sink of lowest temperature available.

This result carries with it the practical rule that from the point of view of power production it is always advantageous to supply as much of the positive heat as possible close to the highest temperature available, and to reject as much of the waste heat as closely to the temperature of the surroundings as is feasible. This result is understandable, because, in the limit, when all the heat is added at the maximum temperature, T_{max}, and all the heat is rejected at the minimum temperature, T_{min}, the cycle transforms into a reversible Carnot cycle whose efficiency is highest.

Any departures from reversible operation will cause additional increases in entropy and hence a further reduction in efficiency.

Following a similar line of argument in the case of reverse operation, it is not difficult to demonstrate that the coefficient of performance, or the efficacy of any reversible cycle consuming work, is less than the corresponding values for a reversed Carnot cycle operating between the maximum and minimum temperatures of the given cycle, and that a further reduction occurs in irreversible operation.

The importance of the Carnot cycle can now be appreciated; in spite of the fact that Carnot cycles cannot be readily realized in practice, they provide a standard of comparison against which real engines, refrigerators or heat pumps can be judged. The performance of the latter is judged in relation to how closely they approach the ideal performance of corresponding Carnot cycles.

10.6.5   Regenerative cycle

When a reversible Carnot cycle is performed, the two reversible isothermal processes are bridged by two isentropic processes along which no heat is exchanged. In some cases it is convenient to replace the isentropics by different reversible processes during which elements of heat dQ are exchanged at all intermediate processes. Such a cycle is seen sketched in Figure 10.18(a). When this is the case, it is often advantageous so to arrange the two processes 12 and 34 that the elements of heat dQ, absorbed during one process and rejected during the other, are equal at equal temperatures. This will occur when all along the processes the areas subtended by the two steps in the process confined between any isotherm T and the neighboring isotherm $T + dT$ are equal, as shown in the sketch by the two shaded areas. In order to secure this property, the two processes 12 and 34 must be represented by identical curves in the T, S diagram, one being merely displaced with respect to the other in the direction of the entropy axis. A cycle of this kind can be performed in one of two ways. Normally, sources and sinks will be provided to secure the necessary heat exchange. In the example sketched, Figure 10.18(b), sources will be required along path 12 and sinks will be necessary along the return path 34. Thus, the heat absorbed by the cycle will consist of that added along 12, denoted by $Q_{1,2}$ (area $12ba$), and the isothermal heat $Q_{2,3}$ (area $b23d$). The heat rejected will consist of that extracted along 34 (area $34cd$), and the isothermal heat $Q_{4,1}$ (area $41ac$). It is seen from the diagram that under the present conditions

$$Q_{1,2} = |Q_{3,4}|,$$

and that, therefore

$$W = Q_{2,3} - |Q_{4,1}|,$$

since the heats $Q_{1,2} = -Q_{3,4}$ cancel when all the quantities of heat are added around the

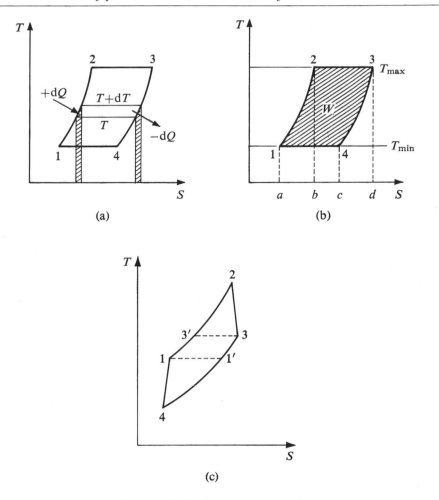

FIGURE 10.18. *Regenerative cycle.*

cycle. The efficiency of the cycle will be

$$\eta = \frac{Q_{2,3} - |Q_{4,1}|}{Q_{1,2} + Q_{2,3}}.\qquad(10.56)$$

This cycle constitutes a particular case of the general reversible cycle, and, therefore, its efficiency must be inferior to that of the corresponding Carnot cycle spanning the temperatures $T_{\max}$ and $T_{\min}$. Hence,

$$\eta < \frac{T_{\max} - T_{\min}}{T_{\max}}.\qquad(10.57)$$

The same cycle can be operated differently and advantage can be taken of the fact that the quantity of heat $Q_{3,4}$ rejected during one phase is equal to the heat $Q_{1,2}$ required during another phase. Moreover, at any temperature T, the element of heat rejected at that temperature along 34 is exactly equal to the element of heat dQ re-

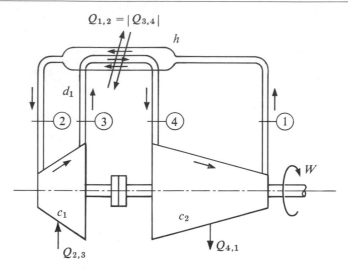

FIGURE 10.19. *Heat regeneration.*

quired along 12 at the same temperature. It is, therefore, possible to supply heat along 12 by utilizing the heat rejected along 34. This can be achieved in one of two ways. First the quantities of heat $-dQ$ rejected along 34 can be stored in an infinite number of heat reservoirs, each element being stored at the appropriate temperature T; these quantities of heat can subsequently be retrieved at the appropriate temperature when the system performs process 12, the transfer of heat occurring reversibly, that is with a zero temperature drop. Alternatively, when the whole cycle is realized in a steady-flow system in a manner similar to that described earlier in Section 9.4 and illustrated in Figure 10.19 (where a turbine c_1 and a turbocompressor c_2 are used), it is possible to employ a *counterflow heat exchanger* which facilitates the transfer of heat between the two processes, 34 and 12. The working fluid at state 2 is passed through cylinder c_1 which changes its state to 3 by expansion. It continues to flow through the duct d_1, where its state is changed to 4 and then through cylinder c_2 where it is further changed to state 1 by compression. The fluid is then passed through the heat exchanger h, where it is made to absorb heat $Q_{3,4}$ in counterflow from the fluid flowing from 3 to 4. Since $T_2 = T_3$ and $T_1 = T_4$, heat can be, at least in principle, exchanged completely reversibly.

The preceding manner of utilizing the heat rejected in one part of the cycle in order to absorb it in another is known as *heat regeneration* (also called "recuperation"). The advantage of employing heat regeneration becomes apparent when the efficiency of such a regenerative cycle is computed. The "expensive" heat now consists only of heat $Q_{2,3}$, but the work remains unaltered. Hence,

$$\eta_{\text{reg}} = \frac{Q_{2,3} - |Q_{4,1}|}{Q_{2,3}}. \tag{10.56a}$$

Thus

$$\eta_{\text{reg}} > \eta.$$

Moreover, as is easy to see from the consideration of the areas in Figure 10.18(b),[†] the efficiency of the regenerative cycle becomes equal to that of a Carnot cycle spanning T_{max} and T_{min}. Alternatively, it is seen that the change in entropy of the system consisting of the engine and all the sources is

$$\Delta S = \int_1^2 \frac{dQ}{T} + \frac{Q_{2,3}}{T_{max}} + \int_3^4 \frac{dQ}{T} + \frac{Q_{4,1}}{T_{min}} = 0.$$

However, for a regenerative cycle

$$\int_1^2 \frac{dQ}{T} + \int_3^4 \frac{dQ}{T} = 0,$$

and

$$\frac{Q_{2,3}}{T_{max}} - \frac{|Q_{4,1}|}{T_{min}} = 0,$$

from which it follows that

$$\eta_{reg} = \frac{Q_{2,3} - |Q_{4,1}|}{Q_{2,3}} = \frac{T_{max} - T_{min}}{T_{max}} = \eta_{Carnot}. \tag{10.57a}$$

Herein lies the great advantage of using heat regeneration in practice.

Heat cannot always be regenerated as completely as in the ideal cycle discussed previously. For example, when the processes 23 and 41 are not isothermal, Figure 10.18(c), heat regeneration can only be used along 13′ and 31′, always assuming that the paths 13′ and 31′ are identical in shape.

Heat regeneration is used to great practical advantage in gas turbines and in steam turbines.[‡] It is clear, however, that in practice ideal regeneration of the kind described here will not be feasible. Consequently, in practical applications, the improvements in efficiency achieved by this means falls short of the ideal, and the resulting efficiency is smaller than the corresponding Carnot efficiency.

List of Symbols for Chapter 10

Latin letters

C	Constant
E	Energy
$\mathbf{F}$	Vector associated with an arbitrary Pfaffian
G	Weight
g	Function defined in equation (10.36)
g_1, g_2	Functions defined in equations (10.16a)
$\mathbf{G}$	Stretched vector associated with integrable Pfaffian
h	Height
h	Function defined in equation (10.36)

[†] The two areas $a14c$ ($Q_{4,1}$) and $b23d$ ($Q_{2,3}$) have equal width, $14 = 23$, and their heights are proportional to T_{min} and T_{max}, respectively.
[‡] Schmidt, E., *Thermodynamics*, translated by J. Kestin, (Oxford: Clarendon Press, 1949), pp. 165, 252, and 386.

i	Unit vector
j	Unit vector
K	Function defined in equation (10.20)
k	Parameter, equation (10.6)
k'	Parameter
k	Unit vector
M	Functional coefficient in Pfaffian, defined in equation (10.3)
N	Functional coefficient in Pfaffian, defined in equation (10.3)
n	Number of subsystems in system; number of independent variables
P	Functional coefficient in Pfaffian, defined in equation (10.15); pressure
Q	Heat; functional coefficient in Pfaffian, defined in equation (10.15)
R	Functional coefficient in Pfaffian, defined in equation (10.15)
S	Entropy
s	Vectorial coordinate
T	Temperature on thermodynamic scale
T_3	Thermodynamic temperature at triple point of water
U	Internal energy
U	Potential defined on p. 470
V	Volume
W	Work
W_{loss}	Work "lost," defined in equation (10.46)
w	Intergrand in Pfaffian expression, equation (10.4)
X_i	Representative functional coefficient in Pfaffian, defined on p. 469
X_j	Representative functional coefficient in Pfaffian, defined on p. 469
x	Coordinate
x'	Coordinate
x_i	Representative independent variable
Y_i	Generalized force
y	Coordinate
y'	Coordinate
Z_i	Generalized displacement
z	Coordinate
z'	Coordinate

Greek letters

ϵ	Coefficient of performance of refrigerator (See Chapter 9)
ϵ_f	Efficacy of heat pump (See Chapter 9)
η	Efficiency
η_r	Relative efficiency
θ	Temperature on empirical scale
θ_3	Empirical temperature at triple point of water
λ	Integrating denominator $(=1/\mu)$
μ	Integrating factor $(=1/\lambda)$
μ'	Integrating factor
ν	Integrating factor
Φ	Potential associated with integrable Pfaffian

ϕ Potential associated with integrable Pfaffian

ψ Potential for orthogonal family of curves; arbitrary function defining a surface, equation (10.21)

Subscripts

irr   Refers to irreversible process or cycle

reg   Refers to regenerative process

Superscripts

°   Refers to reversible process or cycle

CHAPTER 11

The Calculation of Entropy
and Entropy Diagrams

Whether we choose to introduce the concept of entropy by the elementary methods of Clausius, by the Born-Carathéodory, more elegant formulation of the Second Law of thermodynamics, or by the postulational method, we come to the conclusion that the difference in the entropy of a uniform system between two equilibrium states 1 and 2 must be computed with the aid of the Clausius integral

$$S_2 - S_1 = \int_1^2 \frac{\mathrm{d}Q^\circ}{T} \quad \text{(along reversible path)}, \tag{11.1}$$

where $\mathrm{d}Q^\circ$ denotes the heat exchanged along a *reversible* path, and where T denotes the *thermodynamic* temperature. Owing to the importance of this detail in thermodynamics, we emphasize once again that the use of the concept of the entropy implies that the properties of the system under consideration are understood well enough for us to be in a position to *indicate* a reversible path between any two states 1 and 2. As already intimated in Section 4.6, this is not always the case; thus, in order to apply the equations of thermodynamics to such systems, research must be directed towards *identifying* such a reversible path.

In equation (11.1), it is possible to assign an arbitrary value $S_1 = S^*$ to state 1 if the latter is chosen as a reference state. Thus, at any state

$$S = \int_{\text{reference state}}^{\text{any state}} \frac{\mathrm{d}Q^\circ}{T} + S^* \tag{11.1a}$$

along any reversible path from the reference state (with asterisk) to the arbitrary state (without asterisk). We further remind the reader that the path of integration need not be related to the process under consideration; the former *must* be reversible, the latter need not.

In some cases the expression for the reversible heat $\mathrm{d}Q^\circ$ may not be known. If, however, the expressions for the change $\mathrm{d}E$ in the energy of the system and the reversible work $\mathrm{d}W^\circ$ are known, we can utilize the First Law of thermodynamics

$$\mathrm{d}Q^\circ = \mathrm{d}E + \mathrm{d}W^\circ, \tag{11.2}$$

and write

$$S = \int\limits_{\text{reference state}}^{\text{any state}} \frac{dE + dW^{\circ}}{T} + S^{*} \qquad \text{(along any reversible path).} \qquad (11.1b)$$

When dQ°, dE, and dW° are known, that equation is chosen which leads to a more convenient integration.

In order to illustrate the applications of the preceding equations, we now propose to derive expressions for the change in the entropy of two simple systems, and then for several irreversible processes.

11.1   Incompressible fluids and perfect gases

As our first example, we shall derive expressions for the entropy of incompressible fluids (or incompressible solids subjected to a uniform external pressure) and perfect gases. The thermal equation of state of an incompressible fluid (or solid) is $v = \text{const}$, and that for a perfect gas is $PV = mRT$. The latter is true on the stipulation that the perfect-gas temperature is identical with the thermodynamic temperature. A proof of this important relation will be given in Section 12.3, and a more careful treatment of the present problem will only subsequently become possible. For the present, and for the sake of acquiring practice in applications, we shall be satisfied with a more heuristic argument.

In incompressible fluids and perfect gases, equation (11.1b) assumes the form

$$S_2 - S_1 = \int_1^2 \frac{dU + P\,dV}{T}, \qquad (11.3)$$
$$\text{any reversible path}$$

which is equivalent to

$$S_2 - S_1 = \int_1^2 \frac{dH - V\,dP}{T} \qquad (11.4)$$

as already anticipated in equation (9.51b). The preference for equation (11.4) over equation (11.3) is of a pedagogical nature only, there being no fundamental difference between them.

In order to perform the integration, it is necessary to express the enthalpy and the volume in terms of pressure P and, preferably, temperature T. This naturally poses the question about the extent to which the thermal equation of state determines the system's enthalpy. A rigorous answer to this question must also be deferred (to Sections 12.2 and 12.6), but it is clear at this stage that some relation of this kind must exist. In order to bring it into evidence, we shall employ W. Nusselt's[†] method of elementary cycles which makes use of the proposition that the areas encompassed by reversible cycles must be equal in the P, v and T, s diagrams.

[†] *Forsch. Gebiete Ingenieurw.*, **3** (1932), 173.

11.1.1   One of Maxwell's reciprocal relations

The elementary cycle to be considered is seen sketched in Figure 11.1. It consists of two reversible isobaric processes at $P = \text{const}$ and $P + dP = \text{const}$, respectively; the remaining two processes are chosen to be isothermal, one at $T = \text{const}$ and the other at $T + dT = \text{const}$. The area enclosed by this cycle in the P, v diagram is, to first order, equal to $dP \cdot dv$. Similarly, the corresponding area in the T, s diagram, also to first order, is equal to $ds \cdot dT$. A close study of the diagram in Figure 11.1 reveals that the cycle is traversed in a clockwise direction in the P, v diagram and in a counter-clockwise direction in the T, s diagram. Therefore,

$$dP \cdot dv = -ds \cdot dT. \qquad (11.5)$$

From the existence of the equations of state $v(T, P)$ and $s(P, T)$, it follows that along the isobar in the P, v diagram we must have

$$dv = \left(\frac{\partial v}{\partial T}\right)_P dT,$$

and, similarly, along the isothermal in the T, s diagram, we have

$$ds = \left(\frac{\partial s}{\partial P}\right)_T dP.$$

Substitution into equation (11.5) shows that the equality of the areas demands that

$$\left(\frac{\partial v}{\partial T}\right)_P dT \cdot dP = -\left(\frac{\partial s}{\partial P}\right)_T dP \cdot dT,$$

that is, that

$$\left(\frac{\partial s}{\partial P}\right)_T = -\left(\frac{\partial v}{\partial T}\right)_P. \qquad (11.6)$$

This is an example of one of *Maxwell's reciprocal relations* which will be studied systematically in Section 12.1. It will then transpire that a pure substance obeys a

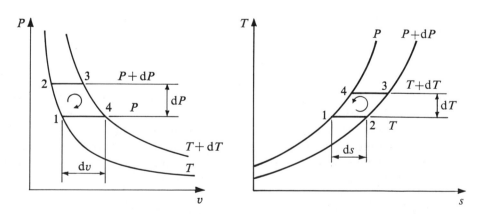

FIGURE 11.1. *Elementary derivation of one of Maxwell's reciprocal relations.*

total of four reciprocal relations of this type. Readers familiar with the properties of Jacobians can obtain it directly from the fact that

$$\frac{\partial(T,\,s)}{\partial(P,\,v)} = 1;$$

hence,

$$\left(\frac{\partial s}{\partial P}\right)_T = -\frac{\partial(T,\,s)}{\partial(P,\,T)} = -\frac{\partial(P,\,v)}{\partial(P,\,T)} = -\left(\frac{\partial v}{\partial T}\right)_P.$$

11.1.2 *Dependence of internal energy and enthalpy on pressure*

We can now revert to equation (9.51b) in its differential form

$$\mathrm{d}h = T\,\mathrm{d}s + v\,\mathrm{d}P$$

for a unit mass of substance, and apply it to a reversible, isothermal process, whence

$$\left(\frac{\partial h}{\partial P}\right)_T = T\left(\frac{\partial s}{\partial P}\right)_T + v. \tag{11.7}$$

Application of Maxwell's equation (11.6) allows us to express the rate of change of enthalpy with pressure at constant temperature in terms of quantities which are derivable from the thermal equation of state $v = v(P, T)$. Hence,

$$\left(\frac{\partial h}{\partial P}\right)_T = -T\left(\frac{\partial v}{\partial T}\right)_P + v. \tag{11.8}$$

We apply this relation in turn to an incompressible fluid or solid and to a perfect gas. In the former case, $v = $ const, and

$$\left(\frac{\partial h}{\partial P}\right)_T = v = \text{const.} \tag{11.9}$$

This proves that the enthalpy of an incompressible fluid or solid must be a linear function of pressure, as can be verified by direct integration. We integrate from a reference state to a current state and realize that the constant of integration must be a function of temperature. Hence,

$$h - h^* = \int_{P^*}^{P} \left(\frac{\partial h}{\partial P}\right)_T \mathrm{d}P + \phi(T) = v(P - P^*) + \phi(T). \tag{11.10}$$

The enthalpy of an incompressible fluid or solid is the sum of a linear function of pressure and an undetermined function of temperature. The function $\phi(T)$ is not determined by the equation of state $v = v(P, T)$, and additional measurements are required to find it.

The internal energy $u = h - Pv$ can now be computed directly from equation (11.10):

$$u - u^* = (h - Pv) - (h^* - P^*v) = \phi(T). \tag{11.11}$$

Thus, the internal energy of a perfect fluid turns out to be a function of temperature alone by virtue of the application of the Second Law of thermodynamics in the form of Maxwell's equation (11.6) and the equation of state $v = $ const.

The preceding fact formed our point of departure in Section 7.2 in which it was shown that, as a further consequence,

$$c_p = c_v = c,$$

with

$$\mathrm{d}u(T) = c(T)\,\mathrm{d}T \quad \text{and} \quad \mathrm{d}h(P, T) = c(T)\,\mathrm{d}T + v\,\mathrm{d}P. \qquad (11.12\text{a, b})$$

The integrals of these equations were noted in equations (7.12) and (7.13).

We now turn to the perfect gas $(Pv = RT)$ and establish with the aid of equation (11.8) that

$$\left(\frac{\partial h}{\partial P}\right)_T = 0. \qquad (11.13)$$

Here, the enthalpy h is treated as function $h(P, T)$ of pressure and temperature, and the vanishing of the derivative signifies that the pressure P does not, in fact, appear. Thus, the enthalpy of a perfect gas depends on temperature alone. The same is, evidently, true of the internal energy, $u = h - Pv$, of a perfect gas because the product $Pv = RT$ itself is a function of temperature alone. Considering u as a function of pressure and temperature, $u = u(P, T)$, we can write at once

$$\left(\frac{\partial u}{\partial P}\right)_T = 0. \qquad (11.14)$$

The same is also true if we treat the internal energy of a perfect gas as a function of temperature and specific volume $u = u(v, T)$, and we can write

$$\left(\frac{\partial u}{\partial v}\right)_T = 0. \qquad (11.14\text{a})$$

However, in the variables $u = u(P, v)$, we cannot assert that the derivatives vanish, and must write

$$\left(\frac{\partial u}{\partial P}\right)_v \neq 0 \qquad \left(\frac{\partial u}{\partial v}\right)_P \neq 0. \qquad (11.14\text{b})$$

The preceding facts were assumed provisionally in Section 7.3 and led to the conclusion that

$$\mathrm{d}u(T) = c_v(T)\,\mathrm{d}T, \quad \mathrm{d}h(T) = c_p(T)\,\mathrm{d}T \quad \text{and} \quad c_p(T) - c_v(T) = R.$$

In selecting values for the specific heats account must be taken of the fact that the perfect-gas law is an asymptotic one and that it represents the properties of real gases in the limit of $P \to 0$. Hence, the specific heats must also be extrapolated to zero pressure, and to emphasize this fact we shall provide them as well as their integrals with a superscript °. In this new notation, the preceding equations and their integrals will be written

$$\mathrm{d}u^\circ(T) = c_v^\circ(T)\,\mathrm{d}T \qquad u^\circ(T) = \int_{T^*}^{T} c_v^\circ(T)\,\mathrm{d}T \qquad (11.15\text{a, b})$$

$$\mathrm{d}h^\circ(T) = c_p^\circ(T)\,\mathrm{d}T \qquad h^\circ(T) = \int_{T^*}^{T} c_p^\circ(T)\,\mathrm{d}T \qquad (11.16\text{a, b})$$

$$c_p^\circ(T) - c_v^\circ(T) = R. \qquad (11.17)$$

This notation has already been used in Table XVI.

When constant values of the specific heats are chosen, a suitable average value is selected.

The vanishing of the derivative $(\partial u/\partial P)_T$ in equation (11.14) may appear to contradict the result of the Frandsen experiment contained in equation (6.84). This contradiction is, however, only superficial, because the result of the Frandsen experiment refers to a *real* gas. The discrepancy between these two equations merely poses the question as to how far is it possible to use equations derived from the perfect-gas law to represent the properties of real gases. The reader will find a complete answer to this vexing question in Volume II.

The second doubt arises from the realization that in certain circumstances the properties of a gas can be approximated by those of an incompressible fluid. In a perfect gas both enthalpy *and* internal energy depend on temperature alone, equations (11.15a, b) and (11.16a, b), whereas for an incompressible fluid, only the internal energy is a function of temperature, the enthalpy depending on *both* pressure and temperature, equations (11.12a, b). Thus, when the incompressible fluid approximation is applied to a gas, the reader may be in doubt as to whether to assign to it the properties expressed in equations (11.12a, b) or those expressed in equations (11.15a, b) and (11.16a, b). A moment's thought shows that this is a matter of consistency and that there is no choice. The Second Law of thermodynamics demands that the approximations for internal energy and enthalpy must be consistent with the approximation used for the thermal equation of state *in a given problem*. Thus, in a flow problem involving a gas, equations (11.12a, b) must be used if the assumption $v = \text{const}$ has been made. When another flow problem is studied, the new constant specific volume may be computed from $Pv = RT$; this implies that on changing problems, the function $\phi(T)$ in equations (11.10) and (11.11) must be chosen with reference to the new range of states which the gas is expected to traverse in the new problem.

A similar doubt arises in connection with the specific heat. A gas is characterized by two specific heats, c_p and c_v, whose values differ considerably, whereas an incompressible fluid is characterized by a single specific heat, c. Thus, when the incompressible-fluid approximation is used for a gas, a suitable choice must be made. This choice must be related to the range of states encountered in the problem. In fluid mechanics, the values of the single specific heat $c(T)$ are replaced by those of $c_p(T)$. Similar problems involving the flow of liquids do not pose the same quandary because their thermodynamic properties are much closer to the adopted model; in particular, the difference between their two specific heats, c_p and c_v, is genuinely negligible.

Before returning to the problem of calculating entropy, it is necessary once more to remind the reader that the derivations of this section were predicated on the fact that the thermodynamic temperature T is identical with the perfect-gas temperature θ. The proof of this is still outstanding, but the reader should notice that the reasoning in Section 12.3, where it is given, is independent of the present conclusions, and could be given immediately after Chapters 9 or 10; it has been deferred for pedagogical reasons only.

11.1.3   Entropy

Equations (11.12b) and (11.15b) in conjunction with equation (11.4) permit us now to perform the integration for entropy explicitly.

For an *incompressible fluid* (or solid compressed uniformly)

$$dS = \frac{mc\,dT}{T},\qquad (11.18)$$

and

$$S_2 - S_1 = m \int_1^2 \frac{c(T)}{T}\,dT = m \int_1^2 c\,d\ln T.\qquad (11.18a)$$

The function

$$s(T) = \int \frac{c(T)}{T}\,dT$$

must be tabulated, because the relation $c(T)$ is usually quite complex. It can be obtained graphically as an area of c *versus* $\ln T$, as is seen from equation (11.18a). When $c = $ const is assumed, the integration can be carried out explicitly, and yields

$$S_2 - S_1 = mc\,\ln T_2/T_1.\qquad (11.18b)$$

It is remarkable that the entropy of an incompressible fluid or solid is a *function of temperature alone*.

For an *ideally perfect gas*, with $V/T = mR/P$, we obtain

$$dS = m\left\{c_p\,\frac{dT}{T} - R\,\frac{dP}{P}\right\}.\qquad (11.19)$$

Here $c_p = $ const, and integration could proceed at once, except for the fact that it is customary to introduce the ratio of specific heats,

$$\gamma = c_p/c_v.$$

In fact, since $R = c_p - c_v$, we have

$$\frac{R}{c_p} = \frac{c_p - c_v}{c_p} = \frac{\gamma - 1}{\gamma},\qquad (11.20)$$

and equation (11.19) can be transformed to

$$dS = mc_p\left\{\frac{dT}{T} - \frac{\gamma - 1}{\gamma}\,\frac{dP}{P}\right\}.\qquad (11.19a)$$

The integral of this equation is

$$S_2 - S_1 = mc_p\,\ln\left\{\frac{T_2/P_2^{\frac{\gamma-1}{\gamma}}}{T_1/P_1^{\frac{\gamma-1}{\gamma}}}\right\};\qquad (11.19b)$$

in it, the entropy difference is expressed in terms of the variables P and T. It is convenient to record the equivalent forms of this equation in terms of the pairs of variables P, v and v, T. This is best done with the aid of the logarithmic form of the perfect-gas law:

$$\frac{dP}{P} + \frac{dv}{v} = \frac{dT}{T}\qquad (11.20a)$$

and by eliminating first dT/T and then dP/P from equation (11.19a). In this manner, we obtain for $S(v, P)$ the differential form

$$dS = m\left\{c_p \frac{dv}{v} + c_v \frac{dP}{P}\right\} = mc_v\left\{\gamma \frac{dv}{v} + \frac{dP}{P}\right\}. \tag{11.21}$$

Upon integration, we are led to the desired relation

$$S_2 - S_1 = mc_v \ln\left\{\frac{P_2 v_2^\gamma}{P_1 v_1^\gamma}\right\}. \tag{11.21a}$$

In an entirely analogous sequence of steps, by eliminating dP/P from equation (11.21), we would derive

$$dS = m\left\{c_v \frac{dT}{T} + R \frac{dv}{v}\right\} = mc_v\left\{(\gamma - 1)\frac{dv}{v} + \frac{dT}{T}\right\}, \tag{11.22}$$

which integrates to

$$S_2 - S_1 = mc_v \ln \frac{T_2 v_2^{\gamma - 1}}{T_1 v_1^{\gamma - 1}}. \tag{11.22a}$$

In the case of a *semiperfect gas*, it is not common to introduce the ratio γ into the expressions, and integration is normally performed only for the pairs of variables T, v and T, P. The differential form (11.19) is still valid, except that now c_p is a function of temperature, and that the extrapolated values c_p° ought to be used. Direct integration of equation (11.19) yields

$$S_2 - S_1 = m\left\{\int_{T^*}^{T_2} \frac{c_p^\circ(T)}{T} dT - \int_{T^*}^{T_1} \frac{c_p^\circ(T)}{T} dT - R \ln\frac{P_2}{P_1}\right\}.$$

The function

$$s_p^\circ(T) = \int_{T^*}^{T} \frac{c_p^\circ(T)}{T} dT \tag{11.23}$$

is usually tabulated for various gases and for an agreed reference temperature T^*. Tables XVI have been constructed for $T^* = 0°K$, and with this notation the entropy equation assumes the convenient form

$$S_2 - S_1 = m\left\{s_p^\circ(T_2) - s_p^\circ(T_1) - R \ln\frac{P_2}{P_1}\right\}. \tag{11.24}$$

Similarly, by eliminating dP/P with the aid of equation (11.20a), which retains its validity, we can write

$$ds = \frac{c_v^\circ(T)dT}{T} + R \frac{dv}{v}. \tag{11.25}$$

Introducing the second auxiliary function

$$s_v^\circ = \int_{T^*}^{T} \frac{c_v^\circ(T)}{T} dT, \tag{11.25a}$$

we obtain the required equation in the form

$$S_2 - S_1 = m\left\{s_v^\circ(T_2) - s_v^\circ(T_1) + R \ln\frac{v_2}{v_1}\right\}. \tag{11.25b}$$

The relation between the auxiliary functions $s_p^\circ(T)$ and $s_v^\circ(T)$ which are known as *standard entropies* at constant pressure and volume, respectively, as well as the reasons for these terms will be explored more fully in Volume II; we shall then also be in a position to determine the behavior of the integrands $c_p^\circ(T)/T$ and $c_v^\circ(T)/T$ in the limit when $T \to 0$, and to show that the integrals are convergent. The auxiliary function $s_v^\circ(T)$ is used only seldom.

It is convenient to write down for future reference the forms which are assumed by equations (11.24) and (11.25b) when molar units are employed:

$$S_2 - S_1 = n\{s_p^\circ(T_2) - s_p^\circ(T_1) - \mathbf{R} \ln P_2/P_1\} \qquad (11.26a)$$

and

$$S_2 - S_1 = n\{s_v^\circ(T_2) - s_v^\circ(T_1) + \mathbf{R} \ln v_2/v_1\}. \qquad (11.26b)$$

Evidently, the molar standard entropies are not the same as those computed for mass units, because molar specific heats must be used in their definitions. In order to obtain the values for mass units, it is sufficient to divide the molar quantities by the molecular mass M of the gas.

Before turning to the next topic, we wish to draw the reader's attention to the fact that the entropy of a compressible perfect gas, unlike that of an incompressible fluid, is *not* a function of temperature alone; it depends on *temperature* and on *pressure* or *volume*, in addition.

The preceding equations allow us to obtain a solution to the problem of finding the equation of an isentropic process which was discussed in an elementary way in Section 5.14.5. Remembering that $dS = 0$ for such a process, we can deduce at once that for an ideally perfect gas, equations (11.19b), (11.21a), and (11.22a) lead to the three equivalent relations:

$$T/P^{\frac{\gamma-1}{\gamma}} = K_1, \quad Pv^\gamma = K_2, \quad Tv^{\gamma-1} = K_3, \qquad (11.26c, d, e)$$

where K_1, K_2, and K_3 are constants whose value is determined by the properties at the initial state.

Similarly, equations (11.26a) and (11.26b) allow us to establish analogous relations for a semiperfect gas. Thus, in T, P or T, v coordinates, we have

$$\frac{P}{P_1} = \frac{\exp[s_p^\circ(T)/\mathbf{R}]}{\exp[s_p^\circ(T_1)/\mathbf{R}]} \quad \text{or} \quad \frac{v}{v_1} = \frac{\exp[-s_v^\circ(T)/\mathbf{R}]}{\exp[-s_v^\circ(T_1)/\mathbf{R}]},$$

respectively. In order to facilitate calculations, the functions

$$p_r(T) = \exp[s_p^\circ(T)/\mathbf{R}] \quad \text{and} \quad v_r(T) = \exp[-s_v^\circ(T)/\mathbf{R}] \qquad (11.26f, g)$$

are usually tabulated, see Table XVI. With these abbreviations

$$\frac{P}{P_1} = \frac{p_r(T)}{p_r(T_1)} \quad \text{or} \quad \frac{v}{v_1} = \frac{v_r(T)}{v_r(T_1)}$$

along an isentrope passing through state 1, described by the parameters P_1, T_1, v_1. The symbols without subscript denote an arbitrary state along the isentrope passing through state 1, that is, they refer to the locus for which $s = s_1$.

11.2   Entropy and Mollier charts

The temperature-entropy, or heat diagram, mentioned in Section 9.12, and the enthalpy-entropy, or Mollier chart, give a very clear representation of the properties of pure substances, particularly in the neighborhood of the phase boundaries and in the vapor phase. Mollier diagrams have proved particularly useful in practice and were used widely in the design of steam plant and in refrigeration before the advent of digital computers.

The diagrams for perfect gases can be drawn easily because they possess very simple geometrical properties. The diagrams for pure substances must be discussed in purely descriptive terms; they are based on experimental results which cannot be represented by simple algebraic expressions. For the sake of being definite, we shall discuss principally the properties of steam, ignoring, however, the anomalies of water substance which have been adequately covered in Section 7.4.9. According to the resolution adopted by the Fifth International Conference on the Properties of Steam which met in 1956 in London, all tabulations and charts should be based on the convention that the enthalpy as well as the entropy of saturated water at the triple point is zero:

$$h_3' = s_3' = 0 \quad \text{at } P_3 = 0.006028 \text{ atm} \ (= 0.006112 \text{ bar}) \quad \text{and} \quad T_3 = 0.01°C. \quad (11.27)$$

11.2.1   The temperature-entropy diagram for an incompressible fluid and a perfect gas

The temperature-entropy diagram for an incompressible fluid or solid under uniform pressure cannot be drawn at all, because for them the entropy is a function of temperature alone, equation (11.18a). Hence, entropy and temperature do not constitute a pair of independent variables.

In the case of ideally perfect and semiperfect gases, the desired lines of constant internal energy, u, enthalpy, h, pressure, P, and specific volume, v, are drawn on the basis of the respective equation in terms of temperature T and entropy s. Lines of constant internal energy and enthalpy are identical with the horizontal isotherms, because both thermodynamic potentials are functions of temperature alone. The lines of constant specific volume, v, and pressure, P, are best deduced from the differential forms

$$ds = c_v \frac{dT}{T} + R \frac{dv}{v} = c_p \frac{dT}{T} - R \frac{dP}{P} \quad (11.28)$$

known to us from equations (11.22) and (11.19).

We begin with the simpler case of an ideally perfect gas (c_p = const; c_v = const). Choosing an arbitrary reference state P^*, v^*, T^* such that

$$P^* v^* = RT^*$$

and standardizing with

$$h^* = s^* = 0$$

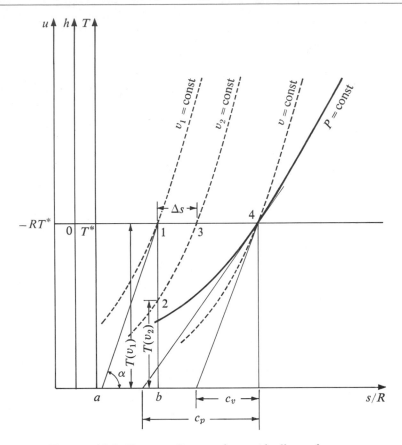

FIGURE 11.2. *Entropy diagram for an ideally perfect gas.*

at the reference state, we can write the integrals of equations (11.22) and (11.19) as

$$s(v,\, T) = c_v \ln \frac{T}{T^*} + R \ln \frac{v}{v^*}, \qquad (11.29a)$$

$$s(P,\, T) = c_p \ln \frac{T}{T^*} - R \ln \frac{P}{P^*}. \qquad (11.29b)$$

Evidently, these forms are entirely equivalent to those given earlier.

Mathematically, the two forms (11.29a) and (11.29b) are identical which shows that the gemoetrical properties of isochores do not differ from those of isobars, except for a change in constants and one change in sign.

A temperature-entropy diagram for an ideally perfect gas is shown in Figure 11.2. The isochores are represented by the equation

$$T = T^* \left(\frac{v^*}{v} \right)^{\gamma - 1} \exp(s/c_v) \qquad (11.30)$$

which is easily obtained from equation (11.29a). This demonstrates that isochores are exponential curves, and that a change from one value of the parameter v, say v_1, to another, say v_2, merely changes all abscissae in the ratio $T(v_2)/T(v_1) = (v_1/v_2)^{\gamma-1}$, as indicated in the sketch. This ratio is the same along both isochores. A deformation of all ordinates of an exponential curve by a constant factor is equivalent to a parallel bodily displacement of the curve in the direction of the axis of abscissae. Indeed, at constant temperature the difference

$$\Delta s = s_3 - s_1 = R \ln \frac{v_2}{v_1} \qquad (11.31)$$

is the same for two isochores, regardless of temperature. Thus, the horizontal distance between any two points on an isotherm intersecting the two isochores is the same.

Instead of tracing isochores in dimensional units, it is more convenient to express these as dimensionless multiples v/v^* of the reference volume v^*. Thus, along the reference isotherm

$$\frac{s}{R} = \ln \frac{v}{v^*} \qquad (T^* = \text{const}).$$

The existence of this relation allows us to add a logarithmic scale along the isotherm $T = T^*$ and to read off the values of these ratios from it, as shown in Figure 11.3, where s/R rather than s has been chosen as the abscissa. Alternatively, a sliding

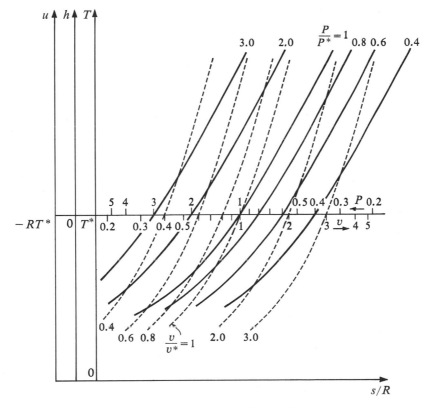

FIGURE 11.3. *Logarithmic scale for isochores.*

scale on a strip of paper can be employed and placed along any isotherm $T = \text{const}$ with unity coinciding with the intersection of $T = \text{const}$ with $v/v^* = 1$. In principle, only the isochore $v/v^* = 1$ need be drawn, and it is useful to remember that the values of v increase to the right.

It is not difficult to show that the subtangent of any exponential is a constant. In our case, Figure 11.2,

$$\overline{ab} = \frac{\overline{1b}}{\tan \alpha} = \frac{T}{(\partial T / \partial s)_v} = c_v$$

as seen from equation (11.28).

The equivalent statements for isobars can be formulated by analogy without further derivation. Isobars are the exponentials

$$T = T^* \left(\frac{P}{P^*} \right)^{\frac{\gamma - 1}{\gamma}} \exp(s/c_p) \tag{11.32}$$

so that their constant subtangents are equal to c_p as indicated in Figure 11.2. Since $c_p > c_v$† for any substance, isochores are steeper than isobars at a particular point in the diagram. The pressure increases to the left, and the logarithmic scale for it along $T^* = \text{const}$ is an inverted one.

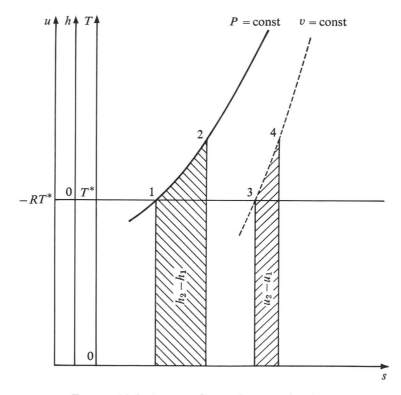

FIGURE 11.4. *Areas under isochores and isobars.*

† This is true for all substances, not just gases, see Section 12.5.

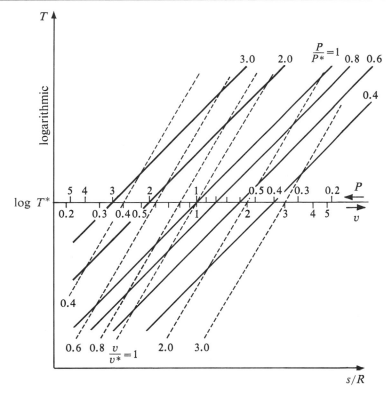

FIGURE 11.5. *Logarithmic diagram.*

Since the area under any curve which represents a reversible process in a T, s diagram is proportional to the heat $\int T ds$ exchanged during the process, provided that the scale for temperature is extended to absolute zero, it follows that areas under isobars represent changes in enthalpy and those under isochores represent changes in internal energy. This has been indicated in Figure 11.4.

Since the internal energy $u = c_v T - c_v T^*$ and the enthalpy $h = c_p T - c_p T^*$, it is convenient to add proportional scales for these properties, as indicated in Figures 11.2, 11.3, and 11.4.

The form of the equations for the isochores and isobars, equations (11.30) and (11.32), demonstrates that a geometrically simpler diagram can be obtained if $\log T$ is plotted instead of the temperature itself. Isochores and isobars then become families of parallel straight lines. Such a simplified diagram has been sketched in Figure 11.5. The ordinary diagram can be easily cross-plotted from the latter.

The modifications introduced by the variability of the specific heats of semiperfect gases with temperature into the structure of entropy diagrams are rather slight. The enthalpy and internal energy ceases to be proportional to the absolute temperature, but lines of $h = h^\circ = \text{const}$ as well as those of $u = u^\circ = \text{const}$ continue to coincide with the isotherms. The only difference is that now the scales for h and u cease to be proportional to T. Any one of the scales T, u, h can be chosen linear, and the remaining two can be established by reference to tables.

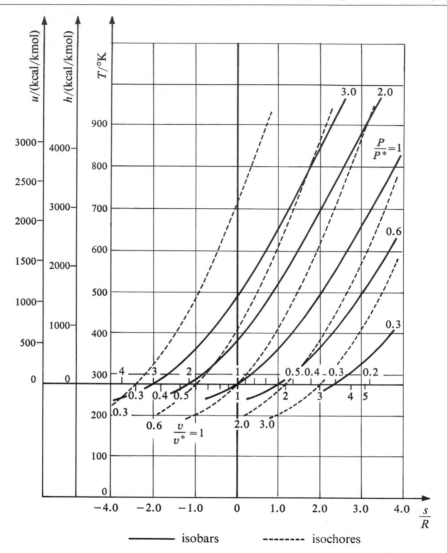

FIGURE 11.6. *T, s diagram for air treated as a semiperfect gas:* $T^* = 0°C$.

Isochores and isobars are described by the equations

$$s(v, T) = s_v^\circ(T) - s_v^\circ(T^*) + R \ln \frac{v}{v^*}, \qquad (11.33a)$$

$$s(P, T) = s_p^\circ(T) - s_p^\circ(T^*) - R \ln \frac{P}{P^*}, \qquad (11.33b)$$

that is, by equations (11.25b) and (11.24), with $s_p^\circ(T)$ tabulated. Since

$$s_v^\circ(T) = \int_{T^*}^T c_v \frac{dT}{T} = \int_{T^*}^T (c_p - R) \frac{dT}{T} = \int_{T^*}^T c_p \frac{dT}{T} - R \int_{T^*}^T \frac{dT}{T}, \qquad (11.34)$$

we have

$$s_v^\circ(T) - s_v^\circ(T^*) = s_p^\circ(T) - s_p^\circ(T^*) - R \ln T/T^*,$$

and $s_v^\circ(T) - s_v^\circ(T^*)$ can be calculated from tables, for example, from Tables XVI. These relations demonstrate that isobars and isochores cease to be exponential curves. On changing the value of the parameter v/v^* or P/P^*, the ordinates are no longer multiplied by a constant ratio, but the curves are still translated horizontally with reference to a logarithmic scale along $T = T^*$, in the same way as before. Since the differential forms in equation (11.28) are the same for ideally perfect and semiperfect gases, it is easily seen that the subtangents are proportional to $c_p(T)$ and $c_v(T)$ respectively, and the variation of these subtangents along an isochore or an isobar presents a graphic picture of the variation of the corresponding specific heat with temperature.

The sketch in Figure 11.6 represents a T, s diagram for air treated as a semiperfect gas with scales for enthalpy and internal energy. The diagram is easily drawn, because only the base curves $P/P^* = 1$ and $v/v^* = 1$ need to be plotted from tables; the others are obtained by translation. The reference state has been assumed at $T^* = 0°C$, the reference pressure P^* being arbitrary. Needless to add, in this as well as in the previous diagrams, one isochore intersects all isobars and vice versa, but each at one point only.

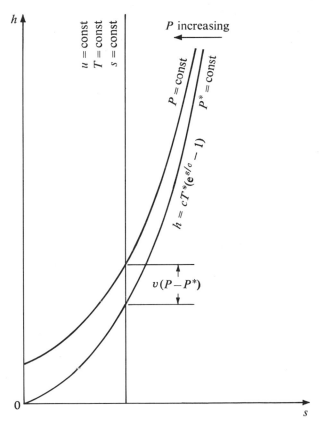

FIGURE 11.7. *Mollier diagram for an incompressible fluid.*

This is evident physically (it can also be verified mathematically), since a pair of values of pressure and specific volume determines uniquely one state.

Mollier (h, s) diagrams for gases do not differ materially from entropy (T, s) diagrams and need not be described.

The Mollier diagram for an incompressible fluid with $c = $ const is shown sketched in Figure 11.7. Since entropy is a function of temperature alone, isotherms are now vertical lines and the same is true about internal energy. Lines of constant density cannot be drawn, because $v = $ const everywhere. The equation of a line of constant pressure is obtained by the elimination of temperature from equations (11.18b) and (7.10). Replacing P_2 by P and P_1 by P^*, we find that

$$h = cT^*(e^{s/c} - 1) + v(P - P^*).\qquad(11.35)$$

This demonstrates that an isobar is an exponential curve and $P = P^* = $ const passes through $h = s = 0$ by definition of the reference state. The basic curve exp (s/c) must be

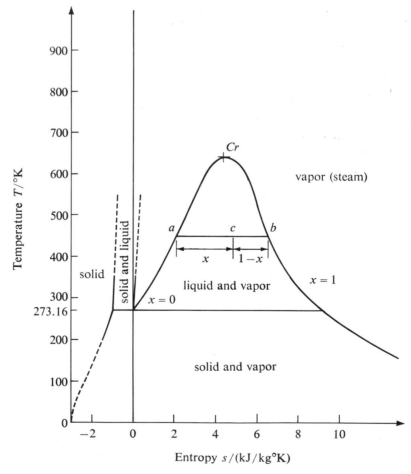

FIGURE 11.8. *Phase boundaries for H_2O in T, s diagram. (Anomalies and allotropic forms of ice ignored.)*

shifted vertically downwards by unity and multiplied by cT^* to obtain the isobar $P^* = $ const. Any other isobar is identical, except that it is displaced vertically by $v(P - P^*)$, that is, upwards for $P > P^*$ and downwards for $P < P^*$.

11.2.2   The temperature-entropy diagram for a pure substance

The phase boundaries of a pure substance in the T, s diagram are shown sketched in Figure 11.8. This diagram has been drawn for water, but its anomalies have been ignored. Similarly, the existence of allotropic forms of ice has been disregarded. The boundary curve which encircles the liquid-vapor region displays a characteristic domed shape with the critical point at its maximum. In this region, as well as in the remaining two two-phase regions, isotherms are also isobars. Furthermore, the intercept ab is divided by a state-point c into parts which are proportional to x and $1 - x$, respectively, in a manner analogous to Figure 7.9. As we remember, this is due to the fact that for wet steam

$$s = s' + x(s'' - s') = s'' - (1 - x)(s'' - s'). \tag{11.36}$$

Lines of constant dryness fraction are seen sketched in Figure 11.9. It is noteworthy that the line $x = 0.5$ is nearly an isentropic. Since an isothermal process is also isobaric, the reversible heat required to evaporate a unit mass of liquid, the latent heat of evaporation l, is equal to the enthalpy difference:

$$Q° = l = h'' - h';$$

hence, the change in entropy is

$$s'' - s' = \frac{Q°}{T} = \frac{l}{T}. \tag{11.37}$$

The usefulness of T, s diagrams turns on the circumstance that areas under reversible processes are equal to the (reversible) heat exchanged in their performance. The sketch in Figure 11.9 shows a typical, subcritical isobar P. The isobars are very close to the boundary curve in the liquid region, become horizontal in the two-phase region, and then slope upwards tending to an exponential shape characteristic of gases (Section 11.2.1). Area $abb'a'$ represents the heat added reversibly during the isobaric process of evaporation, ab. Thus, it represents the latent heat l of steam at pressure P (and the corresponding saturation temperature). Similarly, area $acc'a'$ represents the enthalpy difference $h_c - h'$ of wet steam at state c and the corresponding saturated water at a.

The heat required to turn saturated steam, state b, isobarically into superheated steam at state d is sometimes called the superheat; it is represented by area $bdd'b'$ which is also equal to the enthalpy difference $h_d - h''$. Along an isobar, $dh = T ds$ so that the specific heat

$$c_p = \left(\frac{\partial h}{\partial T}\right)_P = T\left(\frac{\partial s}{\partial T}\right)_P. \tag{11.38}$$

It is easy to show that the subtangent $d''d'$ intercepted by a tangent to the isobar at a point d is given by the same expression, as was done for a gas in Section 11.2.1.

The critical isobar has a point of inflection at the critical point and its tangent is therefore horizontal there. Thus, at the critical point itself the subtangent becomes

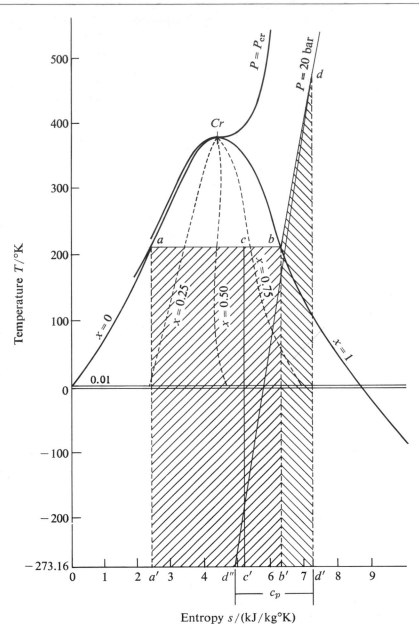

FIGURE 11.9. *Meaning of areas in T, s diagram and lines of constant dryness fraction.*

infinite, which shows that

$$c_p \to \infty \quad \text{at critical point.} \tag{11.39}$$

It is also infinite along the evaporation line *ab*.

Remembering that the area under an isochore, Figure 11.10, in a *T*, *s* diagram represents the difference between internal energies, we conclude that

$$u_b - u_a = \text{area } abb'a' = T \, ds \quad \text{along } v = \text{const.}$$

Remembering further that

$$c_v = \left(\frac{\partial u}{\partial T}\right)_v,$$

it is simple to show that the subtangent $b''b'$ of the isochore at point b represents the specific heat c_v of steam at state b, and that

$$c_v = T\left(\frac{\partial s}{\partial T}\right)_v. \tag{11.40}$$

The diagram of Figure 11.11 shows the course of isobars (full lines), isochores (broken lines), and isenthalpics (chain-dotted lines) for steam in a T, s diagram. The values of enthalpy can be calculated by measuring areas under isobars, and points of

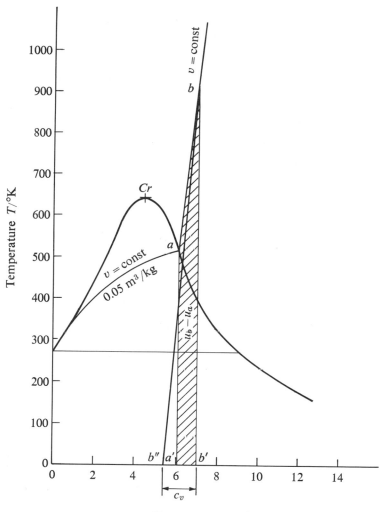

Entropy $s/(\text{kJ/kg}°\text{K})$

FIGURE 11.10. *An isochore.*

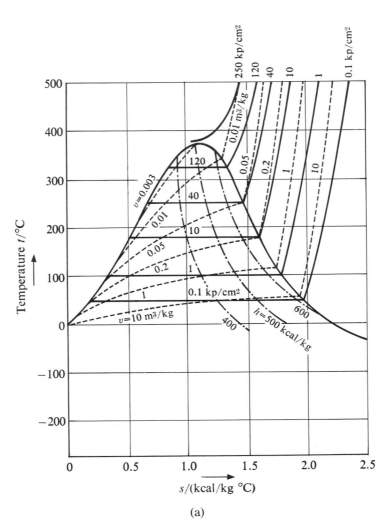

(a)

FIGURE 11.11. *Isobars (full lines), isochores (broken lines) and isenthalpics (chain-dotted*

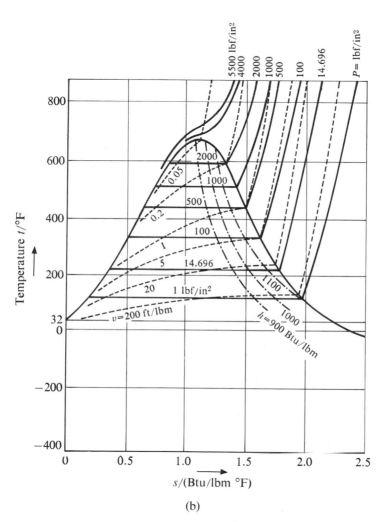

(b)

ines) of steam in a T, s diagram, drawn approximately to scale. (a) Metric units. (b) British units.

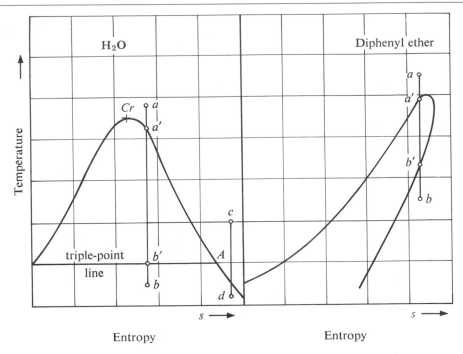

FIGURE 11.12. *The dome for diphenyl ether compared with that of water.*

equal enthalpy can be formed into isenthalpics. In the region of superheated steam, the isenthalpics converge asymptotically to the shape of isotherms. The isochores in the superheated region are similar in shape to isobars, except that their course is steeper.

As the states become further removed from the two-phase region with pressure decreasing, the isobars, isochores, and isenthalpics progressively assume the shapes and regularities which are characteristic for a perfect gas.

The domes of certain organic fluids, for example, diphenyl ether, possess a somewhat different shape which is displayed in Figure 11.12. With such substances it is possible to expand a gas isentropically, state a in the figure, cause it to liquefy completely at a' and subsequently to evaporate at b' ending the process at b in the superheated vapor region. No such possibility exists in water in which isentropic expansion always leads to the appearance of liquid droplets at a' or of snow if the process starts at an entropy which exceeds that at point A, as illustrated by the isentropic cd in the diagram.

11.2.3   *The Mollier chart for a pure substance*

The enthalpy-entropy diagram introduced into engineering thermodynamics by R. Mollier is very advantageous owing to the importance of enthalpy in applications. In a closed system, the difference in enthalpy is equal to the heat exchanged in a reversible isobaric process. In open systems, the adiabatic work is

$$\dot{W} = \dot{m}(h_1 - h_2) \qquad \text{with } Q = 0,$$

and the heat exchanged without the performance of work is given by

$$\dot{Q} = \dot{m}(h_2 - h_1).$$

Finally, in irreversible throttling processes, $h_1 = h_2$. The use of entropy as the second coordinate allows us easily to determine the end state of an isentropic process, and the principle of entropy increase points the direction in which the end state of a real, adiabatic process will be shifted in an adiabatic process as compared with an idealized isentropic.

A typical h, s diagram or *Mollier chart* is shown sketched in Figure 11.13, in which the main phase boundaries have been drawn; it is noteworthy that the critical point Cr is no longer at the top of the dome of the boundary curve. Owing to the fact that both coordinates constitute specific (extensive properties), the set of states at the triple point is located inside a triangle in complete analogy with the u, v diagram of Figure 7.13. The diagram in Figure 11.14 shows the appearance of a Mollier diagram for steam. The lines of constant dryness fraction can be drawn if it is remembered that isobars are identical with isotherms, and if it is realized that they must be straight in the two-phase region. This follows from the fact that $dQ° = dh = T\,ds$ along an isobar. Hence, the slope

$$\left(\frac{\partial h}{\partial s}\right)_{P,T} = T \tag{11.41}$$

is constant. The intercepts of these straight lines are divided into parts which are proportional to x and $1 - x$, respectively, because the two relations

$$h = h' + x(h'' - h')$$

and

$$s - s' + x(s'' - s')$$

are linear.

The relation derived in equation (11.27) remains valid in the superheated region; the slope $(= T)$ ceases to be constant there, except along an isotherm. It follows that an

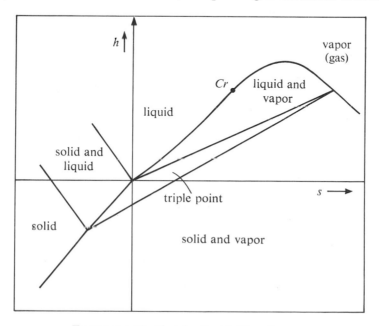

FIGURE 11.13. *Sketch of a Mollier diagram.*

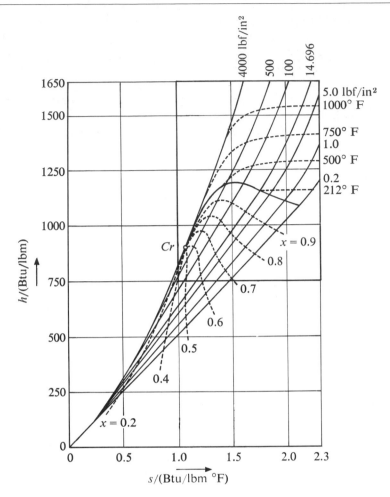

FIGURE 11.14. *The Mollier chart for steam.*

isotherm intersects all isobars at the same angle. At large degrees of superheat the isotherms become nearly horizontal, in conformity with the property that the enthalpy of a perfect gas is a function of temperature only.

The isobars cross the boundary curve continuously, but the isotherms do not. The common isobars-isotherms in the two-phase region merge with the boundary curve near the water region, and the various curves intersect each other at acute angles. For this reason that part of the diagram is useless in practice, and only the framed portion of the diagram in Figure 11.14 is normally included in a working Mollier chart. Figure 11.15 contains a replica of a Mollier chart for steam. The Mollier charts for other working fluids, such as refrigerants or noble gases in the neighborhood of the liquefaction line, assume a similar appearance, even though the numerical values are quite different. As the pressure is lowered and the state moves away from the two-phase region, the Mollier chart asymptotically transforms into one for a perfect gas.

The Mollier chart in Figure 11.15 contains in the left-hand top corner a scale for the graphical computation of velocities when steam is made to expand through a channel

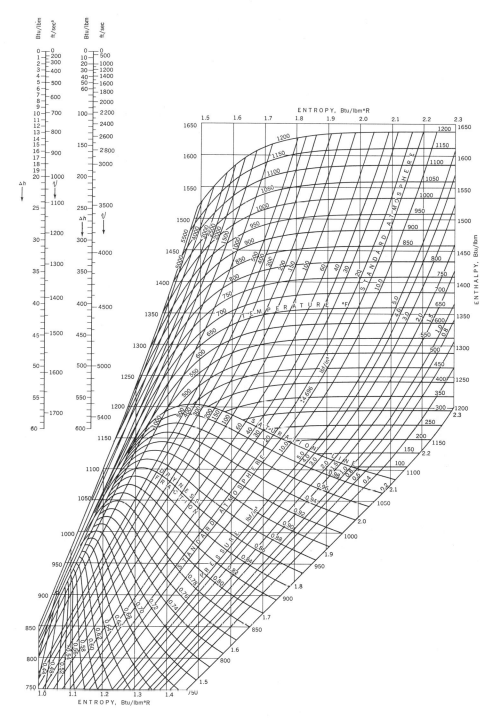

FIGURE 11.15. *The Mollier chart for steam. The right-hand Δh, V scale corresponds to the enthalpy scale of the main chart. The left-hand Δh, V scale has been extended tenfold, to enable small velocities to be calculated accurately. (Abstracted by permission from* Thermodynamic Properties of Steam, *by Joseph H. Keenan and Frederick G. Keyes, John Wiley & Sons, Inc.)*

from rest. It was shown in Section 6.12.1 that under such conditions, the velocity is given by the equation

$$\mathcal{V} = \sqrt{2\Delta h}$$

where Δh denotes the difference between the stagnation enthalpy h_0 and that at the section where the velocity is measured. The required conversion factors have been included in the diagram.

List of Symbols for Chapter 11

Latin letters

c	Specific heat
c_p	Specific heat at constant pressure
c_v	Specific heat at constant volume
E	Energy
H	Enthalpy
h	Specific enthalpy
l	Latent heat of evaporation
m	Mass
P	Pressure
Q	Heat
R	Gas constant
$\mathbf{R}$	Universal gas constant
S	Entropy
s	Specific entropy
s_p°	Specific entropy function at zero pressure (constant pressure)
s_v°	Specific entropy function at zero pressure (constant volume)
T	Thermodynamic temperature
U	Internal energy
u	Specific internal energy
V	Volume
v	Specific volume
W	Work
x	Dryness fraction

Greek letters

γ	Ratio of specific heats ($= c_p/c_v$)
ϕ	Constant of integration, equation (11.10)

Superscripts

$*$	Reference state
$\circ$	Reversible process; extrapolation to zero pressure
$'$	Saturated liquid
$''$	Saturated vapor
$\cdot$	Time rate of change

Subscripts

3	Refers to triple point
0	Refers to stagnation point

CHAPTER **12**

Some Consequences of the First Part of the Second Law of Thermodynamics (Relations between Properties)

12.1 Maxwell's relations

In the present chapter we shall restrict our attention to simple systems possessing two independent variables. It is known from Section 4.9 and from the many specific examples that the reversible work of such a system can be represented in the form of a truncated Pfaffian

$$dW° = Y \, dZ,$$

where Y is an intensive, and Z an extensive property of the system. In order to be more specific, we shall discuss some of the consequences which flow from the first part of the Second Law of thermodynamics in terms of a simple chemical system, that is, a pure substance in a single phase, realizing that their extension to rods stressed elastically, paramagnetic salts, charged dielectrics, galvanic cells, and so on is obtained by an obvious change in the symbols. For such a system

$$dW° = P \, dV,$$

and the First Law for a unit mass, or one mol of the system can be written

$$du = dQ° - dW° = dQ° - P \, dv.$$

Introducing the statement that $dQ° = T ds$, we obtain that

$$du = T \, ds - P \, dv. \tag{12.1}$$

In this expression all symbols represent properties of the system. This clearly signifies that there must exist some relations between the derivatives of internal energy on the one hand, and temperature and pressure on the other, since du constitutes a perfect differential. Furthermore, the condition of integrability (3.26) must be satisfied in equation (12.1), and this leads to a relation between the derivatives of the factors T and P in the Pfaffian expression, (12.1). These facts were first noticed by J. C. Maxwell who thus succeeded in writing down expressions which make such relations explicit. For this reason, the succeeding equations are known as *Maxwell's relations*.

A close scrutiny of equation (12.1), which is a result of the application of the First Law and of the first part of the Second Law to a reversible process in a simple system, reveals that if the internal energy were given as a function

$$u = u(s, v) \qquad (12.2)$$

of entropy and internal energy, then its total differential would be written in a form reminiscent of equation (12.1). In fact

$$du = \left(\frac{\partial u}{\partial s}\right)_v ds + \left(\frac{\partial u}{\partial v}\right)_s dv. \qquad (12.1a)$$

Since equations (12.1) and (12.1a) express the same perfect differential, the respective factors of ds and dv in them must be identical. This leads to the discovery of the first two, so-called *reciprocity relations*, namely,

$$\left.\begin{aligned}
\left(\frac{\partial u}{\partial s}\right)_v &= T(s, v), \\[2mm]
\left(\frac{\partial u}{\partial v}\right)_s &= -P(s, v).
\end{aligned}\right\} \qquad (12.3a, b)$$

The independent variables, the specific or molar entropy s and the specific or molar volume v in this case, have been shown explicitly in equation (12.3) to serve as a reminder that the partial derivatives in equation (12.3) have been obtained from the form (12.2). This does not alter the fact that T and P constitute the values of the two intensive parameters, absolute thermodynamic temperature T and pressure P, at a given state. Thus, equations (12.3) constitute relations which must necessarily be satisfied by the properties of a simple system at any state whatsoever. The existence of a substance for which this were not the case would be inconsistent with the Second Law of thermodynamics and would, therefore, make it possible to devise a perpetual-motion engine of the second kind with such a substance as its working fluid.

If a relation of the form (12.2) could be obtained for a substance, say as a result of fitting an expression to a set of experimental data, it would be possible to evaluate the functions $T(s, v)$ and $P(s, v)$ by simple differentiation, using the reciprocity relations (12.3). It would further be possible to eliminate the entropy from these two functions and to obtain a relation

$$F(P, v, T) = 0 \qquad (12.4)$$

between pressure, volume, and absolute thermodynamic temperature, that is, the thermal equation of state. It would also be possible to calculate the enthalpy of the substance

$$h(s, v) = u(s, v) + P(s, v) \cdot v \qquad (12.5)$$

as a function of the variables s and v, and finally, by differentiation, it would be possible to determine the specific heat

$$c_v(s, v) = \left(\frac{\partial u}{\partial T}\right)_v = \frac{(\partial u/\partial s)_v}{(\partial T/\partial s)_v}.$$

Referring to equation (12.3a), and assuming that the relation $u = u(s, v)$ is known, we compute

$$c_v = \frac{T}{(\partial T/\partial s)_v},$$ (12.6)

or

$$c_v = \frac{(\partial u(s,\,v)/\partial s)_v}{(\partial^2 u(s,\,v)/\partial s^2)_v}.$$ (12.6a)

Similarly, it would be possible to compute

$$c_p = \left(\frac{\partial h}{\partial T}\right)_P,$$

except that now the procedure would be somewhat more complex. Nevertheless, it would involve differentiation only.

The preceding remarks lead to the conclusion that all properties which have so far been used to analyze the state of a simple system, namely,

$$P,\ T,\ h,\ c_p,\ c_v$$

could be computed directly from the relation $u = u(s,\,v)$ in equation (12.2). It follows that the relation $u(s,\,v)$ constitutes a *fundamental equation* as defined in Section 3.8.

There exist two obstacles which prevent us from making practical use of the possibility revealed in the preceding paragraph. First, it must be clearly appreciated that the symbol T in equation (12.1) stands for the thermodynamic temperature of the system, and that no empirical temperature, θ, can be substituted for it; if θ denotes the temperature measured on the perfect-gas temperature scale, this cannot be done, either, without first showing that the two are identical. We shall accomplish this in Section 12.3, but it is still worth emphasizing that for any other empirical temperature, T would be replaced by an empirical function $\Theta(\theta)$ of the empirical temperature θ, as shown in equation (9.35b). The second obstacle is presented by the fact that entropy can neither be controlled nor measured directly in the laboratory. In order to control it, that is, to maintain it at a constant value during an experiment, it would be necessary to provide an ideal, adiabatic enclosure and to ensure that the process is reversible. In order to measure it directly, it would be necessary to measure heat fluxes and associated temperature changes, according to the equation $ds = dQ^\circ/T$ in a *reversible* process. It is not possible to fulfill any of these conditions in practice. Consequently, at present, the observation that the relation $u = u(s,\,v)$ constitutes a fundamental equation is of limited utility only. In spite of this, it is important owing to the consequences which can be derived from it. The independent variables s and v appearing in the function $u(s,\,v)$ are called the *canonical variables* for the potential u, to emphasize the intrinsic simplicity of the relation.

The condition of integrability applied to the form of equation (12.1) leads to the so-called *reciprocal relation*

$$\left(\frac{\partial T}{\partial v}\right)_s = -\left(\frac{\partial P}{\partial s}\right)_v.$$ (12.7)

We have used the integrability condition of a perfect differential to draw conclusions about properties for the first time in Section 8.4.3, where it led to a relation between the modulus of elasticity, E, and the linear coefficient of thermal expansion, α, of a thin elastic rod.

The question naturally poses itself as to whether the preceding is *the only* fundamental equation. In other words, is it possible to obtain alternative fundamental equations in terms of some other independent variables? This question can be investigated systematically with respect to the two pairs of variables

$$T, s \quad \text{and} \quad P, v.$$

The problem posed here can be rephrased in general terms with reference to the perfect differential†

$$dZ(x, y) = X\, dx + Y\, dy \tag{12.8}$$

in which

$$X = \left(\frac{\partial Z}{\partial x}\right)_y; \qquad Y = \left(\frac{\partial Z}{\partial y}\right)_x. \tag{12.9}$$

It is now desired to change the variables, and to replace x, y as independent variables by the derivatives X, Y. This type of transformation in which a change in independent variables involves the selection of derivatives as new independent variables is known as a *Legendre transformation*. In geometry, it is referred to as a *contact transformation*.‡ In order to appreciate the effect of performing Legendre transformations upon equation (12.1) it is not necessary to study the complete theory relevant to the problem.§ Instead, it is sufficient to consider the effect of replacing the function $Z(x, y)$, by the *modified function*

$$A(X, Y) = Z(x, y) - xX - yY \tag{12.10}$$

---

† Here Z and Y denote general symbols, not the generalized displacement and generalized force in $dW° = Y dZ$.

‡ By means of a contact transformation, the equation of a curve on a plane, conceived as a geometric locus of points (x, y) possessing some mathematical property, is replaced by an equation in which the tangent dy/dx at a point and the intercept of this tangent on the axis of ordinates are used as independent variables. Thus, the curve is conceived of as an envelope of a family of straight lines. Similarly, a surface in space is represented as the envelope of a family of planes whose equations are described by the slopes of their traces on the z, x and z, y planes and the intercept on the z axis.

§ The interested reader may wish to consult Callen, H. B., *Thermodynamics* (Wiley, 1960), p. 90 ff. Legendre transformations play an important part in advanced dynamics. In dynamics, it is found that the so-called Lagrangian, that is, a function $\mathcal{L}$ of the generalized coordinates $q_1, \ldots, q_n$, and the generalized velocities $u_1, \ldots, u_n$ of a complex mechanical system moving with $2n$ degrees of freedom completely describes the dynamic behavior of the system. By applying Legendre transformations, it is possible to determine all equivalent functions which also completely describe the motion of the system. In particular, it is often convenient to replace the velocities $u_1, \ldots, u_n$ as independent variables by the generalized momenta

$$p_i = \frac{\partial \mathcal{L}}{\partial u_i}.$$

When this is done, a new function, the so-called Hamiltonian $\mathcal{H}(p_1, \ldots, p_n; q_1, \ldots, q_n)$ is obtained. The Hamiltonian can then be shown to be entirely equivalent to the Lagrangian. It is worth noting that the Lagrangian or Hamiltonian functions play an essential part in statistical mechanics where properties of thermodynamic systems are studied in terms of complex mechanical models. Hence, there exists an important connection between the fundamental equation of state of a thermodynamic system and the Lagrangian or the Hamiltonian function of its model.

in which the products of the *conjugate* pairs of variables X, x and Y, y have been subtracted from the original function Z. Differentiating the function (12.10) we shall obtain in it the two terms

$$-\mathrm{d}(xX) = -X\,\mathrm{d}x - x\,\mathrm{d}X,$$
$$-\mathrm{d}(yY) = -Y\,\mathrm{d}y - y\,\mathrm{d}Y,$$

in addition to $\mathrm{d}Z$, which is given by equation (12.8). Now, the first terms above will cancel the terms $X\,\mathrm{d}x$ and $Y\,\mathrm{d}y$ in equation (12.8), leaving

$$\mathrm{d}A(X, Y) = -x\,\mathrm{d}X - y\,\mathrm{d}Y. \tag{12.11}$$

It is seen that replacing the original function Z by the modified function A has the effect of removing the terms in which x and y appear as independent variables, and replacing them by the conjugate variables X and Y. Hence, our goal of changing the independent variables and replacing them by the derivatives (12.9) can be achieved without complication, if the dependent variable is changed simultaneously. In the new form, the new reciprocity relations

$$x = -\left(\frac{\partial A}{\partial X}\right)_Y; \quad y = -\left(\frac{\partial A}{\partial Y}\right)_X \tag{12.9a}$$

are obtained in analogy with equation (12.9).

There is no need to replace *both* variables at the same time. The modified function

$$B = Z - xX, \tag{12.10a}$$

will lead to

$$\mathrm{d}B(X, y) = -x\,\mathrm{d}X + Y\,\mathrm{d}y, \tag{12.11a}$$

and similarly for

$$C = Z - yY,$$

$$\mathrm{d}C(x, Y) = X\,\mathrm{d}x - y\,\mathrm{d}Y,$$

in which the transformations $x \to X$, $y \to Y$ have been introduced one at a time. The resulting rule is simple, and easy to memorize. In order to interchange the roles of a variable in a perfect differential and of its coefficient, it is necessary to *subtract* the product of the two from the dependent variable. The perfect differential of the resulting *modified function* will contain a term, with *a negative sign*, in which the roles of the two variables have been reversed as desired. In each case new reciprocity and new reciprocal relations are obtained, and it is seen that for two independent variables it is possible to obtain a total of *four* forms, including the original, by interchanging the roles of the conjugate pairs of variables P, v and T, s one at a time, and then both together.

Reverting to the simple system, we can establish the very convenient Table 12.1† which contains all possible transformations, as discussed before.

The preceding considerations, summarized in Table 12.1, have led to the discovery of the following four fundamental equations

$$u(v, s), \quad h(P, s), \quad f(v, T), \quad \text{and} \quad g(P, T), \qquad (12.12)$$

and to the introduction of the three potentials

$$\left.\begin{array}{l} h = u + Pv, \\ f = u - Ts, \\ g = h - Ts = f + Pv = u + Pv - Ts. \end{array}\right\} \qquad (12.13a, b, c)$$

The first new potential is the familiar enthalpy, h. The second new potential, f, is called the Helmholtz function. Finally, the potential g is called the Gibbs function. The latter two potentials are also sometimes referred to as the free energy, f, and the free enthalpy, g, respectively. They will play an important part in the further development of the subject in Volume II. The names adopted for those potentials are not, unfortunately, in general use. Although the preceding terminology seems to be the most consistent one, it has not, as yet, gained universal acceptance. In particular, the name free *energy*‡ is frequently applied to the potential g, called here free *enthalpy*. It is, consequently, necessary to be very cautious when studying different reference books or research papers on this subject, and to verify the definitions, rather than to rely on the name of the potential, in order to avoid confusion.

TABLE 12.1
Maxwell's Reciprocity and Reciprocal Relations.

No.	Potential	Independent canonical variables	Conjugate variables (reciprocity relations)	Thermodynamic (reciprocal, or Maxwell's) relations	Name adopted for potential
1.	U, u $du = T\,ds - P\,dv$	v, s	$T = \left(\dfrac{\partial u}{\partial s}\right)_v$ $P = -\left(\dfrac{\partial u}{\partial v}\right)_s$	$\left(\dfrac{\partial T}{\partial v}\right)_s = -\left(\dfrac{\partial P}{\partial s}\right)_v$ $= \dfrac{\partial^2 u}{\partial v\,\partial s}$	Internal energy
2.	H, h $h = u + Pv$ $dh = T\,ds + v\,dP$	P, s	$T = \left(\dfrac{\partial h}{\partial s}\right)_P$ $v = \left(\dfrac{\partial h}{\partial P}\right)_s$	$\left(\dfrac{\partial T}{\partial P}\right)_s = \left(\dfrac{\partial v}{\partial s}\right)_P$ $= \dfrac{\partial^2 h}{\partial P\,\partial s}$	Enthalpy
3.	F, f $f = u - Ts$ $df = -s\,dT - P\,dv$	v, T	$s = -\left(\dfrac{\partial f}{\partial T}\right)_v$ $P = -\left(\dfrac{\partial f}{\partial v}\right)_T$	$\left(\dfrac{\partial s}{\partial v}\right)_T = \left(\dfrac{\partial P}{\partial T}\right)_v$ $= -\dfrac{\partial^2 f}{\partial v\,\partial T}$	Free energy or Helmholtz function
4.	G, g $g = h - Ts$ $= f + Pv$ $= u + Pv - Ts$ $dg = -s\,dT + v\,dP$	P, T	$s = -\left(\dfrac{\partial g}{\partial T}\right)_P$ $v = \left(\dfrac{\partial g}{\partial P}\right)_T$	$\left(\dfrac{\partial s}{\partial P}\right)_T = -\left(\dfrac{\partial v}{\partial T}\right)_P$ $= -\dfrac{\partial^2 g}{\partial P\,\partial T}$	Free enthalpy or Gibbs function

† After A. Sommerfeld. See *Thermodynamics and Statistical Mechanics*, transl. by J. Kestin (Academic, 1956), p. 44.
‡ Very common in textbooks on chemical thermodynamics.

Some authors, notably M. Planck,[†] prefer to replace the Helmholtz function f, and the Gibbs function g, respectively, by the related functions

$$j = s - \frac{u}{T} = -\frac{f}{T} \qquad (12.13\text{d})$$

known as the Massieu function, and

$$y = s - \frac{h}{T} = -\frac{g}{T} \qquad (12.13\text{e})$$

known as the Planck function. The pairs of potentials f, j and g, y can be used interchangeably, and there is no advantage in retaining them all. Sometimes, the use of the Massieu and Planck functions leads to slight simplifications in derivations, but the results are, of course, entirely equivalent. In accordance with modern usage, and to preserve the symmetry of Table 12.1, we shall restrict ourselves exclusively to the use of the Gibbs and Helmholtz potentials. It is, however, clear that an analog of Table 12.1 can be obtained by considering the alternative form of equation (12.1), namely,

$$\mathrm{d}s = \frac{1}{T}\,\mathrm{d}u + \frac{P}{T}\,\mathrm{d}v,$$

in which $s(u, v)$ is the fundamental equation. Applying the Legendre transformation, we would be led to consider the modified functions

$$s - \frac{Pv}{T}, \quad s - \frac{u}{T} = j, \quad \text{and} \quad s - \frac{Pv}{T} - \frac{u}{T} = y.$$

Such an alternative procedure, apart from leading to equations whose formal appearance is different, would contribute nothing new to our understanding of the subject.

The fundamental equation $u = u(s, v)$ represents an extensive property in terms of two extensive canonical variables. Recalling Euler's theorem from Section 7.5.3, we can state that u must be a homogeneous function of degree one in s and v. We can also say, and confirm in Table 12.1, that both partial derivatives, being limits of ratios of extensive properties, must themselves be intensive in character. Similar observations can be made about the remaining forms and it is worth noting that $g = g(P, T)$ is the only equation with two intensive properties chosen as independent. A Legendre transformation performed on $u = u(s, v)$ replaces one extensive property with an intensive property as the canonical variable.

The thermodynamic relations implied in Maxwell's reciprocal relations, sometimes called *the* Maxwell relations, are very useful in the study of the thermodynamic properties of substances. They express certain derivatives, such as $(\partial P/\partial s)_v$ in line 1 of Table 12.1, by other derivatives, such as $(\partial T/\partial v)_s$ in this case. A close scrutiny of all four relations reveals that usually one of the two is more easily measured than the other. This is particularly true of the relations in lines 3 and 4 in Table 12.1, because derivatives of entropy, which cannot be measured directly, are expressed in terms of derivatives which involve the thermal equation of state $F(P, v, T) = 0$ only. The relation in line 4 is of course identical with that previously derived in an *ad hoc* manner as equation (11.6) in Section 11.1.1.

[†] See his *Theory of Heat* (*Introduction to Theoretical Physics*, Vol. V) transl. by H. L. Brose (Macmillan, 1932).

The thermal equation of state is most easily measured, and is usually the first one to be established by direct measurement for a substance whose properties are being tabulated. Moreover, measurements which lead to the thermal equation of state can be performed with great precision. For example, in moderate ranges of pressure, say up to several hundred atmospheres, pressures can be measured with a precision of 1 part in 50,000 (that is, 0.002%), specific volumes with a precision of 1 part in 10,000 (that is, 0.01%), and absolute temperatures with an error of the order of 0.001°K for temperatures which are not too high, that is, with a precision of 0.0003%.

In order to appreciate the importance of such measurements, as well as their limitations, it is necessary to examine in detail the reasons which preclude the thermal equation of state from being a fundamental equation.

12.2   The thermal equation of state

In order to ascertain that the thermal equation of state

$$F(P, v, T) = 0 \qquad (12.14)$$

is not a fundamental one, it is best to attempt to calculate entropy with its aid. This choice is based on two observations. First, a scrutiny of the four reciprocal relations in Table 12.1 reveals that only the derivatives

$$\left(\frac{\partial P}{\partial T}\right)_v = f_1(T, v)$$

and

$$-\left(\frac{\partial v}{\partial T}\right)_P = f_2(T, P)$$

can be obtained readily from equation (12.14). Since the functions $f_1(T, v)$ and $f_2(T, P)$ are obtained from the empirical equation (12.14) by differentiation, the procedure will entail some loss in accuracy. This, however, is not serious, if the data for equation (12.14) have been measured as precisely as it is possible to do. Secondly, it is clear from the remarks in Section 12.1 that entropy must be calculated, since it cannot be measured in practice, and its knowledge is essential for the establishment of a fundamental equation.

In this manner, by the use of the relations in lines 3 and 4, of Table 12.1 the calculation of entropy can be reduced to either of the two integrations:

$$\int_{v*}^{v} \left(\frac{\partial s}{\partial v}\right)_T dv = \int_{v*}^{v} f_1(T, v) \, dv, \qquad (12.15a)$$

$$\int_{P*}^{P} \left(\frac{\partial s}{\partial P}\right)_T dP = \int_{P*}^{P} f_2(T, P) \, dP. \qquad (12.15b)$$

Here, the reference state is denoted by $P*, v*$, the corresponding value of temperature, $T*$, being given by the relation

$$F(P*, v*, T*) = 0.$$

More explicitly, equation (12.15a) yields the difference

$$s(v, T) - s(v*, T) = F_1(T, v)$$

and equation (12.15b) leads to

$$s(P, T) - s(P^*, T) = F_2(T, P),$$

where

$$F_1(T, v) = \int_{v^*}^{v} f_1(T, v) \, dv \quad \text{and} \quad F_2(T, P) = \int_{P^*}^{P} f_2(T, P) \, dP. \quad (12.15c, d)$$

It is clear that the constants of integration $s(v^*, T)$ and $s(P^*, T)$ cannot be assigned arbitrary values, because both integrations have been performed at a constant temperature T which differs from the reference temperature T^*. This can be done for the reference state only. If the arbitrary value is denoted by

$$s(v^*, T^*) \quad \text{or} \quad s(P^*, T^*)$$

for the two cases, we can rewrite the preceding equations as

$$s(v, T) - s(v^*, T^*) = F_1(T, v) + \{s(v^*, T) - s(v^*, T^*)\} = F_1(T, v) + \phi_1(T)$$
$$(12.16a)$$

and

$$s(P, T) - s(P^*, T^*) = F_2(P, T) + \{s(P^*, T) - s(P^*, T^*)\} = F_2(P, T) + \phi_2(T).$$
$$(12.16b)$$

The two expressions in brackets

$$\phi_1(T) = s(v^*, T) - s(v^*, T^*) \qquad (12.17a)$$

and

$$\phi_2(T) = s(P^*, T) - s(P^*, T^*) \qquad (12.17b)$$

are both functions of temperature and neither of them can be evaluated with the aid of the data contained in the thermal equation of state (12.14). They require an additional calculation of entropy differences along the reference isochore $v^* - \text{const}$ in the case of equation (12.17a) or along the reference isobar, $P^* = \text{const}$, in the case of equation (12.17b). In order to perform these calculations, it is necessary to obtain additional information of an empirical nature, see Section 12.5. At this stage, it is sufficient to note that the thermal equation of state does not completely determine entropy, and hence does not constitute a fundamental equation.

With reference to equations (12.16a) and (12.16b), it is possible to make one observation of interest. In these two equations, only the terms $F_1(T, v)$ or $F_2(T, P)$ are determined by the equation of state. It is, therefore, feasible that different substances can be found for which the form of the thermal equation of state is identical but for which the functions $\phi_1(T)$ and $\phi_2(T)$ are different. Thus, their behavior, as far as the thermal equation of state is concerned, is identical, whereas those properties which are not completely determined by the thermal equation of state, such as entropy, whose values also involve the differing functions $\phi_1(T)$ and $\phi_2(T)$, will be different. In fact, we have already encountered such substances in the perfect gas. It will be recalled from Section 3.10 that the perfect-gas law is identical for all gases when the molar specific volume is used. On the other hand, equations (12.16a) and (12.16b) are valid if the symbol v in them is interpreted as the molar specific volume. It follows that the functions $F_1(T, v)$ and $F_2(T, P)$ are identical for all perfect gases, and that only the values of the functions $\phi_1(T)$ and $\phi_2(T)$ will be different for them. A quick reference to Table XVI demonstrates that the molar entropy, the molar specific heats, or the molar enthalpy of real gases, extrapolated to zero pressure, differ from gas to gas, in spite of the fact that their thermal equations of state become *identical* in the same limit.

It is easy to show that for all perfect gases

$$F_1(T, v_m) = \mathbf{R} \ln v_m/v_m^*, \tag{12.18a}$$

$$F_2(T, P) = -\mathbf{R} \ln P/P^*, \tag{12.18b}$$

where the subscript $_m$ has been added to emphasize the fact that molar quantities are stipulated. Indeed, since

$$Pv_m = \mathbf{R}T \tag{12.19}$$

it is seen that

$$f_1(T, v_m) = \mathbf{R}/v_m \quad \text{and} \quad f_2(T, P) = -\mathbf{R}/P,$$

and equations (12.18a) and (12.18b) follow directly by integration from equations (12.15c, d).

It is noticed that in equation (12.19) the perfect-gas temperature θ has been replaced by the thermodynamic temperature T. This is in anticipation of the result which was alluded to before, and which we are now in a position to derive.

12.3   Relation between the perfect-gas and the thermodynamic temperature scales

We now proceed to investigate the relation between the, so far, purely conceptual thermodynamic temperature scale T on the one hand, and the, so far, purely empirical prefect-gas temperature scale θ on the other. A moment's reflection should convince the reader that such a comparison cannot be carried out by reasoning alone and that recourse must be had to some empirical information, that is, to results of experiments. Furthermore, experiments can only be carried out with real gases. Consequently, care must be taken not to invoke the hypothetical properties of perfect gases.† Finally, it must be realized that available experimental results provide an excess of information over that which is essential for our purpose; this means that the succeeding line of reasoning is not the only one possible. It is suggested, however, that it is very economical in the number of empirical facts employed.

In order to provide a strict comparison between the temperature scales T and θ, use will be made of two empirical facts and of one fact which is fundamental to the concept of a temperature scale. Since temperature scales provide a means of assigning numerical values to corresponding isotherms, as set out in detail in Section 2.5, it follows that $T = \text{const}$ implies $\theta = \text{const}$ and vice versa. Hence, whenever one appears

---

† In some textbooks the proof of the identity of the two scales is carried out with reference to the perfect-gas thermal equation of state. Such a course is admissible only if it can be shown that *all* properties of a real gas extrapolate to those of a perfect gas in the limit of $P \to 0$. That this is unlikely is clear from the fact that the equation $Pv_m = \mathbf{R}\theta$ is not a fundamental one. The exact relation between the properties of a perfect gas and the extrapolated properties of its real counterpart when the limit $P \to 0$ is imposed, will be studied in Volume II. It will then become clear that the two sets of properties are by no means identical. Care has been taken to avoid such unsound reasoning (leading to a correct result!) in this book.

as an index in a partial derivative, it can be replaced by the other. For example

$$\left(\frac{\partial y}{\partial x}\right)_T \equiv \left(\frac{\partial y}{\partial x}\right)_\theta,$$

where x and y denote any properties whatsoever.

The first empirical fact which will be drawn into our considerations asserts that for moderate pressures, the thermal equation of state for *real* gases can be represented in the form of a so-called virial series

$$Pv = A(\theta) + B(\theta) \cdot P + C(\theta) \cdot P^2 + \cdots . \tag{12.20}$$

The coefficients $A(\theta)$, $B(\theta)$, ... are known as the first, second, ... *virial coefficient*, and each of them is a function of the empirical, perfect-gas temperature, in terms of which the measurements implied in equation (12.20) are assumed to have been performed. In fact, since

$$\theta = \lim_{P \to 0} \frac{Pv}{(Pv)_3} \theta_3,$$

we have

$$\theta = \frac{A}{A_3} \theta_3,$$

and since

$$R = \frac{\lim_{P \to 0} (Pv)_3}{\theta_3},$$

we also have

$$A = R\theta. \tag{12.20a}$$

The second experimental fact required for our purpose is the result of the Washburn experiment performed by F. D. Rossini and M. Frandsen, and described in detail in Section 6.18. This can be stated in the form of the assertion that

$$\lim_{P \to 0} \left(\frac{\partial u}{\partial P}\right)_\theta = \lim_{P \to 0} \left(\frac{\partial u}{\partial P}\right)_T$$

is finite, irrespective of the value at which the temperature has been kept constant during a measurement, equation (6.84).

It has been shown on two examples that Maxwell's reciprocal relations provide links between the thermal equation of state and the remaining properties of a substance. In the present case, we need to evaluate the partial derivative $(\partial u/\partial P)_T$ and to investigate its behavior as the pressure is extrapolated to zero. In order to do this we rewrite equation (12.1) for a constant temperature path, and obtain

$$\left(\frac{\partial u}{\partial P}\right)_T = T\left(\frac{\partial s}{\partial P}\right)_T - P\left(\frac{\partial v}{\partial P}\right)_T .$$

The derivative $(\partial s/\partial P)_T$ can now be replaced by $-(\partial v/\partial T)_P$ from line 4 in Table 12.1.

Thus, we obtain the relation

$$\left(\frac{\partial u}{\partial P}\right)_T = -T\left(\frac{\partial v}{\partial T}\right)_P - P\left(\frac{\partial v}{\partial P}\right)_T, \tag{12.21}$$

in which all the derivatives on the right-hand side can be evaluated by differentiation only from the virial equation (12.20). Equation (12.21), having been derived from equation (12.1) and the Maxwell relations, contains only the thermodynamic temperature T. On the other hand, equation (12.20) contains only the empirical, perfect-gas temperature θ. Since they will now occur in one equation, a direct comparison between the two scales will become possible.

Carrying out the differentiations indicated, and remembering that T and θ are connected by a single-valued functional relationship, we obtain

$$\left(\frac{\partial v}{\partial T}\right)_P = \frac{\dfrac{dA}{d\theta}\dfrac{d\theta}{dT}}{P} + \frac{dB}{d\theta}\frac{d\theta}{dT} + \frac{dC}{d\theta}\frac{d\theta}{dT}P + \cdots$$

and

$$\left(\frac{\partial v}{\partial P}\right)_T = -\frac{A}{P^2} + C + \cdots.$$

Here, in view of the relation $T(\theta)$, the chain-rule of differentiation was used. Thus,

$$\frac{dA}{dT} = \frac{dA}{d\theta}\frac{d\theta}{dT} \cdots.$$

Substitution into equation (12.21) leads to

$$\left(\frac{\partial u}{\partial P}\right)_T = \left(\frac{\partial u}{\partial P}\right)_\theta = \frac{1}{P}\left\{A - T\frac{dA}{d\theta}\frac{d\theta}{dT}\right\} - T\frac{dB}{d\theta}\frac{d\theta}{dT} - P\left\{C + T\frac{dC}{d\theta}\frac{d\theta}{dT}\right\} + \cdots. \tag{12.22}$$

The detailed form of equation (12.22) is actually of minor importance, since we wish to concentrate on its form in the limit when the pressure is extrapolated to zero at *constant temperature*, because the result of such an extrapolation is known from the Washburn experiment. On performing this passage to the limit in equation (12.22), it is seen that all terms, starting with the third, will vanish. The second term will remain, since it is a constant at constant temperature, but the first term will tend to infinity, since the term

$$A - T\frac{dA}{d\theta}\frac{d\theta}{dT} \tag{12.22a}$$

in the bracket is a constant during this passage to the limit. This is a conclusion which contradicts experimental evidence. It is clear, therefore, that agreement with the experimental result can be secured only on condition that the term (12.22a) *vanishes identically*. If this is the case, the term multiplying $1/P$ in equation (12.22) will be removed, and the simplified equation will lead to a result which agrees with what is known from experiment. Furthermore, this is the only possibility, since the term (12.22a) remains constant during the passage to the limit, because it contains functions of temperature only.

We are thus forced to accept the result that

$$A - T \frac{dA}{d\theta} \frac{d\theta}{dT} = 0 \tag{12.23}$$

for all temperatures. Substituting the value for A from equation (12.20a) we find that

$$\frac{d\theta}{\theta} = \frac{dT}{T}, \tag{12.23a}$$

which constitutes a differential equation whose solution demands that T and θ should be *proportional to each other*. Indeed, it follows from equation (12.23a) that

$$\ln \theta = \ln T + \ln K,$$

where K is a constant of integration, so that

$$\theta = KT.$$

The value of the constant of integration, K, must be fixed by convention. If the convention is adopted that on both scales the triple point of water shall be assigned the common value

$$T_3 = \theta_3 = 273.16°K,$$

it follows that

$$\theta = T, \tag{12.24}$$

as we have set out to prove.

In this manner, equation (12.22) transforms to

$$\left(\frac{\partial u}{\partial P}\right)_T = -T \frac{dB}{dT} - P\left\{C + T \frac{dC}{dT}\right\} + \text{higher-order terms.}$$

Since the virial coefficients $B, C, \ldots$ are functions of temperature alone, it is seen that the preceding expression assumes the form

$$\left(\frac{\partial u}{\partial P}\right)_T = f_1(T) - f_2(T) \cdot P + \cdots, \tag{12.25}$$

where

$$f_1(T) = -T \frac{dB}{dT} \quad \text{and} \quad f_2(T) = C + T \frac{dC}{dT}. \tag{12.25a}$$

At low pressures, $P \to 0$, and equation (6.84) from Section 6.18 is retrieved in the limit.

The preceding argument leads to the conclusion that the thermodynamic temperature scale is identical with the perfect-gas temperature scale on condition that the convention of assigning the same arbitrary value to a single isotherm is followed. This statement provides an operational basis for the measurement of thermodynamic temperatures. It should, however, be realized that this basis is somewhat incomplete, because it is limited to the range in which precise determinations with gas thermometers (thermometers filled with real gases!) are possible. In principle, this circumstance limits the operational (but not fundamental) definition of thermodynamic temperature to the lowest temperature at which a gas can still exist over a reasonable range of pressures.

We can take it as the temperature of liquefaction of helium, say at a pressure of 100 Torr, that is approximately 1.8°K for the isotope He^3, or approximately 2.7°K for the isotope He^4. In practice, the critical temperature of 5.2°K for He^4 provides a more realistic lower limit. Thus, there is a need to establish an operational basis for measuring lower temperatures on the thermodynamic temperature scale with reference to a system other than a gas. The second limitation occurs at very high temperatures when the materials of construction of the bulb of a gas thermometer begin to fail.

At the present time the limits are much narrower than those discussed in the preceding paragraph and are confined to the range of temperatures in which a comparison between the International Practical Temperature Scale and the perfect-gas temperature scale exists, as discussed in Section 2.8. The reason for it lies in the fact that practical measurements can only be performed with the instruments specified in the International Temperature Scale, as opposed to gas thermometers.

The high-temperature limit is extended by replacing the gas thermometer by a radiation pyrometer whose operation is based on a fundamental physical law, Planck's law of blackbody radiation.† The low temperature limit, of great importance to the study of the properties of substances at very low temperatures and in the corresponding branch of technology known as *cryogenics*, is extended with reference to the vapor-pressure curves of the isotopes of helium (Section 2.8) or to paramagnetic systems (Section 8.5.8).

Another possibility of creating an operational basis for the thermodynamic temperature scale, so far unused in practice, will be discussed in Volume II in connection with the Clausius-Clapeyron equation for phase transition.

Having established the exact equivalence of the thermodynamic and the perfect-gas temperature scales, we shall no longer find it necessary to use the two distinctive symbols, T and θ, to denote them. We shall now retain the symbol T for both, as we have done provisionally in Chapter 11. It will be realized that it is now possible to imagine that the substitution of T for θ has been carried out in all previous expressions, because the distinction was introduced in order to provide a safeguard against circular reasoning. The same is true about the numerical data quoted previously. For this reason, the symbol T was used for absolute temperature in the tables of data at the end of the book.

12.4   The use of Jacobians in thermodynamics

Maxwell's reciprocal relations, and relations of the type of equations (12.6) or (12.21), can be easily derived when the Jacobian notation is used. The need for a shorthand, and expeditious, method of derivation will be appreciated if it is realized that interest now centers on the eight properties

$$P, v, T, s, u, h, f, \text{ and } g$$

to which the two specific heats and their ratio

$$c_p, c_v, \text{ and } \gamma$$

† See Schmidt, E., *Thermodynamics*, transl. by J. Kestin (Oxford: Clarendon Press, 1949), p. 465 ff.; Sommerfeld, A., *Thermodynamics and Statistical Mechanics* (*Lectures on Theoretical Physics*, Vol. V) transl. by J. Kestin (Academic, 1956), pp. 135 and 246. See equation (2.38) in Section 2.8.

may be added. Limiting attention to the first group of eight properties, since none of the second group of three is ever used as an independent variable, it is found that for a simple system it is possible to select one of 28 alternative pairs of independent variables, as already remarked in Section 3.7. The number of first partial derivatives which can be formed with the aid of eight variables is equal to the number of permutations of $n = 8$ symbols, taken $r = 3$ at a time, or

$$P^3_8 = 8 \cdot 7 \cdot 6 = 336$$

of which, however, only one half will be independent, since for any symbols,

$$\left(\frac{\partial x}{\partial y}\right)_z = \left[\left(\frac{\partial y}{\partial x}\right)_z\right]^{-1},$$

showing that the partial derivatives will appear in pairs of which one is the reciprocal of the other. Thus, a total of 168 partial derivatives will come into consideration. Among these, two, of course, will be equal to the specific heats

$$c_v = \left(\frac{\partial u}{\partial T}\right)_v \quad \text{and} \quad c_p = \left(\frac{\partial h}{\partial T}\right)_P.$$

It is to be expected that such a multitude of parameters will satisfy a large number of relations and that only some of them will be needed, or helpful, in the understanding or in the applications of thermodynamics. Thus, without attempting to be comprehensive, we shall write down those relations that appear to us to be of interest.[†]

The usefulness of the Jacobian notation turns primarily on the area property quoted in Section 3.7.3. Equation (12.25) expresses the fact that the area encompassed by any closed curve in the P, v (or Y, Z) plane is equal to that enclosed by its image in the T, s plane. It follows that the Jacobian of the transformation $(P, v) \rightarrow (T, s)$ is constant throughout the plane and that it is identically equal to unity everywhere, that is, that

$$\frac{\partial(P, v)}{\partial(T, s)} = 1, \tag{12.26}$$

Section 9.12, equation (9.61). In other words, the mapping $(P, v) \rightarrow (T, s)$ is *isometric*, or area-preserving. Applying the property of Jacobians expressed in equation (3.39), we can also write

$$\frac{\partial(P, v)}{\partial(x, y)} = \frac{\partial(T, s)}{\partial(x, y)}, \tag{12.27}$$

where x, y denote an arbitrary pair of variables. By a judicious choice of the pair of variables x, y it is possible to derive a large number of thermodynamic relations. Since x, y denote *arbitrary* variables, their choice can be consciously governed by the demands of the problem at hand. In particular, the identity in equation (12.27) can be utilized to express certain derivatives which may occur in a problem in terms of more convenient variables, more precisely, in terms of variables which enter easily measurable equations of state. For example, it may be advantageous to express partial derivatives in terms of such other partial derivatives as contain only the variables P, v,

---

[†] A comprehensive and systematic listing can be found in Bridgman, P. W., *A Condensed Collection of Thermodynamic Formulas* (Harvard Univ. Press, 1925; reprinted by Dover, 1961).

and T, in view of the importance of the thermal equation of state in measurement. This procedure involves the application of the "cancelling rule" displayed in equation (3.45a).

The preceding remarks do not lead to a universal formula which includes all others as special cases, but demonstrate that with the aid of the identity (12.27) it is possible to proceed systematically towards a set goal; in other words, it permits the formulation of an algorithm. By way of example, we shall investigate all the consequences which flow from equation (12.27) when x, y are chosen from among the four variables P, v, T, s. There are in all six combinations of these, but the pairs (P, v) and (T, s) would obviously lead to trivial results. Hence, there remain the four combinations

$$v, s; \quad P, s; \quad T, v; \quad \text{and} \quad P, T.$$

Substituting the first pair, we obtain

$$\frac{\partial(P, v)}{\partial(v, s)} = \frac{\partial(T, s)}{\partial(v, s)} \quad \text{or} \quad -\left(\frac{\partial P}{\partial s}\right)_v = \left(\frac{\partial T}{\partial v}\right)_s,$$

which is Maxwell's first reciprocal relation, Table 12.1. It is evident that the remaining substitutions will lead to the derivation of the remaining three Maxwellian reciprocal relations.†

12.5   The specific heats

The study of the mathematical properties of the two specific heats of a simple homogeneous system, useful in itself, affords several additional examples of the ease with which thermodynamic relations can be derived when Jacobians are employed. It will be remembered that the two specific heats are defined as

$$c_v = \left(\frac{\partial u}{\partial T}\right)_v, \tag{12.28a}$$

$$c_p = \left(\frac{\partial h}{\partial T}\right)_P, \tag{12.28b}$$

which are symmetric with respect to each other, in that each of them constitutes a partial derivative of a potential, internal energy u or enthalpy h, with respect to temperature when the canonical variable other than the entropy is maintained constant, Table 12.1. Thus, a comparable symmetry must be expected to exist in the two sets of expressions.

The first useful step is to relate the specific heats to the other canonical variable for the respective potential, namely, to entropy. This has been done already for c_v in equation (12.6) which can be written as

$$c_v(T, v) = T\left(\frac{\partial s}{\partial T}\right)_v. \tag{12.29a}$$

---

† Many generations of thermodynamicists have searched for easy mnemonic rules which would make it possible to write down the four reciprocal relations from memory. It appears that the use of Jacobian notation together with the identity (12.27) achieves the purpose with a minimum of effort.

Similarly, and by an analogous derivation, it is possible to show that

$$c_p(T, P) = T\left(\frac{\partial s}{\partial T}\right)_P. \tag{12.29b}$$

The equations (12.29a, b) exhibit the symmetry between the expressions for the two specific heats.

By the use of Jacobians we can obtain two expressions for the difference $c_p - c_v$, in the following manner. Equation (12.29a) can be written

$$c_v = T\frac{\partial(s, v)}{\partial(T, v)}.$$

In order to obtain c_p from equation (12.29b) on the right-hand side of the preceding equation, it is evidently necessary to introduce $\partial(T, P)$. In this manner

$$c_v = T\frac{\partial(s, v)/\partial(T, P)}{\partial(T, v)/\partial(T, P)} = T\frac{\left(\frac{\partial s}{\partial T}\right)_P\left(\frac{\partial v}{\partial P}\right)_T - \left(\frac{\partial s}{\partial P}\right)_T\left(\frac{\partial v}{\partial T}\right)_P}{\left(\frac{\partial v}{\partial P}\right)_T}.$$

This transforms to

$$c_v = c_p - T\frac{\left(\frac{\partial s}{\partial P}\right)_T\left(\frac{\partial v}{\partial T}\right)_P}{\left(\frac{\partial v}{\partial P}\right)_T},$$

which can be written in the simple form

$$c_p - c_v = -T\left\{\left(\frac{\partial v}{\partial T}\right)_P\right\}^2 \Big/ \left(\frac{\partial v}{\partial P}\right)_T \tag{12.30a}$$

if account is taken of Maxwell's fourth reciprocal relation (Table 12.1). The symmetric expression is obtained simply by replacing v with P and vice versa, as is easily inferred from a comparison on the forms in equations (12.29a) and (12.29b). Alternatively, steps analogous to the preceding ones can be followed. Hence,

$$c_p - c_v = -T\left\{\left(\frac{\partial P}{\partial T}\right)_v\right\}^2 \Big/ \left(\frac{\partial P}{\partial v}\right)_T. \tag{12.30b}$$

It will be shown in Volume II that for any stable substance, that is for any real substance, we must have

$$\left(\frac{\partial P}{\partial v}\right)_T < 0, \tag{12.31a}$$

or, what amounts to the same

$$\left(\frac{\partial v}{\partial P}\right)_T < 0. \tag{12.31b}$$

The inequalities express the fact that during isothermal compression ($\Delta P > 0$), the volume of the system must decrease ($\Delta V < 0$), and vice versa. Thus, equations (12.30a) and (12.30b) demonstrate that

$$c_p - c_v > 0 \quad \text{or} \quad c_p > c_v,$$

as anticipated in Sections 5.14.2 and 11.8.1.

It is useful to introduce the coefficients of thermal expansion, tension, and isothermal compressibility from equations (3.16), (3.18) into equations (12.30a) and (12.30b), whence we obtain

$$c_p - c_v = T\beta^2 v/\kappa \tag{12.32a}$$

or

$$c_p - c_v = TP^2 v\kappa\pi^2. \tag{12.32b}$$

The two equations (12.32a) and (12.32b) are identical, in view of the relation in equation (3.35); they are very useful in computing the difference in the specific heats $c_p - c_v$ for substances for which the isothermal compressibility and the coefficient of thermal expansion are easily measured or nearly constant, that is essentially for liquid and solid phases. The importance of the preceding expressions for the difference $c_p - c_v$ is enhanced by the fact that the specific heat at constant pressure is more easily measured than that at constant volume, because in a calorimeter it is simpler to maintain the pressure constant than its volume. In practice, calorimetric determinations of the specific heat c_v are made only exceptionally.

The equivalent inequalities (12.31a, b) will be derived rigorously in Volume II as already stated. Nevertheless, it is useful to demonstrate their validity by a more heuristic, physical argument. In order to do this we shall consider the system sketched in Figure 12.1, in which a quantity of the substance is contained in a cylinder closed by a weighted, ideal piston. The weight G is so chosen that equilibrium with the internal pressure P of the substance prevails. The cylinder remains in contact with a reservoir of temperature T which ensures that the temperature remains constant throughout. It is clear that a change in the weight G by a positive or negative amount $\pm\Delta G$ must result in a new position of equilibrium. We now proceed to show that this will be impossible if

$$\left(\frac{\partial P}{\partial v}\right)_T > 0. \tag{12.33}$$

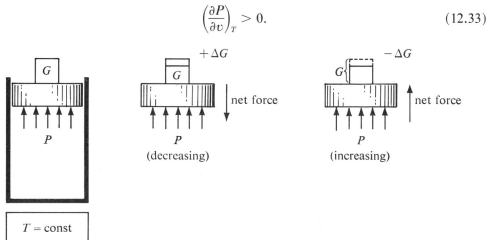

FIGURE 12.1. *Stability of a simple system.*

Suppose that a weight ΔG has been added to the piston. The piston will then experience a downward force and will accelerate downwards, that is, in the direction of decreasing volume. On the other hand, on the hypothesis expressed by the inequality (12.33), a new position of equilibrium, if it exists, must entail an increase in volume. It is seen, therefore, that the piston will move away from the potential new position of equilibrium, and in doing so will be opposed by a decreasing pressure so that it will increase its acceleration as a result. Consequently, and contrary to observation, it will fail to reach a new position of equilibrium. Similarly, for a decrease in weight by an amount $-\Delta G$, the piston will accelerate upwards, and its acceleration will be augmented by the increasing internal pressure P, as demanded by the erroneous assumption (12.33). It will be seen to move away from a possible position of equilibrium (at a decreased volume) under the action of an increasing force.

The rigorous proof of inequality (12.31a) in Volume II will also yield the result that $c_v > 0$, hence, it will follow that $c_p > 0$. Consequently,

$$\gamma \geq 1. \tag{12.34}$$

It follows, furthermore, that the internal energy of any system, as well as its enthalpy, must be monotonically increasing functions of temperature, at constant volume for internal energy, and at constant pressure for enthalpy. These conclusions follow immediately if equations (12.28a, b) are imagined integrated with respect to temperature for $c_v > 0$ and $c_p > 0$, respectively.

The two specific heats can be related to the thermal equation of state in a simple way by evaluating the right-hand sides of equations (12.29a) and (12.29b) with the aid of equations (12.16a) and (12.16b). Noting that

$$F_1(T, v) = \int_{v^*}^{v} \left(\frac{\partial P}{\partial T}\right)_v dv \quad \text{and that} \quad F_2(T, P) = -\int_{P^*}^{P} \left(\frac{\partial v}{\partial T}\right)_P dP,$$

we obtain

$$c_v(T, v) = T\int_{v^*}^{v} \left(\frac{\partial^2 P}{dT^2}\right)_v dv + T\frac{d\phi_1(T)}{dT} \tag{12.35a}$$

and

$$c_p(T, P) = -T\int_{P^*}^{P} \left(\frac{\partial^2 v}{\partial T^2}\right)_P dP + T\frac{d\phi_2(T)}{dT}. \tag{12.35b}$$

These relations are very important, because they provide a method of obtaining the two functions ϕ_1 and ϕ_2 which appear in the expressions for entropy. It is easy to see that these functions are directly related to the specific heats. More precisely, if the specific heat c_v is known as a function of temperature along the reference isochore v^*, or if the specific heat c_p is known as a function of temperature along the reference isobar P^*, the functions ϕ_1 and ϕ_2 can be determined from the relations

$$\frac{d\phi_1(T)}{dT} = \frac{c_v(T, v^*)}{T},$$

$$\frac{d\phi_2(T)}{dT} = \frac{c_p(T, P^*)}{T},$$

which integrate to

$$\phi_1(T) = \int_{T^*}^{T} \frac{c_v(T, v^*)}{T} \, dT, \tag{12.36a}$$

$$\phi_2(T) = \int_{T^*}^{T} \frac{c_p(T, P^*)}{T} \, dT. \tag{12.36b}$$

Either of the integrations now involves a function of one variable, temperature T only, and consequently the values of ϕ_1 and ϕ_2 can be fixed arbitrarily for the reference temperature $T = T^*$. They have been fixed at

$$\phi_1(T^*) = \phi_2(T^*) = 0 \tag{12.36c}$$

in the preceding two expressions.

Equations (12.36a) and (12.36b) demonstrate that the entropy of a substance can be completely determined if the thermal equation of state is known from experiment, and if *in addition* one of the specific heats is known as a function of temperature, along an isochore for c_v or along an isobar for c_p, it being clear that equations (12.29a) and (12.29b) provide two alternative, but equivalent expressions for entropy. This fact can be recorded in the equations:

$$s(v, T) - s(v^*, T^*) = \int_{v^*}^{v} \left(\frac{\partial P}{\partial T}\right)_v \, dv + \int_{T^*}^{T} \frac{c_v(T, v^*)}{T} \, dT, \tag{12.37a}$$

$$s(P, T) - s(P^*, T^*) = -\int_{P^*}^{P} \left(\frac{\partial v}{\partial T}\right)_P \, dP + \int_{T^*}^{T} \frac{c_p(T, P^*)}{T} \, dT. \tag{12.37b}$$

These circumstances were recognized, even though not explicitly, in Section 11.1.3. In the case of a perfect gas $c_v^\circ(T) = \lim c_v(T, v^*)$ with $v^* \to \infty$ and $c_p^\circ(T) = \lim c_p(T, P^*)$ when $P^* \to 0$. The quantities $s_v^\circ(T)$ and $s_p^\circ(T)$ denote values of the last integrals in equations (12.37a, b).

Having calculated entropy, either as a function of the variables P, v or of the variables P, T we are in a position to calculate all other properties, including internal energy and enthalpy. That this can be done in principle, is clear from Table 12.1. A convenient method of achieving this aim will be outlined in the next section. At this stage it should be noted that the knowledge of the thermal equation of state together with the variation of one specific heat with temperature along the reference isochore or isobar constitutes the experimental information which is both *necessary and sufficient* to establish all the thermodynamic properties of a substance. Together, they play the part of a fundamental equation. It is evident that the above does not constitute the *only* possibility and that certain measurements can be replaced by others, thus, requiring a different scheme of computation. However, the present scheme has been used most widely, notably in the calculation of steam tables,† because precise experimental data of this kind can be obtained reasonably easily.

---

† See, for example, Keenan, J. H., and Keyes, F. G., *Thermodynamic Properties of Steam* (Wiley, 1936). Schmidt, E., *VDI-Wasserdampftafeln* [6th ed. A (kcal, at), ed. B (Joule, bar), Springer, 1963]. Vukalovich, M. P., *Thermodynamic Properties of Water and Steam* (6th ed.; Moscow State Publishing-House, 1958).

In turn, the specific heats at all other states can be computed from the relations which result when the values (12.36a, b) are substituted in (12.35a, b), or

$$c_v(T, v) = T\int_{v*}^{v} \left(\frac{\partial^2 P}{\partial T^2}\right)_v dv + c_v(T, v*),$$ (12.38a)

$$c_p(T, P) = -T\int_{P*}^{P} \left(\frac{\partial^2 v}{\partial T^2}\right)_P dP + c_p(T, P*).$$ (12.38b)

The last two equations can also be written in the form

$$\left(\frac{\partial c_v}{\partial v}\right)_T = T\left(\frac{\partial^2 P}{\partial T^2}\right)_v \quad \text{or} \quad \left(\frac{\partial c_p}{\partial P}\right)_T = -T\left(\frac{\partial^2 v}{\partial T^2}\right)_P,$$ (12.39a, b)

which show that the dependence of the specific heats on volume or pressure is completely determined by the thermal equation of state, whereas their complete dependence on temperature is not. Equations (12.39a, b) have been first derived by R. Clausius. Their utility is somewhat limited, since even an accurate thermal equation of state will lead to rather inaccurate values of the second derivatives which appear on the right-hand sides of the preceding equations.

12.6   Internal energy and enthalpy

In this section we shall continue our inquiry into the extent to which the thermal equation of state determines the thermodynamic potentials of a simple chemical system, and will turn our attention to internal energy and enthalpy. It is evident from a scrutiny of Table 12.1 and from the derivation contained in Section 12.3 that reference must now be made to the forms of the respective total differentials

$$\begin{aligned}du &= Tds - P\,dv,\\ dh &= Tds + v\,dP,\end{aligned}$$ (12.40a, b)

and that the simplest formulae will be obtained if only one of the canonical variables, s, v for internal energy and s, P for enthalpy, will be eliminated. Hence, we shall concentrate on the functions

$$u(T, v) \quad \text{and} \quad h(T, P),$$

noting, further, the symmetry in equations (12.40a, b) which must result in a certain symmetry in the above expressions for internal energy and enthalpy. No such symmetry could be expected with a different choice of variables.

Applying equations (12.40a, b) to an isothermal path, we obtain

$$\left(\frac{\partial u}{\partial v}\right)_T = T\left(\frac{\partial s}{\partial v}\right)_T - P$$

and

$$\left(\frac{\partial h}{\partial P}\right)_T = T\left(\frac{\partial s}{\partial P}\right)_T + v.$$

Eliminating the derivatives of entropy with the aid of the third and fourth reciprocal relations, we obtain the desired formulas, namely

$$
\left.\begin{aligned}
\left(\frac{\partial u}{\partial v}\right)_T &= T\left(\frac{\partial P}{\partial T}\right)_v - P, \\
\left(\frac{\partial h}{\partial P}\right)_T &= -T\left(\frac{\partial v}{\partial T}\right)_P + v.
\end{aligned}\right\}
\qquad (12.41\mathrm{a,\ b})
$$

Equation (12.41b) is already familiar to the reader as equation (11.8) when it was derived in a less systematic manner. Both equations can be contracted, if it is noted that the terms $-P$ and v can be absorbed in the derivatives by transforming the dependent variables in them to P/T and v/T, respectively. We then obtain the equations

$$
\left.\begin{aligned}
\left(\frac{\partial u}{\partial v}\right)_T &= T^2\left(\frac{\partial (P/T)}{\partial T}\right)_v, \\
\left(\frac{\partial h}{\partial P}\right)_T &= -T^2\left(\frac{\partial (v/T)}{\partial T}\right)_P,
\end{aligned}\right\}
\qquad (12.42\mathrm{a,\ b})\dagger
$$

whose equivalence with equations (12.41a, b) can be verified by carrying out explicitly the differentiations indicated. These equations can now be integrated with respect to a reference state P^*, v^*, T^*, in the same manner as was done for entropy in Section 12.2. Integration yields

$$
u(v,\ T) - u(v^*,\ T) = T^2 \int_{v^*}^{v} \left(\frac{\partial (P/T)}{\partial T}\right)_v \, \mathrm{d}v,
$$

$$
h(P,\ T) - h(P^*,\ T) = -T^2 \int_{P^*}^{P} \left(\frac{\partial (v/T)}{\partial T}\right)_P \, \mathrm{d}P.
$$

Proceeding in the same way as in the case of entropy in Section 12.5, we find that

$$
\left.\begin{aligned}
c_v(v,\ T) &= \left(\frac{\partial u}{\partial T}\right)_v = \int_{v^*}^{v} \frac{\partial}{\partial T}\left[T^2\left(\frac{\partial (P/T)}{\partial T}\right)_v\right]\mathrm{d}v + \frac{\mathrm{d}u(v^*,\ T)}{\mathrm{d}T} \\
c_p(P,\ T) &= \left(\frac{\partial h}{\partial T}\right)_P = -\int_{P^*}^{P} \frac{\partial}{\partial T}\left[T^2\left(\frac{\partial (v/T)}{\partial T}\right)_P\right]\mathrm{d}P + \frac{\mathrm{d}h(P^*,\ T)}{\mathrm{d}T}.
\end{aligned}\right\}
\ (12.43\mathrm{a,\ b})
$$

At $v = v^*$ and $P = P^*$, respectively, the integrals vanish, and the functions of temperature $u(v^*,\ T)$ and $h(P^*,\ T)$ can be expressed in terms of the respective specific heats by integration. Thus,

$$
u(v^*,\ T) - u(v^*,\ T^*) = \int_{T^*}^{T} c_v(v^*,\ T)\mathrm{d}T,
$$

$$
h(P^*,\ T) - h(P^*,\ T^*) = \int_{T^*}^{T} c_p(P^*,\ T)\mathrm{d}T,
$$

† These equations can also be written in terms of derivatives with respect to the reciprocal temperatures $1/T$ as follows:

$$
\left(\frac{\partial u}{\partial v}\right)_T = -\left(\frac{\partial (P/T)}{\partial (1/T)}\right)_v,
$$

$$
\left(\frac{\partial h}{\partial P}\right)_T = \left(\frac{\partial (v/T)}{\partial (1/T)}\right)_P,
$$

which may prove convenient for graphical evaluation.

and finally

$$
\left.
\begin{aligned}
u(v, T) - u(v^*, T^*) &= \int_{v^*}^{v} T^2\left(\frac{\partial (P/T)}{\partial T}\right)_v \, \mathrm{d}v + \int_{T^*}^{T} c_v(v^*, T)\mathrm{d}T, \\
h(P, T) - h(P^*, T^*) &= -\int_{P^*}^{P} T^2\left(\frac{\partial (v/T)}{\partial T}\right)_P \, \mathrm{d}P + \int_{T^*}^{T} c_p(P^*, T)\mathrm{d}T.
\end{aligned}
\right\}
\quad (12.44\text{a, b})
$$

The last two equations demonstrate, as was the case with entropy, that the internal energy and enthalpy of a pure substance can be computed when the thermal equation of state is known from experiment, together with the variation with temperature of one of the specific heats along the reference isochore or isobar, as the case may be. It is evident that, in principle, only one of the functions u or h need be evaluated. If the function $h(v, T)$ were needed, it is simplest to use the relation

$$h(v, T) = u(v, T) + P(v, T) \cdot v.$$

Alternatively, if $u(P, T)$ were required, it could be obtained from

$$u(P, T) = h(P, T) - P \cdot v(P, T).$$

It is also noteworthy that the thermal equation of state completely determines the dependence of internal energy on volume or of enthalpy on pressure. The variation of these two functions with temperature is given jointly by the thermal equation of state and one of the specific heats, taken along an isochore or an isobar, respectively. The constants $u(v^*, T^*)$ and $h(P^*, T^*)$ can, of course, be assigned completely arbitrary values.

Equations (12.43a, b) could now be used to calculate the specific heats at any state, but it is easy to see that they are identical with the previously derived equations (12.33a, b), as they should be. As already remarked, their utility for the evaluation of the two specific heats is only moderate because even an accurate empirical function leads to second derivatives which are of marginal accuracy only. In practice, it is preferable to determine the enthalpy of a substance by direct measurements. As a rule, these yield an empirical form of the function $h(P, T)$ since the intensive parameters, pressure P and temperature T, are most easily controlled in the laboratory. When a set of measurements of this type is available, the specific heat c_p can be obtained by a single differentiation from its definition

$$c_p(P, T) = \left(\frac{\partial h(P, T)}{\partial T}\right)_P.$$

The knowledge of the specific heat c_v is seldom required. However, if needed, equation (12.30a) can be used, noting that the function on its right-hand side is expressed in terms of the independent variables P and T.

12.7 Isentropic processes

During isentropic processes, the entropy of the system remains constant, and the process can be discussed in terms of derivatives which are analogous to the coefficients of thermal expansion, tension and isothermal compressibility. The rate of change of volume with temperature is described by the derivative

$$\left(\frac{\partial v}{\partial T}\right)_s$$

and the rate of change of pressure with temperature, by

$$\left(\frac{\partial P}{\partial T}\right)_s.$$

The preceding derivatives are not, habitually, formed into relative coefficients, like the coefficient of thermal expansion, or tension. On the other hand the relative change of volume with pressure

$$\kappa_s = -\frac{1}{v}\left(\frac{\partial v}{\partial P}\right)_s$$

is sometimes referred to as the *isentropic compressibility*.

As already emphasized on several prior occasions, it is advantageous to express the preceding quantities in terms of derivatives which can be deduced from the thermal equation of state. Accordingly, following the algorithm discussed in Section 12.4, we write for the first one

$$\left(\frac{\partial v}{\partial T}\right)_s = \frac{\partial(v, s)}{\partial(T, s)} = \frac{\partial(v, s)/\partial(v, T)}{\partial(T, s)/\partial(v, T)} = -\frac{(\partial s/\partial T)_v}{(\partial s/\partial v)_T}$$

$$= \frac{c_v}{T}\left(\frac{\partial v}{\partial s}\right)_T = -\frac{c_v}{T}\frac{\partial(v, T)}{\partial(s, T)} = \frac{c_v}{T}\frac{\partial(v, T)}{\partial(P, v)} = -\frac{c_v}{T}\left(\frac{\partial T}{\partial P}\right)_v, \qquad (12.45)$$

or, alternatively

$$\left(\frac{\partial v}{\partial T}\right)_s = -\frac{c_v}{T\pi P} = -\frac{c_v\kappa}{T\beta}. \qquad (12.45a)$$

Similarly, it is possible to show that

$$\left(\frac{\partial P}{\partial T}\right)_s = \frac{c_p}{T}\left(\frac{\partial T}{\partial v}\right)_P \qquad (12.46)$$

or

$$\left(\frac{\partial P}{\partial T}\right)_s = \frac{c_p}{Tv\beta}. \qquad (12.46a)$$

In the last equation, all quantities, except the coefficient of thermal expansion, are positive. Thus, the rate of change of temperature with pressure in an isentropic process, or $(\partial T/\partial P)_s$, has the same sign as the coefficient of thermal expansion. Normally, the coefficient of thermal expansion is positive, which proves that, normally, upon isentropic compression, the temperature of the system increases, and decreases upon expansion. Water, and a few other substances, such as bismuth, exhibit anomalous behavior in certain ranges, as already remarked in Section 7.4.2. It will be remembered that in those ranges their specific volume decreases upon heating at constant pressure which is equivalent to their having a negative coefficient of thermal expansion. For example, at a pressure of 1 atmosphere, the specific volume of water decreases when its temperature is increased from 0°C to 4°C, and in this range

$$\beta < 0, \quad \text{so that} \left(\frac{\partial T}{\partial P}\right)_s < 0 \qquad \text{(water 0°C to 4°C at 1 atm)}.$$

Consequently, upon isentropic compression in the above range of temperatures, the temperature of water will decrease, increasing upon isentropic expansion. This behavior is termed anomalous because it is at variance with that expected from most substances.

For the isentropic compressibility, it is possible to write

$$\kappa_s = -\frac{1}{v}\left(\frac{\partial v}{\partial P}\right)_s = -\frac{1}{v}\frac{\partial(v, s)}{\partial(P, s)} = -\frac{1}{v}\frac{\partial(v, s)/\partial(v, T)}{\partial(P, s)/\partial(P, T)}\frac{\partial(v, T)}{\partial(P, T)}$$

$$= -\frac{1}{v}\frac{(\partial s/\partial T)_v}{(\partial s/\partial T)_P}\left(\frac{\partial v}{\partial P}\right)_T = -\frac{1}{v}\frac{c_v}{c_p}\left(\frac{\partial v}{\partial P}\right)_T, \tag{12.47}$$

or

$$\kappa_s = \frac{\kappa}{\gamma}. \tag{12.47a}$$

Since, as shown earlier, $\gamma > 1$, the isentropic compressibility is always *smaller* in absolute value than the corresponding isothermal compressibility.

Introducing the values for the difference $c_p - c_v$ from equations (12.30a, b) or (12.31a, b), we can obtain the useful relations:

$$\left(\frac{\partial v}{\partial P}\right)_s = \left(\frac{\partial v}{\partial P}\right)_T + \frac{T}{c_p}\left[\left(\frac{\partial v}{\partial T}\right)_P\right]^2, \tag{12.48a}$$

$$\left(\frac{\partial P}{\partial v}\right)_s = \left(\frac{\partial P}{\partial v}\right)_T - \frac{T}{c_v}\left[\left(\frac{\partial P}{\partial T}\right)_v\right]^2. \tag{12.48b}$$

Alternatively,

$$\kappa_s = \kappa - \frac{T\beta^2 v}{c_p}, \tag{12.49a}$$

$$\frac{1}{\kappa_s} = \frac{1}{\kappa} + \frac{T\beta^2 v}{\kappa^2 c_v}. \tag{12.49b}$$

12.8 The Joule-Thomson coefficient

The Joule-Thomson, porous plug or throttling experiment was first discussed in Section 6.17.3 where it was shown that it can be used to determine the partial derivative $(\partial T/\partial P)_h$ since during the process the enthalpy of the final state of equilibrium is equal to that of the initial state of equilibrium. By the application of the cyclic relation in equation (3.34), or by the use of the properties of Jacobians, it is easy to demonstrate that

$$\left(\frac{\partial T}{\partial P}\right)_h = \frac{\partial(T, h)}{\partial(P, h)} = \frac{\partial(T, h)/\partial(P, T)}{\partial(P, h)/\partial(P, T)} = -\frac{(\partial h/\partial P)_T}{(\partial h/\partial T)_P},$$

or

$$\left(\frac{\partial T}{\partial P}\right)_h = -\frac{(\partial h/\partial P)_T}{c_p}. \tag{12.50}$$

The coefficient $(\partial h/\partial P)_T$ can be measured directly during an isothermal throttling process (Section 6.17.3); alternatively, it can be determined from the thermal equation of state, as already discussed in Section 12.6, equation (12.41b). In this manner

$$\mu = \left(\frac{\partial T}{\partial P}\right)_h = \frac{T\left(\frac{\partial v}{\partial T}\right)_P - v}{c_p} = \frac{T^2}{c_p}\left[\frac{\partial(v/T)}{\partial T}\right]_P. \qquad (12.51)\dagger$$

Joule-Thomson experiments involving adiabatic or isothermal throttling are frequently performed for the purpose of providing experimental material either to determine the specific heat c_p with the aid of equation (12.50), or to provide additional experimental data which can be used as tests of consistency for direct measurements of specific heats and the thermal equation of state. The values of the specific heat c_p are not required for the whole range of states, since c_p can be represented as the sum of the specific heat measured at a constant pressure P^*, and of derivatives which can be obtained from the thermal equation of state, equation (12.38b). Whether one or another relation can or should be used depends on a careful assessment of errors. In this connection it is necessary to bear in mind that two relations which are mathematically equivalent may lead to results which are incommensurate as far as their probable errors are concerned. The results of measurements on Joule-Thomson coefficients are not extremely accurate. A typical accuracy is one of 1–2%. Nevertheless, the measurements can be very useful.

The diagram of the variation of the adiabatic Joule-Thomson coefficient implied in Figure 6.28 or for the isothermal Joule-Thomson coefficient $(\partial h/\partial P)_T$ implied in Figure 6.30 are typical for all substances.

It is useful to determine the rate of change of entropy along the line $h = $ const which characterizes the Joule-Thomson process (but does not represent it, since the process is irreversible). From the familiar relation (Table 12.1)

$$ds = \frac{1}{T}dh - \frac{v}{T}dP$$

it follows at once that

$$\left(\frac{\partial s}{\partial P}\right)_h = -\frac{v}{T}. \qquad (12.52)$$

Since during a process $P_2 < P_1$, we must consider that $dP < 0$, and hence, that $ds > 0$, as might have been foreseen.

12.9 The Joule coefficient

The inquisitive reader will have grasped that the Joule experiment involving the unresisted expansion of a gas provides an analog of the throttling, porous plug experiment. It is, therefore, not difficult to write down the following three equations which are the exact counterparts of equations (12.50), (12.51) and (12.52) of the preceding section. Thus,

$$\left(\frac{\partial T}{\partial v}\right)_u = -\frac{(\partial u/\partial v)_T}{c_v},$$

† Also

$$\left(\frac{\partial T}{\partial P}\right)_h = -\frac{1}{c_p}\left(\frac{\partial(v/T)}{\partial(1/T)}\right)_P$$

that is,

$$\left(\frac{\partial T}{\partial v}\right)_u = \frac{P - T(\partial P/\partial T)_v}{c_v} = -\frac{T^2}{c_v}\left[\frac{\partial(P/T)}{\partial T}\right]_v, \tag{12.51a}†$$

and

$$\left(\frac{\partial s}{\partial v}\right)_u = \frac{P}{T}. \tag{12.52a}$$

The preceding equations can be commented upon in terms analogous to those in the preceding section. It must, however, be added that the process of unresisted adiabatic expansion is of very little practical importance compared with the Joule-Thomson process. The latter can be used, as the reader will recall, for the liquefaction of gases as well as for the study of thermodynamic properties (Section 12.8). The same cannot be said about the Joule experiment under discussion mainly because its accuracy is very poor. In fact, Gay-Lussac first devised the process of unresisted expansion when he set out to study the properties of gases in 1806. Later, Joule repeated the experiment, only to discover its unreliability and lack of precision. He, therefore, together with Sir William Thomson (the future Lord Kelvin), devised the throttling process which is much more amenable to being performed accurately. As far as the study of the properties of gases is concerned, the Washburn experiment performed by Rossini and Frandsen in 1932 (Section 6.18.2) constituted a further step forward. For this reason, no important experimental results on the coefficients $(\partial T/\partial v)_u$ and $(\partial u/\partial v)_T$ are available. They can, if found necessary, be *evaluated* from the equations of this section, but their experimental determination would not be undertaken since superior methods of achieving the same aims can always be found.

The reader is naturally curious to know whether the variation in temperature with pressure at constant internal energy is also connected with an inversion, in analogy with the Joule-Thomson process. The answer to this question is positive. We shall revert to it in connection with a more detailed discussion of the virial equation for gases in Volume II.

12.10   Condition for internal energy and enthalpy to be functions of temperature only

Under certain conditions, the internal energy or the enthalpy of a system can become functions of temperature alone, singly or simultaneously. Since the volume or pressure dependence, respectively, of these two properties are completely determined by the thermal equation of state, it is clear that any one of the preceding conditions imposes a mathematical restriction on the form of the thermal equation of state.

The internal energy will become a function of temperature alone when it is independent of specific volume, that is, when

$$\left(\frac{\partial u}{\partial v}\right)_T = 0. \tag{12.53}$$

† Also

$$\left(\frac{\partial T}{\partial v}\right)_u = \frac{1}{c_v}\left(\frac{\partial(P/T)}{\partial(1/T)}\right)_v$$

Equivalently, as seen from equation (12.42a), this implies that

$$\left(\frac{\partial(P/T)}{\partial T}\right)_v = 0,$$

or, upon integration, that

$$\frac{P}{T} = f(v), \tag{12.54}$$

where the function $f(v)$ plays the part of a constant of integration, and is quite arbitrary.

In an analogous manner, the enthalpy becomes independent of pressure, and hence a function of temperature alone, when

$$\left(\frac{\partial h}{\partial P}\right)_T = 0, \tag{12.53a}$$

that is, by the integration of equation (12.42b), when

$$\frac{v}{T} = \phi(P), \tag{12.54a}$$

with an arbitrary form of $\phi(P)$.

For example, the perfect-gas law $Pv = RT$ is of this form with

$$f(v) = \frac{R}{v} \quad \text{and} \quad \phi(P) = \frac{R}{P}.$$

Both conditions (12.53a, b) are satisfied simultaneously if and only if

$$\frac{P}{f(v)} = \frac{v}{\phi(P)} = T,$$

so that

$$P\phi(P) = vf(v);$$

this is possible only on condition that

$$\phi(P) = \frac{A}{P} \quad \text{and} \quad f(v) = \frac{B}{v},$$

where A and B are both equal, and equal to a constant, say R. Thus,

$$Pv = RT$$

is the only form for which the two conditions are satisfied simultaneously. For example, the equation of state

$$v = \text{const}$$

of an incompressible fluid is not of form (12.54) or (12.54a). However, for $v = \text{const}$, the derivative (12.53) cannot be formed, and it is necessary to stipulate $(\partial u/\partial P)_T = 0$. Reference to equation (12.21) shows that $v = \text{const}$ implies $(\partial u/\partial P)_T = 0$, and reference to equation (12.42b) shows that $(\partial h/\partial P)_T \neq 0$, or, more precisely, that $(\partial h/\partial P)_T = v$.

In the case of a general system whose state depends on two independent variables Y and Z such that

$$dW^\circ = Y\,dZ, \quad \text{and} \quad h = u + YZ,$$

the most general form of the equation $F(Y, Z, T) = 0$ which leads to

$$\left(\frac{\partial u}{\partial Z}\right)_T = 0$$

is

$$Y = T \cdot f(Z). \tag{12.53b}$$

If we consider a paramagnetic salt, we put $Y = \mathscr{H}$ and $Z = \mathscr{M}$, and the required form is

$$\mathscr{H} = T \cdot f(\mathscr{M}).$$

Curie's equation of state $\mathscr{M} = C\mathscr{H}/T$ (Section 8.5.8) is also of a form which describes a substance whose internal energy is a function of temperature alone.

The analogous condition for enthalpy leads to

$$\frac{Z}{T} = \phi(Y) \quad \text{or to} \quad \frac{\mathscr{M}}{T} = \phi(\mathscr{H}) \tag{12.54b}$$

which is not satisfied by Curie's equation.

It is clear that if $u = u(T)$, then the specific heat $c_v = (\partial u/\partial T)_v$, or, more generally, the specific heat $c_z = (\partial u/\partial T)_z$, is also a function of temperature alone. However, the enthalpy $h = u + Pv$ or $h = u + YZ$ need not be a function of temperature alone.

Similarly, if the enthalpy is a function of temperature only, the specific heat c_p or c_Y must also be functions of temperature exclusively. However, specific heats c_v or c_z need not possess that property. Evidently, in the case of a perfect gas both conditions are satisfied simultaneously.

12.11 Simple examples of fundamental equations

Though unobtainable by direct measurement, a fundamental equation of state contains within it a statement of all thermodynamic properties of a system; these describe the equilibrium states which the system is capable of achieving under all circumstances. (It does not, however, contain enough information to describe the system's transport properties which govern its behavior as it performs quasistatic irreversible processes.) Given a fundamental equation of state—in whatever form—we can deduce from it a complete set of tables, diagrams and similar aids to analysis. The difficulty usually resides in formulating such an equation of state for practical systems with sufficient accuracy and over a sufficiently wide range of states. With the advent of computers, it is possible to handle very complex relations and the thought is expressed that, ultimately, all thermodynamic properties of substances will become available in the form of computer programs, each based on an appropriate fundamental equation of state.†

---

†The Sixth International Conference on the Properties of Steam which met in 1963 in Providence and New York appointed an International Formulating Commission and charged it with the task of working in this direction.

The task of deriving a fundamental equation of state can be carried out explicitly when the properties of the system are simple enough, and we now propose to display two such examples. In all cases we shall follow the algorithm established in Section 12.5 which relies on the fact that the thermal equation of state combined with the knowledge of one specific heat function is equivalent to a fundamental equation of state. As usual, we shall denote the arbitrary reference state by a star superscript, and stipulate that two potentials assume the value zero there.

The fundamental equation $h = h(s, P)$ for an incompressible fluid or solid subjected to uniform pressure and possessing a constant specific heat c has already been derived when its temperature-entropy chart was discussed in Section 11.2.1. It is equation (11.84), namely,

$$h = cT^*(e^{s/c} - 1) + v^*(P - P^*). \tag{12.55}$$

The equation $u = u(s, v)$ cannot be derived, because $v = v^*$ is now a constant and not an independent variable. In general, it is worth noting that the family of isobars (but not isotherms or isochores) in a Mollier h, s diagram represents the level lines of the fundamental equation $h = h(s, v)$ and define it geometrically.

The fundamental equations $u(s, v)$ and $h(s, P)$ for an ideally perfect gas are equally easy to derive. All that is required is to eliminate the temperature from the equations for energy and entropy, namely,

$$u = c_v(T - T^*) \quad \text{and} \quad s = c_v \ln \frac{Tv^{\gamma-1}}{T^*(v^*)^{\gamma-1}}.$$

The result is

$$u = c_v T^* \left\{ \left(\frac{v^*}{v}\right)^{R/c_v} e^{s/c_v} - 1 \right\}, \tag{12.56}$$

where $\gamma - 1 = R/c_v$ has been substituted. In an analogous manner, we would obtain

$$h = c_p T^* \left\{ \left(\frac{P}{P^*}\right)^{R/c_p} e^{s/c_p} - 1 \right\}, \tag{12.56a}$$

from

$$h = c_p(T - T^*) \quad \text{and} \quad s = c_p \ln \frac{T/P^{(\gamma-1)/\gamma}}{T^*/(P^*)^{(\gamma-1)/\gamma}}.$$

Evidently, h and u cannot vanish simultaneously, because $h - u = Pv = RT$. Hence, the arbitrary constants in equations (12.56) and (12.56a) are not quite the same.

List of Symbols for Chapter 12

Latin letters

A	Function defined in equation (12.11); first virial coefficient
B	Function defined in equation (12.10a); second virial coefficient
C	Function; third virial coefficient
c_p	Specific heat at constant pressure

c_v	Specific heat at constant volume
F, f	Helmholtz function (or free energy)
f	Function defined in equation (12.54)
G, g	Gibbs function (or free enthalpy)
G	Weight
H	Enthalpy
h	Specific enthalpy
$\mathcal{H}$	Hamiltonian; magnetic field intensity
j	Massieu function
K	Constant of proportionality between perfect-gas and thermodynamic temperature scales.
$\mathcal{L}$	Lagrangian
$\mathcal{M}$	Magnetization
n	Number of degrees of freedom
P	Pressure
p	Generalized momentum
Q	Heat
q	Generalized coordinate
R	Gas constant
$\mathbf{R}$	Universal gas constant
s	Specific entropy
T	Thermodynamic temperature
U	Internal energy
u	Specific internal energy; generalized velocity
V	Volume
v	Specific volume
W	Work
X	General variable, equation (12.8)
x	Independent variable
Y	General variable, equation (12.8); intensive parameter or generalized force
y	Independent variable; Planck function
Z	General variable, equation (12.8); extensive parameter or generalized displacement
z	Independent variable

Greek letters

α	Linear coefficient of thermal expansion
β	Coefficient of thermal expansion
γ	Ratio of specific heats, c_p/c_v
θ	Empirical temperature scale
κ	Isothermal coefficient of compressibility
κ_s	Isentropic coefficient of compressibility
μ	Joule-Thomson coefficient
π	Coefficient of tension
ϕ_1, ϕ_2	Functions defined in equations (12.17a, 12.17b)
ϕ	Function defined in equation (12.54a)

Superscripts

*	Reference state
°	Reversible process

Subscripts

3	Triple point
m	Molar quantity

CHAPTER 13

Some Consequences of the Second Part of the Second Law of Thermodynamics. Entropy Production

13.1 General remarks

Chapters 11 and 12 were devoted to the exploration of some of the consequences of the first part of the Second Law of thermodynamics. These reduced themselves to the determination of relations between the thermodynamic properties of systems. Such relations must be satisfied by all systems if their behavior is to be consistent with the existence of the thermodynamic potential which is called entropy. The thermodynamic relations between properties are, naturally, insufficient to determine the properties themselves, but lead to an understanding of the minimum amount of experimentation required to determine them completely.

The present chapter will be devoted to the exploration of some of the consequences of the second part of the Second Law of thermodynamics which asserted that the entropy of an adiabatic system must increase when an irreversible process takes place within it. Thus, our attention will be focused on irreversible processes. Another, and equivalent, way of stating the principle of entropy increase is to assert that an irreversible process generates entropy. This was done in a preliminary way in Section 10.6, where it also transpired that in the particular cases examined there, this increase in entropy could be related in a simple way to the work termed "lost" or rendered "unavailable" owing to the irreversible process, for example, in equation (10.47). This mode of expression allows us to free ourselves from the need to analyze all processes in terms of an adiabatic system and displays the connection between the entropy generated by an irreversible process and the concept of energy dissipated by a system, undoubtedly known to the reader from his studies of friction in mechanics or of related dissipative phenomena in electricity and magnetism.

13.2 Engine efficiencies

As our first example, Figure 13.1, we consider an *adiabatic system* consisting of a source of heat, T, a sink of heat, T_0, and a cyclic engine e which operates irreversibly.

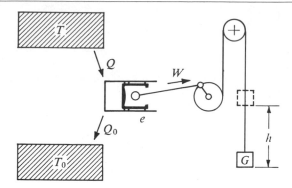

FIGURE 13.1. *Irreversible cyclic engine.*

During one cycle, the engine extracts heat Q, rejects heat Q_0, and produces work

$$W = Q - |Q_0|, \qquad (13.1)$$

symbolized by the weight G which is raised over a distance h in a standard gravitational field.

The change in entropy of the engine per cycle is zero, because the engine reverts periodically to its initial state. Hence, the change in the entropy of the system is associated with the source and sink only. Bearing in mind the idealized properties of the latter, we can write

$$\Delta S = \Delta S_{\text{source}} + \Delta S_{\text{sink}} = -\frac{Q}{T} + \frac{|Q_0|}{T_0} > 0, \qquad (13.2)$$

because in (imaginary) reversible processes of heat addition and extraction, the source will lose entropy $\Delta S_{\text{source}} = -Q/T$, whereas the sink will gain entropy $\Delta S_{\text{sink}} = +|Q_0|/T_0$. By the second part of the Second Law, the algebraic sum (13.2) must be positive.

It is instructive to compare the operation of the real engine e in Figure 13.1 with that of a *reversible* Carnot engine c, Figure 13.2, which consumes the same quantity of heat $Q^\circ = Q$ per cycle. The Carnot engine will reject a different quantity of heat, Q_0°, and will produce work

$$W^\circ = Q - |Q_0^\circ| \neq W, \qquad (13.3)$$

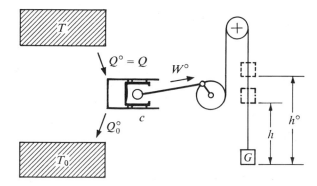

FIGURE 13.2. *Reversible Carnot engine.*

thus, raising weight G over a different distance $h°$. In this case

$$\Delta S° = \Delta S_{\text{source}} + \Delta S_{\text{sink}} = -\frac{Q}{T} + \frac{|Q_0°|}{T_0} = 0, \tag{13.4}$$

as we know from Sections 9.11 and 10.6.3. It is easy to see from equations (13.1) and (13.3) that

$$|Q_0| = Q - W = |Q_0°| + (W° - W).$$

Hence,

$$\Delta S = -\frac{Q}{T} + \frac{|Q_0°|}{T_0} + \frac{W° - W}{T},$$

or, in view of equation (13.4),

$$\Delta S = \frac{W° - W}{T}. \tag{13.5}$$

Since the latter quantity is positive, it is seen that

$$W° > W,$$

which means that the work of a reversible Carnot engine exceeds that of any other engine operating between the same source and sink for the same amount of heat consumed. Thus, the quantity

$$W_{\text{loss}} = W° - W$$

can be regarded as work lost, dissipated, or made unavailable owing to the irreversible nature of the real engine; it represents the work which could be obtained ideally, but which is lost to us actually. Since $|Q_0| = |Q_0°| + (W° - W)$, it is evident that the difference W_{loss} is rejected to the sink by the real engine in addition to heat $Q_0°$. Thus, compared with a Carnot engine, a real engine produces less work and rejects more heat for the same amount of heat consumed. The same result would be achieved if we operated the reversible engine c, raised the weight G to height $h°$ ($W° = Gh°$) and then *lowered* it to height $h(W = Gh)$, converting the equivalent of the work lost

$$W_{\text{loss}} = G(h° - h)$$

into heat by friction or Joule heat, and rejecting this heat to the sink in addition to the previously rejected heat $|Q_0°|$. Thus, the entropy of the system is raised by an amount $\Delta S = (W° - W)/T$. For this reason, we are justified in *saying* that the real engine *produces* the amount of entropy ΔS from equation (13.5) by virtue of the fact that it performs an irreversible process.

   In engineering applications, the ratio $W/W°$ of the real work measured on the brake of a reciprocating engine to that which could be obtained ideally under identical circumstances is usually represented as the product of two factors

$$\frac{W}{W°} = \frac{W}{W_i} \cdot \frac{W_i}{W°},$$

where W_i denotes the work

$$W_i = \oint P \, dV,$$

which is measured by an indicator connected to the real engine. Such an indicator traces the variation of pressure with volume inside the cylinder and represents the quantity of work which could be obtained if the engine were mechanically perfect. The ratio

$$\eta_m = \frac{W}{W_i} \tag{13.6}$$

is called the mechanical efficiency of the engine; it represents the loss of work by mechanical imperfections, such as friction between the piston and cylinder, friction in the bearings and the work consumed by auxiliary mechanisms, for example, a fuel pump, a camshaft drive, and so on. The ratio

$$\eta_r = \frac{W_i}{W^\circ} \tag{13.7}$$

represents the loss compared with the most ideal operation in the circumstances — a Carnot cycle in the present case. This ratio is variously known as the *relative efficiency*, *efficiency ratio*, or the *diagram factor* of the engine. The ratio

$$\eta_0 = \frac{W}{Q} \tag{13.8}$$

is known as the *brake thermal efficiency* of the engine. Evidently,

$$\eta_0 = \frac{W}{Q} = \frac{W^\circ}{Q} \cdot \frac{W_i}{W^\circ} \cdot \frac{W}{W_i} = \eta_C \eta_r \eta_m, \tag{13.9}$$

where η_C is the Carnot efficiency, W°/Q, of the most ideal cycle. The ratio

$$\eta_i = \frac{W_i}{Q} \tag{13.10}$$

is called the indicated thermal efficiency, and

$$\eta_0 = \eta_i \eta_m. \tag{13.11}$$

Since

$$W^\circ - W = W^\circ \left(1 - \frac{W}{W^\circ}\right) = W^\circ (1 - \eta_r \eta_m),$$

it is seen that the quantity of entropy produced per cycle

$$\Delta S = \frac{W^\circ}{T_0} (1 - \eta_r \eta_m)$$

is related to the product $\eta_r' = \eta_r \eta_m$ of relative and mechanical efficiency.[†] Thus, the various efficiencies defined above, and widely used in engineering practice, constitute alternative and dimensionless measures of the amount of entropy produced by the inevitable, irreversible processes in a real engine. In more practical cases, a comparison is made with an idealized, reversible cycle which more nearly corresponds to the operation of the actual engine than the most efficient, Carnot cycle, because it is realized that the latter can never be attained or even approached in practice.

† See also equation (10.51).

13.3   Calorimetric mixing

As a further example, we shall examine the process of temperature equalization between two systems 1 and 2 which are allowed to come to equilibrium within an adiabatic enclosure, Figure 13.3, as a consequence of the removal of a slide. This is a process which occurs in an adiabatic calorimeter when a body of temperature T_1 is immersed, say, in a quantity of water of temperature T_2, without a change in phase. Thus, chemical reactions, mixing, evaporation, melting, allotropic changes, and so on are excluded from further consideration at the moment; we shall revert to the process of mixing in Section 13.5. We shall further assume that the systems are incompressible and that the specific heats c_1 and c_2 of the two systems are constant and independent of temperature, denoting the products m_1c_1 and m_2c_2 of mass and specific heat by the symbols C_1 and C_2. The quantities C_1 and C_2 are known as the water equivalents or as the heat capacities† of the systems.

By the application of the First Law, we can evaluate the temperature T_m which sets in when final equilibrium has been attained. Thus,

$$T_m = \frac{C_1 T_1 + C_2 T_2}{C_1 + C_2}. \tag{13.12}$$

In order to calculate the change in entropy during the process, we shall replace the actual phenomenon by two reversible processes. During one, the system 1 is cooled from T_1 to T_m by an infinite succession of sinks of heat. Hence

$$\Delta S_1 = C_1 \int_{T_1}^{T_m} \frac{dT}{T} = C_1 \ln \frac{T_m}{T_1},$$

because $dQ° = C\, dT$. Similarly, the reversible heating of system 2 from T_1 to T_m will produce a change in entropy

$$\Delta S_2 = C_2 \int_{T_2}^{T_m} \frac{dT}{T} = C_2 \ln \frac{T_m}{T_2}.$$

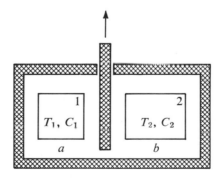

FIGURE 13.3. *Calorimetric mixing.*

---

† In books on chemical thermodynamics, the term "heat capacity" is often used for the quantity which we prefer to call "specific heat."

Evidently, $\Delta S_2 > 0$ and $\Delta S_1 < 0$, but the algebraic sum

$$\Delta S = C_1 \ln \frac{T_m}{T_1} + C_2 \ln \frac{T_m}{T_2} = \ln \left(\frac{T_m}{T_1}\right)^{C_1} \left(\frac{T_m}{T_2}\right)^{C_2} > 0, \qquad (13.13)$$

as demanded by the principle of entropy increase.

Denoting†

$$\alpha_1 = \frac{C_1}{C_1 + C_2} \quad \text{and} \quad \alpha_2 = \frac{C_2}{C_1 + C_2},$$

we can write

$$T_m = \alpha_1 T_1 + \alpha_2 T_2,$$

and

$$\Delta S = (C_1 + C_2) \ln T_m - C_1 \ln T_1 - C_2 \ln T_2 > 0.$$

Dividing by $C_1 + C_2$, we conclude that

$$\ln (\alpha_1 T_1 + \alpha_2 T_2) > \ln T_1^{\alpha_1} + \ln T_2^{\alpha_2},$$
$$\alpha_1 T_1 + \alpha_2 T_2 > T_1^{\alpha_1} \cdot T_2^{\alpha_2}.$$

In the special case $\alpha_1 = \alpha_2 = \frac{1}{2}$, the preceding inequality becomes

$$\tfrac{1}{2}(T_1 + T_2) > (T_1 \cdot T_2)^{\frac{1}{2}}. \qquad (13.14)$$

This is the well-known rule which states that the arithmetical mean of two numbers is always greater than their geometrical mean. It is curious that this rule can be derived by the application of the Second Law of thermodynamics.

In the case of *n* bodies, equation (13.12) becomes

$$T_m = \frac{\sum_n C_i T_i}{\sum_n C_i},$$

whereas equation (13.14) changes to

$$\Delta S = \ln \prod_n \left(\frac{T_m}{T_i}\right)^{C_i} > 0,$$

where $\prod_n$ denotes the product of *n* terms $(T_m/T_i)^{C_i}$

Retracing our preceding steps, we can easily derive a generalized form of the mathematical rule (13.14). This reads

$$\sum_n \alpha_i T_i > \prod_n T_i^{\alpha_i} \quad \text{with} \quad \sum_n \alpha_i = 1.$$

The equation states that the arithmetical mean of the weighted sum of *n* quantities T_i, formed with the weighting factors α_1, is greater than the weighted geometrical mean in which the weighting factors appear in the exponents.

The calculation of the amount of work made unavailable in this process is left as an exercise for the reader.

---

† See Sommerfeld, A., *Thermodynamics and Statistical Mechanics* translated by J. Kestin (*Lectures on Theoretical Physics*, Vol. V) (Academic, 1956) p. 358. Purely algebraic proofs of these propositions can be found in Hardy, G. H., Littlewood, J. E., Pólya, G., and Szegö, G. *Inequalities* (Cambridge Univ. Press, 1934), p. 17.

13.4 Adiabatic throttling

When a gas is throttled *adiabatically*, its enthalpy h_2 after the throttle is equal to that before the throttle, h_1. Consequently, the calculation of entropy can proceed along an imaginary, reversible isenthalpic process between states 1 and 2, and we may write

$$S_2 - S_1 = \int_1^2 \frac{dQ^\circ}{T} \qquad \text{(along } h = \text{const).}$$

The First Law of thermodynamics, in the form

$$dQ^\circ = dh - v\,dP \qquad (13.15)$$

leads to the conclusion that

$$dQ^\circ = -v\,dP \qquad \text{along } h = \text{const,}$$

per unit mass of gas. Hence,

$$s_2 - s_1 = -\int_1^2 \frac{v}{T}\,dP \qquad \text{along } h = \text{const.} \qquad (13.16)$$

In order to evaluate this integral, it is necessary to know the relation between the composite property v/T and the pressure P along an isenthalpic line. In most cases this relation is quite complex, as we shall see in detail in Volume II. Restricting attention to perfect gases, we remember that $h = $ const implies $T = $ const, and that $v/T = R/P$. With these restrictions, equation (13.16) can be easily integrated to give

$$s_2 - s_1 = -\int_1^2 R\,\frac{dP}{P} = R\,\ln\frac{P_1}{P_2}. \qquad (13.17)$$

The increase in entropy upon throttling, always remembering the restrictive conditions under which equation (13.17) has been derived, is seen to depend on the pressure ratio P_1/P_2 alone, regardless of the particular value of enthalpy. For example, throttling from 100 atm to 10 atm produces the same amount of entropy as throttling from 1 atm to 0.1 atm. Moreover, per one mol

$$s_2 - s_1 = \mathbf{R}\,\ln\frac{P_1}{P_2}; \qquad (13.17a)$$

thus, the amount of entropy produced in the system per one mol turns out to be independent of the chemical nature of the gas.

It is now useful to verify directly that during the process of adiabatic throttling ($Q = 0$) the resulting entropy increase *cannot* be obtained by integrating the actual amount of heat, divided by the absolute temperature, in conformity with Clausius' inequality discussed in Section 9.11.

If the gas were to undergo the same change of state as it does during adiabatic throttling, that is, if the gas were to perform a reversible process at constant enthalpy, it would be capable of producing positive work

$$W^\circ = \int_1^2 P\,dv \qquad \text{at } h = \text{const,}$$

per unit mass. In order to integrate the expression for work, it is now necessary to know the relation between P and v along an isenthalpic. A glance at Figure 6.28 suggests that at low enough pressures and at sufficiently high temperatures, an isenthalpic line is close to an isotherm over a wide range of states. Consequently, in the range of applicability of our present equations, $h = $ const implies $T = $ const and $Pv = $ const, and the gas can be treated as perfect. For a perfect gas, the two become exactly identical. Thus,

$$P \, dv + v \, dP \approx 0, \quad \text{and} \quad P \, dv \approx -v \, dP,$$

and

$$W^\circ \approx -\int_1^2 v \, dP \qquad \text{along } T \approx \text{const.}$$

This is the amount of work which could be obtained from the gas (naturally, at the expense of an equivalent quantity of heat and internal energy), but which is lost owing to the irreversibility of the process. Upon comparing with equation (13.17), it is seen that

$$s_2 - s_1 \approx -\frac{\int_1^2 v \, dP}{T} = \frac{W_{\text{loss}}}{T}, \tag{13.18}$$

since $W_{\text{loss}} = W^\circ$.

When an incompressible fluid is throttled, the requirement that the enthalpy, equation (7.13), must be the same at the initial as at the final state leads to the relation

$$v(P_1 - P_2) = \int_{T_1}^{T_2} c(T) \, dT, \tag{13.18a}$$

which allows us to calculate the change in temperature for a given pressure drop. With $c = $ const,

$$v(P_1 - P_2) = c(T_2 - T_1). \tag{13.18b}$$

The entropy increase upon throttling is

$$s_2 - s_1 = c \ln T_2/T_1 \qquad (\text{for } c = \text{const}), \tag{13.18c}$$

as we know from equation (13.18a). Thus, the requirement that $s_2 > s_1$ shows that $T_2 > T_1$ and that, therefore, $P_1 > P_2$, as confirmed by experiments.

13.5 Mixing and diffusion

When discussing the process of calorimetric mixing in Section 13.3, we were careful to point out that the equations for entropy increase discussed there did not apply to cases when mixing involved the diffusion of one substance into another. We shall now proceed to discuss this possibility, leaving the related case when a chemical reaction can also occur to Volume II. In the course of this analysis, we shall discover that the process of mixing several chemically distinct substances entails an additional increase in entropy, that is, an increase in entropy which exists even if the components are at the same temperature and pressure. That this must be so can be foreseen from the fact that isothermal mixing constitutes an irreversible process, it being clear that the reverse process of separation never occurs spontaneously.

Bearing in mind the complexities of mixing outlined in Sections 6.13 and 7.5, we shall concentrate on ideal mixtures, starting with gases. It is recalled that the adiabatic diffusion of gases at low enough densities (strictly speaking, in the limit $\rho \to 0$) is isothermal, isobaric and isochoric at the same time. Thus, outwardly nothing changes, and the only parameter which varies during the process is the composition. In cases like this, it is often said that the composition constitutes an *internal parameter* of the system.

Our aim is to relate the entropy of the ideal mixture of perfect gases to the sum of the entropies of the components, when measured at the same pressure and temperature, and thus to compute the amount of entropy produced when an ideal mixture is created by diffusion from a number of components of equal pressure and temperature consequent upon the removal of the partitions between them.

13.5.1 Semipermeable membranes

To achieve our aim, it is necessary to devise a *reversible* process of mixing. A way of accomplishing this was first indicated clearly by J. H. van 't Hoff who introduced the concept of a *semipermeable membrane* or *partition* into the study of thermodynamics, after their existence in nature had been discovered by the botanist W. Pfeffer.

A semipermeable membrane is imagined to possess the property that it is completely impervious to one gas, with respect to which it behaves like a solid wall, being completely permeable to any other. Thus, as far as any other gas is concerned, the semipermeable membrane is unable to offer resistance to its pressure. The other gases pass through it unhindered, and are, so to speak, ignored by the membrane. This property of a semipermeable membrane is illustrated in Figure 13.4 in which the material of membrane a is supposed to be impervious to gas 1 but permeable to gas 2. A piston made of this material experiences a force PA when exposed to gas 1 on one side of it, but no force at all when exposed to gas 2.

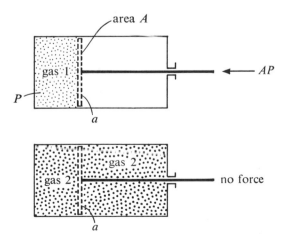

FIGURE 13.4. *Idealized properties of a semipermeable membrane.*

Contrary to what might be supposed at first, semipermeable membranes are quite common in nature, but their ability to discriminate between substances is not as extreme as that stipulated here. Walls of organic cells constitute semipermeable membranes, and the chemical processes of life depend crucially on this fact. Without semipermeable membranes, organic life, as we know it, would be impossible. Artificial approximations to semipermeable membranes can be made of thin, incandescent sheets of palladium or platinum which are permeable to hydrogen, even though the equalization of pressure across such a wall may take a long time. Liquid films are permeable to gases which dissolve in the liquid, such as sulphur dioxide or ammonia in water, but gases which are not easily soluble will be held back. A further example is afforded by the clay wall of a Daniell cell, Section 8.2, which impedes the mixing of the solutions of copper and zinc sulphate but allows ions of SO_4^{--} to pass freely. Thus, the concept of a perfect semipermeable membrane constitutes an idealization from observation of a kind which is quite common in thermodynamics. The limitations of making wider industrial use of semipermeable membranes are due to the fact that there exist no good structural materials which possess this property to a sufficient degree of perfection.

13.5.2   *Equilibrium across a semipermeable membrane*

When a mixture of two gases 1 and 2 at pressure P is contained behind a piston a_2, Figure 13.5, which is permeable to gas 2 but impervious to gas 1, a quantity of gas 2 will pass through it on to the other side. At equilibrium, the pure gas 2 will assume a pressure $\widetilde{P}_2 < P$. The maintenance of equilibrium requires the application of a static force AP_1 which is due entirely to the pressure P_1 exerted on the piston by gas 1 in the mixture. At a given temperature, the characteristic pressure $\widetilde{P}_i$ which establishes itself behind a piston permeable to component i depends on the total pressure P and on the composition of the mixture. We shall call this pressure the *membrane pressure* of the component. It will be seen presently that in an ideal mixture of perfect gases, the membrane pressure $\widetilde{P}_i$ is identical with the partial pressure of the component, that is, with the pressure which would be exerted by it if it alone occupied the total volume V of the mixture at the temperature under consideration.

On examining Figure 13.5, it might appear that the net force acting on piston a_2 is equal to $A(P - \widetilde{P}_2)$. This would be the case if the piston were impermeable to both gases, and care must be taken not to confuse this case with the case when the piston

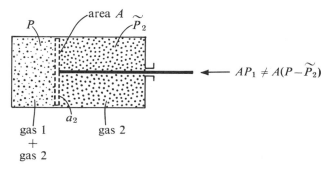

FIGURE 13.5. *Membrane equilibrium.*

is permeable to gas 2 only. The equality $AP_1 = A(P - \widetilde{P}_2)$ is satisfied only in the exceptional case when the mixture is ideal and contains perfect gases. Otherwise,

$$AP_1 \neq A(P - \widetilde{P}_2).$$

The preceding representation allows us to think (microscopically) that gas 2 exerts pressure $\widetilde{P}_2$ in the mixture, and that the sum of the membrane pressures of the components fails to be equal to the total pressure P owing to forces exerted between the molecules of different gases when they exist in close proximity.

13.5.3   Reversible separation

With the aid of semipermeable walls, it is possible to construct, at least conceptually, devices which can be used to separate or to mix gases *reversibly*. One such device is shown sketched in Figure 13.6. The arrangement consists of two cylinders, b_1 and b_2, which can slide with respect to each other without friction. Cylinder b_1 is connected rigidly with piston a_2 which is permeable to gas 2, whereas cylinder b_2 is closed with a membrane a_1 which is permeable only to gas 1. The remaining walls are impermeable to both gases. At state a the cylinders are collapsed and contain a homogeneous mixture of gases 1 and 2 at pressure P and temperature T in volume V. When the cylinders are moved apart quasistatically, state b, the left compartment of cylinder b_1 will contain a quantity of gas 1 in membrane equilibrium with the mixture. Similarly, the right compartment of cylinder b_2 will contain a quantity of gas 2 in membrane equilibrium with the mixture. The process of pulling the cylinders apart requires no expenditure of work. The forces acting on cylinder b_1 stem from gas 1 alone, the pure gas on the left wall, and gas 1 in the mixture on the right wall. Thus, all forces acting on cylinder b_1 are in equilibrium and the same is true of cylinder b_2. The process is imagined performed isothermally, but, as we already know, the process is also adiabatic, and no exchange of heat takes place. At state c, the gases are separated completely, and this result has been achieved *reversibly* with $W° = Q° = 0$. Performing the process in the reverse direction, we could perform *reversible mixing* also with $Q° = W° = 0$.

It is now apparent that the membrane pressures $\widetilde{P}_1$ and $\widetilde{P}_2$ are equal to the partial pressures $P_1 = x_1 P$ and $P_2 = x_2 P$ of the component gases in the mixture (see Section 7.5), if the latter is ideal and if the gases are perfect. Thus, in this case the membrane pressure of a component is synonymous with its partial pressure. In the study of non-ideal mixtures the term "partial pressure" is frequently used for what we call here "membrane pressure." However, this usage does not lead to ambiguities, because the concept of a partial pressure, as it was defined in Section 7.5 (the pressure exerted by the component when it alone occupies the total volume of the mixture at the temperature of the mixture), has no physical significance, and only membrane pressures need to be considered. Nevertheless, in this book, a clear distinction will be made between these two concepts.

Since no heat is exchanged, no work is expended, and the process is reversible, the First and Second Laws lead to the conclusion that the energy of the system as well as its entropy are equal in states a and c. Thus,

$$U(T, n_1, n_2) = n_1 u_1(T) + n_2 u_2(T), \tag{13.19}$$

where the symbols without subscript refer to the mixture, and those with subscripts

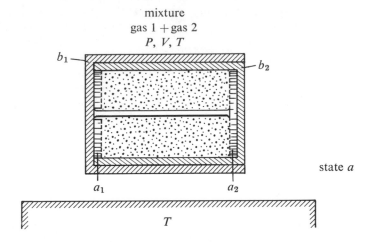

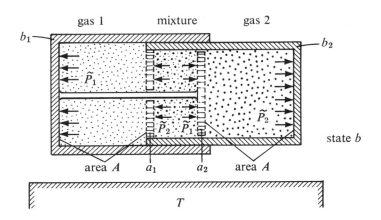

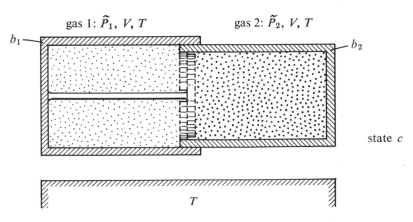

FIGURE 13.6. *Reversible separation of gases.*

refer to the component gases. Similarly,

$$S(P, T, n_1, n_2) = n_1 s_1(P_1, T) + n_2 s_2(P_2, T). \tag{13.20}$$

The preceding equations can be immediately generalized to α component gases:

$$U(T, n_1, \ldots, n_\alpha) = \sum_1^\alpha n_i u_i(T), \tag{13.19a}$$

$$S(P, T, n_1, \ldots, n_\alpha) = \sum_1^\alpha n_i s_i(P_i, T). \tag{13.20a}$$

The symbol P has been omitted in the list of variables for internal energy, because the internal energy of a perfect gas is independent of pressure. The same cannot be done for entropy as is clear from equations (11.19b) and (11.24).

Equation (13.20a) expresses the Gibbs-Dalton rule which states that *the entropy of an ideal mixture of perfect gases is equal to the sum of the entropies of its components, each taken at the common temperature but at the **partial** pressure of the component in the mixture.*

Introducing the mol fractions $x_i = n_i/n$, we can also write

$$\left. \begin{aligned} u(T, x_1, \ldots, x_{\alpha-1}) &= \sum_1^\alpha x_i u_i(T), \\ s(P, T, x_1, \ldots, x_{\alpha-1}) &= \sum_1^\alpha x_i s_i(P_i, T), \end{aligned} \right\} \tag{13.21a, b}$$

remembering that only $\alpha - 1$ fractions are independent since

$$\sum_1^\alpha x_i = 1.$$

Similar equations can be written in terms of mass units.

13.5.4   Entropy of mixing

In equations (13.20a) and (13.21b), the specific quantities for the components are not measured at the total pressure P of the mixture, which would be preferable. In order to derive such alternative relations, it is possible to make use of the device shown in Figure 13.7. Accordingly, we start with state a when two gases are separated, each under pressure P but occupying the *partial volumes* V_1 and V_2, respectively, as shown at the top of Figure 13.7. Before reversible mixing can take place, it is necessary to reduce the pressure of the components to the anticipated partial pressures. This must be done *reversibly*. Therefore, during process $a \rightarrow b$ both gases are expanded isothermally (and hence, also isoenergetically, because they are perfect) in the two expansion cylinders e_1 and e_2 and charged into the two compartments of the mixing box m.

During the processes of reversible isothermal expansion, work W_1 and W_2 is performed by each gas, and the quantities of heat Q_1 and Q_2 must be exchanged with the surroundings at temperature T. From the First Law it is known that

$$W_1 = Q_1 \quad \text{and} \quad W_2 = Q_2, \tag{13.22}$$

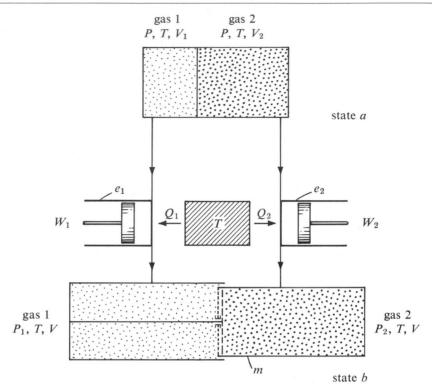

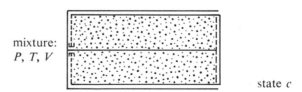

FIGURE 13.7. *Reversible mixing.*

because for a perfect gas isothermal processes are isoenergetic. The reversible mixing during process $b \rightarrow c$ is also adiabatic. Hence, the only quantities of heat exchanged reversibly are Q_1 and Q_2, and both are exchanged at constant temperature. Therefore,

$$S_c - S_a = \int_a^c \frac{dQ^\circ}{T} = \frac{Q_1 + Q_2}{T} = \frac{W_1 + W_2}{T};$$ (13.23)

in view of equation (13.22). The reversible work W of an isothermal expansion can be calculated with the aid of the integral

$$W = \int_a^b P \, dV,$$

where $P = n\mathbf{R}T/V$ for a perfect gas. Hence,

$$W_1 = n_1\mathbf{R}\,T\ln\frac{V}{V_1} \quad\text{and}\quad W_2 = n_2\mathbf{R}\,T\ln\frac{V}{V_2}. \tag{13.24}$$

Substitution into equation (13.23) allows us to calculate the total change in entropy

$$\Delta S = S(P,\,T,\,n_1,\,n_2) - \{S_1(P,\,T) + S_2(P,\,T)\} = n_1\mathbf{R}\,T\ln\frac{V}{V_1} + n_2\mathbf{R}\,T\ln\frac{V}{V_2}. \tag{13.25}$$

Recalling that $x_i = n_i/n = V_i/V = P_i/P$, we can also write

$$\Delta S = n_1\mathbf{R}\ln\frac{P}{P_1} + n_2\mathbf{R}\ln\frac{P}{P_2} \tag{13.25a}$$

or

$$\Delta S = n\mathbf{R}(x_1\ln 1/x_1 + x_2\ln 1/x_2), \tag{13.26}$$

with similar equations for mass quantities.

When the gases are allowed to diffuse through each other adiabatically, that is, isothermally when they are perfect, upon the removal of the partition at state a, state c will result directly and irreversibly. In this process, the change in entropy is the same as that calculated for the reversible process between the same end states. Since the arguments of the logarithmic terms are greater than unity, the entropy of the final state exceeds that of the initial state. Equations (13.25a) and (13.26) represent *the entropy generated during the irreversible process*. The form of equation (13.25a), when compared with equation (13.17a), allows us to recognize that the increase in entropy is the same as if each gas were to be regarded as a throttle for the other. Similarly, the form of equation (13.23) shows that the amount of entropy generated during the irreversible process is equal to

$$\Delta S = \frac{W_{\text{loss}}}{T},$$

where $W_{\text{loss}} = W_1 + W_2$ represents the work which could be obtained if the process were reversible, and which is not made available during the irreversible process.

The preceding equations can be written at once for α components in the mixture:

$$S(P,\,T,\,n_1,\,\ldots,\,n_\alpha) - \sum_1^\alpha n_i s_i(P,\,T) = \mathbf{R}\sum_1^\alpha n_i\ln\frac{P}{P_i} = \mathbf{R}\sum_1^\alpha n_i\ln\frac{n}{n_i}, \tag{13.27}$$

or, upon division by $n = \Sigma n_i$,

$$s(P,\,T,\,x_1,\,\ldots,\,x_{\alpha-1}) - \sum_1^\alpha x_i s_i(P,\,T) - n\mathbf{R}\sum_1^\alpha x_i\ln(1/x_i), \tag{13.27a}$$

with analogous equations in mass units. The expressions

$$\mathbf{R}\sum_1^\alpha n_i\ln P/P_i = \mathbf{R}\sum_1^\alpha n_i\ln n/n_i = n\mathbf{R}\sum_1^\alpha x_i\ln(1/x_i) \tag{13.28}$$

are known as the *mixing terms*, because their presence is due entirely to the mixing process.

13.5.5   Work of reversible separation

In order to separate the components in a mixture, it is necessary to supply *work*. When separation is performed reversibly and isothermally, for example by reversing the processes shown schematically in Figure 13.7, it is necessary to supply work

$$W = T\Delta S$$
$$= n\mathbf{R}T\Sigma x_i \ln (1/x_i). \tag{13.29}$$

For an *equimolar* mixture of two perfect gases of equal parts by volume,

$$W = n\mathbf{R}T(\tfrac{1}{2} \ln 2 + \tfrac{1}{2} \ln 2) = 0.693 \, n\mathbf{R}T.$$

The work of reversible separation increases with temperature, decreasing for mixtures of unequal parts. This work is independent of the chemical nature of the components; it depends exclusively on the total number of mols n (and composition), that is, on the product

$$n\mathbf{R}T = mRT = PV.$$

13.5.6   Gibbs' paradox

The mixing terms (13.28) obviously do not exist if the components are identical, for then no diffusive process sets in when the partition is removed. On the other hand, the full amount of entropy is produced even if the gases differ from each other ever so slightly. Thus, when the properties of the gases are made to approach each other continuously, the same amount of entropy is produced at each stage, provided the composition is the same, except in the limit, when it suddenly vanishes. This conclusion is certainly unexpected. It is known under the name of *Gibbs' paradox* after J. W. Gibbs who was the first to notice it. As pointed out by A. Sommerfeld,[†] in view of the *atomistic nature* of substances, including gases, the difference between their properties can never be made vanishingly small, and the mental process of continuously changing their properties to a common limit has no counterpart in nature. As long as the gases are distinguishable by some operational means, the full amount of entropy is produced. Consequently, the full amount of entropy is produced if two (chemically indistinguishable) isotopes of the same gas are mixed. Even further, the diffusion of ortho- and para-hydrogen which differ merely by their spins produces the full amount of entropy. The latter disappears only if the molecules are *completely indistinguishable*.

The limiting process which leads to Gibbs' paradox is carried out at constant composition and stipulates continuously variable properties. This process must be clearly distinguished from a limiting process in which the properties are kept constant but the composition is varied. For example, in the case of two gases, the change in entropy is

$$\Delta S = -n\mathbf{R}[x \ln x + (1 - x) \ln (1 - x)], \tag{13.30}$$

where x is the mol fraction of one component, $1 - x$ being that of the other. In the first process, nothing changes in the equation. In the second process if $x = x_1 \to 0$ then $x_2 = 1 - x \to 1$. Since $\lim x \ln x = 0$ when $x \to 0$, it is seen that the mixing term ΔS tends continuously to zero when less and less of one component is involved. Naturally,

† *Thermodynamics and Statistical Mechanics*, translated by J. Kestin (Academic, 1956), p. 80.

when $x_2 = 1 - x \to 0$ with $x_1 = x \to 1$, the limit $\Delta S = 0$ is also reached continuously. Consequently, by symmetry, there must exist a maximum in ΔS,

$$\Delta S_{\max} = n\mathbf{R} \ln 2, \tag{13.30a}$$

for an equimolar mixture when $x_1 = x_2 = 0.5$. In a mixture of α components, the contribution of component i tends to zero when its molar fraction x_i tends to zero. Thus, we are often justified in ignoring the contributions to the mixing term which stem from the ever-present impurities in gases.

13.5.7 Dilute solutions

It is recalled from Section 7.5.8 that a dilute solution of $\alpha - 1$ solutes in solvent 1 is also ideal. Making use of equation (7.71) which resulted from a Taylor-series expansion in the small parameters $n_i \ll n_1$, we can write for the volume

$$V = n_1 v_1(T, P) + \sum_2^\alpha n_i v_i(T, P), \tag{13.31}$$

and for the energy

$$U = n_1 u_1(T, P) + \sum_2^\alpha n_i u_i(T, P). \tag{13.31a}$$

The entropy of the solution can be calculated by employing a reversible mixing box, as was done for perfect gases. However, in order to vary the method, we prefer to perform a direct integration of the familiar equation

$$dS = \frac{dQ^\circ}{T} = \frac{dU + P \, dV}{T},$$

equation (11.1b). We shall integrate along a path of *constant composition* with variable pressure and temperature. Hence,

$$dS = n_1 \frac{du_1 + P \, dv_1}{T} + \sum_2^\alpha n_i \frac{du_i + P \, dv_i}{T}.$$

In this manner, we obtain α perfect differentials of the form

$$dS_i(T, P) = n_i \frac{du_i + P \, dv_i}{T},$$

and

$$S = n_1 s_1(T, P) + \sum_2^\alpha n_i s_i(T, P) + C(n_1, n_2, \ldots, n_\alpha).$$

The constant of integration $C(n_1, n_2, \ldots, n_\alpha)$ is constant only with respect to the variables of integration P and T, and its value must depend on the mol numbers n_i. In order to determine this constant, we shall follow a suggestion made by M. Planck[†] and utilize the fact that the pressure P and temperature T are arbitrary. Accordingly, we imagine that the pressure has been lowered and that the temperature has been raised sufficiently for *all components* to evaporate and to turn into perfect gases. With the aid of this stratagem, it becomes clear that the constant of integration C must be equal

[†] *Theory of Heat (Introduction to Theoretical Physics*, Vol. V) transl. by H. L. Brose (Macmillan, 1932), p. 120; or Fermi, E., *Thermodynamics* (Dover, 1956), p. 115.

to the mixing term for an ideal solution of perfect gases given in equation (13.28). Hence,

$$C(n_1, n_2, \ldots, n_\alpha) = -\mathbf{R}n_1 \ln \frac{n_1}{n_1 + n_2 + \cdots + n_\alpha} - \mathbf{R} \sum_2^\alpha n_i \ln \frac{n_i}{n_1 + n_2 + \cdots + n_\alpha}.$$

It is convenient to simplify these terms by making use of the fact $n_i/n_1 \ll 1$. The first term can be expanded into the series

$$n_1 \ln \frac{n_1}{n_1 + n_2 + \cdots + n_\alpha} = n_1 \ln \frac{1}{1 + \dfrac{n_2}{n_1} + \cdots + \dfrac{n_\alpha}{n_1}} \approx n_1 \ln \left(1 - \frac{n_2}{n_1} - \cdots - \frac{n_\alpha}{n_1} \right)$$

$$\approx -(n_2 + n_3 + \cdots + n_\alpha).$$

The typical term for a solute becomes simply

$$n_i \ln \frac{n_i}{n_1 + n_2 + \cdots + n_\alpha} \approx n_i \ln \frac{n_i}{n_1} \qquad (i \geqslant 2).$$

It follows that

$$S(P, T, n_1, \ldots, n_\alpha) - n_1 s_1(T, P) - \sum_2^\alpha n_i s_i(T, P)$$

$$= -\mathbf{R}(n_1 + n_2 + \cdots + n_\alpha) - \mathbf{R} \sum_2^\alpha n_i \ln \frac{n_i}{n_1}.$$

We can replace the functions $s_1(T, P)$, $s_2(T, P), \ldots,$ by the related functions

$$\sigma_1 = s_1(T, P) \quad \text{but} \quad \sigma_i = s_i(T, P) + \mathbf{R}. \tag{13.32}$$

With this notation

$$S(P, T, n_1, \ldots, n_\alpha) - n_1 \sigma_1(T, P) - \sum_2^\alpha n_i \sigma_i(T, P) = \mathbf{R} \sum_2^\alpha n_i \ln \frac{n_i}{n_1}. \tag{13.33}$$

The form of this equation is very similar to that for gases, which usually comes as a surprise, particularly when a different method of derivation is used, because it is not clear why the universal gas constant $\mathbf{R}$ should appear in a formula for liquid or solid solutions. When first discovered, equation (13.33) was met with general incredulity, but its validity has since been confirmed experimentally beyond any reasonable doubt whatever.

Since liquids and solids are, to all intents and purposes, incompressible, the functions σ are independent of pressure

$$\sigma_i(T, P) \approx \sigma_i(T), \tag{13.32a}$$

because the functions $s_i(T, P) \approx s_i(T)$ are also independent of pressure, equation (11.18a).

13.5.8   *Nonideal mixtures; fugacity and activity*

Owing to the complexity of the mixing process, the calculation of the entropy of mixing of nonideal solutions is also quite complex. In principle, the scheme adopted in connection with Figure 13.7 could be used for this purpose, but in practice this is not possible. Retracing the steps one by one, it becomes clear that additional quantities of heat will be exchanged during the reversible processes under consideration. Thus, in general, $Q_i \neq W_i$. Furthermore, the process $b \rightarrow c$ would cease to be adiabatic. Since experimental material concerning these quantities of heat is seldom available directly, a somewhat different path is followed in applications. The central idea, due to G. N. Lewis, consists in preserving the same *form* of the equations as they apply to ideal mixtures of perfect gases and to introduce correction functions for *nonideality* in the mixture and for the *imperfection* of the gas. Furthermore, it turns out that it is inconvenient to do this for the entropy directly, and that it is preferable to insert the correction terms in the expression for the Gibbs function $G = H - TS$. In this manner the problem is reduced to an empirical determination and subsequent tabulation of these correction functions—the *fugacity* of a pure component and the *activity* of a component in a mixture. The concepts of fugacity and activity will be discussed in Volume II. In anticipation, we shall attempt to introduce them here in a purely heuristic way.

In an ideal mixture of perfect gases, the membrane pressure

$$\widetilde{P}_i = x_i P \tag{13.34}$$

is identical with the partial pressure and depends only on the mol fraction of the component in question. The imperfection of the gas is taken into account by replacing the membrane pressure of the gas by its fugacity, $\widetilde{P}^*$, at membrane pressure, and the nonideality of the mixture is taken into account by replacing the mol fraction by the activity a_i of the component in a mixture, so that

$$\widetilde{P}_i^* = a_i P. \tag{13.35}$$

The fugacity depends on the membrane pressure P_i and on the temperature

$$\widetilde{P}_i^* = \widetilde{P}_i^*(T, \widetilde{P}_i), \tag{13.35a}$$

whereas the activity depends on the pressure, temperature and composition. Since the fugacity as well as the total pressure are intensive properties, the activity must also be intensive, and can depend only on the $\alpha - 1$ independent mol fractions. Thus,

$$a_i = a_i(T, P, x_1, \ldots, x_{\alpha - 1}). \tag{13.35b}$$

In the limit of zero pressure, equation (13.35) must transform asymptotically into equation (13.34). For this reason

$$\lim_{P \to 0} \widetilde{P}_i^* / \widetilde{P}_i = 1 \quad \text{and} \quad \lim_{P \to 0} a_i / x_i = 1. \tag{13.36}$$

In an ideal mixture $\sum_1^\alpha x_i = 1$, but in a nonideal mixture

$$\sum_1^\alpha a_i \neq 1 \quad \text{and} \quad \sum_1^\alpha \widetilde{P}_i^* \neq P,$$

even though

$$\lim_{P \to 0} \sum_1^\alpha a_i = 1 \quad \text{and} \quad \lim_{\widetilde{P}_i \to 0} \sum_1^\alpha \widetilde{P}_i^* = P. \tag{13.36a}$$

The ratio

$$\gamma_i = a_i / x_i \tag{13.36b}$$

is known as the *activity coefficient* of the component in the mixture.

13.6   Open system

We are now in a position to return to the study of open systems abandoned in Section 6.15 at a point when it became clear that the process of mixing substances of different chemical composition was beyond our grasp at the time. The diagram in Figure 13.8 reproduces that from Figure 6.18, but it is now assumed that mass dm differs chemically or by isotopic composition (or merely by the spin) from the main system. We continue to stipulate provisionally that the system within boundary C is one of uniform state. In order to introduce mass dm quasistatically and reversibly into the system, it is necessary to provide the semipermeable partition a. This implies that mass dm is in membrane equilibrium with the open system. Hence its pressure is $\tilde{P}_\xi$ and it will be assumed that its temperature is equal to that of the main system, T. In this manner, the adding or extracting of mass dm has become fully reversible, and this will enable us to write the Second as well as the First Law of thermodynamics for this open system.

The expression for the First Law is identical with that in equation (6.36), except that $h_\xi = u_\xi + \tilde{P}_\xi v_\xi$. With an eye on future applications, we shall write the equation for d$W_e = 0$, we shall admit a deforming boundary with d$W = P\,$dV, and we shall neglect kinetic and potential energy. The inclusion of all such additional terms is simple, and can be performed when required. With these restrictions

$$dQ^\circ = dU - h_\xi dm + P\,dV. \tag{13.37}$$

The total change in entropy, dS, of the open system consists of the change in entropy produced by adding mass dm, performing work $P\,$dV, and exchanging heat dQ°. The work of adding mass dm appears in the term h_ξ. Hence, at state a, when mass dm is outside, the entropy of the combined system is $S + s_\xi\,$dm. Similarly, at state b, when the mass has been added to the open system inside C, the entropy is $S + dS$. The change in entropy, d$S - s_\xi\,$dm must be equal to the quotient dQ°/T of heat over temperature. If equal temperatures of system and subsystem had not been stipulated, it would be necessary to include an additional entropy term due to temperature equalization, thus, com-

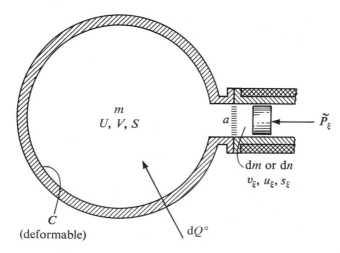

FIGURE 13.8. *Open system.*

plicating the expression for no apparent purpose. Hence,

$$T(dS - s_\xi \, dm) = dQ^\circ,$$

and substitution from equation (13.37) leads to

$$dU = T \, dS - P \, dV + g_\xi \, dm. \tag{13.38}$$

The property

$$g_\xi = h_\xi - T s_\xi \tag{13.38a}$$

of the mass dm in membrane equilibrium with the mixture represents the *Gibbs function* (or free enthalpy) for the substance of mass dm at state ξ. When this substance is pure, the term *chemical potential* is used for it, and the symbol μ is then preferred:

$$\mu_\xi = h_\xi - T s_\xi \quad \text{(pure component; membrane equilibrium)}. \tag{13.38b}$$

There is no difficulty in generalizing equation (13.38) for the case when several pure substances, each in membrane equilibrium with the mixture in the open system, are charged into ($dm > 0$) or discharged from ($dm < 0$) it. It is simply necessary to sum all terms $\mu_i \, dm_i$. We prefer to write this more general form in mol units:

$$dU = T \, dS - P \, dV + \sum_i \mu_i \, dn_i, \tag{13.39}$$

where

$$\mu_i = h_i - T s_i \quad \text{(in membrane equilibrium)}. \tag{13.39a}$$

Equation (13.39) is frequently known under the name of *Gibbs' equation*. It plays a very important part in chemical thermodynamics because it is valid even in cases when the open system contains a reacting mixture. The extension from the present, implied case of an inert mixture to that of a reacting mixture rests on a simple concept, and will be dealt with in Volume II. This circumstance explains why the Gibbs function g_ξ for a pure component in membrane equilibrium with a mixture is known as its *chemical potential*. At this stage, however, it is clear that it is equally applicable to a homogeneous open phase which gains or loses mass to another phase during a process of evaporation, condensation, and so on.

Equation (13.39) connects the changes in the properties of the open system, denoted by capital letters, with those of the substances (denoted by μ_i) which enter or leave it reversibly and isothermally during an elementary process. From its derivation, as well as from our remarks about potentials of varying masses (Section 5.5), it is understood that it is not really an equation for an open system. When the mass of a system varies, we cannot meaningfully speak of a change in energy or entropy owing to the existence of arbitrary constants in their definition. Thus, equation (13.39) must be applied to an open system whose mass remains constant, that is, to a system which loses as much mass through some channels, as it gains through others. Alternatively, it may be used for several open systems, such as a number of open phases in a heterogeneous inert or reacting closed system, whose total mass remains constant but within which each phase separately suffers a change in mass. If this were not so, the potentials for the various masses could not be normalized. The preceding restriction is not serious, and merely reflects the circumstance that all equations of thermodynamics derive, ultimately, from equations for closed systems. This is a consequence of the fact that any process must be studied in terms of a closed system, and that the writing of equations for open systems is done for convenience and efficiency in the analysis.

It is very important to realize that equation (13.39) contains only properties each of whose change is independent of the details of the process. A reversible path was chosen to make it possible to apply the Second Law of thermodynamics correctly. In most practical cases of interest, no semipermeable partition will be available and the process will be carried out quasistatically but not always reversibly. Nevertheless, equation (13.39) retains its validity in the same way as the equation for a change in entropy, necessarily obtained by integration along a reversible path, correctly represents the change in the entropy regardless of the details of an actual process.

The extension of equation (13.39) to a finite rate is immediate, and we can put it in the form

$$\frac{\mathrm{d}U}{\mathrm{d}t} = T\frac{\mathrm{d}S}{\mathrm{d}t} - P\frac{\mathrm{d}V}{\mathrm{d}t} + \sum_i \mu_i \frac{\mathrm{d}n_i}{\mathrm{d}t}. \tag{13.40}$$

However, the extension of the equation to a continuous system requires some caution. A continuous system normally sustains a variable temperature field, whereas equation (13.39) demands that each mass entering or leaving must have the same temperature as the contents of the open system. Consequently, the equation cannot be rewritten for a finite continuous system; it must be written for an elementary volume ΔV first, and integrated over the whole volume afterwards. We record this form in mass units for future use:

$$\frac{\mathrm{d}}{\mathrm{d}t}(\rho u\,\Delta V) = T\frac{\mathrm{d}}{\mathrm{d}t}(\rho s\,\Delta V) - P\frac{\mathrm{d}}{\mathrm{d}t}(\Delta V) + \sum \mu_i \frac{\mathrm{d}}{\mathrm{d}t}(\rho\,\Delta V), \tag{13.40a}$$

where the quantities ρ, u, T, s, P, and μ_i represent time-dependent spatial fields. The complete continuum form of this equation must contain the work of shearing stresses which has been omitted here. When electric or magnetic phenomena play a part, or when surface tension effects become important and, finally, when motion and action at a distance through various fields intervene, the equation will require more terms but will not differ from the simple form in equation (13.39) in any essential respect.

Equation (13.39) can be given several equivalent, alternative forms by applying to it Legendre transformations in the same way as in Section 12.1. The only difference now consists in the appearance of the sum $\sum_i \mu_i \, \mathrm{d}n_i$ which will remain unaffected by such transformations if they are confined to the pairs of variables P, V and T, S. Together with equation (13.39), the following four forms are obtained:

$$\left.\begin{aligned}
\mathrm{d}U &= \quad T\,\mathrm{d}S - P\,\mathrm{d}V + \sum_i \mu_i\,\mathrm{d}n_i, \\[4pt]
\mathrm{d}H &= \quad T\,\mathrm{d}S + V\,\mathrm{d}P + \sum_i \mu_i\,\mathrm{d}n_i, \\[4pt]
\mathrm{d}F &= -S\,\mathrm{d}T - P\,\mathrm{d}V + \sum_i \mu_i\,\mathrm{d}n_i, \\[4pt]
\mathrm{d}G &= -S\,\mathrm{d}T + V\,\mathrm{d}P + \sum_i \mu_i\,\mathrm{d}n_i.
\end{aligned}\right\} \tag{13.41a, b, c, d}$$

These equations show that the fundamental equations for a homogeneous mixture are of one of the forms

$$
\left.\begin{aligned}
U &= U(S,\, V,\, n_i),\\
H &= H(S,\, P,\, n_i),\\
F &= F(T,\, V,\, n_i),\\
G &= G(T,\, P,\, n_i).
\end{aligned}\right\}
\qquad\text{(13.42a, b, c, d)}
$$

It is, of course, remembered that the variations in the mol numbers n_i are not completely arbitrary, because the mass must remain constant. Hence, these equations are subject to the restriction that

$$
m = \Sigma\, n_i M_i = \text{const,}
\qquad\text{(13.43)}
$$

where M_i denotes the molar mass of species i. All reciprocal and reciprocity relations listed in Table 12.1 retain their validity when $n_i = \text{const}$. Thus, for such a system, for example,

$$
T = \left(\frac{\partial U}{\partial S}\right)_{V,\, n_i}
\qquad\text{(13.44)}
$$

or

$$
\left(\frac{\partial T}{\partial V}\right)_{S,\, n_i} = -\left(\frac{\partial P}{\partial S}\right)_{V,\, n_i},
\qquad\text{(13.44a)}
$$

and similarly for all other relations. Here, the subscript n_i denotes that *all* mol numbers must remain constant during the process of differentiation.

It is clear that it is now possible to derive additional reciprocal and reciprocity relations, for example,

$$
\left(\frac{\partial \mu_i}{\partial n_j}\right)_{T,P,\, n_k} = \left(\frac{\partial \mu_j}{\partial n_i}\right)_{T,P,\, n_k}
\quad\text{or}\quad
\left(\frac{\partial \mu_i}{\partial n_j}\right)_{S,V,\, n_k} = \left(\frac{\partial \mu_j}{\partial n_i}\right)_{S,V,\, n_k},
\qquad\text{(13.45a, b)}
$$

where n_k denotes all the variable mol numbers *except* the one with respect to which the differentiation is performed. Relations of this kind will become important in Volume II.

13.7 Entropy production during quasistatic irreversible processes

All natural processes, even those as occur at very slow rates, are irreversible. Thus, in contrast with the limiting case of a reversible process when the system traverses a continuous sequence of equilibrium states, the states traversed during a real quasistatic process are not true states of equilibrium. In fact, the system becomes a continuous one because it is possible to detect variations in its properties throughout its extent. For example, in the presence of friction there will exist temperature gradients caused by the appearance of heat fluxes. When the system is in motion, there will exist variations in pressure or stress in addition to a velocity field, and as a consequence, the energy and all other properties will vary continuously, first from point to point at any instant of time, and then with time, during a process, at any point.

In many processes, these departures from equilibrium are not large, and we can assign to the system uniform, average properties and so describe its state as it varies quasistatically with time during a process. We describe its instantaneous quasi-equilibrium or near-equilibrium states by indicating those properties which the system would assume if it were allowed to reach equilibrium adiabatically. In particular, a value of entropy can also be assigned to such a system. It follows that the relations between properties, as they describe a near-equilibrium state, are the same as for a true equilibrium state. In many cases the departures from equilibrium at any instant are too large to permit the assignation of a uniform quasistate to the whole system. For such cases, it is necessary to develop a complete continuum version of classical thermodynamics. We shall outline this development in Volume II, but we can foresee now that the continuous system will be subdivided at every instant of time t into elementary systems of volume ΔV, with $\Delta V \to 0$, each of which will be treated as a uniform system in a near-equilibrium state performing a quasistatic, irreversible process with the flow of time. It is thus important to develop efficient methods of analysis. The main improvement consists in removing the necessity to consider the surroundings of the system whenever the Second Part of the Second Law is applied. This is achieved by the introduction of the concept of entropy production which is a simple adaptation of the concept of work lost and the amount of entropy produced by a system which performs an irreversible process between two equilibrium states. We encountered these concepts in Sections 4.7, 10.6, 11.2, and 11.4.

Accordingly, we consider an arbitrary quasistatic, irreversible process as illustrated in Figure 13.9. The fact that only two variables, a generalized force Y and a generalized displacement Z, are shown, imposes no limitations on our results and the reader should satisfy himself that this is the case. In order to calculate the change in entropy during an elementary step ab in the process, we compare it with a step $a°b°$ in an identical sequence of equilibrium states which thus constitutes a reversible process. The First Law can now be written in two versions: for the irreversible process

$$dU = dQ - dW, \tag{13.46}$$

and for the reversible process

$$dU = dQ° - dW°. \tag{13.46a}$$

Naturally, $dQ \neq dQ°$ and $dW \neq dW°$. The change in internal energy, being independent of the path, must be the same for identical steps. On comparing these two equations, we deduce that

$$dQ° - dQ = dW° - dW \qquad (=dW_{\text{loss}}). \tag{13.46b}$$

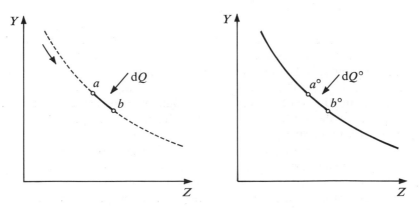

FIGURE 13.9. *Quasistatic, irreversible process.*

The difference $dW° - dW$ represents the work lost, already familiar to us; it is equal to the difference between the reversible heat $dQ°$ of ideal process $a°b°$ and the heat dQ of real process ab.

The change in entropy for either process is computed as

$$dS = \frac{dQ°}{T}$$
$$= \frac{dQ}{T} + \frac{dW_{loss}}{T}. \qquad (13.47)$$

The examples considered earlier suggest that dW_{loss} should always be positive in an irreversible process, being zero for a reversible process. This signifies that an irreversible process produces $(dW > 0)$ less work and absorbs less heat than a comparable reversible process. Similarly, it consumes $(dW < 0)$ more work and rejects more heat than a comparable reversible process. Evidently, this observation, if it is general, must be a consequence of the second part of the Second Law, that is, a consequence of the principle of entropy increase.

In order to apply the second part of the Second Law, it is necessary to consider the entropy of the system as well as that of the reservoir with which it exchanges heat. For the reversible process $a°b°$ the reservoir *must* be at temperature T, but it may be of a different temperature for process ab. For the sake of simplicity, we shall *assume* that the heat reservoir is at temperature T in both cases. This limits the application of the resulting equations and experience teaches that this restriction is apt to be overlooked on occasion. We emphasize this detail for this reason, noting that the corresponding equation for a source of temperature $T_0 \neq T$ can be written down with ease. Thus,

$$dS \geq \frac{dQ}{T} \qquad (13.48)$$

(otherwise we would write $dS \geq dQ/T_0$), the sign of equality relating to reversible processes only. A comparison with equation (13.47) shows that, indeed,

$$\frac{dW_{loss}}{T} \geq 0. \qquad (13.49)$$

In fluid mechanics, the term dW_{loss} is known as the dissipation function. The ratio

$$d\theta = \frac{dW_{loss}}{T}, \qquad (13.50)$$

which we designate as the entropy *produced* or *generated* by the irreversible process, has an important physical interpretation and plays a crucial part in continuum thermodynamics. In order to see this, we rewrite equation (13.47) to read

$$dS = \frac{dQ}{T} + d\theta \qquad (\theta \geq 0) \qquad (13.51)$$

for a small step during time dt. Alternatively, equation (13.51) can be written as a rate equation

$$\dot{S} = \frac{\dot{Q}}{T} + \dot{\theta} \qquad (\dot{\theta} \geq 0). \qquad (13.51a)$$

Either of these equations can be interpreted to mean that the entropy S of the system is affected by two factors: by the flow of heat Q and by the appearance of additional entropy θ. This additional entropy is zero when the process is reversible, and always positive when the process is irreversible. Thus, we are justified in saying that the system develops *sources* which *create* entropy during an irreversible process, rather like a source "creates" water in the open where it would not exist were it not for the presence of the source. The second part of the Second Law asserts that *sinks* of entropy are impossible in nature, which is merely a more graphic way of saying that θ and $\dot\theta$ must be positive definite, or zero for reversible processes.

The term dQ/Tdt or $\dot Q/T$ can be interpreted as a flux of entropy. The boundary is crossed by heat (at the uniform temperature T), and the ratio of this flux to temperature can be defined as a flux of entropy. There are no restrictions on the sign of this quantity, and we may say that this flux either contributes towards, or drains away the system's entropy. During a reversible process, only this flux can affect the entropy of the system. This terminology suggests that we interpret entropy as a kind of weightless fluid whose quantity is conserved (like that of matter) during a reversible process. However, during an irreversible process, this fluid is *not* conserved; it cannot disappear, on the contrary, it is created by sources throughout the system. This interpretation need not disturb the reader, nor should it induce him to take it too literally. It provides an easy mode of expression, and is in the same category of concepts as those associated with the phrases "flux of heat," "flux of energy," "source of heat," and so on. In fluid mechanics, this graphic language is very effective, and there are no objections to copying it in thermodynamics.

In the case of a continuous system, we shall select a small element of volume ΔV and area ΔA, and write (in mass units)

$$\frac{d}{dt}(\rho s\,\Delta V) = \frac{1}{T}(\dot q\,\Delta A) + \frac{d}{dt}(\rho\theta\,\Delta V). \qquad (13.52)$$

Here $\dot q = \lim_{A\to 0} \dot Q/A$ denotes the heat flux, or rate of flow of heat per unit area and time. Frequently, the strength of the entropy source, $\dot\theta$, is expressed per unit volume rather than mass; when this is the case the last term will be written $(d/dt)\,(\theta\Delta V)$.

A very useful form of equation (13.51) is obtained when dQ is expressed in it in terms of energy and work, equation (13.46). Rearranging terms, we prefer to put it in the form

$$dU = T\,dS - dW - T\,d\theta, \qquad (13.53)$$

where

$$T\,d\theta = dW_{\text{loss}} = dW^\circ - dW. \qquad (13.53a)$$

This form is reminiscent of equation (13.39) for an open system performing a quasistatic process of mixing. In particular, it is seen that the total (irreversible) work for the process is $dW = PdV$ and that

$$d\theta = -\frac{\sum\limits_i \mu_i\,dn_i}{T} \qquad (\sum\limits_i \mu_i\,dn_i < 0), \qquad (13.54)$$

or that

$$dW_{\text{loss}} = dW^\circ - P\,dV = -\sum\limits_i \mu_i\,dn_i. \qquad (13.55)$$

The form of equation (13.39) suggests that the energy U appears in it as a function of entropy S, volume V and the numbers of mols n_i in the mixture; the latter constitute internal variables. Thus, there are more than two independent variables which describe the state. In a reversible process (no addition or subtraction of mass with $dn_i \equiv 0$, or a process when $\sum_i \mu_i \, dn_i \equiv 0$), the work would be $P \, dV$. In actual fact, a quantity of work $-\sum_i \mu_i \, dn_i$ (so-called chemical work in a chemical reaction) is lost, and a corresponding amount of entropy $-\sum_i \mu_i \, dn_i/T$ is generated. A process for which $\sum_i \mu_i \, dn_i \equiv 0$ is, therefore, reversible.

When the reversible work $dW°$ is of the form of a single Pfaffian $Y \, dZ$, and the system performs a quasistatic, irreversible process, the work is

$$dW = Y \, dZ - T \, d\theta \qquad (d\theta > 0), \tag{13.56}$$

the heat is

$$dQ = dU + Y \, dZ - T \, d\theta \quad \text{or} \quad dQ = T \, dS - T \, d\theta. \tag{13.56a, b}$$

The areas under the curve of a quasistatic, irreversible process in Y, Z and T, S coordinates no longer represent the heat or work, but the sums $dW° = dW + T \, d\theta$ in Y, Z coordinates and $dQ° = dQ + T \, d\theta$ in T, S coordinates. This has been indicated in Figure 13.10.

Equation (13.56b) allows us to recognize that it is possible to perform a quasistatic process at constant entropy on condition that

$$dQ = -T \, d\theta.$$

A process of this kind has been termed quasi-isentropic in Section 9.11. It differs from an isentropic process, which is reversible by definition, in that it is not adiabatic. Since $d\theta$ is always positive, a quasi-isentropic process requires the system to be cooled at a prescribed rate.

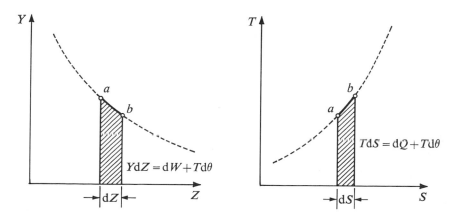

FIGURE 13.10. *Meaning of areas in the work and heat diagrams for quasistatic, irreversible processes.*

13.8   Systems exchanging heat with a single reservoir

The great majority of processes of interest in thermodynamics occur, at least approximately, when a system is free to exchange heat with a single, infinite reservoir of heat of temperature T_0. Most processes, whether industrial or experimental occur in the terrestrial atmosphere. The latter constitutes the only heat reservoir which is not artificially produced. Such processes start with a collection of bodies which are in thermal, and very often also in mechanical, but not necessarily in chemical equilibrium with the atmosphere, and end when the collection of bodies has once again achieved thermal and mechanical equilibrium with the atmosphere. In the production of power, we always start with some substance — the fuel — which is capable of undergoing a chemical reaction with the oxygen of the atmosphere. In the example of the jet engine discussed in Section 6.11, the fuel and the air, including oxygen, enter the system at a temperature and pressure equal to that of the atmosphere. The pressure of the system is increased inside the system, and after a series of processes has taken place, the combustion gases, that is, a mixture of oxygen, nitrogen and several, usually gaseous, oxides are returned to the atmosphere where, ultimately, they reach thermal and mechanical equilibrium with it. In a steam installation, a solid, often pulverized, fuel may be supplied and burned in a furnace in a stream of preheated air. The steam in the plant either circulates through it cyclically or is produced from water which enters the system at room temperature and atmospheric pressure. The combustion gases are exhausted into the atmosphere, and so is the steam if it does not stay in the circuit. Otherwise, it is condensed by cooling with the aid of a stream of water which enters and leaves the system at atmospheric pressure, its initial temperature being atmospheric. When a small quantity of fuel is burned in a bomb calorimeter in an atmosphere of compressed oxygen, we realize that the bomb calorimeter is charged in the atmosphere and that the compressed oxygen was sent to us in a high-pressure cylinder from a factory, where it had previously been extracted from the surrounding atmosphere or produced in a chemical plant from reactants which entered it at atmospheric temperature and pressure.

Many examples of the type just described could be quoted, but the preceding ones should suffice to convince the reader of the great importance of studying separately that class of irreversible processes which is characterized by the feature that only one reservoir of heat at T_0 is available for the exchange of heat (any others are included in the system). The formulation of the problem contains the simplification that no allowance has been made for the diurnal and seasonal changes in the temperature of the atmosphere.

The central problem is to determine the maximum work which can be obtained when the system changes its state from a given state 1 with $T_1 = T_0$ to another given state 2 with $T_2 = T_0$, being allowed to assume any temperature in between. When work W must be done upon the system to produce a desired change of state $1 \rightarrow 2$, for example, to compress a gas or to separate a mixture of gases into its components, the work is negative, and we are interested in the minimum (absolute) value of $|W|$ required to produce this change. The method of analysis is essentially identical with that used in the preceding section, except that now states 1 and 2 are not assumed to be arbitrarily close; they are, however, thought of as equilibrium states. To vary the method somewhat, we shall write our result in the form of an inequality and identify the entropy production term at the end of our argument.

13.8.1 *Maximum work in constant-volume processes*

The first case to be considered will involve an arbitrary system contained in a rigid vessel as shown in Figure 13.11; this will exclude mechanical equilibrium with the atmosphere. Moreover, to obtain a slightly more general expression we shall, at first, not stipulate that the temperatures T_1 and T_2, at equilibrium states 1 and 2, respectively, are necessarily equal to the temperature T_0 of the heat source. In all cases, the temperature *during* the irreversible process $1 \to 2$ is left arbitrary.

The arrangement sketched in Figure 13.11 constitutes an adiabatic system; its operation does not conflict with the Second Law (the Kelvin-Planck statement), because we do *not* now stipulate that the system performs a *cyclic* process; on the contrary, it performs an irreversible process $1 \to 2$ as a consequence of the removal of some constraint.

The First Law leads to the relation

$$Q_0 - W = E_2 - E_1, \tag{13.57}$$

whereas the principle of entropy increase stipulates that

$$S_2 - S_1 - \frac{Q_0}{T_0} \geq 0, \tag{13.58}$$

the sign of equality referring to a reversible process. Replacing Q_0, which may be positive or negative, by its expression from equation (13.57), we obtain

$$W \leq E_1 - E_2 - T_0(S_1 - S_2). \tag{13.59}$$

Thus, the Second Law of thermodynamics imposes the condition that the work W obtained in an irreversible process between prescribed states 1 and 2 (sign of inequality) is always smaller than that in a reversible process between the same states (sign of equality). Specializing to the case when only internal energy is involved, we conclude

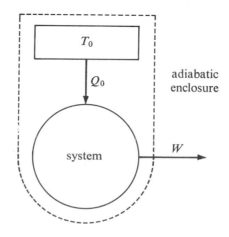

FIGURE 13.11. *Maximum or minimum work for system of constant volume.*

that the *maximum* work is

$$W^\circ_{max} = U_1 - U_2 - T_0(S_1 - S_2); \tag{13.59a}$$

it can be obtained by performing any reversible process between the prescribed states. Conversely, the minimum (absolute) amount of (negative) work required to produce a desired change in state is

$$|W^\circ_{min}| = U_2 - U_1 - T_0(S_2 - S_1). \tag{13.59b}$$

The maximum (or minimum) work is seen to differ from the loss (or gain) in internal energy; the balance is made up by the term

$$Q'_0 = T_0(S_1 - S_2) = -Q_0 \tag{13.60a}$$

known as the *bound* or *unavailable* energy. Similarly, the minimum work is not equal to the *gain* in energy $U_2 - U_1$, but differs from it by the quantity

$$|Q'_0| = T_0(S_2 - S_1) = Q_0. \tag{13.60b}$$

The bound energy may be positive or negative, depending on the change in entropy; it can be computed if the properties of the system are known.

As an example of the application of the preceding relations, we shall consider the case when the system depicted in Figure 13.12 consists of a single reservoir of temperature T and an engine operating on a cycle. The change in the energy of the system during an integral number of cycles will be equal to the heat Q given up or acquired by the reservoir T. Similarly, the only change in the entropy of the system will be the loss $-Q/T$ suffered by the heat reservoir. Thus, in equation (13.59a) we substitute

$$U_1 - U_2 = Q \quad \text{and} \quad S_1 - S_2 = Q/T$$

and obtain

$$W_{max} = Q\left(1 - \frac{T_0}{T}\right).$$

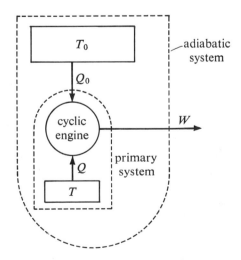

FIGURE 13.12. *Cyclic engine.*

This is another way of saying that a reversible Carnot cycle whose efficiency is equal to $\eta = 1 - T_0/T$ produces the maximum amount of work possible under the circumstances and that its efficiency is the highest possible. It is easy to verify with the aid of equation (13.60a) that

$$Q_0^\circ = - (Q - W_{max}^\circ)$$

which shows that the heat Q_0° is *rejected* by the system and flows in a direction opposite to that assumed in Figure 13.12. The heat rejected can also be represented as

$$Q_0' = |Q_0^\circ| = \frac{Q}{T} T_0,$$

which is the bound, or unavailable energy from equation (13.60a). For $Q > 0$ and $T < T_0$ the preceding equations yield the known statements about a reversed reversible cycle operating as a refrigerator, whereas the case $Q < 0$ and $T > T_0$ corresponds to an ideal, Carnot heat pump. It is, of course, realized that equations (13.59a, b) and (13.60a, b) apply to more complex cases than just Carnot engines.

The maximum work given by the expression in equation (13.59a) is sometimes called *available work*. It represents that work which is available in the system at state 1 in the presence of heat reservoir T_0 *before* the internal constraints have been removed, making it possible for the system to perform the process $1 \rightarrow 2$. When the irreversible process $1 \rightarrow 2$ has taken place, a quantity of work $W < W_{max}^\circ$ is actually delivered by the system. The difference

$$W_{loss} = W_{max}^\circ - W \tag{13.61}$$

is the work lost or dissipated. Since, however, no energy can be lost, in the strict sense of the word (First Law of thermodynamics), the quantities of heat Q_0 will differ according as to whether the change from state 1 to state 2 has taken place naturally, Q_0, or reversibly, Q_0°. It is clear, of course, that in order to force the system to perform a reversible process between states 1 and 2, it is necessary suitably to rearrange the details of the process. From the application of the First Law, we obtain

$$U_2 - U_1 = Q_0^\circ - W_{max}^\circ = Q_0 - W,$$

and upon comparing with equation (13.61) it is seen that

$$W_{loss} = W_{max}^\circ - W = Q_0^\circ - Q_0.$$

This equation shows that the work W_{loss} which remains unrecovered reappears in the heat reservoir, for

$$-Q_0 = -Q_0^\circ + W_{loss} \quad \text{or} \quad |Q_0| = |Q_0^\circ| + W_{loss}. \tag{13.62}$$

In other words, instead of rejecting a quantity of heat $-Q_0^\circ$, a larger quantity of heat, $|Q_0^\circ| + W_{loss}$ is now rejected. When the process is conducted reversibly, the total change in the entropy of the system and reservoir T_0 is zero. Now, however, the change in the entropy of the system together with the source is positive, and the change in the entropy of the system proper is

$$S_2 - S_1 > \frac{Q_0}{T_0};$$

it can be positive or negative, depending on circumstances. The difference between the two cases, the reversible and irreversible, can be computed easily. It is clear that

$$S_2 - S_1 = \frac{Q_0^\circ}{T_0}$$

and that

$$S_2 - S_1 = \frac{Q_0}{T_0} + \frac{W_{\text{loss}}}{T_0}. \tag{13.63}$$

Thus, the entropy change in the system, $S_2 - S_1$, can be regarded as the sum of two terms, the change in entropy due to the absorption of heat Q_0, or the *rejection* of heat $-Q_0$, and the additional term

$$\Delta\theta = \frac{W_{\text{loss}}}{T_0} \tag{13.64}$$

which has been created by the system by virtue of its having performed an irreversible process. This additional amount of entropy appears in the heat reservoir T_0, because now its entropy has increased by an amount

$$-\frac{Q_0}{T_0} = -\frac{Q_0^\circ}{T_0} + \Delta\theta. \tag{13.65}$$

Depending on the direction of flow of the quantity of heat Q_0, the entropy of the heat reservoir T_0 either increases by an additional amount $\Delta\theta$ or decreases by an amount which is less by $\Delta\theta$ than it would be in a reversible process *between the same two states 1 and 2*.

In the particular case when

$$T_1 = T_2 = T_0,$$

equations (13.59) and (13.59a) can be rewritten

$$W \leq F_1 - F_2 \tag{13.66}$$

or

$$\left. \begin{array}{l} W_{\text{max}}^\circ = F_1 - F_2 \\ |W_{\text{min}}^\circ| = F_2 - F_1 \end{array} \right\} \tag{13.66a, b}$$

and

$$\left. \begin{array}{l} W = F_1 - F_2 - W_{\text{loss}}, \\ |-W| = F_2 - F_1 + W_{\text{loss}}, \end{array} \right\} \tag{13.67a, b}$$

where

$$F = U - TS$$

is the Helmholtz function known to the reader from Section 12.1. Hence, when an irreversible process occurs between two states 1 and 2 of a system which is in thermal equilibrium with a large reservoir at the beginning and at the end of the process, but not necessarily *during* the process, the *maximum, or available work is equal to the decrease in the Helmholtz function* between these two states, on condition that the work $P_0 \Delta V$ of the atmosphere is zero. The preceding equations are, of course, valid when the direction of flow of heat Q_0 or of work W is opposite to that stipulated in Figure 13.11, as already mentioned.

The particular case when $W = 0$ is of great practical importance. For example, the process may involve a chemical reaction carried out in a rigid bomb. Equation (13.66) then yields

$$F_1 \geqq F_2, \tag{13.68}$$

the sign of equality being reserved for reversible processes. This equation shows that during a spontaneous irreversible process, for example, a chemical reaction, which occurs in a rigid vessel so that heat is exchanged with a single reservoir under circumstances when the system is in thermal equilibrium with that reservoir at the beginning and at the end of the process, *the Helmholtz function must decrease*. This statement constitutes a special case of the general principle of entropy increase and applies only under the restrictions stated earlier.

The relations which obtain in the case of a reversible process during which $T_1 = T_2 = T_0$ can be given a very lucid physical interpretation in the following way. The First Law expresses the principle of energy conservation and asserts that the change in energy is balanced by heat *and* work:

$$U_2 - U_1 = Q_0^\circ - W_{max}^\circ.$$

Thus, only the *difference* between heat and work can be expressed in terms of the properties of the system. Under the particular conditions when $V_1 = V_2$ and $T_1 = T_2 = T_0$, both heat *and* work can be *separately* represented in terms of the properties of the system, since then

$$W_{max}^\circ = F_1 - F_2$$

and

$$Q_0^\circ = T_0(S_2 - S_1).$$

For this reason H. von Helmholtz called the difference $F_1 - F_2$ "free energy," a synonym for available energy, and denoted the negative of the difference $T_0(S_2 - S_1)$ as the bound, or unavailable energy.

It is noteworthy that for a reversible cycle both the maximum work and the unavailable energy vanish separately. This is an alternative way of stating that no net work can be obtained with the aid of a cycle and a single heat source.

13.8.2 *Maximum work in a constant-pressure process*

In the preceding section we have disregarded the circumstance that the terrestrial atmosphere usually intervenes in our processes. Its influence was neutralized by the provision of a rigid vessel of constant volume which constituted a permanent constraint impeding the attainment of mechanical equilibrium with the atmosphere. We now propose to repeat all the preceding arguments with this modification in view.

The system under consideration is shown sketched in Figure 13.13. It consists of a cylinder closed with the aid of an ideal piston which is, in turn, loaded with a weight G. In this manner, the pressure of the system remains constant at a value P_0 which need

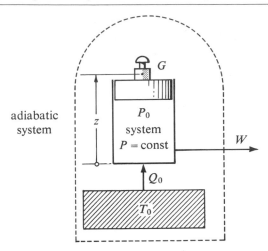

FIGURE 13.13. *Maximum (or minimum) work for a constant-pressure system.*

not, at this stage, necessarily be assumed equal to the atmospheric pressure. Thus, it is imagined that the exterior of the cylinder and piston are at zero pressure. The system exchanges positive or negative heat, Q_0, with a single reservoir of temperature T_0 and exchanges positive or negative work, W. The sign convention for the quantities Q_0 and W is that shown in the sketch, it being noted that it agrees with the general sign convention as far as the system proper is concerned. Thus, the only difference with the case discussed in connection with Figure 13.11 is in the work of the piston which is subtracted from W in recognition of the fact that it cannot be made available in a process of this kind.

It will be convenient to include the weight G with the system, because by this device it will not be necessary to limit attention to strictly isobaric processes. During an irreversible process, the pressure inside the system may exceed the pressure P_0 or be lower than P_0, thus causing the piston and weight to oscillate. However, the initial and final equilibrium pressures P_1 and P_2, respectively, will both be equal to P_0, or

$$P_1 = P_2 = P_0.$$

The First Law of thermodynamics can be written

$$Q_0 - W = E_2 - E_1, \tag{13.69}$$

where now E includes the potential energy Gz of the weight. Here z is measured from the bottom of the cylinder, as shown, and since $G = AP_0$, where A is the cross-sectional area of the piston, we have $Gz = P_0V$. Limiting our attention to processes which involve only the internal energy U, we can rewrite equation (13.69) as

$$Q_0 - W = U_2 - U_1 + P_0(V_2 - V_1).$$

Alternatively, we have

$$Q_0 - W = H_2 - H_1. \tag{13.70}$$

It is recalled that equation (13.70) is also valid for an open system in steady flow under the assumption that the effect of shear need not be taken into account in calculating pumping work. Thus, the ensuing theory will also be valid for the system shown sketched in Figure 13.14. The steady-flow open system which exchanges heat Q_0 and work W per m units of mass of substance flowing through it at a rate $\dot{m}$ has been closed with the aid of fictitious cylinders and pistons, each maintaining a constant pressure, one at inlet and the other at exit.

The change in the potential energy of piston 1 during time dt is $-G_1 dz_1$ and that of piston 2 is $+G_2 dz_2$, and their algebraic sum is

$$G_2\, dz_2 - G_1\, dz_1 = A_2 P_2\, dz_2 - A_1 P_1\, dz_1.$$

However the terms $A_2 dz_2$ and $A_1 dz_1$ are equal to the volume changes dV_2 and dV_1, respectively. It is thus easy to see that when a given mass $dm = \dot{m}\, dt$ has passed through the system, the expression for the First Law of thermodynamics will become identical with that in equation (13.70).

Retracing all the steps outlined in Section 13.8.1 for the case when $V_1 = V_2$, we can write the principle of entropy increase in the form

$$S_2 - S_1 - \frac{Q_0}{T_0} \geq 0. \tag{13.71}$$

Equations (13.70) and (13.71) now lead to

$$W \leq T_0(S_2 - S_1) - (H_2 - H_1). \tag{13.72}$$

It is therefore concluded that

$$W^\circ_{\text{max}} = (H_1 - H_2) - T_0(S_1 - S_2) \tag{13.73}$$

and that

$$|W^\circ_{\text{min}}| = (H_2 - H_1) - T_0(S_2 - S_1). \tag{13.73a}$$

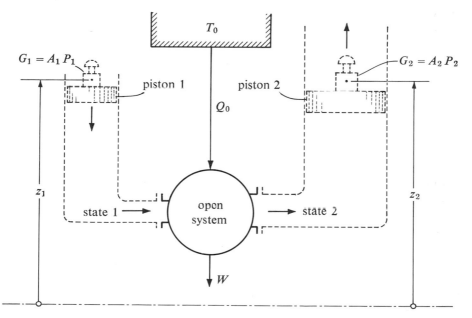

FIGURE 13.14. *Maximum (or minimum) work for steady-state open system.*

Once again, $W_{\max}^{\circ}$ can be interpreted as the available work, and the term $T_0(S_2 - S_1)$ as the unavailable work, compared with the heat $H_2 - H_1$ which would be released in the absence of work, that is, for $W = 0$. In an actual, irreversible process the work performed will be less than the maximum available during a reversible process and the difference

$$W_{\text{loss}} = W_{\max}^{\circ} - W$$

is not made available during the process. The quantity of heat Q_0 is also smaller than the quantity of heat Q_0° exchanged during the reversible process used here as a standard of comparison. Since

$$H_2 - H_1 = Q_0^{\circ} - Q = W_{\max}^{\circ} - W,$$

we also have

$$W_{\text{loss}} = W_{\max}^{\circ} - W = Q_0^{\circ} - Q_0,$$

in complete analogy with the rigid system treated earlier. The portion of the available work which cannot be delivered by the irreversible process appears in the form of heat rejected to the reservoir, T_0, or as a quantity of heat which has failed to be extracted from it. In analogy with equation (13.62) we can also write

$$-Q_0 = -Q_0^{\circ} + W_{\text{loss}} \quad \text{or} \quad |Q_0| = |Q_0^{\circ}| + W_{\text{loss}}. \tag{13.74}$$

The change in the entropy of the system can again be represented as the sum of that which occurs during the reversible process and that which is created by the irreversible process:

$$-\frac{Q_0}{T_0} = -\frac{Q_0^{\circ}}{T_0} + \Delta\theta, \tag{13.75}$$

where

$$\Delta\theta = \frac{W_{\text{loss}}}{T_0}.$$

The entropy created during the process appears in the reservoir of temperature T_0.
  In the particular case when

$$T_1 = T_2 = T_0,$$

equations (13.72) and (13.73) can be written

$$W \leq G_1 - G_2 \tag{13.76}$$

or

$$\left. \begin{array}{l} W_{\max}^{\circ} = G_1 - G_2 \\ |W_{\min}^{\circ}| = G_2 - G_1 \end{array} \right\} \tag{13.77a, b}$$

and

$$\left. \begin{array}{l} W = G_1 - G_2 - W_{\text{loss}}, \\ |W| = G_2 - G_1 + W_{\text{loss}}, \end{array} \right\} \tag{13.78a, b}$$

where $G = H - TS$ denotes the Gibbs function.[†] It plays the same part in the present process as the Helmholtz function F played in the case of a rigid system.

The analogy carries over to the statement that the Gibbs function must decrease during a spontaneous process when $W = 0$, or

$$G_1 \geq G_2, \tag{13.79}$$

the sign of equality being characteristic of a reversible process.

In practical applications, the equations of the present section are needed much more frequently than those for rigid systems. This is due to the ubiquitous presence of the atmosphere and to the greater ease with which industrial processes can be performed in flow systems than in closed, rigid cylinders. It must be realized that in the case of the open, steady-flow system sketched in Figure 13.14, the maximum, or minimum work is always associated with the case when $P_1 = P_2 = P_0$. In the contrary case, the existing pressure differences could be utilized for the production of additional work, for example, by isothermal, reversible expansion. This is precisely the case which is of most practical interest, since in all engineering installations substances are loaded at atmospheric pressure, and useful or waste products are discharged into the atmosphere. When $P_1 = P_2$, the case depicted in Figure 13.14 becomes, really, identical with that shown in Figure 13.13. In order to see this, it is sufficient to adopt the Lagrangian point of view and to imagine that the system in terms of which the analysis is conducted consists of a fixed mass of state 1 and that its changes are followed as it passes through the interior of the open system, emerging finally at the exit at state 2.

It may be worth mentioning here that an oscillating piston will transfer some of the work performed by it to the atmosphere. This amount is small, and our theory neglects it completely.

In concluding our remarks on systems exchanging heat with one reservoir, it may be worth while drawing the reader's attention to the fact that the considerations of this and the preceding section become trivial when applied to simple systems whose state is determined by two properties, for then, with $T_1 = T_2$ and either $P_1 = P_2$ or $V_1 = V_2$, we must have $G_1 = G_2$ or $F_1 = F_2$, respectively. The importance of the concept of maximum work emerges only when more complex systems are examined, particularly when phase transformations or chemical reactions come into play.

The maximum work in an open system of variable composition can be inferred from equations (13.41c, d). At $T = $ const, $V = $ const

$$dW_{max}^\circ = -dF = -\sum_i \mu_i \, dn_i, \tag{13.80a}$$

and at $T = $ const, $P = $ const, similarly

$$dW_{max}^\circ = -dG = -\sum_i \mu_i \, dn_i. \tag{13.80b}$$

List of Symbols for Chapter 13

Latin letters

A	Area
a	Activity
C	Heat capacity; constant of integration

[†] The Gibbs function, G, should not be confused with the weight, G, which occurred earlier in this section.

c	Specific heat
E	Energy
F	Helmholtz function
G	Weight; Gibbs function
g	Gibbs function
H	Enthalpy
h	Height; specific enthalpy
m	Mass
n	Number of systems; number of mols
P	Pressure
$\widetilde{P}$	Membrane pressure
$\widetilde{P}*$	Fugacity
Q	Heat accepted from source
Q_0	Heat rejected to sink
Q_0'	Bound or unavailable energy
R	Gas constant
$\mathbf{R}$	Universal gas constant
S	Entropy
s	Specific entropy
T	Absolute temperature; temperature of heat source
T_0	Temperature of heat sink
T_m	Equilibrium temperature following process of calorimetric mixing
t	Time
U	Internal energy
u	Specific internal energy
V	Volume
V_1, V_2	Partial volumes
v	Specific volume
W	Work
W_i	Indicated work
W_{loss}	Work dissipated
x	Mol fraction
Y	Generalized force
Z	Generalized displacement
z	Displacement

Greek letters

α	General summation index; number of components in system
α_1, α_2	Ratios of heat capacities or weighting factors
γ	Activity coefficient
η_c	Carnot efficiency
η_i	Indicated thermal efficiency
η_m	Mechanical efficiency
η_0	Brake thermal efficiency
η_r	Relative efficiency or efficiency ratio
η_r'	Product of η_r and η_m
θ	Entropy generated by irreversible process

μ	Chemical potential
ρ	Density
σ	Function defined in equation (13.32)

Superscripts

$^{\circ}$	Reversible process
$\cdot$	Time rate of change

Subscripts

$_{1,\,2}$	Refers to systems 1, 2
$_{max}$	Maximum value
$_{min}$	Minimum value
$_{\xi}$	Refers to state of mass entering open system

Index

ABCDEFGHIJ 7069876